TREATISE ON ANALYTICAL CHEMISTRY

A comprehensive account in three parts

PART I
THEORY AND PRACTICE

PART II
ANALYTICAL CHEMISTRY
OF THE ELEMENTS

PART III
ANALYSIS OF INDUSTRIAL PRODUCTS

TREATISE ON ANALYTICAL CHEMISTRY

Edited by I. M. KOLTHOFF
School of Chemistry, University of Minnesota

and PHILIP J. ELVING
Department of Chemistry, University of Michigan

with the assistance of ERNEST B. SANDELL
School of Chemistry, University of Minnesota

PART II
**ANALYTICAL CHEMISTRY
OF THE ELEMENTS
VOLUME 1**

INTERSCIENCE PUBLISHERS, NEW YORK-LONDON

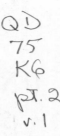
Copyright © 1961 by
INTERSCIENCE PUBLISHERS, INC.

ALL RIGHTS RESERVED
LIBRARY OF CONGRESS CATALOG CARD NUMBER 59-12439

Distributed by
Interscience Publishers, Inc., 250 Fifth Avenue, New York 1, N. Y.

For Great Britain and Northern Ireland:
Interscience Publishers Ltd., 88/90 Chancery Lane, London, W. C. 2

PRINTED IN U.S.A. BY MACK PRINTING CO., EASTON, PA.

TREATISE ON ANALYTICAL CHEMISTRY

PART II

ANALYTICAL CHEMISTRY
OF THE ELEMENTS

SECTION A

Systematic Analytical Chemistry of the
Elements

VOLUME 1: INORGANIC NOMENCLATURE
GENERAL CONCEPTS
HYDROGEN · WATER
INERT GASES · ALKALI METALS

AUTHORS OF VOLUME 1

H. F. BEEGHLY   JAMES I. HOFFMAN
GERHARD A. COOK   SILVE KALLMAN
W. CONARD FERNELIUS   JOHN MITCHELL, JR.

Preface to Part II

Part II of the Treatise critically reviews the analytical chemistry, inorganic and organic, of all of the elements. It is not encyclopedic in nature and in that sense it is not an attempt to compete with the excellent *Handbuch der analytischen Chemie*, edited by Professor Wilhelm Fresenius and Professor Gerhart Jander.

Section A deals with the analytical chemistry of the various elements. Through a harmonious cooperation between the authors and the editors, it has been possible to present the material in a uniform way with emphasis on critically selected approaches and procedures. In brief, the reader is first given a short summary of the occurrence of the element, of industrial processes involving it, and of its toxicology. This introduction is followed by a description of the analytically important physical and chemical properties of the element. Sections covering distinctive features in the sampling of materials containing the element and outlining its separation and isolation are followed by systematic discussions of the current situation in respect to the detection and quantitative determination of the element and the analysis of its most important compounds. The discussion of each element is concluded by selected references for the determination of the element in specific materials and by a group of critically selected general laboratory procedures.

In order to assure a critical treatment, authors have been invited who have a rich experience in the field of the particular element and who were willing to assume responsibility for selecting recommended procedures.

Section A of Part II is largely devoted to the analysis and determination of the elements in their inorganic forms. In Section B of Part II of the Treatise, which is at present in preparation, the determination of the elements as such in organic compounds and as components of organic functional groups is systematically covered. The differences between organic and inorganic analysis are now not as sharp as formerly. Determination of inorganic constituents in various types of bonding is gaining more and more importance.

A systematic treatment of the detection of the elements and of their functional groups is reserved for Section C of Part II after the quantitative treatment because qualitative analysis often uses the same properties

that are used for the quantitative determination.   Principles of separation
and identification in qualitative analysis are frequently the same as those
used for separation and determination in quantitative analysis.

It is probably most convenient as well as most logical to have the order
of the discussions of the analytical chemistry of the individual elements or
of groups of related elements in Section A of Part II of the Treatise parallel
the occurrence of the elements in the familiar Periodic Table arrangement.
Consequently, Section A will be issued in seven or eight volumes organized
on the basis of the Periodic Table.   The order in which the volumes are
issued will be determined to a considerable extent by the order in which
allied groups of manuscripts are completed.   To minimize the possible
delays in publication which may arise as a consequence of delayed completion of some manuscripts, it may be necessary to take certain liberties in
the arrangement of the individual chapters, including some slight deviations
from the Periodic Table arrangement.

I. M. KOLTHOFF

P. J. ELVING

Authors of Volume 1

H. F. Beeghly

Research and Development Department, Jones & Laughlin Steel Corporation, Pittsburgh, Pennsylvania.

Gerhard A. Cook

Research Laboratory, Linde Company, Division of Union Carbide Corporation, Tonawanda, New York.

W. Conard Fernelius

Research Department, Koppers Company, Inc., Pittsburgh, Pennsylvania.

James I. Hoffman

Chief, Metallurgy Division, National Bureau of Standards, Washington, D. C.

Silve Kallman

Research Director, Ledoux & Company, Inc., Teaneck, New Jersey.

John Mitchell, Jr.

Polychemicals Department, E. I. du Pont de Nemours & Company, Inc., Wilmington, Delaware.

PART II. ANALYTICAL CHEMISTRY OF THE ELEMENTS

CONTENTS—VOLUME 1

SECTION A. Systematic Analytical Chemistry of the Elements

PRINCIPLES OF INORGANIC NOMENCLATURE

By W. Conard Fernelius, *Koppers Company, Inc., Pittsburgh, Pennsylvania*

Contents

Contents (*continued*)

I. INTRODUCTION

Every chemist has need of a knowledge of nomenclature (*1*) to present his findings and ideas in a manner that will be completely understood by his contemporaries and (*2*) to enable him to read understandingly the records of previous chemical investigators. The treatment of inorganic nomenclature presented here should acquaint the reader with (*1*) the historically important nomenclature developments, (*2*) the present state of national and international agreement, and (*3*) suitable practices for areas in which there has been, as yet, only limited agreement.

The first aim of a good system of chemical nomenclature is that there should be a specific and unique name for each individual chemical species. Aims almost as important are that the name should indicate (*1*) the composition and (*2*), where convenient, the structure of a compound. Beyond these qualifications, chemical names should be developed along some logical and systematic pattern so that they are easily and exactly reproduced and adapted to new compounds. It is hardly surprising that all these aims are not realized at all times and that compromises have to be made. Furthermore, as the knowledge of chemical combination expands, established patterns of nomenclature are strained, and new ones proposed. Even theories widely accepted at a given period are apt to leave an imprint upon nomenclature practices. Hence, it is appropriate to trace briefly the major developments in inorganic nomenclature before detailing modern practices.

A. THE SYSTEM OF GUYTON DE MORVEAU, LAVOISIER, AND OTHERS

In 1782 Guyton de Morveau (15,16) made the first attempt to replace the chaotic practices then current by a rational system of nomenclature. This system was elaborated in a joint publication (1787) by Guyton de Morveau, Lavoisier, Berthollet, and Fourcroy (17) and given wide publicity by Lavoisier (1789) in his *Traite Elementaire de Chemie* (20). This system was adapted by Berzelius (3) to the Germanic languages, and English followed either the direct translation (inverted form) from French or the Berzelius pattern. Gradually, the latter displaced the former.

The fundamental principles of the new nomenclature were that the name of a compound should exhibit (*1*) the elements of which it was composed and (*2*), as far as possible, the relative proportions thereof. The combinations of oxygen with other elements played a dominant role in this new system of names. The product of the union of oxygen with a simple non-metallic substance was called an acid, whereas that of the union with a metallic substance was called an oxide. The union of an acid and an oxide produced a salt. The acids or oxides were given names (much like those of Linnaeus for plants and animals) of which the generic part was the work "acid" or "oxide" and the specific part was an adjective derived from the other element in the compound: e.g., *acide sulfurique* and *oxide plombique* (or, in English, sulfuric acid and plumbic oxide). The same principle supplied names for sulfides and phosphides.

In case a substance combined with oxygen to produce more than one acid or oxide, these were distinguished by an alteration of the termination or by the addition of a Greek prefix: *acide sulfureux* and *acide sulfurique* (sulfurous and sulfuric acids); *oxide de plomb blanc* and *oxide plombique* (lead monoxide and lead dioxide).

The names adopted for salts consisted of a generic part derived from the acid and a specific part from the metallic base: *l'oxide de plomb* + *l'acid sulfurique* → *le sulfate de plomb* (lead oxide + sulfuric acid → lead sulfate). The names for salts of acids containing an element in varying degrees of oxidation were given varying terminations: *sulfite de soude* and *sulfate de soude* (sodium sulfite and sodium sulfate); *nitrite de baryte* and *nitrate de baryte* (barium nitrite and barium nitrate).

B. ESTABLISHED PRACTICE IN THE ENGLISH LANGUAGE

In English, the system which has become standard practice shares the simplicity of the original proposal for French. Binary compounds are systematically designated by two words, the first referring to the more electropositive constituent, and the second, ending in *-ide*, referring to the more electronegative constituent, as sodium chlor*ide*. In case the metal exhibits two oxidation states, the lower is indicated by the termination *-ous*, and the higher by *-ic*, as cupr*ous* oxide and cupr*ic* oxide. Some ternary compounds containing well-established radicals are named as though they were binary compounds: e.g., sodium hydroxide, calcium cyanide, and potassium amide.

Ternary compounds are also named by giving the more electropositive constituent first. The various oxidation states of the more electronegative element are designated by a system of prefixes and terminations added to a stem characteristic of the element.

Acids		Salts	
HClO	*hypochlorous*	NaClO	*hypochlorite*
HClO$_2$	chlor*ous*	NaClO$_2$	chlor*ite*
HClO$_3$	chlor*ic*	NaClO$_3$	chlor*ate*
HClO$_4$	*per*chlor*ic*	NaClO$_4$	*per*chlor*ate*

The name cyan*ate* indicates that the compound bearing this name contains oxygen, in contrast to cyan*ide*.

C. MODIFIED FORMS IN COMMON USE

Because there were situations not covered by the original proposal, additional practices found acceptance. Where elements exhibited more than two states of oxidation, the naming of binary compounds could be handled in the following manner:

TiCl$_2$	titanium dichloride
TiCl$_3$	titanium trichloride
TiCl$_4$	titanium tetrachloride
N$_2$O	dinitrogen (mon)oxide, nitrous oxide
NO	(mono)nitrogen (mon)oxide, nitric oxide
N$_2$O$_3$	(di)nitrogen trioxide
NO$_2$	nitrogen dioxide
N$_2$O$_4$	(di)nitrogen tetroxide
N$_2$O$_5$	(di)nitrogen pentoxide

Another approved method of indicating proportions of constituents is the Stock system (see Section I-F).

Occasionally, an element forms more than four acids, and other combinations of prefixes and suffixes have been resorted to; H$_4$P$_2$O$_6$, intermediate between H$_3$PO$_3$ and H$_3$PO$_4$, is known as *hypo*phosphor*ic* acid; and the salts M$_2$FeO$_3$, intermediate between M$_2$FeO$_4$ and MFeO$_2$, are sometimes known as *per*ferr*ites*. Here again the Stock system offers definite advantages. For a long time use has been made of *ortho-*, *meta-*, and *pyro-* or of numerical prefixes to denote stages of hydroxylation of acids. In many instances special names have been created to deal with unusual situations. Examples are the thionic acids, H$_2$S$_x$O$_6$ ($x = 2$ to 6); dithionous acid (instead of hydrosulfurous acid), $H_2S_2O_4$; and nitroxylic acid (instead hydronitrous acid), H_2NO_2.

D. SYSTEMS OF COMPOUNDS

Although the nomenclature system of Guyton de Morveau was designed particularly for oxygen compounds, it was early recognized that other elements could play much the same role in many compounds as does oxygen in the familiar oxygen salts. These relationships received their maximum systematization in E. C. Franklin's concept of systems of compounds (12–14). Consider the following formulas and their names on this basis:

KBO_2	KBS_2	KBF_4	$KB(NH)_2$
potassium	potassium	potassium	potassium
borate	*thio*borate	*fluo*borate	*ammono*borate
$CaCO_3$	$CaCS_3$	$CaSiF_6$	$CaCN_2$
calcium	calcium	calcium	calcium
carbonate	*thio*carbonate	*fluo*silicate	*ammono*carbonate
Na_3PO_4	Na_3PS_4	$NaPF_6$	Na_2PN_2
sodium	sodium	sodium	sodium
phosphate	*thio*phosphate	*fluo*phosphate	*ammono*phosphate

Note that Franklin used *ammono-* because the use of the prefix *nitro-* was already well established in an entirely different capacity.

Although the pattern of nomenclature just outlined in very useful, it does lead to some difficulties. Many quaternary compounds exist which contain oxygen and another electronegative element. Consider the series M_2CO_3, M_2CO_2S, M_2COS_2, and MCS_3, which are called carbonates, (mono)-thiocarbonates, dithiocarbonates, and trithiocarbonates, respectively. However, in practice both the prefixes *mono-* and *tri-* have been omitted, and there is no agreement as to whether the omission of a prefix should signify the mono- or the completely substituted compound: e.g., thiosulfate, $S_2O_3{}^{2-}$, and chloroplatinate, $PtCl_6{}^{2-}$. The situation is somewhat more complicated where oxygen and fluorine are present in the same compound because one is bivalent and the other univalent and the coordination number toward fluorine is different from that toward oxygen: e.g., H_3PO_4, H_2PO_3F, HPO_2F_2, and HPF_6. Also, investigators have not been consistent in choosing the same reference state for the names of the oxygen salts and the halogen salts. Thus, for rhenium(IV), the salts M_2ReO_3 are known as rhenites whereas the chloro salts M_2ReCl_6 are known as chlororhenates. Names like ferrocyanide and ferricyanide seem to be archaic remnants of a time when all such compounds were regarded as double salts.

E. COORDINATION COMPOUNDS

The approach of Werner (29) to the problem of naming ternary and higher-order compounds was from an entirely different point of view. By considering all such substances as complex or coordination compounds, he succeeded in naming a wide variety of compounds according to a single general pattern. To designate the oxidation state of the element serving as the center of coordination, Werner chose the characteristic endings suggested by Brauner (4):

$$
\begin{array}{llllllll}
\text{I} & \text{II} & \text{III} & \text{IV} & \text{V} & \text{VI} & \text{VII} & \text{VIII} \\
\text{a} & \text{o} & \text{i} & \text{e} & \text{an} & \text{on} & \text{in} & \text{en}
\end{array}
$$

The essentials of the Werner scheme of nomenclature are indicated in Table I.

TABLE I
Comparison of the Werner and Stock Systems

Formula	Werner name	Stock name
$[Cr(NH_3)_6]^{3+}(NO_3{}^-)_3$	hexamminechrom*i* nitrate	hexamminechromium(III) nitrate
$[Pt(H_2O)_2(NH_3)_4]^{4+}(Cl^-)_4$	diaquotetrammineplat*e* chloride	diaquotetrammineplatinum-(IV) chloride
$[CoCl(NO_2)(en)_2]^+Br^-$ (en = $H_2NCH_2CH_2NH_2$)	chloronitrobis(ethylenedi-amine)cobalt*i* bromide	chloronitrobis(ethylenedi-amine)cobalt(III) bro-mide
$H^+[AgCl_2]^-$	hydrogen dichloroargen-ta*ate*	hydrogen dichloroargentate-(I) or dichloroargentic(I) acid
$(K^+)_3[Fe(CN)_5(H_2O)]^{3-}$	potassium pentacyano-aquoferro*ate*	potassium pentacyanoaquo-ferrate(II)
$(Na^+)_2[SSO_3]^{2-}$	sodium thiotrioxosulfur*on*-ate	sodium thiotrioxosulfate(VI)

Werner's system was both logical and general; yet it never attained general adoption. Books have been written on complex compounds in which no names, only formulas, are used. In the spoken language, especially English, the necessity for stressing the significant vowels probably militated against general acceptance of Werner's scheme.

F. THE STOCK SYSTEM

Stock (21,22,24,27) sought to correct many nomenclature difficulties by introducing the use of Roman numerals in parentheses to indicate the state or states of oxidation.

$TiCl_2$	titanium(II) chloride	FeO	iron(II) oxide
$TiCl_3$	titanium(III) chloride	Fe_2O_3	iron(III) oxide
$TiCl_4$	titanium(IV) chloride	Fe_3O_4	iron(II, III) oxide

For anions, only the termination -*ate* is used followed by Roman numerals in parentheses. Examples are K_2MnO_3, potassium manganate(IV); K_2PtCl_4, potassium (tetra)chloroplatinate(II); K_2PtCl_6, potassium (hexa)-chloroplatinate(IV); K_2ReCl_6, potassium (hexa)chlororhenate(IV); Na_4-$Fe(CN)_6$, sodium (hexa)cyanoferrate(II); and $Na_3Fe(CN)_6$, sodium (hexa)cyanoferrate(III). Thus a set of prefixes and terminations to indicate composition becomes unnecessary.

The Stock system is easily extended to include other coordination compounds (see Table I). Even the preparation of the interesting substances represented by the formulas $Na_4[Ni(CN)_4]$ and $K_4[Pd(CN)_4]$ created no nomenclature problem because according to the Stock system these become sodium tetracyanonickelate(0) and potassium tetracyano-palladate(0). However, there are times when the state of oxidation of the central atom is in doubt. To avoid this embarrassment, Ewens and Bassett (7) proposed that instead of the Roman numerals representing the state of oxidation of the central atom, the charge on the ion in Arabic numerals be given in parenthesis.

G. INTERNATIONAL AGREEMENT

The efforts of the first international commission on inorganic nomenclature were brought to an abrupt end by World War I. Resumption of these efforts in 1921 led to a preliminary report in 1926 (6,23) and a comprehensive set of rules in 1940 (18). These rules have been altered, elaborated, and augmented by a further report in 1957 (see General References). The responsible group is the Commission on the Nomenclature of Inorganic Chemistry appointed by the International Union of Pure and Applied Chemistry (I.U.P.A.C.) (at one time known as the International Union of Chemistry). The cooperating body in the United States is the nomenclature committee of the National Research Council, although its work is greatly aided by committees of the American Chemical Society and its Division of Inorganic Chemistry.

II. ELEMENTS

The symbols for the elements which are approved by the I.U.P.A.C. Commission on the Nomenclature of Inorganic Chemistry are given in Table II. The terms in parentheses after the names of the elements are used when forming names derived from those of the elements. Isotopes

TABLE II
Elements

Name	Symbol	Atomic number	Name	Symbol	Atomic number
Actinium	Ac	89	Lanthanum	La	57
Aluminum	Al	13	Lead (Plumbum)	Pb	82
Americium	Am	95	Lithium	Li	3
Antimony	Sb	51	Lutetium	Lu	71
Argon	Ar	18	Magnesium	Mg	12
Arsenic	As	33	Manganese	Mn	25
Astatine	At	85	Mendelevium	Md	101
Barium	Ba	56	Mercury	Hg	80
Berkelium	Bk	97	Molybdenum	Mo	42
Beryllium	Be	4	Neodymium	Nd	60
Bismuth	Bi	83	Neon	Ne	10
Boron	B	5	Neptunium	Np	93
Bromine	Br	35	Nickel[c]	Ni	28
Cadmium	Cd	48	Niobium	Nb	41
Calcium	Ca	20	Nitrogen	N	7
Californium	Cf	98	Nobelium	No	102
Carbon	C	6	Osmium	Os	76
Cerium	Ce	58	Oxygen	O	8
Cesium[a]	Cs	55	Palladium	Pd	46
Chlorine	Cl	17	Phosphorus	P	15
Chromium	Cr	24	Platinum	Pt	78
Cobalt	Co	27	Plutonium	Pu	94
Copper (Cuprum)	Cu	29	Polonium	Po	84
Curium	Cm	96	Potassium	K	19
Dysprosium	Dy	66	Praseodymium	Pr	59
Einsteinium	Es	99	Promethium	Pm	61
Erbium	Er	68	Protactinium	Pa	91
Europium	Eu	63	Radium	Ra	88
Fermium	Fm	100	Radon	Rn	86
Fluorine	F	9	Rhenium	Re	75
Francium	Fr	87	Rhodium	Rh	45
Gadolinium	Gd	64	Rubidium	Rb	37
Gallium	Ga	31	Ruthenium	Ru	44
Germanium	Ge	32	Samarium	Sm	62
Gold (Aurum)	Au	79	Scandium	Sc	21
Hafnium	Hf	72	Selenium	Se	34
Helium	He	2	Silicon	Si	14
Holmium	Ho	67	Silver (Argentum)	Ag	47
Hydrogen[b]	H	1	Sodium	Na	11
Indium	In	49	Strontium	Sr	38
Iodine	I	53	Sulfur	S	16
Iridium	Ir	77	Tantalum	Ta	73
Iron (Ferrum)	Fe	26	Technetium	Tc	43
Krypton	Kr	36	Tellurium	Te	52

(*continued*)

TABLE II (*continued*)

Name	Sym-bol	Atomic number	Name	Sym-bol	Atomic number
Terbium	Tb	65	Uranium	U	92
Thallium	Tl	81	Vanadium	V	23
Thorium	Th	90	Xenon	Xe	54
Thulium	Tm	69	Ytterbium	Yb	70
Tin (Stannum)	Sn	50	Yttrium	Y	39
Titanium	Ti	22	Zinc	Zn	30
Tungsten[d]	W	74	Zirconium	Zr	40

[a] I.U.P.A.C. recommends *caesium*.

[b] D and T are acceptable for ^{2}H and ^{3}H, respectively.

[c] I.U.P.A.C. recommends that derived names be formed from the Latin name *niccolum*. It is unlikely that niccolate will replace nickelate in the American literature.

[d] I.U.P.A.C. recommends that derived names be formed from *wolfram*. However, tungstate is too well established to be replaced by wolframate.

are designated by the mass number along with the symbol for the elements: oxygen-18, ^{18}O (I.U.P.A.C. recommendation), O^{18} (usual practice in the United States.). However, hydrogen is an exception: hydrogen-2, deuterium, D; and hydrogen-3, tritium, T. These isotope symbols are used in both formulas and names: ^{32}PCl$_3$, phosphorus (^{32}P) trichloride, or phosphorus-32 trichloride; ^{15}NH$_3$, ammonia (^{15}N), or ammonia nitrogen-15; HOSO$_2$^{35}SH, thiosulfuric (^{35}SH) acid; ^{15}NO$_2$NH$_2$, nitramide (^{51}NO$_2$).

Although a symbol may be used in a general sense for the element, it may also be used for a single atom and with subscripts for a molecule of the element. In the latter cases, the names should indicate the state of aggregation or the allotropic modification.

Symbol	Trivial name	Systematic name
H	atomic hydrogen	monohydrogen
O$_2$	(common) oxygen	dioxygen
O$_3$	ozone	trioxygen
P$_4$	white phosphorus (yellow phosphorus)	tetraphosphorus
S$_8$	λ-sulfur	*cyclo*octasulfur or octasulfur
S$_n$	μ-sulfur	*catena*polysulfur or polysulfur

For the nomenclature of solid allotropic forms, the rules under Section III may be applied.

III. FORMULAS

In any consideration of formulas, it must be recognized that several kinds of formulas are in common use by chemists. The *empirical formula* is the *simplest* formula expressing the stoichiometric composition of the compound in question. Such a formula may be supplemented by an indication of the crystal structure, especially where polymorphism exists: e.g., ZnS (cub.) for sphalerite and ZnS (hex.) for wurtzite; or AuCd (CsCl type) and AuCd (o-rh). Suitable abbreviations follow:

cub. = cubic; c. = body-centered; f. = face-centered
tetra. = tetragonal   trig. = trigonal
o-rh. = orthorhombic   mon. = monoclinic
hex. = hexagonal   tric. = triclinic

It should be noted that an empirical formula is the only kind of formula that can be written for a true electrolyte or a "giant" molecule such as silica, SiO_2.

The *molecular formula* indicates the composition of the molecules of a compound: e.g., S_2Cl_2 and $H_4P_2O_6$ instead of SCl and H_2PO_3. Such formulas are valid only for compounds consisting of discrete molecules where a molecular weight may be determined. The *structural formula* indicates the sequence and spatial arrangement of the atoms in a molecule. Such a representation may be simple or complex according to the complexity of the molecule. The determination of structures for most inorganic compounds had to wait for the development of x-ray and similar techniques. Hence, the use of structural formulas is not so well developed in inorganic chemistry as in organic chemistry. However, there is no excuse for writing formulas with an order inconsistent with known structures; e.g., the thiocyanate ion should always be written NCS^- and not CNS^-, cyanic acid HOCN, and fulminic acid HONC. The prefixes *cis-*, *trans-*, *sym-*, *asym-*, etc., are used for further indications of structure: e.g., *cis*-[$PtCl_2$-($NH_3)_2$].

When writing formulas, the more electropositive constituent is always placed first. For ionic compounds this means that the cation precedes the anion. For other types of compounds it may be necessary to be a bit arbitrary. Unless there is good evidence to the contrary, for binary compounds between nonmetals that constituent is placed first which appears earlier in the sequence

B, Si, C, Sb, As, P, N, H, Te, Se, S, At, I, Br, Cl, O, F

In intermetallic compounds the constituents are placed in the following order:

Fr, Cs, Rb, K, Na, Li
Ra, Ba, Sr, Ca, Mg, Be
103, No, Md, Fm, Es, Cf, Bk, Cm, Am, Pu, Np, U, Pa, Th, Ac, Lu-La, Y, Sc
Hf, Zr, Ti
Ta, Nb, V
W, Mo, Cr
Re, Tc, Mn
Pt, Ir, Os, Pd, Rh, Ru, Ni, Co, Fe
Au, Ag, Cu
Hg, Cd, Zn
Tl, In, Ga, Al
Pb, Sn, Ge
Bi, Sb
Po
Nonmetals (except Sb) in the order previously given

For compounds containing more than one electropositive or more than one electronegative constituent, the sequence is the same as for the naming of double salts (see Section VI-B).

However, usage for the ternary oxygen compounds HNO_3, $HClO_4$, H_2SO_4, etc., does not follow this practice.

IV. BINARY COMPOUNDS

The order of the parts of a name for a binary compound is the same as that for writing a formula. The name of the electropositive constituent is not modified, whereas that of the electronegative constituent is modified to end in *-ide*. However, when a binary hydrogen compound is named as an acid, the two names are contracted, and the termination *-ic* is used: e.g., *hydrochloric* acid for HCl. The stoichiometric proportions are denoted either by means of Greek numerical prefixes (*mono-*, *di-*, *tri-*, *tetra-*, *penta-*, *hexa-*, *octa-*, *ennea-*,* *deca-*, *hendeca-*,* and *dodeca-*) or by the

TABLE III
Order of Elements in Formulas and Names of Binary Compounds

Li_3N	lithium nitride	S_2Cl_2	disulfur dichloride
SF_6	sulfur hexafluoride	As_2Se_3	(di)arsenic (tri)selenide
SiC	silicon carbide	OF_2	oxygen difluoride
Cl_2O	(di)chlorine oxide	S_4N_4	(tetra)sulfur (tetra)nitride (known to be a nitride)
ClO_2	chlorine dioxide		
MnO_2	manganese(IV) oxide	BaO_2	barium peroxide
$Pb_2^{II}Pb^{IV}O_4$	dilead(II) lead(IV) oxide or trilead tetraoxide		

* In organic nomenclature, nona- is used instead of ennea-, and undeca- instead of hendeca-.

use of Roman numerals to indicate the oxidation state (see Section I-C), as shown in Table III.

Names for simple cations and anions follow directly from the names for binary compounds: e.g., Cu^+, copper(I) ion; Cu^{2+}, copper (II) ion; S^{2-}, sulfide ion; N^{3-}, nitride ion; B^{3-}, boride ion, etc. Note that the use of the terminations -*ous* and -*ic* applied to the cation is rapidly disappearing. Some unusual cations require specific names: e.g., NO^+, nitrosyl cation; NO_2^+, nitryl ion; UO_2^{2+}, uranyl ion; and $H_2NO_3^+$, nitric acidium ion.

The hydrides are a special group in that certain trivial names persist. Further, the other names are derived according to a different pattern.

BH_3	borane	B_2H_6	diborane
CH_4	methane	C_2H_6	ethane
		C_2H_2	acetylene
SiH_4	silane	Si_2H_6	disilane
NH_3	ammonia	N_2H_4	hydrazine
		HN_3	hydrogen azide
PH_3	phosphine	P_2H_4	diphosphine
AsH_3	arsine	As_2H_4	diarsine
SbH_3	stibine		
H_2O	water	H_2O_2	hydrogen peroxide

Cations formed by the addition of a proton to these hydrides have the termination -*ium:* e.g., H_3O^+, oxonium; PH_4^+, phosphonium; but $N_2H_5^+$, hydrazinium (1+), and $N_2H_6^{2+}$, hydrazinium (2+). Anions formed by the loss of a proton have characteristic names ending in -*ide:* e.g.,

OH^-	hydroxide	O_2^-	superoxide
O_2^{2-}	peroxide	O_3^-	ozonide
S_2^{2-}	disulfide	$NHOH^-$	hydroxylamide
I_3^-	triiodide	$N_2H_3^-$	hydrazide
HF_2^-	hydrogen difluoride	C_2^{2-}	acetylide
N_3^-	azide	SH^-	hydrogen sulfide
NH^{2-}	imide	O_2H^-	hydrogen peroxide
NH_2^-	amide		

There are a few ternary compounds that are named like binary compounds These include hydroxides, amides, and cyanides.

V. TERNARY COMPOUNDS

A. OXYGEN ACIDS AND THEIR SALTS

For most of the oxygen acids, names based on the Lavoisierian pattern are still in use (see Table IV). For names of the corresponding salts,

TABLE IV
Names for Oxo Acids

H_3BO_3	orthoboric acid or (mono)boric acid	H_3AsO_2	arsenious acid
$(HBO_2)_n$	metaboric acid	$HSb(OH)_6$	hexahydroxoantimonic acid
$(HBO_2)_3$	trimetaboric acid	H_2SO_4	sulfuric acid
$H_4B_2O_4$	hypoboric acid	$H_2S_2O_7$	disulfuric or pyrosulfuric acid
H_2CO_3	carbonic acid		
HOCN	cyanic acid	H_2SO_5	peroxy(mono)sulfuric acid[a]
HNCO	isocyanic acid		
HONC	fulminic acid	$H_2S_2O_8$	peroxydisulfuric acid[a]
H_4SiO_4	orthosilicic acid	$H_2S_2O_3$	thiosulfuric acid
$(H_2SiO_3)_n$	metasilicic acids	$H_2S_2O_6$	dithionic acid
HNO_3	nitric acid	H_2SO_3	sulfurous acid
HNO_4	peroxynitric acid[a]	$H_2S_2O_5$	disulfurous or pyrosulfurous acid
HNO_2	nitrous acid		
HOONO	peroxynitrous acid[a]	$H_2S_2O_2$	thiosulfurous acid
H_2NO_2	nitroxylic acid	$H_2S_2O_4$	dithionous acid
$H_2N_2O_2$	hyponitrous acid	H_2SO_2	sulfoxylic acid
H_3PO_4	(ortho)phosphoric acid	$H_2S_xO_6$	polythionic acids
$H_4P_2O_7$	diphosphoric or pyrophosphoric acid	$(x = 3, 4, \ldots)$	
		H_2SeO_4	selenic acid
$H_5P_3O_{10}$	triphosphoric acid	H_2SeO_3	selenious acid
$H_{n+2}P_nO_{3n+1}$	polyphosphoric acids	H_6TeO_6	(ortho)telluric acid
$(HPO_3)_n$	metaphosphoric acids	H_2CrO_4	chromic acid
$(HPO_3)_3$	trimetaphosphoric acid	$H_2Cr_2O_7$	dichromic acid
$(HPO_3)_4$	tetrametaphosphoric acid	$HClO_4$	perchloric acid
		$HClO_3$	chloric acid
H_3PO_5	peroxy(mono)phosphoric acid[a]	$HClO_2$	chlorous acid
		HClO	hypochlorous acid
$H_4P_2O_8$	peroxydiphosphoric acid[a]	$HBrO_3$	bromic acid
		$HBrO_2$	bromous acid
$(HO)_2OP$—$PO(OH)_2$	hypophosphoric acid	HBrO	hypobromous acid
		H_5IO_6	(ortho)periodic acid
$(HO)_2P$—O—$PO(OH)_2$	diphosphoric(III,V) acid	HIO_3	iodic acid
		HIO	hypoiodous acid
H_2PHO_3	phosphorous acid	$HMnO_4$	permanganic acid
		H_2MnO_4	manganic acid
$H_4P_2O_5$	diphosphorous or pyrophosphorous acid	$HTcO_4$	pertechnetic acid
		H_2TcO_4	technetic acid
HPH_2O_2	hypophosphorous acid	$HReO_4$	perrhenic acid
H_3AsO_4	arsenic acid	H_2ReO_4	rhenic acid

[a] The I.U.P.A.C. commission prefers *peroxo* to *peroxy*, but there is strong pressure to return to the older *peroxy* to obtain acceptance for similar usage among organic chemists.

see Section I-B. However, there is a growing tendency to name some of the less common acids as coordination compounds:

H_2MnO_4 manganic(VI) acid, to distinguish it from H_3MnO_4, manganic(V) acid

$HReO_4$ tetraoxorhenic(VII) acid, to distinguish it from H_3ReO_5, pentaoxorhenic(VII) acid

H_2ReO_4 tetraoxorhenic(VI) acid, to distinguish it from $HReO_3$, trioxorhenic(V) acid; H_3ReO_4, tetraoxorhenic(V) acid; and $H_4Re_2O_7$, heptaoxodirhenic(V) acid

H_2NO_2 dioxonitric(II) acid instead of nitroxylic acid

B. THIO ACIDS AND THEIR SALTS

These are named like the corresponding oxygen compounds.

H_3PO_3S	monothiophosphoric acid
$H_3PO_2S_2$	dithiophosphoric acid
H_2CS_3	trithiocarbonic acid
H_3AsS_3	trithioarsenious acid
H_3AsS_4	tetrathioarsenic acid

C. FUNCTIONAL DERIVATIVES OF ACIDS

Esters of inorganic acids are named in the same way as salts: e.g., dimethyl sulfate, diethyl hydrogen phosphate. The names of the acid halides are formed from the names of the corresponding acid radicals: e.g., sulfuryl chloride and phosphoryl bromide. The I.U.P.A.C. commission has approved the following radical names:

HO	hydroxyl	SO	sulfinyl (thionyl)	ClO	chlorosyl
CO	carbonyl	SO_2	sulfonyl (sulfuryl)	ClO_2	chloryl
NO	nitrosyl	S_2O_5	pyrosulfuryl	ClO_3	perchloryl
NO_2	nitryl	SeO	seleninyl		(and similarly
PO	phosphoryl	SeO_2	selenonyl		for other halogens)
VO	vanadyl	CrO_2	chromyl		
PS	thiophosphoryl	UO_2	uranyl		
CSe	selenocarbonyl	NpO_2	neptunyl		
		PuO_2	plutonyl		
			(similarly for other actinide elements)		

Whenever there is any doubt about the oxidation number of the characteristic element, this uncertainty can be indicated: e.g., $VOCl_3$, vanadyl(V) chloride, and $VOCl_2$, vanadyl(IV) chloride. In other cases acid halides may be named as oxidehalides: e.g., MoO_2Cl_2, molybdenum dioxide dichloride. Inorganic chemistry has few "substitutive names" such as chloramine, NH_2Cl, and dichloroamine, $NHCl_2$. Hence, fluorosulfuric acid, FSO_3H, is to be preferred to fluorosulfonic acid.

The naming of amides and imides continues to cause difficulty. Although the words sulfamide, $SO_2(NH_2)_2$, phosphamide, $PO(NH_2)_3$, and sulfamic acid, NH_2SO_3H, have long standing, they should be replaced by sulfuric diamide, phosphoric triamide, and amidosulfuric acid, respectively.

VI. SALTS

Several aspects of the nomenclature of salts have already been covered in Sections I-B, IV, and V-A. There remain a number of other aspects which require care.

A. SALTS CONTAINING HYDROGEN

Names are formed by adding the word *hydrogen* immediately in front of the name of the anion: e.g., $NaHCO_3$, sodium hydrogen carbonate, and NaH_2PO_4, sodium dihydrogen phosphate.

B. DOUBLE SALTS

The cations are given in the order of increasing valence, and within each valence group in the order of decreasing atomic number, with polyatomic radical ions (e.g., ammonium) at the ends of their appropriate groups.

$KMgF_3$	potassium magnesium fluoride
$TlNa(NO_3)_2$	thallium(I) sodium nitrate or thallium sodium dinitrate
$KNaCO_3$	potassium sodium carbonate
$NH_4MgPO_4 \cdot 6H_2O$	ammonium magnesium phosphate hexahydrate
$NaZn(UO_2)_3(C_2H_3O_2)_9 \cdot 6H_2O$	sodium zinc triuranyl acetate hexahydrate
$Na[Zn(H_2O)_6](UO_2)_3(C_2H_3O_2)_9$	sodium hexaquozinc triuranyl acetate
$NaNH_4HPO_4 \cdot 4H_2O$	sodium ammonium hydrogen phosphate tetrahydrate

Anions are cited in the order of the following groups:

1. H^-
2. O^{2-} and OH^- (in that order)
3. Simple (i.e., one element only) inorganic anions other than H^- and O^{2-}
4. Inorganic anions containing two or more elements, other than OH^-
5. Anions of organic acids and organic substances exerting an acid function

Although the I.U.P.A.C. commission has recommended that within group *3* the ions be cited in the order for nonmetals in binary compounds and within group *4* in the order of increasing number of atoms, an alphabetical listing within groups *3* to *5* seems preferable.

C. OXIDE AND HYDROXIDE SALTS

These salts are regarded as double salts containing O^{2-} and OH^- anions and are so named.

$Mg(OH)Cl$	magnesium hydroxide chloride
$BiOCl$	bismuth oxide chloride
$LaOF$	lanthanum oxide fluoride
$VOSO_4$	vanadium(IV) oxide sulfate
$CuCl_2 \cdot 3Cu(OH)_2$ or $Cu_2(OH)_3Cl$	dicopper trihydroxide chloride
$ZrOCl_2 \cdot 8H_2O$	zirconium oxide (di)chloride octahydrate

D. DOUBLE OXIDES AND HYDROXIDES

Structural studies of many "mixed oxides" and "mixed hydroxides" have shown that these are not saltlike.   Hence, to name them as salts is misleading.   In such cases these materials are named in the same manner as double salts.

$NaNbO_3$	sodium niobium trioxide (*perovskite* type)
$MgTiO_3$	magnesium titanium trioxide (*ilmenite* type)
$FeTiO_3$	iron(II) titanium trioxide (ilmenite)
$LiAlMn_2^{IV}O_4(OH)_4$	lithium aluminum dimanganese(IV) tetraoxide tetrahydroxide

VII. HIGHER-ORDER COMPOUNDS

A. COORDINATION COMPOUNDS

In practice the system of nomenclature used for coordination compounds has proved to be extremely flexible and comprehensive (9,10).   This pattern of nomenclature is being adapted to encompass an increasingly larger portion of the whole of inorganic nomenclature, so that a good guide in any instance is the following suggestion: in case of doubt, try to name the substance as a coordination compound.

A *coordination entity* (complex ion or neutral molecule) (Fig. 1) consists of a central cation (much less often a neutral atom) surrounded by two or

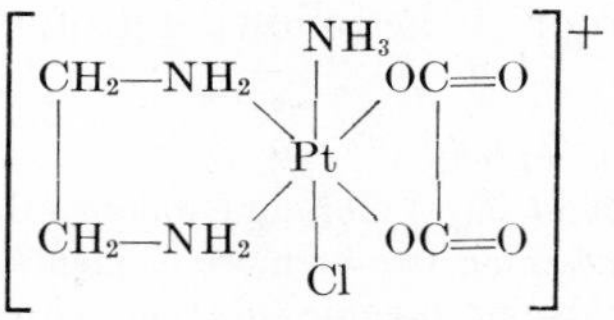

Fig. 1. A coordination entity: Pt^{4+}, central or nuclear atom; 6, C.N. (coordination number); $H_2NCH_2CH_2NH_2$, en; $C_2O_4^{2-}$, ox^{2-}; NH_3 and en, neutral ligands; Cl^- and ox^{2-}, charged ligands; and en and ox^{2-}, chelate ligands.

more *ligands* (anions or neutral molecules).   Each ligand has one or more atoms through which *coordination* to the central or nuclear ion is effected. The number of such atoms surrounding the central ion determines the *coordination number* of the central ion.   The number of atoms through which the ligand is attached to the central ion determines the multiplicity of the ligand (*mono-, bi-, ter-, quadri-*, etc., *-dentate*).   All ligands with more than one point of attachment are known as *chelate* groups.   Since monodentate ligands may carry a charge or be uncharged and multidentate ligands may or may not carry a charge at each point of attachment, the entities resulting from the attachment of ligands to the central ion will have a *charge* equal to the *algebraic sum* of the charges of the constituents. In this way complex cations, complex anions, and neutral units will result. When writing formulas, it is customary to preserve the normal order of cation and anion, to give the symbol of the central atom first in any complex, and to enclose all complex units in brackets to indicate that these units are distinct from any oppositely charged ions which may be present to obtain electrical neutrality.

The nomenclature of coordination compounds is covered by the following rules.

1. Order of Listing Ions

The cation(s) is (are) given first, followed by the anion(s) as elsewhere.

2. Characteristic Endings of Coordinated Groups

The names of neutral and cationic ligands have no characteristic endings, whereas these of anionic ligands end in *-o*. In general, if the anion name ends in *-ide, -ite,* or *-ate,* the final *-e* is replaced by *-o,* giving *-ido, -ito,* and *-ato,* respectively. Certain exceptions which do not follow the general practice will be evident in the list of accepted names for coordinated groups, Table V. (The names of most of the cationic ligands end in *-ium* and thus appear to have a characteristic ending.)

TABLE V
List of Coordinated Groups

A. Negatively charged (anionic) groups
   1. Inorganic
      a. Singly charged groups
        Amido, NH_2^-
        Azido, N_3^-
        Bromo, Br^-
        Chlorato, ClO_3^-
        Chlorito, ClO_2^-
        Chloro, Cl^-
        Cyanato, —OCN^-
        Cyano, CN^-
        Fluoro, F^-
        Hydrazido, $N_2H_3^-$
        Hydro,[a] H^-

(continued)

TABLE V (*continued*)

Hydrogen carbonato, $HCO_3{}^-$
Hydrogen peroxo, $HO_2{}^-$
Hydrogen sulfito, $HSO_3{}^-$
Hydroxo,[b] OH^-
Hydroxylamido, $NHOH^-$
Hypochlorito, ClO^-
Hypophosphito, $PH_2O_2{}^-$
Iodo, I^-
Isothiocyanato, $—NCS^-$
Nitrito, $—ONO^-$
Nitro, $—NO_2{}^-$
Selenocyanato, $—SeCN^-$
Tellurocyanato, $—TeCN^-$
Thiocyanato, $—SCN^-$
Thiolo,[c] SH^-
  b. Doubly charged groups
Carbonato, $CO_3{}^{2-}$
Disulfido, $S_2{}^{2-}$
Imido, NH^{2-}
Oxo, O^{2-}
Peroxo, $O_2{}^{2-}$
Phosphito, $PHO_3{}^{2-}$
Selenato, $SeO_4{}^{2-}$
Selenito, $SeO_3{}^{2-}$
Seleno, Se^{2-}
Sulfato, $SO_4{}^{2-}$
Sulfito, $SO_3{}^{2-}$
Telluro, Te^{2-}
Thio, S^{2-}
Thiosulfato, $S_2O_3{}^{2-}$
  c. Triply charged groups
Arsenato, $AsO_4{}^{3-}$
Nitrido, N^{3-}
Phosphato, $PO_4{}^{3-}$
Phosphido, P^{3-}
 2. Organic
Acetato, $CH_3CO_2{}^-$
Acetylacetonato, $CH_2COCH{=}CO^-{—}CH_3$
Cyclopentadienyl, $C_5H_5{}^-$
Dimethylglyoximato, $HON{=}C(CH_3)C(CH_3){=}NO^-$
Ethanethiolato,[d] $C_2H_5S^-$
Ethoxo,[b] $C_2H_5O^-$
N,N'-Ethylenebis(salicylideneiminoato), $(—CH_2N{=}CHC_6H_4O^-)_2$
Ethynyl, C_2H^-
Methanethiolato,[d] CH_3S^-
Methoxo,[b] CH_3O^-

(*continued*)

TABLE V (*continued*)

Methyl, CH_3^-
Oxalato, $^-OOCCOO^-$
Phenyl, $C_6H_5^-$
Phenylethynyl, $C_6H_5C_2^-$
8-Quinolinolato
Salicylaldehydato, $OHCC_6H_4O^-$
Thiooxalato, $^-SOCCOS^-$

B. Neutral groups
   1. Inorganic
   Ammine, NH_3
   Aquo, H_2O
   Carbonyl, CO
   Nitrosyl, NO
   Thiocarbonyl, CS
   Thionitrosyl, NS
   2. Organic
   Bipyridine
   N,N-Dimethylaminoethylaminoethylsulfide, $(CH_3)_2NCH_2CH_2SCH_2CH_2NH_2$
   Dimethylglyoxime, $HONC(CH_3)C(CH_3)CNOH$
   Ethylene, $H_2C{=}CH_2$
   Ethylenediamine, $H_2NCH_2CH_2NH_2$
   Methylamine, CH_3NH_2
   o-Phenanthroline
   Phenylisocyanide, C_6H_5NC
   1,2,3-Propanetriamine
   Pyridine, C_5H_5N
   Triethylarsine, $(C_2H_5)_3As$
   Triethylphosphine, $(C_2H_5)_3P$
   Triethylphosphite, $(C_2H_5O)_3P$

C. Positively charged (cationic) groups
   1. Inorganic
   Nitrosyl, NO^+
   Hydrazinium, $H_2NNH_3^+$
   2. Organic
   2,3-Diaminopropylammonium, $H_2NCH_2CH(NH_2)CH_2NH_3^+$

---

[a] The I.U.P.A.C. commission recommends hydrido.

[b] There is strong pressure to replace hydroxo, methoxo, etc., by hydroxy, methoxy, etc., respectively, to agree with organic usage.

[c] Mercapto is probably better to agree with approved organic usage.

[d] Methylthio and ethylthio are probably better to agree with organic usage.

3. Order of Classes of Ligands

The name of the central atom is placed after those of the ligands. The order of citation of ligands is anionic ligands followed by neutral and cationic ligands.

4. Order within Classes of Ligands

The anionic ligands are cited in the following order: (*1*) H^-; (*2*) O^{2-}, OH^-; (*3*) other simple anions (one atom only); (*4*) polyatomic inorganic anions; and (*5*) organic anions in alphabetical order. Within group *3* the ions are cited in the order B, Si, C, Sb, As, P, N, H, Te, Se, S, At, I, Br, Cl, oxygen anions other than O^{2-} (e.g., O_2^{2-}), F. Within group *4* anions containing the smallest number of atoms are cited first, and, in the case of two ions containing the same number of atoms, they are cited in the order of decreasing atomic number of the central atoms (e.g., CO_3^{2-} precedes CrO_4^{2-}).

Neutral and cationic ligands are cited in the following order: (*1*) H_2O, NH_3: (*2*) other inorganic ligands in the sequence in which their coordinating elements appear in the list given in group (*3*) above; and (*3*) organic ligands in alphabetical order.

5. Use of Numerical Prefixes

The numerical prefixes *di-*, *tri-*, *tetra-*, etc., are used before all simple expressions, and the multiplicative numerical prefixes *bis-*, *tris-*, *tetrakis*, etc., before complex expressions. All complex expressions are enclosed in parentheses if necessary for clarity.

6. Terminations for Coordination Entities

The characteristic termination for an anionic coordination entity is *-ate*, or *-ic* if named as an acid. There are no characteristic terminations for cationic or neutral coordination entities.

7. Designation of Oxidation State

The oxidation state of the central element is designated by a Roman numeral in parenthesis (Stock system) placed as follows: for a cationic or neutral coordination entity, after the name of the central element; for an anionic entity, after the termination *-ate*. The oxidation states O, $-I$, and $-II$ are recognized. An alternate procedure is the use of prefixes to indicate the number of ions.

Examples of the application of the above rules are shown in Table VI.

TABLE VI
Representative Names for Coordination Compounds

$Li[AlH_4]$	lithium tetrahydroaluminate
$Na[BH_4]$	sodium tetrahydroborate
$K_2[OsNCl_5]$	potassium nitridopentachloroosmate(VI)
$[Co(NH_2)_2(NH_3)_4]OC_2H_5$	diamidotetramminecobalt(III) ethoxide
$[CoN_3(NH_3)_5]SO_4$	azidopentamminecobalt(III) sulfate
$Na_3[Ag(S_2O_3)_2]$	sodium bis(thiosulfato) argentate(I)
$[Ru(HSO_3)_2(NH_3)_4]$	bis(hydrogen sulfito)tetrammineruthe-nium(II)
$NH_4[Cr(SCN)_4(NH_3)_2]$	ammonium tetra(thiocyanato)diammine-chromate(III)
$K[AgF_4]$	potassium tetrafluoroargentate(III)
$K_2[NiF_6]$	potassium hexafluoronickelate(IV)
$Ba[BrF_4]_2$	barium tetrafluorobromate(III)
$Na[AlCl_4]$	sodium tetrachloroaluminate
$Cs[ICl_4]$	cesium tetrachloroiodate(III)
$K[Au(OH)_4]$	potassium tetrahydroxoaurate(III)
$K[CrOF_4]$	potassium oxotetrafluorochromate(V)
$K_2[Cr(O)_2O_2(CN)_2(NH_3)]$	potassium dioxoperoxodicyanoammine-chromate(VI)
$Na[BH(OCH_3)_3]$	sodium hydrotrimethoxoborate
$K_2[Fe_2S_2(NO)_4]$	dipotassium dithiotetranitrosyldiferrate
$[Ni(C_4H_7O_2N_2)_2]$	bis(dimethylglyoximato)nickel(II)
$[Cu(C_5H_7O_2)_2]$	bis(acetylacetonato)copper(II)
$[CoCl_2(C_4H_9O_2N_2)_2]$	dichlorobis(dimethylglyoxime)cobalt(II)
cis-$[PtCl_2(Et_3P)_2]$	cis-dichlorobis(triethylphosphine)plati-num(II)
$[CuCl_2(CH_3NH_2)_2]$	dichlorobis(methylamine)copper(II)
$[Pt(py)_4][PtCl_4]$	tetrapyridineplatinum(II) tetrachloro-platinate(II)
$[Fe(bi\ py)_3]Cl_2$	tris(bipyridine)iron(II) chloride
$[Co(en)_3]_2(SO_4)_3$	tris(ethylenediamine)cobalt(III) sulfate
$[Zn\{NH_2CH_2CH(NH_2)CH_2NH_2\}_2]I_2$	bis(1,2,3-propanetriamine) zinc iodide
$K[PtCl_3(C_2H_4)]$	potassium trichloro(ethylene)platinate-(II) or potassium trichloromonoethyl-eneplatinate(II)
$[PtCl_2\{H_2NCH_2CH(NH_2)CH_2NH_3\}]Cl$	dichloro-(2,3-diaminopropyl ammonium)-platinum(II) chloride
$[Cr(C_6H_5NC)_6]$	hexakis(phenyl isocyanide)chromium
$[Cr(H_2O)_6]Cl_3$	hexaquochromium(III) chloride or hexa-quochromium trichloride
$[Al(OH)(H_2O)_5]^+$	hydroxopentaquoaluminium ion
$[Co(NH_3)_6]ClSO_4$	hexamminecobalt(III) chloride sulfate
$[CoCl(NH_3)_5]Cl_2$	chloropentamminecobalt(III) chloride
$[CoCl_3(NH_3)_2\{(CH_3)_2NH\}]$	trichlorodiammine(dimethylamine)cobalt-(III)

(continued)

TABLE VI (*continued*)

$Na_2[Fe(CN)_5NO]$	disodium pentacyanonitrosylferrate
$K_3[Fe(CN)_5CO]$	tripotassium pentacyanocarbonylferrate
$K[Co(CN)(CO)_2(NO)]$	potassium cyanodicarbonylnitrosylcobaltate(0)
$HCo(CO)_4$	hydrogen tetracarbonylcobaltate($-I$)
$[Ni(CO)_2(Ph_3P)_2]$	dicarbonylbis(triphenylphosphine)nickel(O)
$[Fe(en)_3][Fe(CO)_4]$	tris(ethylenediamine)iron(II) tetracarbonylferrate($-II$)
$K[B(C_6H_5)_4]$	potassium tetraphenylborate
$K[SbCl_5C_6H_5]$	potassium pentachloro(phenyl)antimonate(V)
$K_2[Cu(C_2H)_3]$	potassium triethynylcuprate(I)
$K_4[Ni(C_2C_6H_5)_4]$	potassium tetrakis(phenylethynyl)nickelate(0)
$[Fe(CO)_4(C_2C_6H_5)_2]$	tetracarbonylbis(phenylethynyl)iron(II)
$Fe(C_5H_5)_2$	bis(cyclopentadienyl)iron(II)
$[Fe(C_5H_5)_2]Cl$	bis(cyclopentadienyl)iron(III) chloride
$[Ni(NO)(C_5H_5)]$	nitrosylcyclopentadienylnickel

8. Bridging Groups

A bridging gap is indicated by adding the Greek letter μ immediately before its name and separating this portion from the rest of the complex by a hyphen. Two or more bridging groups of the same kind are indicated by di-μ-, etc. In case more than one kind of bridging group is present in the coordination entity, the letter μ is repeated before the name of each bridging group. If the number of nuclear atoms bound by one bridging group exceeds two, the number shall be indicated by adding a subscript numeral to the μ.

$[(NH_3)_5Cr—OH—Cr(NH_3)_5]Cl_5$	μ-hydroxobis{pentamminechromium(III)} chloride
	di-μ-thiocyanatobisthiocyanatobis-(tripropylphosphine)diplatinum-(II)
$[(CO)_3Fe(CO)_3Fe(CO)_3]$	tri-μ-carbonylbis(tricarbonyliron)
$[(CO)_3Fe(SEt)_2Fe(CO)_3]$	di-μ-ethanethiolatobis(tricarbonyliron)
$[(C_5H_5)(CO)Fe(CO)_2Fe(CO)(C_5H_5)]$	di-μ-carbonylbis(carbonylcyclopentadienyliron)
$[(CO)\{P(OEt)_3\}Co(CO)_2Co(CO)\{P(OEt)_3\}]$	di-μ-carbonylbis{carbonyl(triethyl phosphite)cobalt}
$[Au(CN)(C_3H_7)_2]_4$	cyclotetra-μ-cyanotetrakis(dipropylgold)
$[CuI(Et_3As)]_4$	tetra-μ_3-iodotetrakis{trimethylarsinecopper(I)}
$[Be_4O(CH_3COO)_6]$	μ_4-oxohexa-μ-acetatotetraberyllium

9. Designation of the Point of Attachment

Where ligands are capable of attachment by different atoms, the point of attachment may be denoted by adding the symbol for the atom to which attachment occurs at the end of the name of the ligand.

$$K_2\left[Ni\left(\begin{matrix}S-CO\\|\\S-CO\end{matrix}\right)_2\right]$$ potassium bis(thiooxalato-S,S')nickelate(II)

dichloro{N,N-dimethyl-2,2'-thio-bis(ethylamine-N',S)}

10. Alternate Modes of Linkage of Some Ligands

Structural isomerism in the ligand is designated by the use of different terms for the stoichiometrically equivalent groups or by the method of the rule above.   Recognized terms are

—SCN   thiocyanato   —NCS   isothiocyanato
—NO₂   nitro   —ONO   nitrito

$K_2[Pt(NO_2)_4]$ potassium tetranitroplatinate(II)
$Na_3[Co(NO_2)_6]$ sodium hexanitrocobaltate(III)
$[Co(NO_2)_3(NH_3)_3]$ trinitrotriamminecobalt(III)
$[Co(ONO)(NH_3)_5]SO_4$ nitritopentamminecobalt(III) sulfate
$[Co(NCS)(NH_3)_5]Cl_2$ isothiocyanatopentamminecobalt(III) chloride

11. Structural Isomerism in the Coordination Sphere

Geometrical isomerism is designated by the prefixes *cis-*, *trans-*, *asym-*, or *sym-* or by numbering systems.

a. PLANAR STRUCTURES

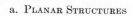

cis-dichlorodiammineplatinum(II)
1,2-dichlorodiammineplatinum(II)

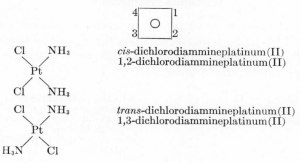

trans-dichlorodiammineplatinum(II)
1,3-dichlorodiammineplatinum(II)

b. Bridged Planar Structures

Et₃As   Cl   Cl
    \ / \ /
     Pt   Pt
    / \ / \
   Cl   Cl   AsEt₃

sym-trans-di-μ-chlorodichlorobis-
    (triethylarsine)diplatinum(II)
di-μ-chloro-1,3-dichlorobis(tri-
    ethylarsine)diplatinum(II)

two other isomers: *asym-* or 1,2-dichloro-
                      sym-cis- or 1,4-dichloro-

c. Octahedral Structures

Cl   cis-dichlorobis(ethylenediamine)cobalt(III) ion
        Cl   1,2-dichlorobis(ethylenediamine)cobalt(III) ion
en
        en

Cl   trans-dichlorobis(ethylenediamine)cobalt(III) ion
en   en   1,6-dichlorobis(ethylenediamine)cobalt(III) ion

Cl

12. Optical Isomerism

Where optical isomerism can occur, the optically active compound is designated by (+)- or (−)- depending upon the sign of rotation; alternatively, *d*- or *l*- may be used. The racemic mixture is designated by (±)- or *dl*-, and the inactive form by *meso-*.

(+)-[Fe(C₁₂H₈N₂)₃]²⁺   (+)-tris(*o*-phenanthroline)iron(II) ion
                              d-tris(*o*-phenanthroline)iron(II) ion
(±)-[Co(en)₂C₂O₄]⁺   (±)-oxalatobis(ethylenediamine)-
                                  cobalt(III) ion
                              dl-oxalatobis(ethylenediamine)cobalt-
                                  (III) ion

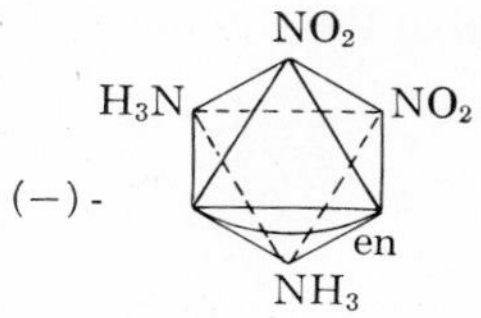

$(-)$-cis-dinitrodiammine(ethylenediamine)cobalt(III) ion
l-1,2-dinitro-5,6-diammine(ethylenediamine)cobalt(III)ion

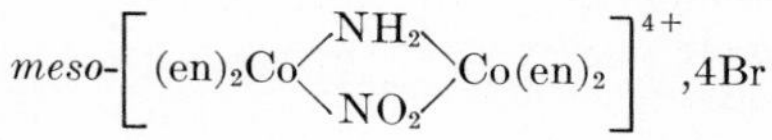

$meso$-μ-amido-μ-nitro-tetrakis(ethylenediamine)dicobalt(III) bromide

13. Coordination of Groups in Lower Functionality than Usual

The nomenclature of compounds involving monocoordination of bi
functional groups and the dicoordination of polyfunctional groups, etc ,
usually can be handled according to the rules previously given. See
Section VII-A-9.

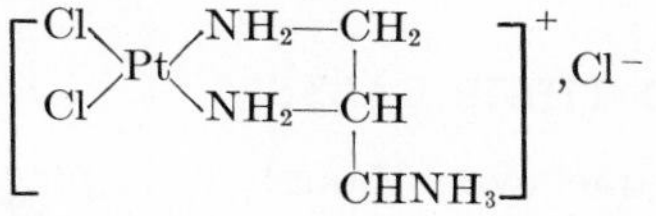

dichloro(2,3-diaminopropylammonium)plati-
num(II) chloride

14. Direct Linkage of Coordination Centers

The direct linking of two centers of coordination is designated by the
prefix bi- before the name of the coordination centers:

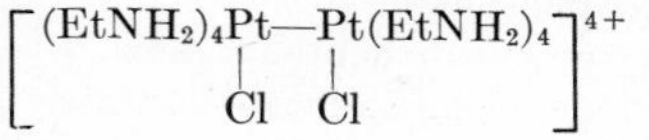

sym-octakis(ethylamine)dichlorobi-
platinum(IV) ion

$Mn_2(CO)_{10}$
or
$(CO)_5Mn$—$Mn(CO)_5$

decacarbonylbimanganese(0)
or
bis{pentacarbonylmanganese(0)}

15. Extended Structures

Where bridging causes an indefinite extension of the structure, it is
best to name compounds primarily on the basis of their over-all composition: e.g., $(Cs^+)_n[(CuCl_3)_n]^{n-}$, $catena$-μ-chlorodichlorocuprate(II).

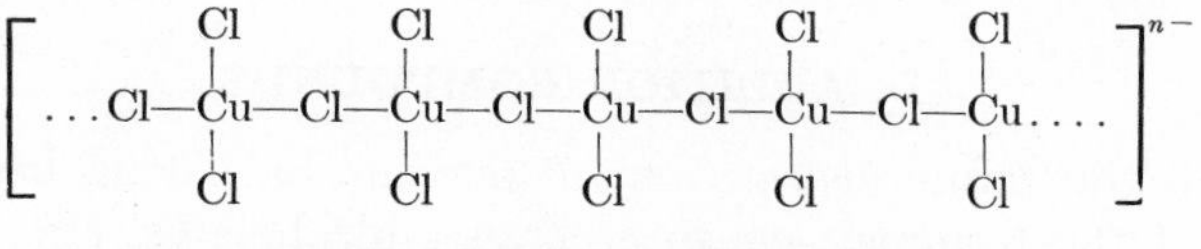

B. ISOPOLYACIDS AND THEIR SALTS

It is sufficient to indicate the number of atoms by Greek prefixes (at
least until isomers are formed). When all atoms have their "normal"

oxidation states (e.g., W^{VI}), it is not necessary to give the numbers of the oxygen atoms, if all the others are indicated.

$K_2S_2O_7$	dipotassium disulfate
$K_2S_3O_{10}$	dipotassium trisulfate
$Na_5P_3O_{10}$	pentasodium triphosphate
$K_2Cr_3O_{13}$	dipotassium tetrachromate
$Na_2B_4O_7$	disodium tetraborate
NaB_5O_8	sodium pentaborate
$Ca_3Mo_7O_{24}$	tricalcium heptamolybdate
$Na_7HNb_6O_{19} \cdot 15H_2O$	heptasodium monohydrogen hexaniobate-15-water
$K_2Mg_2V_{10}O_{28} \cdot 16H_2O$	dipotassium dimagnesium decavanadate-16-water

The previous report of the I.U.P.A.C. commission has permitted alternate names based on the "resolved formulas" for these compounds: thus $Na_2B_8O_{13}$ or $Na_2O \cdot 4B_2O_3$ was sodium (1:4) borate, and $Na_2W_3O_{10}$ or $Na_2O \cdot 3WO_3$ was sodium (1:3) tungstate.

C. HETEROPOLYACIDS AND THEIR SALTS

The central atom is cited last in the name even though it is placed before the other acidic element in the formula. Thus, phosphotungstate is not acceptable. When it is necessary to give the oxidation number, it is often desirable to place it immediately after the atom referred to and not after the ending -ate, in order to avoid ambiguity.

$(NH_4)_2PW_{12}O_{40}$	triammonium dodecatungstophosphate
$(NH_4)_6TeMo_6O_{24} \cdot 7H_2O$	hexaammonium hexamolybdotellurate heptahydrate
$Li_3HSiW_{12}O_{40} \cdot 24H_2O$	trilithium monohydrogen dodecatungstosilicate-24-water
$K_6Mn^{IV}Mo_9O_{32}$	hexapotassium enneamolybdomanganate(IV)
$Na_6P_2^{V}Mo_{18}O_{62}$	hexasodium 18-molybdodiphosphate(V)
$Na_4P_2^{III}Mo_{12}O_{41}$	tetrasodium dodecamolybdodiphosphate(III)
$K_7Co^{II}Co^{III}W_{12}O_{42} \cdot 16H_2O$	heptapotassium dodecatungstocobalt(II)-cobalt(III)ate-16-water
$K_3PV_2Mo_{10}O_{39}$	tripotassium decamolybdodivanadophosphate

The alternate naming system based on "resolved formulas" has not proven satisfactory in practice: e.g., $M_3PO_4 \cdot 12MoO_3$ or $3M_2O \cdot P_2O_5 \cdot 24MoO_3$, 24-molybdo-2-phosphate.

D. ADDITION COMPOUNDS

Although the terms *hydrate* and *ammoniate* have long been accepted, extension of the terminal -ate to etherates, alcoholates, etc., is confusing because of the general acceptance of -ate as the ending of anions.

The names of addition compounds are formed by connecting the names of individual compounds by hyphens and indicating the number of molecules by Arabic numerals. For simple 1:1 compounds it is preferable to place the base (donor) molecule first, followed by the acid (acceptor) (5). When the added molecules are organic, the multiplicative numerals (*bis-*, *tris-*, *tetrakis-*, etc.) instead of Arabic figures may be used to avoid confusion with the organic chemical use of Arabic figures to indicate position of substituents.

$CaCl_2 \cdot 6H_2O$	calcium chloride-6-water (or calcium chloride hexahydrate)
$3CdSO_4 \cdot 8H_2O$	3-cadmium sulfate-8-water
$Na_2CO_3 \cdot 10H_2O$	sodium carbonate-10-water (or sodium carbonate decahydrate)
$AlCl_3 \cdot 4C_2H_5OH$	aluminum chloride-4-ethanol or aluminum chloride-tetrakis-ethanol
$(C_2H_5)_2O \cdot BF_3$	diethyl ether-boron trifluoride
$2CH_3OH \cdot BF_3$	bismethanol-boron trifluoride
$BF_3 \cdot H_3PO_4$	boron trifluoride-phosphoric acid
$BiCl_3 \cdot 3PCl_5$	bismuth trichloride-3-(phosphorus pentachloride)
$TeCl_4 \cdot 2PCl_5$	tellurium tetrachloride-2-(phosphorus pentachloride)
$(CH_3)_4NAsCl_4 \cdot 2AsCl_3$	tetramethylammonium tetrachloroarsenate(III)-2-(arsenic trichloride)
$CaCl_2 \cdot 8NH_3$	calcium chloride-8-ammonia
$8H_2S \cdot 46H_2O$	8-hydrogen sulfide-46-water
$8Kr \cdot 46H_2O$	8-krypton-46-water
$6Br_2 \cdot 46H_2O$	6-dibromine-46-water
$8CHCl_3 \cdot 16H_2S \cdot 136H_2O$	8-chloroform-16-hydrogen sulfide-136-water

These names are not very different form pure verbal descriptions, which may in fact be used: e.g., calcium chloride with 6 waters; compound of aluminum chloride with 4 ethanols, etc.

If it needs to be shown that added molecules from part of a complex, the names are given according to the practice for coordination compounds.

$FeSO_4 \cdot 7H_2O$	iron(II) sulfate heptahydrate
or	or
$[Fe(H_2O)_6]SO_4 \cdot H_2O$	hexaquoiron(II) sulfate monohydrate
$PtCl_2 \cdot 2PCl_3$	platinum(II) chloride-2-(phosphorus trichloride)
or	or
$[PtCl_2(PCl_3)_2]$	dichlorobis(phosphorus trichloride)platinum(II)
$AlCl_3 \cdot NOCl$	aluminum chloride–nitrosyl chloride
or	or
$NO[AlCl_4]$	nitrosyl tetrachloroaluminate
$Et_3N \cdot BF_3$	triethylamine–boron trifluoride
or	or
$[BF_3(Et_3N)]$	trifluoro(triethylamine)boron

VIII. CRYSTALLINE PHASES OF VARIABLE COMPOSITION

For phases with limited variation in composition, the concept of an ideal composition with the sign $\sim$ (circa) is used in writing formulas: $\sim$FeS, $\sim$CuZn. The direction of the deviation may be indicated when required: $\sim$FeS (iron deficient); $\sim$MoC$_2$ (excess carbon). For phases where the variable composition is solely or partially caused by replacement, atoms or atomic groups that replace each other are separated by a comma and placed together between parentheses. If only part of the homogeneity range is referred to, the major constituent is placed first.

(Cu, Ni)	Complete range from pure Cu to pure Ni
K(Br, Cl)	Range from pure KBr to pure KCl
(Li$_2$, Mg)Cl$_2$	Homogeneous phase from LiCl to MgCl$_2$ (one vacant cation position appears for every substitution from 2Li$^+$ to Mg^{2+})
(Mg$_3$, Al$_2$)Al$_6$O$_{12}$	Homogeneous phase from MgAl$_2$O$_4$ to spinel form of Al$_2$O$_3$

A more complete form of notation indicates the variables which define the composition: x = wide variability; ϵ = narrow variability.

Cu$_x$Ni$_{1-x}$	Total number of atoms in lattice is constant
KBr$_x$Cl$_{1-x}$	
Li$_{2x}$Mg$_{1-x}$Cl$_2$	Homogeneous phase from LiCl to MgCl$_2$
Mg$_{3x}$Al$_{2(1-x)}$Al$_6$O$_{12}$	Cannot contain more Mg than MgAl$_2$O$_4$
Fe$_{1-x}$Sb; Fe$_{1-x}$0; Cu$_{2-x}$O	Pure compounds, x = 0; otherwise, cation-deficient structures
Na$_{1-x}$WO$_3$	Sodium tungsten bronzes
PdH$_x$	Solid solution of H in Pd
Li$_{4-x}$Fe$_{3x}$Ti$_{2(1-x)}$O$_6$	
(x = 0–0.34)	Limits of variability defined
Li$_{4-0.35}$Fe$_{3-0.35}$Ti$_{2(1-0.35)}$O$_6$	Composition Li$_{3.65}$Fe$_{1.05}$Ti$_{1.30}$O$_6$

IX. FUTURE DEVELOPMENTS

There are many areas of inorganic chemistry where standardization of nomenclature is needed (8,11,26). These include various strange cations like CH$_3$CO$^+$, which are being found in studies on solutions in nonaqueous solvents; various derivatives of S$_4$N$_4$ such as (NSCl)$_3$, (NSH)$_4$, and S$_{18}$H$_3$H$_5$; certain aspects of coordination compounds; and organometallic compounds, especially those derived from the cyclopentadienyl radical and benzene. Finally, and most important of all, it is essential that there be much greater harmonizing of divergent practices in inorganic and organic nomenclature.

Sooner, or later, whenever there is intense activity in a given field, the need for systematization of nomenclature becomes acute, and solutions are proposed, to be followed by reconciliation of rival solutions and then agreement, at first limited, and later more general. Efforts in two such fields have already reached the stage of deserving consideration here.

A. PHOSPHORUS COMPOUNDS

In 1952 the organic nomenclature groups in this country and Britain agreed on a system of nomenclature for organic compounds of phosphorus (2), which if expanded and if accepted by inorganic chemists will go far toward changing many commonly accepted inorganic names. The system breaks with all tradition and bases all names on the following parent structures:

Hydrides

H_3P	phosphine
H_3PO	phosphine oxide (sulfide, etc.)
H_3PNH	phosphine imide
H_5P	phosphorane

Acids, trivalent

$(HO)_3P$	phosphorous acid
$HP(OH)_2$	phosphonous acid
H_2POH	phosphinous acid
$HOP{=}O$	phosphenous acid

Acids, quinquevalent

$(HO)_3PO$	phosphoric acid
$HPO(OH)_2$	phosphonic acid
$H_2PO(OH)$	phosphinic acid
$HOP({=}O)(O)$	phosphenic acid
H_4POH	phosphoranoic acid
$H_3P(OH)_2$	phosphoranedioic acid
$H_2P(OH)_3$	phosphoranetrioic acid
$HP(OH)_4$	phosphoranetetroic acid
$(HO)_5P$	phosphoranepentoic acid

Structures formed by replacing two hydrogen atoms bound to P in any parent structure (not containing an OH group) by O, S, Se, Te, or NH are named by prefixing *oxo-*, *thiono-*, etc., or *imino-* to the parent name. Structures formed by the operation of replacing (*1*) O in a structure containing an OH group bound to P, (*2*) O and OH simultaneously, (*3*) OH, or (*4*) O in OH in a parent or substituted structure by any group other than O, S, Se, Te, or NH are named by insertion of the appropriate affix (in alphabetical order if more than one) just preceding the valence suffix (*ic, -oic, -ous,* or *-ate, -oate,* or *ite*) in the parent name. For the sake of euphony, an affix beginning with a consonant is always preceded by *o;*

the final *o* is dropped if followed by a vowel.   Doubling an affix does not change its alphabetical order.   Finally, names are given in fundamental radicals attached to another group at the phosphorus atom.

H_2P—	phosphino
$H_2P(O)$—	phosphinyl
$H_2P(S)$—	phosphinothioyl
$H_2P(NH)$—	phosphinimyl
$HP(N)$—	phosphononitridyl
H_4P—	phosphoranyl

These radicals may in themselves be substituted: e.g., chloromethoxy-phosphino, MeOClP.   Representative names are these:

$HP{=}O$	oxophosphine
$HP{=}NH(O)$	iminophosphine oxide
$HP{=}S(S)$	thionophosphine sulfide
$HP{=}NH(NH)$	iminophosphine imide
$(H_2N)_2(HO)PO$	phosphorodiamidic acid
$Cl(HS)PN$	phosphorochloridonitridothioic acid
$Cl_2P(O)H$	phosphonic dichloride
$H_2NP(NH)H_2$	phosphinimidic amide
$(H_2N)_3P$	phosphorous triamide
$(HO)_2(HS)P$	phosphorothious acid
$(HO)(H_2N)PH$	phosphonamidous acid
$ClPH_2$	phosphinous chloride
$H_2NP{=}O(S)$	phosphenothioic amide
$HSP{=}NH$	phosphenimidothious acid

Names based on this pattern are appearing with increasing frequency in the British and American literature, although largely for organic derivatives.   However, the Swedish chemists have made an alternate proposal (19), and the major complication in the field of phosphorus compounds does not use the new names (28).

B. BORON COMPOUNDS

An Advisory Committee on the Nomenclature of Organic Boron Compounds (1,25) (whose membership includes many inorganic chemists) has worked hard to bring order to this field of chemistry.   The recommended names take full account of the peculiar formulas and the peculiar linkages of boron hydrides.   The examples below give only a general idea of the complete system.   The names for the hydrides indicate the number of atoms (both B and H) in the formulas, thus:

BH_3	borane(3)
B_2H_6	diborane(6)
B_5H_9	pentaborane(9)
B_5H_{11}	pentaborane(11)

The names for substitution products follow customary practices.

$C_6H_5BH_2$	phenylborane
$BH(OCH_3)_2$	dimethoxyborane
B_2H_5Cl	chlorodiborane(6)
$B_{10}H_4I_{10}$	decaiododecaborane(14)

However, provision is made for bridge substitution.

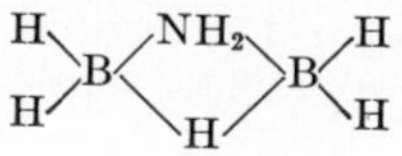

μ-amidodiborane

For certain purposes, it is necessary to number the boron atoms in a hydride: e.g.,

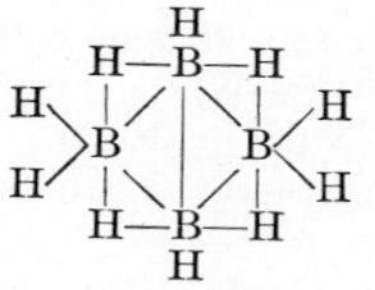

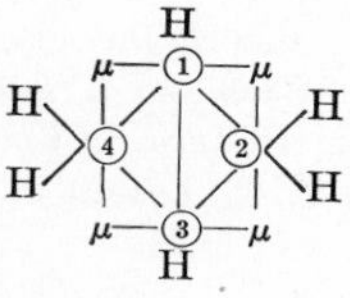

Then names for radicals follow logically.

$(H_2B)_2CH_2$	diborylmethane
B_2H_5-	diboran(6)yl

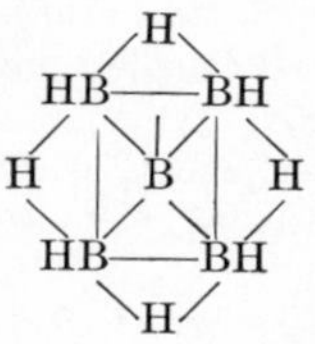

pentabor(9)

Names for addition compounds involve a simple scheme for showing the method of attachment.

$(CH_3)_3N:BH_3$	trimethylamine-borane
$OC:BH_3$	carbon monoxide(C—B)borane
$(CH_3)_2N:BH_2NH_2$	trimethylamine(N—B)aminoborane

Coordination compounds of boron follow existing practice except that the charge on the ion, not the oxidation state, is given in parentheses.

$Na[BF_2(OH)_2]$	sodium dihydroxyfluoroborate (1−)
$Ag[C_6H_5BO(OH)]$	silver oxohydroxyphenylborate (1−)

The metal-boron hydrides are treated as coordination compounds, but note that hydro (for H^-) is given last, not first (Section VII-A-4).

$Na[BH_4]$ sodium tetrahydroborate $(1-)$
$Na[B(OCH_3)_3H]$ sodium trimethoxyhydroborate $(1-)$
$Li[BF_2H_2]$ lithium difluorodihydroborate $(1-)$
$Na[B(CH_3)H_3]$ sodium methyltrihydroborate $(1-)$

The report also includes considerations of polyborates and ring systems.

REFERENCES

1. Advisory Committee on the Nomenclature of Organic Boron Compounds, *The Nomenclature of Boron. Preliminary Report*, July 31, 1957.
2. American Chemical Society Nomenclature, Spelling, and Pronunciation Committee, *Chem. Eng. News*, **30**, 4515 (1952).
3. Berzelius, J. J., *J. phys.*, **73**, 258 (1811).
4. Brauner, B., *Z. anorg. Chem.*, **32**, 10 (1902).
5. Davidson, N., and H. C. Brown, *J. Am. Chem. Soc.*, **64**, 317 (1942).
6. Delepine, M., *Bull. soc. chim.*, [iv]**43**, 289 (1928).
7. Ewens, R. V. G., and H. Bassett, *Chem. & Ind. (London)*, **1949**, 131.
8. Fernelius, W. C., *Chem. Eng. News*, **26**, 161 (1948).
9. Fernelius, W. C., *Advances in Chem. Ser.*, No. 8, 9 (1953).
10. Fernelius, W. C., E. M. Larsen, L. E. Marchi, and C. L. Rollinson, *Chem. Eng. News*, **26**, 520 (1948).
11. Fleischer, M., *Proc. Am. Soc. Testing Materials*, **47**, 1090 (1947).
12. Franklin, E. C., *Am. Chem. J.*, **47**, 285 (1912).
13. Franklin, E. C., *J. Am. Chem. Soc.*, **46**, 2137 (1924).
14. Franklin, E. C., *The Nitrogen System of Compounds*, Reinhold, New York, 1933.
15. Guyton de Morveau, L. B., *J. phys.*, **19**, 310, 382 (1782).
16. Guyton de Morveau, L. B., *Ann. chim. et phys.*, [1]**25**, 205 (1798).
17. Guyton de Morveau, L. B., A. L. Lavoisier, C. L. Berthollet, and A. F. de Fourcroy, *Methode de Nomenclature Chimique*, Paris, 1787.
18. Jorissen, W. P., H. Bassett, A. Damiens, F. Fichter, and H. Remy, *Ber.*, **A73**, 53 (1940); *J. Chem. Soc.*, **1940**, 1404; *J. Am. Chem. Soc.*, **63**, 889 (1941). (The last is available as a reprint from *Chemical Abstracts*.)
19. Larsson, L. B., B. Holmstedt, and E. Tjus, *Acta Chem. Scand.*, **8**, 1563 (1954).
20. Lavoisier, A. L., *Traite Elementaire de Chimie*, 3rd ed., Deterville, Paris, 1801, Vol. I, Part I, pp. 70–81; all of Part II.
21. Ohman, O., *Z. angew. Chem.*, **33**, 326 (1920).
22. Ohman, O., *Z. physik. chem. Unterricht*, **33**, 41 (1920).
23. Remy, H., *Rules for Naming Inorganic Compounds. Committee for the Reform of the Nomenclature of Inorganic Chemistry*, International Union of Chemistry.
24. Rosenheim, A., *Z. angew. Chem.*, **33**, 78 (1920).
25. Schaeffer, G. W., and T. Wartik, "Nomenclature in Boron Compounds," Division of Chemical Literature, 125th Meeting, ACS, Kansas City, Mo., March, 1954, *Paper No. 27*. See reviews of paper, *Chem. Eng. News*, **32**, 1441 (1954), **34**, 560 (1956).
26. Scott, J. D., *Chem. Revs.*, **32**, 73 (1943).
27. Stock, A., *Z. angew. Chem.*, **32**, 373 (1919), **33**, 78 (1920).
28. Van Wazer, J. R., *Phosphorus and Its Compounds*, Vol. I, *Chemistry*, Interscience, New York–London, 1958, pp. 88–91, 346–53.
29. Werner, A., *Neuere Auschaungen auf den Gebiete der anorganischen Chemie*, 3rd ed., Vieweg, Braunschweig, 1913, pp. 92–5.

GENERAL REFERENCES

Cahn, R. S., *An Introduction to Chemical Nomenclature*, Butterworth, London, 1959.

Mitchell, A. D., *British Chemical Nomenclature*, Arnold, London, and Longmans, Green, New York, 1949.

"The Naming and Indexing of Chemical Compounds by Chemical Abstracts," *Chem. Abstr.*, **39**, 5867 (1945). (Available as a reprint.)

Nomenclature of Inorganic Chemistry, 1957 Report of the Commission on the Nomenclature of Inorganic Chemistry, I.U.P.A.C., Butterworth, London, 1959; *J. Am. Chem. Soc.*, **82**, 5523 (1960). (Available as a reprint from Chemical Abstracts Service.)

Patterson, A. M., and E. J. Crane, "Nomenclature, Chemical," in J. F. Thorpe and M. A. Whiteley, *Thorpe's Dictionary of Applied Chemistry*, 4th ed., Longmans, Green, New York, 1947, Vol. VIII, pp. 594–613.

Patterson, A. M., and W. C. Fernelius, "Nomenclature," in R. E. Kirk and D. F. Othmer, *Encyclopedia of Chemical Technology*, Interscience, New York–London, 1952, Vol. 9, pp. 473–84.

Scott, J. D., "Notes on the Nomenclature of Inorganic Compounds," in W. C. Fernelius *Inorganic Syntheses*, McGraw-Hill, New York, 1946, Vol. II, Appendix, pp. 256–67

DETERMINATION OF THE ELEMENTS: GENERAL CONCEPTS

By James I. Hoffman, *National Bureau of Standards, Washington, D. C.*

At the beginning of the century the analytical chemist usually performed all his analyses on one or two samples. For example, in rock analysis, he started with a 1 g. sample, dissolved it, removed in succession the acid group (SiO_2, etc.), the hydrogen sulfide group (Cu, Pb, etc.), the ammonium hydroxide group (Fe, Al, etc.), the ammonium sulfide group (Mn, Zn), the oxalate group (Ca, Sr), and the phosphate group (Mg, Ba). He then determined the various elements in each group and finally the alkalies on a separate sample. At present most industrial analyses are made by taking separate samples for each element or group of elements. The reasons for this change are interesting and important.

In the early days of analytical chemistry, analyses were usually made of natural products, such as rocks, ores, and minerals. Because of the labor involved in the preparation of the sample and also because of occasional scarcity of material it was practical to procure and prepare for analysis only small portions. It became customary, therefore, to make as many analyses as possible on the same sample because material was thereby economized and because each determination was preceded by a necessary senaration. At present our operations are on a larger scale, both in the processing of raw materials and in manufactured products. Inability to obtain a large portion of sample is now exceptional, and analyses made on separate portions for each element or group of elements are quite common. Of course, the more important factor of availability of more efficient methods that do not require preliminary separations is not to be overlooked. The analyst now has at his command methods, reagents, and devices not dreamed of 50 years ago. With these he can make many determinations in minutes which earlier required tedious separations and other operations. The accumulated knowledge now available to the analyst is astounding, and the better this knowledge is organized in the mind of the analytical chemist the more successful he will be in applied analyses.

Sometimes the analyst has a choice between a method that involves separation of an element and one that requires no separation. No rule applies here. Many analysts take a possessive attitude toward the element they are determining, and they obtain much comfort in actually seeing and holding in their hands the aluminum oxide or the cobalt metal they have separated. This pleasure they should not be denied. Those interested in clever methods and instrumentation shun separations and take pride in using color, fluorescence, oxidation state, radioactivity, and other properties to give them an estimate of the quantity of an element in a solution or a phosphor. Here the satisfaction comes from a feeling that time has been saved and much hard work has been avoided. Push-button devices and automation in chemical analysis have sometimes been sneered at, but these aids are as useful to the analyst as are the calculating machine and computer to the banker and the mathematician. The danger in their use lies in the possibility that the users may forget the chemical principles behind their operation.

As late as the first World War an analytical laboratory was considered adequate if it had a supply of beakers, stirring rods, funnels, burets, a few platinum crucibles, Bunsen burners, a combustion furnace, a hood with exhaust fan, a balance, and various other equally inexpensive items. In a few cases luxuries, such as a muffle furnace with temperature control or an electrometric titration apparatus, added to the prestige of the laboratory. However, more likely than not, the electrometric titration apparatus was homemade, and the heating element for the furnace was wound by the analyst. Good quality distilled water could generally be made available, but the quality of chemical reagents was not satisfactory. Thanks to the American Chemical Society's Committee on Chemical Reagents, good quality reagents are now the rule.

In contrast with the modest laboratory of 50 years ago, one now sees laboratories equipped with automatic titrators, spectrometers for use in the visible, ultraviolet, and infrared, mass spectrometers, gas chromatographs, and many other instruments and automatic devices. Papers on devices for use in chemical analysis run into the thousands, and the cost of equipping a modest analytical laboratory may run into hundreds of thousands of dollars. But it is estimated that one man, by the use of these devices, can in many cases turn out 20 times as many reliable results as he could by the older methods.

Automation and instrumentation inevitably lead to a necessity for accurate standards to which the automatically or instrumentally obtained numbers can be related. The reading on a dial or a number on a scale has meaning only if it can be related to a definite quantity. The most desirable standard of reference is one that has approximately the same composition as the material under analysis.   This means that ideally as many standards should be available as there are classes of materials to be analyzed.   This, of course, is impossible, but, by judicious blending or by slight changes in operation, available standards can usually be made to suffice. Fortunately the National Bureau of Standards can furnish over 600 standard samples, many of which are of use in instrumental analysis and automatic devices.   The Bureau's metallic samples are especially useful in spectrographic work, and some of the larger industrial laboratories are now producing their own standards, often in cooperation with the National Bureau of Standards.

The analyst of 50 years ago seldom made use of a spectroscope except for identifying main constituents in ores or minerals or impurities in a final precipitate.   His spectroscope was either a hand scope or an instrument of very low resolution.   Aside from the many indirect applications of the spectroscope, the analyst now uses it extensively to make analyses of materials that fall into the same general class and for which he has standards.   For example, thousands of determinations of the constituents in steels and nonferrous alloys are now made daily in control laboratories with properly calibrated spectroscopes.   In a slightly different category are many operations that do not require strictly quantitative results. Here the spectroscope affords a rapid means of supplying a satisfactory approximate analysis.   Another very important use of the spectroscope is for a preliminary qualitative analysis of a material that the chemist is about to analyze by conventional methods.   Through a knowledge of the approximate composition of the material, the analytical chemist has the advantage of choosing methods that may be more accurate or that will save much time by avoiding steps in a procedure.   For example, if the spectroscopic analysis shows beryllium and lithium, the analyst knows that he must correct his aluminum and sodium results obtained by the usual gravimetric methods, or he must choose methods in which beryllium is not counted with aluminum, or lithium with sodium.

An interesting example of time saving by a preliminary spectroscopic analysis was the purification of gallium in a critical situation during World War II. By a qualitative spectroscopic analysis the impure gallium was shown to contain only metals that are more noble than gallium or such elements as are volatilized when the metal is dissolved in hydrochloric acid (As, Sb). Gallium, having a melting point of 29.78°C., forms a liquid globule when it is warmed in hydrochloric acid, and dissolves slowly. By treating a 100 g. portion with an excess of dilute hydrochloric acid and stopping the reaction when all but 1 or 2 g. was dissolved, a solution of pure gallium chloride was obtained. The 1 to 2 g. globule remaining contained all the more noble metals (Cu, etc.), and the arsenic was volatilized as arsine. Thus, by simply dissolving about 98% of the material and discarding the other 2%, a purification was effected which would have taken days of work by the usual procedures.

X-ray spectroscopy finds application in many analytical laboratories and is capable of yielding very precise results if the material is not too complex. A distinct advantage is that the sample under analysis is not destroyed.

Ion exchange procedures have greatly simplified analytical separations. In the early work on the separation of the rare earths, it was not unusual to make hundreds of recrystallizations of rare earth compounds in order to obtain a pure product (3).* Of course, the product seldom, if ever, was pure by our present standards. Those who have tried to separate niobium from tantalum by the conventional methods, for example, by the use of tannin, can appreciate the advantages of the ion exchange approach. Separations by means of ion exchange have enabled the analyst to make clear-cut separations of the rare earth elements and of niobium and tantalum. The technique has likewise made possible the preparation of these and other elements, such as zirconium and hafnium, in pure form so that the analyst now has pure raw materials for setting up his own standards for use in other methods of determination.

Here a word should be said for advances in other fields of chemistry. Had it not been for the development of tubes and containers of polyethylene, polystyrene, and other similar materials, the use of fluoride solutions for the ion exchange separations of niobium and tantalum would have been impossible or at least very difficult.

It is difficult to find any technique used by the analytical chemist that is more far-reaching in its scope than extraction with solvents. The extraction of ferric iron with ether has been practiced for many years, and the use of ether for this purpose is known to all analytical chemists. The use of ether extraction in the purification of gallium is not so well known, but its use in the purification of uranium for atomic energy purposes (2) has received wide attention. During and since the late war another type of extraction came into extensive use. Here a compound, for example, a cupferrate or an oxinate, is precipitated and is then dissolved and extracted without first filtering the solution (5). Actually in practice the precipitant and extractant are usually added at the same time. The extractant may be ether, chloroform, carbon tetrachloride, or other solvent. Examples of the separation of iron from uranium by the extraction of the oxinate and cupferrate are described by Rodden and by Morrison and Freiser. This type of extraction had been of more or less academic interest until pressure of wartime analyses brought it into more extensive use. Solvent extraction is used for such rare elements as actinium, americium, berkelium, curium,

---

* It is a matter of actual record that James went through 15,000 operations in order to obtain what he considered pure thulium.

polonium, protactinium, and technetium.   The fact that at least 80 elements can be separated by the use of extraction procedures is an indication of the possibilities of solvent extraction in analytical chemistry.

Radioisotopes can be used in many ways for analyses. Unique techniques are possible because of the high sensitivity and simplicity of radioactivity measurements.   Thus, a radioactive substance can be separated completely by use of a nonradioactive carrier, and the amount of the radioactive substance can be ascertained by the dilution of the radioactive material with the nonradioactive substance.   Radioactive materials separated by chromatography are easily located by radioautographs and determined quantitatively by radioactivity assay.   Minute amounts of carbonyl compounds can be determined by reaction with ^{14}C-labeled cyanide; similar techniques might be feasible for determination of metals that form complex cyanides.   Minute traces of tritiated water can be measured easily, and many applications of this property seem possible.   The use of tritium in organic analysis is only one of the applications of radioactive tracers which could make the analyst's problems simple.   It is probable that biochemists and medical people have taken radioisotopes into their research more than the practicing analytical chemist.

The improvements in the techniques mentioned, as well as the increased use of organic reagents in inorganic analysis, have lightened the burden of the analytical chemist.   To a greater or lesser degree we have seen similar advances in colorimetry, turbidimetry, nephelometry, spectrometry, polarimetry, chromatography, petrography, polarography, electromotive and electrolytic techniques, fluorimetry, coulometry, and flame photometry, in addition to many common operations in volumetric and gravimetric analysis.   As a last example of these useful advances the mass spectrograph is an interesting development.   Several decades ago it was "temperamental" and not counted on for quantitative results.   Today it is one of the most useful instruments available to the analyst.   He now uses it to determine bonding energies, the constituents in smog, and the composition of gas mixtures; in all but a few rare cases atomic weights are now more accurately determined spectrographically than by the old painstaking orthodox analytical procedures.

With the methods and techniques at his disposal the analytical chemist usually has sufficient knowledge to enable him to avoid a complete analysis. A complete analysis of a complex material is both time-comsuming and costly but is necessary to furnish the maximum information that can be derived from an analysis.   In many cases the determination of a single element furnishes the required information.   This is especially true in specifications.   A specification for a steel may call for 0.60% manganese and

0.03% sulfur (maximum). Here, one actual determination of manganese is all that is needed. In the case of the sulfur it is only necessary to proceed until it is certain that the sulfur content does not exceed 0.03%. Expediency dictates the determination of manganese and an estimation of sulfur only, whereas completeness might require the determination of a score of elements. Thus, it is seen that good judgment on the part of the analytical chemist is required to avoid unnecessary work but also to avoid the pitfalls of incomplete information. His objective should be to do as little work as possible but as much work as is necessary to obtain the desired result. In general, the over-all composition of the sample must be known if only a few constituents are to be determined. The use of the spectroscope for this purpose has already been mentioned.

To avoid serious errors in wet analysis the analytical chemist must have a comprehensive concept concerning the dissolution of the sample. He must make sure that the element to be determined is not volatilized in the solution treatment. What a shock it is to the uninitiated to dissolve germanium oxide in aqua regia and find that nothing is left in the beaker on evaporation of the solution to dryness! Germanium tetrachloride boils at 86°C. Likewise, residues remaining after acid attack of a sample must be understood. Sand in a sample of phosphate rock remains as an inert residue when the phosphate is dissolved in nitric acid, but not all residues are unattacked parts of the original material. When bronze is dissolved in dilute nitric acid, white metastannic acid separates, and when a tungsten steel is dissolved in aqua regia, yellow tungstic acid separates. Neither the metastannic acid nor the tungstic acid occurred as such in the alloys, but they were formed in the process of dissolution.

Residues insoluble in acid (or sometimes alkaline) solutions must usually be brought into solution by fusion with solid fluxes, either acid or alkaline. Pyrosulfate is an example of the former, and alkali carbonates of the latter. Losses by volatilization can occur during fusions, for example, boron, alkalies, fluorine, etc. Likewise, much consideration must be given to the choice of flux and its effect on later determinations. For example, a silica determination is difficult after a fusion with borax.

If time is not of major importance, decomposition of refractory materials can often be accomplished without the introduction of a non-volatile flux, by heating the material with acids in a closed system so that the temperature of the solvent may be increased beyond that attainable at atmospheric pressure. By such a procedure highly refractory platiniferous materials and even Alundum can be completely dissolved (1).

Decomposition of organic matter prior to determination of inorganic constituents may involve dissolution in acid or alkaline solvents or a preliminary "ashing" treatment. In inorganic analyses most organic matter is probably destroyed by treatment with nitric acid in conjunction with sulfuric or perchloric acid, but here the analyst must perform his operations with full knowledge of the chemistry involved. He must realize that heating organic matter in the presence of sulfuric acid alone will yield sulfur dioxide, which may reduce certain elements; he must also realize that perchloric acid will oxidize many elements to higher valences; thus chromium may form volatile chromyl chloride, CrO_2Cl_2, in the presence of hydrochloric acid; finally the explosive nature of mixtures of organic matter and perchloric acid must not be overlooked.

For the determination of constituents such as alumina, silica, iron, alkalies, and other inorganic substances in foods, leaves, and similar materials, careful ignition until the organic matter is driven off is usually satisfactory. However, if elements such as fluorine or sulfur are to be determined, certain compounds or mixtures are added to the organic matter to retain the sulfur or fluorine. Eschka's mixture (2 parts by weight of calcined MgO and 1 part of anhydrous Na_2CO_3) is usually used for sulfur, and aluminum nitrate may be used for fluorine. The aluminum nitrate or Eschka's mixture is ground with the organic matter, and then the ignition is carried out at as low a temperature as possible to avoid loss of sulfur or fluorine. Other special treatments are used for the decomposition of rubber, plastics, asphalt, petroleum products, etc., but their discussion would be out of place here.

The conception of a blank determination in inorganic analysis needs appraisal. The exhortation on the part of authors to "carry a blank through all steps of the procedure" is intended to relieve the analyst of all responsibility for such factors as impurities in the reagents, dust in the atmosphere, attack of the solutions on glassware, attack of fluxes on crucibles, solubility of precipitates, and many others. The custom of carrying a blank along with each set of determinations is a good one because it will reveal large sources of error introduced through impure reagents, atmospheric dust, attack on glassware, errors in manipulation, etc. However, there are loopholes leading to error even if the analyst carefully measures all reagents for his blank and performs all operations with it just as he does for the actual determination he is making. Several examples will make this clear.

It is common practice in many analyses to precipitate iron and aluminum with ammonium hydroxide and weigh the precipitate as $Al_2O_3 + Fe_2O_3$ after filtration and ignition. The iron is then titrated in a solution of the oxides, and its equivalent Fe_2O_3 subtracted from the combined weights to obtain the alumina. Now consider the conditions that exist in the blank solution as compared with the solution under analysis. Both contain the impurities in the sodium carbonate used in the fusion and in the other reagents used. Both also contain the silica and boron dissolved out of the glassware. However, ordinarily the blank contains little or no iron or aluminum, and, when ammonium hydroxide is added, no precipitate is formed in the blank. Thus the silica and boron escape, whereas in the solution under analysis the boron, silica, some sodium salts, and phosphates, if present, are included in the precipitate. These are, therefore, included in the weight of the combined $Al_2O_3 + Fe_2O_3$, whereas the blank does not reflect their presence. Consequently, the reported result for Al_2O_3 will be high. (See also Chapter 3 of Part I.)

Another pertinent example is the precipitation of barium sulfate in applied analyses in the presence of substances such as iron, aluminum, and sodium salts. The materials going into the blank and into the solution under analysis are again carefully weighed or measured. Conditions in both are kept the same until the barium chloride is added. If a precipitate appears in the blank, solubility effects are approximately compensated. If no precipitate appears in the blank, it only shows that no major contamination by sulfur occurred. To be a true blank, a precipitate of barium sulfate must appear in the blank in an environment similar to that of the solution under analysis. A small blank may not always lead to the correct answer.

A practical solution to the problem of the blank determination is to add to the blank a known small amount of the element to be determined. If the amount obtained in the blank determination is greater than the amount added in the beginning, the excess is subtracted; if it is less, as it may well be in the case of barium sulfate, the correction is made in the other direction. Standard solutions of the more common elements are usually available in a laboratory and can be used in blank determinations without much extra work. This system of making blank determinations applies in titrimetric and colorimetric as well as in gravimetric work. Furthermore, in careful analyses it is difficult to reconcile the logic of running triplicate or quadruplicate determinations and only a single blank. It may be just as important to run duplicate blanks as duplicate determinations.

The planning and design of experiments and the treatment of results obtained in analysis will be discussed elsewhere in this Treatise. It is sufficient to note here that much time and labor can be saved by intelligent planning of experiments and skillful interpretation of the results obtained.

To be successful an analytical chemist must have certain qualities of a detective. He must always be on guard lest he weigh something he does not intend to weigh, lest he titrate what he does not intend to titrate, or lest he dissolve what he wishes to remain insoluble.   He must always view with suspicion.   In his work he needs fingerprints of his reagents.   He needs to know that ammonium hydroxide precipitates gallium under the same conditions as aluminum and that ether extracts iron and gallium almost equally well from hydrochloric acid solutions.   He needs to know much more about all his reagents.   In fact, he should have fingerprints or tables that would give him this information.   Attempts have been made (4) to furnish such fingerprints for many of the common reagents, but, unfortunately, this work has not been systematically extended to include newer reagents that have appeared in the last 20 years.

There are good methods for the determination of every element if it occurs alone, but very seldom can the element be determined in a mixture of elements by the same method without some modification.   One example will suffice.   The analysis of a simple rock is straightforward but is greatly complicated by the presence of one unusual element such as niobium. Without niobium, the silica is obtained in a nearly pure form; in the presence of niobium the silica will be greatly contaminated by this element.   The trouble does not end here; the "R_2O_3" will also be contaminated because separation of the niobium with the silica was not complete.   Now correction for niobium in the iron and aluminum (R_2O_3) must also be made.   This is not easy.   If an attempt is made to titrate the iron after putting a solution of the R_2O_3 through a Jones reductor, erroneous results will be obtained owing to uncertain reduction of an unknown quantity of niobium.   At present, ion exchange methods furnish means of getting out of the difficulties caused by niobium, but, in order to be effective, the analyst must know about the interference and also how to circumvent it.   It is evident that the selection of a method for a given analysis is a most important part of the analytical process, and it is equally certain that interference in methods should be pointed out by authors.

Thousands of papers have appeared in the analytical literature in the last two decades.   Too many of them ignore realistic interferences that may be operating.   Editors and reviewers might well improve the quality of the analytical literature by decreasing its quantity through a stronger insistence on statements of interferences, whether such interferences be in gravimetric, potentiometric, photometric, or any other kind of analytical work.

The accuracy demanded in an analysis plays an important role in the selection of the method and in the decision to apply corrections for interferences.   In the determination of fundamental constants, such as atomic weights or the value of the faraday, the most painstaking search for possible errors or interferences is justified, whereas in routine control analysis a simple color comparison in Nessler tubes may furnish all the information needed.

The foregoing is not intended to depict a simple life for the analytical chemist. The new reagents and improved techniques only enable him to keep abreast of new alloys, new ceramic bodies, and newly discovered elements. Fifty years ago he was seldom asked to determine more than 25 elements; now he is likely to be asked to determine any one of a hundred, and it is significant that some of these he cannot determine without instruments. We have, therefore, arrived at a stage in chemical analysis where we can not entirely substitute automation and instrumentation for human beings, nor can we expect an analyst to count the alpha particles emitted by a sample of uranium without the aid of an instrument. The complexity of present-day materials enforces an interdependence between instruments and the conventional human skills, and this interdependence will be enhanced as time goes on because future technology will undoubtedly demand the determination of smaller and smaller percentages of an element in a mixture. Parts in a million or parts in a billion will become more common. The alert analytical chemist is therefore faced with the fact that he is practicing a science (or an art) which requires a knowledge of all the other branches of chemistry and one that is making an increasing use of physics as well.

REFERENCES

1. Gordon, C. L., E. Wichers, and W. G. Schlecht, *J. Research Natl. Bur. Standards*, **30**, 107 (1943); **33**, 363, 451, 457 (1944).
2. Hoffman, J. I., *J. Wash. Acad. Sci.*, **38**, 233 (1948), and U. S. Pat. 2,690,376 (Sept. 28, 1954).
3. James, C., *J. Am. Chem. Soc.*, **33**, 1342 (1911).
4. Lundell, G. E. F., and J. I. Hoffman, *Outlines of Methods of Chemical Analysis*, Wiley, New York, 1938.
5. Rodden, C. J., *Analytical Chemistry of the Manhattan Project*, McGraw-Hill, New York, 1950; G. H. Morrison and H. Freiser, *Solvent Extraction in Analytical Chemistry*, Wiley, New York, 1957.

HYDROGEN

By H. F. Beeghly, *Jones & Laughlin Steel Corporation, Pittsburgh, Pennsylvania*

Contents

I. INTRODUCTION

Hydrogen (H_2) has the lowest atomic weight and its atom the simplest structure among the elements. Under normal conditions it is a tasteless, colorless, odorless, diatomic gas with the lowest density of any substance. Hydrogen has a valence of one and acts like a metal in its reactions.

Hydrogen exists in nature in the ortho and para isomers. At normal temperatures, the ratio of ortho to para is generally considered to be 3:1. The physical properties of ortho- and parahydrogen differ.

Two isotopes of hydrogen exist in nature. Heavy hydrogen or deuterium (D_2) is present in normal hydrogen in small concentrations. A third isotope of hydrogen, tritium (T_2), of mass three is radioactive. It may exist in ortho and para forms similarly to ordinary hydrogen.

The easiest of the elementary gases to prepare, hydrogen may have been first recognized in the sixteenth century by Paracelcus in the gas liberated by the action of sulfuric acid on iron. Cavendish established the nature of the gas and proved in 1781 that it burned in air to form water. Lavoisier gave it the name hydrogen in 1783.

II. OCCURRENCE

Because of the ease with which hydrogen reacts with other elements, especially oxygen, little free hydrogen exists on earth. It is found in air in less than 1 p.p.m. concentration and elsewhere only in mixtures with other gases in certain volcanic and natural gases. Free hydrogen has been found occluded in meteorites, and it is present in the sun, many stars, and nebulae.

In the combined state, hydrogen is very abundant. It comprises 11.19% of water; it is an essential constituent of all acids, metal hydroxides, hydrides, hydrocarbons, and animal and vegetable matter; and it is present in most organic compounds.

Free deuterium is rare in nature. It is found combined principally as deuterium oxide and occurs to the extent of approximately 1 part in 6000 in rain water.

Tritium does not occur naturally.

Compounds containing hydrogen are very important in industrial processes and products. Major uses are for synthesis of ammonia and hydrogen chloride, in conjunction with nitrogen or chlorine, respectively, for hydrogenation of oils, fats, and hydrocarbons, and for reduction, sintering, and annealing operations in metallurgical processes. Hydrogen is an important raw material for the synthesis of organic compounds on an industrial scale.

A relatively new and growing use for hydrogen, in the form of water, organic compounds, or hydrides, is as a moderator in nuclear reactors designed for research or production of power. Deuterium, usually as the oxide, is a valuable moderator for neutrons and is so used.

Liquid hydrogen is used in cryogenic devices and in propulsion equipment. These uses, which require large quantities of hydrogen, are finding increasing application.

Hydrogen reacts with many metals to form hydrides; certain of these compounds are becoming important as reducing agents in organic synthesis.

When passed through an electric arc, hydrogen absorbs enough energy to dissociate into single atoms. Molecular hydrogen forms again with liberation of much heat. This reaction is utilized commercially in welding.

Hydrogen frequently is a minor constituent of metals. Since the effect of the hydrogen impurity in metals is to impair their mechanical properties, it is an undesired contaminant, and much effort has been expended in devising reliable methods for sampling and analysis of metals for hydrogen.

III. STORAGE, SHIPMENT, AND TOXICOLOGY

Hydrogen is nontoxic. The principal hazards in its use result from its flammability. Its mixture with oxygen may be highly explosive.

The reactions of hydrogen with other elements, e.g., fluorine, may also be explosive, and many of its compounds are highly corrosive or toxic.

Hydrogen is shipped and stored in high-pressure steel tanks. For low-temperature high-pressure handling, austenitic stainless steel, aluminum, or copper containers are used.

Tritium is radioactive and toxic; therefore, the precautions necessary for handling beta-emitting isotopes must be observed in working with tritium or with tritium-containing compounds.

Reference works on the toxicology of the different hydrogen compounds or reactions to be worked with should be consulted before experimental work is started. The *Dangerous Properties of Industrial Materials* by Sax (6) will be useful.

IV. PREPARATION

Hydrogen may be prepared on a laboratory scale by such methods as these: (1) electrolysis of water; (2) reaction of a dilute acid on a metal, e.g., of sulfuric acid on zinc or iron; (3) reaction of a hydride, e.g., calcium hydride, with water; or (4) heating a metallic hydride, e.g., titanium hydride, to liberate hydrogen.

Commercial production of hydrogen is carried out on a very large scale. Processes used include (1) the catalytic reaction of hydrocarbons or methanol with steam, (2) the electrolysis of water, (3) the reaction of steam with water or producer gas and further reaction over an iron oxide catalyst, (4) the thermal decomposition of hydrocarbons, and (5) the dissociation of ammonia. Details of these methods may be found in Kirk-Othmer's work (4).

Deuterium, as deuterium oxide, may be separated from water by electrolysis. The dual temperature exchange between hydrogen sulfide and water is used in production plants for preparation of D_2O (2). Deuterium oxide provides a starting material for preparation of deuterium and its compounds. These, in general, can be synthesized in the same way and undergo the same reactions as hydrogen.

Tritium is an unstable beta-emitting isotope that can be obtained as a by-product of nuclear transmutation processes. It may be prepared from lithium-6 by bombardment with neutrons as illustrated by the reaction

$$_3^6Li + _1^0n \longrightarrow _1^3T + _2^4He$$

In general, tritium undergoes the same reactions as hydrogen and deuterium and can be used to synthesize tritium compounds by essentially the same methods used for these isotopes. Because tritium is toxic, precautions that are not necessary with the other hydrogen isotopes must be observed in handling it.

V. PROPERTIES

Table I lists some of the physical properties of hydrogen. Table II and Figs. 1 and 2 (4a) give the solubility of hydrogen in water. Tables

TABLE I
Physical Properties of Hydrogen

Isotopes	Hydrogen	Deuterium	Tritium
Symbol	H	D	T
Normal state	Diatomic (H_2)	Diatomic (D_2)	Diatomic (T_2)
Atomic weight	1.0081	2.0147	3.0170
Isomers	ortho, para		ortho, para
Melting point, °C.	−259.14	−254.4	
Boiling point, °C.	−252.6	−249.4	
Density, g./liter			
at 0°C. and 760 mm. (gas)	0.0899		
at −253°C. (liquid)	70.8		
at −262°C. (solid)	80.7		
Specific gravity (air = 1)	0.0695		
Molar volume, at 20°K. and saturated pressure (liquid)	28.232	23.525	
Heat capacity, C_p, cal./g., at 0 to 200°C.	3.44		
Heat capacity, C_v, cal./g., at 0 to 200°C.	2.46		
Latent heat of fusion, cal./g., at −259°C.	13.89		
Latent heat of vaporization, cal./g., at −253°C.	107		
Critical temperature, °C.	−239.9		
Critical pressure, atm.	12.98		
Critical density, g./liter	31.2		
Critical volume, cm.^{3}/mole	66.95		
Gross heat of combustion, cal./g.	33.940		
Entropy, $S°$, gas	31.21	34.602	
Type of radiation	Stable	Stable	β, 0.18 m.e.v., 12.5 yr.
Limits of inflammability			
in air, vol. %	4.0/74.20		
in oxygen, vol. %	4.65/93.9		

TABLE II

Solubility of Hydrogen in Water

t, °C.	Solubility, cc./g., reduced to 0°C. and 1 atm.								
	1 atm.	25 atm.	50 atm.	75 atm.	100 atm.	300 atm.	500 atm.	700 atm.	1000 atm.
0	0.0214	0.5363	1.068	1.601	2.130	6.139	9.838	13.370	18.001
10	0.0193	0.4870	0.9690	1.435	1.932	5.579	8.980	12.214	16.623
20	0.0178	0.4498	0.8945	1.341	1.785	5.158	8.328	11.362	15.592
30	0.0163	0.4263	0.8475	1.271	1.689	4.897	7.922	10.818	14.928
50	0.0141	0.4067	0.8090	1.212	1.612	4.695	7.613	10.389	14.404
80	0.0085	0.4203	0.8385	1.254	1.667	4.866	7.885	10.757	14.867
100	0.0000	0.4615	0.9120	1.355	1.805	5.220	8.429	11.512	15.775

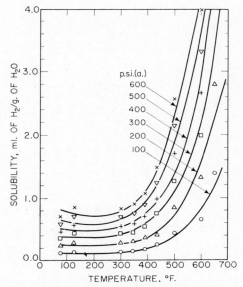

Fig. 1. Variation in solubility of hydrogen in water with temperature (4a).

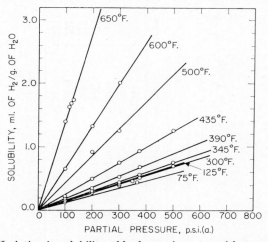

Fig. 2. Variation in solubility of hydrogen in water with pressure (4a).

III, IV, and V show the solubility of hydrogen in aqueous acids and bases, aqueous solutions of salts, and a number of organic compounds.

Liquid hydrogen has the highest specific heat of any known liquid. The thermal conductivity of hydrogen is approximately seven times that of air;

TABLE III
Solubility of Hydrogen in Aqueous Acids and Bases

Concn. of solvent, N	Solubility, ml. of H_2/ml. of solvent, at 25°C. and 1 atm.					
	HCl	HNO₃	H₂SO₄	CH₃COOH	KOH	NaOH
0.0	0.0193	0.0193	0.0193	0.0193	0.0193	0.0193
0.5	0.0186	0.0188	0.0183	0.0192	0.0167	0.0165
1.0	0.0179	0.0183	0.0177	0.0191	0.0142	0.0139
2.0	0.0168	0.0174	0.0163	0.0188		0.0097
3.0	0.0159	0.0167	0.0150	0.0186		0.0072

this property is used in analyzing for hydrogen in other gases, e.g., in mixtures with air, carbon monoxide, or nitrogen, and for deuterium in hydrogen. Hydrogen is a nonconductor of electricity. Being the lightest and smallest atom, it diffuses readily through many substances and rapidly through metals such as iron at room temperature. It is necessary to keep this characteristic in mind when sampling and storing certain metals for hydrogen analyses.

Atomic hydrogen is much more reactive than molecular hydrogen; it will form hydrides with sulfur, phosphorus, and arsenic and will reduce many metal oxides and salts to the metal. In the electrometric force series of the elements, in which they are tabulated in the order of their relative affinities for positive electricity as well as their relative oxidizing and reducing capacities, hydrogen is used as the reference point. The voltages tabulated are obtained by measurement against a normal hydrogen electrode. The hydrogen ion surrenders its positive charge to any element above hydrogen in the series, and the farther the separation, the greater the discharging tendency.

Hydrogen gas will completely reduce hot oxides of iron, lead, nickel, and copper to the metals. Under pressure, hydrogen will precipitate from aqueous solutions metals that have less tendency to ionize than hydrogen itself. Such metals as bismuth, cobalt, copper, lead, mercury, and nickel (but not iron or zinc) may be precipitated in this way. When the acid formed becomes sufficiently concentrated to attack the metal, the reaction comes to a standstill.

Hydrogen is soluble sparingly in water and to an appreciably greater extent in organic compounds. It is dissolved by many metals, including copper, iron, manganese, nickel, palladium, platinum, and tantalum; the hydrogen here is not considered to be chemically combined. Metals such as iron and palladium may be loaded by electrolysis to contain 100 to 1000 times, respectively, their volumes of hydrogen. Other metals that

TABLE IV.   Solubility of Hydrogen in Aqueous Salt Solutions

Concn., g. of salt/ 100 g. of soln.	Solubility, ml. of H_2/ml. of soln., at 15°C. and 1 atm.											
	$BaCl_2$	$CaCl_2$	$LiCl$	$NaCl$	KCl	Na_2CO_3	K_2CO_3	$NaNO_3$	KNO_3	NH_4NO_3[a]	$MgSO_4$	Na_2SO_4
1.0					0.0187			0.0184		0.0187		
1.2				0.0191					0.0184			
2.1				0.0176	0.0176	0.0164		0.0177	0.0182	0.0184		
2.8							0.0163					
3.3	0.0185											
3.4		0.0162								0.0182		
3.5			0.0162									
3.6	0.0184											
3.8				0.0176	0.0167							
4.5				0.0171				0.0169				0.0151
4.7									0.0168	0.0177		
5.0											0.0150	
5.6								0.0160				
6.1		0.0145		0.0164								
6.4	0.0173											
7.0	0.0172											
7.3			0.0137									
7.5				0.0149	0.0149							
8.4							0.0139	0.0137	0.0156			0.0154
8.8						0.0118						
10.2											0.0116	
11.3		0.0114					0.0084			0.0164		
12.1				0.0128								
14.8			0.0099	0.0093								
16.5							0.0076					
16.6					0.0101				0.0131			
19.2								0.0105				
19.8												0.0077
23.8											0.0050	
24.1				0.0060			0.0046					

[a] At 20°C

TABLE V
Solubility of Hydrogen in Organic Compounds

Compound	Solubility[a]			
Acetone	$l_{40} = 0.1131$	$l_{20.9} = 0.0968$	$l_0 = 0.0783$	$l_{-40.6} = 0.0498$
Benzene	$l_{41.3} = 0.0844$	$l_{22.9} = 0.0700$	$l_0 = 0.0585$	
Carbon tetrachloride	$l_{38.8} = 0.0928$	$l_{20.9} = 0.0794$	$l_0 = 0.0050$	
Ethyl ether		$l_{21.1} = 0.1409$	$l_0 = 0.1188$	$l_{-40} = 0.0800$
Chlorobenzene	$l_{40} = 0.0702$	$l_{21.2} = 0.0595$	$l_0 = 0.0479$	$l_{-40.9} = 0.0303$
Ethyl acetate		$l_{20} = 0.0788$		
Methyl acetate	$l_{40.9} = 0.1051$	$l_{20.9} = 0.0891$	$l_0 = 0.0730$	$l_{-40.1} = 0.0447$
Amyl acetate		$l_{20} = 0.0743$		
Isobutanol		$l_{20} = 0.0929$		
Ethanol	$\beta_{40} = 0.0840$	$\beta_{20.3} = 0.0769$		

[a] l, ml. of H_2 (at temperature shown and 1 atm.) dissolved in 1 ml. of compound when partial pressure of H_2 is 1 atm.; β, ml. of H_2 (at 0°C. and 760 mm.) dissolved in 1 ml. of compound when partial pressure of H_2 is 1 atm.

may dissolve hydrogen or react chemically to form the hydrides include the rare earths, thorium, titanium, uranium, zirconium, magnesium, beryllium, and the alkali and alkaline earth metals.

VI. SAMPLING

The sampling of hydrogen-containing materials for analysis requires care to obtain a representative specimen and care that the hydrogen content of the specimen, as sampled, does not change prior to analysis.

The sampling and analysis of organic materials for hydrogen will be considered in another volume and will not be covered in this chapter.

Many inorganic materials contain water of hydration or are, in varying degrees, desiccants. Industrial materials frequently are analyzed for "free" moisture, for "combined" moisture, and for hydrogen on the dry material. Analyses may be reported on a dry basis or on an as received basis. In any event the specimen, once obtained, must be stored in a tightly closed container until analyses are made; otherwise, adsorbed moisture may lead to an erroneous hydrogen value.

The sampling of metals to be analyzed for hydrogen presents a special problem. Elements such as iron, nickel, cobalt, and copper, which dissolve hydrogen in the solid state without formation of a compound, involve a different consideration from metals such as titanium, zirconium, and uranium, with which hydrogen reacts to form hydrides. In the absence of compound formation, the gas diffuses with relative ease and rapidity. Samples, once obtained, must be stored in a manner that prevents loss.

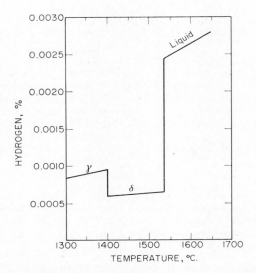

Fig. 3. The solubility of hydrogen in iron at 1 atm. pressure (10).

On the whole, steel presents the most difficult sampling problem and will be considered in most detail.

Hydrogen may enter steel from pickling, from electrolysis (electroplating), from high-temperature, high-pressure atmospheres, or, during the steelmaking operation, from water vapor, fuels, or water in the materials used to make the steel (such as scrap, hot metal, ferroalloys, and slag-making constituents). Water vapor, from the air used for combustion of the fuel, from the atmosphere during pouring of the molten steel, and from refractories, constitutes the source of hydrogen most difficult to eliminate. The solubility of hydrogen in iron, shown in Fig. 3 (11), varies with temperature and is much higher at the temperature of molten steel than at room temperature. The gas diffuses rapidly in steel and is readily lost during solidification, hot working, machining, or storage at room temperature.

Sampling of liquid steel for hydrogen analysis is very difficult, and special precautions also are necessary in sampling the cold metal.

The techniques for sampling molten steel may be grouped as rapid cooling methods, which are designed to retain the hydrogen in the solid steel in a supersaturated condition, or slow cooling methods, which try to collect the hydrogen evolved as the metal solidifies and cools.

The rapid cooling methods generally use a copper mold to cast a pin- or wedge-shaped specimen. Fig. 4 (3) illustrates a sampling device of this type. The copper tube is inserted in a spoon of molten metal, and the

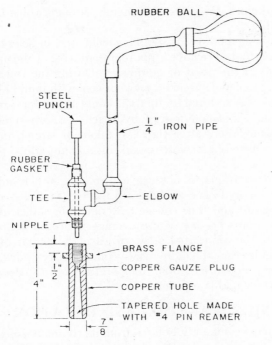

Fig. 4. Sampling mold for hydrogen in molten steel (3).

metal drawn into the tube where it quickly solidifies. The resulting pin is analyzed immediately or stored at low temperature until it can be analyzed. Alternatively, it may be sealed in a glass tube or stored under mercury, and the evolved gas collected. With the latter methods, both the collected gas and the metal sample must be analyzed for hydrogen.

The slow cooling sampling methods generally use an evacuated steel tube closed at the bottom with a thin steel diaphragm. The lower end is inserted into a spoon of molten steel, the diaphragm melts, and steel is drawn into the tube. Any gas evolved during solidification is collected in the tube or in an attached balloon. The solid metal is analyzed for hydrogen, and the amount found is added to the amount of hydrogen evolved during solidification.

Because hydrogen diffuses so readily in steel even at room temperature and because the solubility of the gas at room temperature is so low, steels sampled a few days after they have been rolled will be found to have a uniformly low hydrogen content. Exceptions to this situation are large sections (pieces more than 1 inch in their smallest dimension) and steels coated with cadmium, tin, or bearing metals through which hydrogen does not diffuse readily.

The most reliable method for sampling solid steel in heavy sections is to use a trepanning tool to remove a pin representative of the cross section of the bar or ingot at the point of sampling. During the trepanning operation, the cutting tool and specimen are kept cool with liquid nitrogen or dry ice. Specimens can be stored for up to 72 hours at temperatures of $-70°C$. or lower without significant loss of hydrogen. Alternatively, they may be analyzed immediately after they are taken or stored under mercury, the hydrogen collected as it evolves, and this amount added to the amount found by analysis.

The major precautions to observe in sampling other industrially important metals for hydrogen analysis are these: (1) to be cognizant that hydrogen segregates and thus choose material from sufficient locations to secure samples representative of the average hydrogen content or, alternatively, sample the segregated areas to learn the extent of segregation; and (2) to recognize that the more reactive metals may hydride by reaction with atmospheric moisture at room temperature and thus store them in a way that will prevent this reaction.

VII. SEPARATION AND ISOLATION

Hydrogen is most commonly isolated from its compounds by oxidation to water. When present in the sample as elemental hydrogen, it usually can be recovered by holding the specimen at reduced pressure. Recovery is more rapid if the specimen is heated at the same time.

Once converted to water, hydrogen may be detected by reactions with anhydrous cobaltous salts or copper sulfate, which change color as they hydrate, with dipicrylamine (color change), or with aluminum sulfide (liberation of H_2S), by condensation on a cool surface, or by use of spectroscopic methods. More complete coverage of methods for detection and determination of water will be found in another volume.

Elemental hydrogen reacts with molybdenum trioxide to form the intense blue color of molybdenum indigo. This reaction has been used for the detection of hydrogen in investigating the decomposition of water and ammonia.

The heat liberated by reaction of hydrogen with a catalyst has been made the basis for continuous automatic hydrogen detection devices.

Hydrogen in a hydrocarbon can be oxidized to water without oxidation of the hydrocarbon and detected as water. For example, free hydrogen in methane will oxidize when passed over copper oxide at 300°C. without oxidation of the methane.

Hydrogen may be absorbed from mixtures of other gases on spongy palladium or in anthraquinonedisulfonic acid in the presence of colloidal platinum and recovered by heating.

Deuterium in hydrogen may be detected by thermal conductivity measurements or with the infrared or mass spectrometer. The difference in density, refractive index, or freezing point may be used after the mixture of gases is converted to a deuterium oxide–hydrogen oxide mixture.

Tritium in mixtures of hydrogen or deuterium or both may be detected by sensitive counting techniques and direct measurement of beta particles and by spectroscopy.

VIII. IDENTIFICATION OF COMPOUNDS

X-ray and electron diffraction methods are useful in identifying hydrogen compounds. The amplitude of x-ray scattering by the elements is proportional to their atomic numbers. Consequently, the amount of information that can be gained by x-ray diffraction investigation of materials containing hydrogen is limited when the gas is present in conjunction with heavy elements.

With neutron diffraction, the light element can generally be detected with about the same precision and sensitivity as the heavy element. So far, this method has been used for simpler types of problems. As more intense neutron sources become generally available, the technique of neutron diffraction promises to be a most valuable method for solving analytical problems involving positions of the hydrogen atoms. It should prove equally valuable in the investigation of the crystal chemistry of hydrogen compounds of the heavy elements and in problems involving hydrogen in metals.

Neutron diffraction may be used to supplement and confirm x-ray diffraction data, or it may be used independently. Shull and co-workers appear to have been the first to use neutron diffraction to obtain information on the structures of sodium hydride and sodium deuteride (7). The structures of uranium hydride and of thorium and zirconium hydrides and deuterides were determined a short time later (5).

IX. DETERMINATION

The earliest procedure used for the determination of hydrogen was direct combustion. More recently vacuum fusion and hot extraction methods have been devised and have special value for determination of hydrogen in metals.

A procedure illustrative of each of these methods will be given. Many variations of each are possible.

A. COMBUSTION METHOD

The combustion method is most frequently used for determining hydrogen in minerals, slags, and inorganic compounds. The earliest method for determining hydrogen in metals, it has largely been replaced by the hot extraction and vacuum fusion techniques.

The procedure for determination of hydrogen by direct combustion must vary according to the composition of the sample and its volatility. Before setting up the apparatus for this method, references that give detailed information about the properties of the compound or material to be analyzed (8) should be consulted.

The very strong tendency for glass, quartz, porcelain, etc., to adsorb moisture must be recognized and guarded against in all procedures involving analyses for small amounts of hydrogen. Otherwise, erratic hydrogen and excessive blank values will be obtained through liberation of adsorbed moisture.

In many inorganic materials, it is necessary to distinguish between water and hydrogen. This differentiation often may be made by heating the specimen in dry nitrogen at 110°C. and weighing the liberated water. It should be remembered that the desiccant used to dry the nitrogen should also be used to adsorb the liberated moisture. A too-effective desiccant will remove water from the absorbent, and low hydrogen values will result; the converse may also occur. Essentially the same apparatus can be used as for the determination of hydrogen.

Procedure

Prepare a powdered mixture of approximately 10 parts of lead chromate with 1 part of potassium chromate. Mix the finely divided sample with approximately five times its weight of the chromate mixture, and transfer to a porcelain boat. A 2 to 10 g. sample generally may be used.

Place the boat in a combustion tube packed as illustrated in Fig. 5 and connected at the exit end to an absorbent tube containing a drying agent. Magnesium perchlorate trihydrate (Dehydrite) is satisfactory. Follow the boat with a roll of copper gauze. Close the entrance end of the tube, and pass dry air through the system until all moisture is removed. Continue passing a slow current of air (1 to 2 ml./second) through the system, heat the lead chromate in the exit end of the tube to within the range of 300 to 400°C., and then gradually heat the section of the tube under the sample; at the same time begin heating the tube at the entrance end. The section of the tube containing the boat should reach a temperature of 600 to 800°C. Volatilization or combustion should not begin in the sample until the chro-

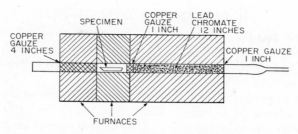

Fig. 5. Combustion tube for hydrogen determination.

mate in the exit end has reached temperature. Oxygen may be substituted for air if the sample is difficult to oxidize. When burning is complete, any moisture collected in the exit end of the tube or connections must be driven into the absorption tube. Continue the current of air or oxygen until the absorption tube is judged to have reached constant weight. Disconnect and close the absorption tube, allow to cool, preferably in the balance case, and weigh after opening the tube momentarily to equalize the pressure. The increase in weight of the absorption tube is due to water, and the amount of hydrogen can be calculated from it.

For substances known to be free of sulfur or halogens, a copper oxide packing can be used in place of the granular chromates, and the sample does not have to be mixed with chromates. By inserting an absorber for carbon dioxide in the train, the carbon content of the sample also can be determined.

Care must be taken that oxidation of the sample is complete and that all of the hydrogen is converted to water and driven into the absorption tube.

The hydrogen content of metals and of metal hydrides can be determined in essentially the same way by using either a solid specimen or millings. Considerable care and time are required to assure complete oxidation. Because the hydrogen content of metals is generally very low, a large sample (25 to 50 g.) should be used. The oxidation rate should be kept slow to prevent formation of oxide fumes, which would contaminate the adsorption system. A good arrangement is to oxidize the specimen in one furnace connected in series to a second tube containing the copper oxide and enclosed by a second furnace. With this arrangement, the temperature of the sample and of the copper oxide can be varied and controlled independently of each other.

The Karl Fischer method is applicable to determination of free water in many inorganic materials (e.g., estimation of the moisture content of ores or minerals) and to determination of water or crystallization.

B. VACUUM FUSION METHOD

Much effort has been directed to the accurate estimation of hydrogen in metals because the gas always impairs their mechanical properties. Amounts of hydrogen as low as 0.0005 wt. % may have a significant effect on metal properties.

The vacuum fusion method is based upon the fusion of a metal in the presence of carbon in vacuum. Tin, platinum, or iron (for nonferrous metals) may be added to the bath. Under these conditions all oxides are reduced to carbon monoxide, and nitrogen and hydrogen are liberated. The evolved gases are collected and analyzed by appropriate procedures, including (1) low-pressure manometric, (2) macro or micro Orsat, (3) gravimetric, and (4) thermal conductivity techniques.

The vacuum fusion method may be used for determination of hydrogen in practically all metals. Since the hydrogen contents of metals are very small, the materials from which the apparatus is constructed adsorb moisture tenaciously, and high temperatures and high vacuum are used to liberate and remove the hydrogen from the metal, care must be exercised to avoid high or erratic blank values. The temperature of fusion and removal of the hydrogen is in the range of maximum solubility for hydrogen in the metal, the converse of what would be ideal. Most analyses for hydrogen are made not on pure metals but rather on binary or more complex alloys. Constituents of these may vaporize and deposit in cooler parts of the apparatus, where they serve as getters to trap hydrogen evolved from the sample. With sufficiently high temperatures and vacuum and high-capacity pumps, this gettering is minimized. Addition of tin or platinum to the bath facilitates evolution of hydrogen. For nonferrous alloys, addition of iron to the bath may be used to advantage.

The specimen should be a solid chunk and can be of any convenient shape small enough for loading into the apparatus. As a general principle, the specimen should be chosen to have the least possible surface in order to minimize the possibility of errors from surface contamination. Powdering, milling, or filing is not a satisfactory way of taking specimens from a metal for analysis. When the hydrogen content of metal powders or other finely divided materials must be determined, they should be compressed into pellets.

Acid cleaning or pickling of the specimen should be avoided, and abrasive cleaning should be used with caution. Outer heavy scale or contamination can best be removed by slowly turning the specimen in a lathe at room temperature or lower. Special care must then be exercised to remove traces of oil, grease, or other hydrocarbons from the specimen prior to analysis. A dip in trichloroethylene followed by a rinse in clean acetone

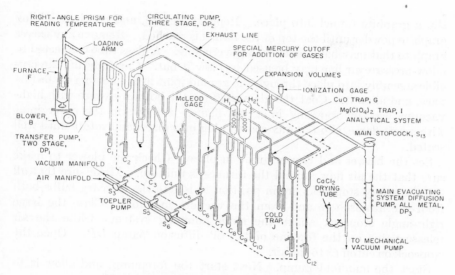

Fig. 6. Diagram of vacuum fusion apparatus (1).

may be used.   Clean rubber gloves or tweezers should be used for handling the specimens.

Fig. 6 illustrates schematically a vacuum fusion apparatus suitable for the determination of hydrogen in metals.   Such apparatus can be purchased commercially or can be constructed.   There can be considerable variation in details of the apparatus and the analytical procedure.   The following technique is typical and very similar to the method tentatively adopted by the American Society for Testing Materials for electronic nickel (1).

Procedure

Weigh the sample, and insert into the sample-loading tube on furnace F (Fig. 6).   Samples weighing from 0.5 to 2.0 g. may be accommodated, depending on the gas content of the metal.   At least 10 samples may be loaded into the side arm at one loading.   Close the side arm by sealing the cap at the end with a high-vacuum wax such as Apiezon W.

Place a $1^1/_2$ inch layer of graphite powder in the bottom of the quartz tube.   Do not compact the graphite.   Place a graphite crucible on top of this powder in alignment with the axis of the quartz tube.   Place a suitable cap on top of the crucible, and pour graphite powder into the quartz tube to reach the top of the crucible.   Remove the cap, and gently slip a graphite funnel into place.   Replace the cap, and continue adding graphite powder until the top of the funnel is reached.   Remove any excess graphite that may have fallen into the crucible.   A glass tube connected to a low-pressure air line may be used to blow it out.   Carefully lift the crucible assembly into place through the ground joint in the bottom of the furnace, and align it.   Coat the glass plug for the bottom closure with high-vacuum wax by warming in a soft flame.   Also warm the outer joint with a soft flame, slip the wax-coated plug into place, and rotate until well seated.

Set the blower and blower guide in place.   Check the blower to make sure that the air flow around the furnace is uniform.   Make sure that all the three-way stopcocks are in position to isolate the mercury bulbs both from the atmosphere and from the vacuum manifold.   Close the large right-angle stopcock above the main pumping system.   Close the air release valve on the foreline of the oil diffusion pump DP_3.   Open the stopcock on cutoff C_2 to the air.

Start the manifold pump.   Next start the forepump, and allow it to run until it is operating quietly (2 or 3 minutes).

Very slowly and cautiously open the large right-angle stopcock S_{13}, located above the metal diffusion pump, until the mercury begins to rise slowly in the various tubes.   Leave the stopcock in this position.   In no case should the system be pumped down in less than 6 to 10 minutes.

When the mercury has reached a height of about 3 to 4 inches in all the tubes, lower the mercury column carefully by turning the stopcocks momentarily to connect the mercury reservoir bulbs with the vacuum manifold.   Leave the stopcock on cutoff C_2 open to the atmosphere at all times. Tubes C_1, C_2, C_4, C_7, C_8, C_9, C_{10}, C_{11}, and C_{12} will need no further attention since the mercury will not now reach the cutoff.

Cutoffs C_3, C_5, and C_6 will require attention during pump-down to keep mercury from rising into the bulbs of the Toepler pump and the McLeod gage, and into the side arm of the gas addition tube C_6.   Cutoff C_5 on the McLeod gage is in the lowest position and will require the most attention.   Keep manipulating stopcocks S_3, S_5, and S_6 in such a fashion that the mercury does not reach the cutoff in any case.   When no further upward movement is visible in tube C_2, fully open the main stopcock.   Do this slowly.   Next turn on the main diffusion pump and the transfer and circulating mercury diffusion pumps.

At this point it is a good practice to adjust the height of all the mercury columns (with the exception of C_2, which is left all the way up) to a point just below the cutoff.   The special cutoff C_6 may be permanently closed, and the mercury sealed off by closing the stopcock in the stem.

After one-half to three-quarters of an hour, the pressure in the system as checked by the McLeod gage should be so low that the McLeod gage shows no differential in the heights of the mercury in the two capillary columns. Pumping for a minimum of 1 hour is necessary before applying heat to the furnace. Fine graphite outgasses very rapidly when first heated and may fluff out and into the system if caution is not used.

Outgas the furnace assembly by heating the graphite crucible to a temperature of 2400°C. for at least 2 hours. Turn on the air blower at the same time as the induction heater. Raise the temperature slowly to permit evacuation of the gases evolved and, also, to avoid displacement of the graphite powder. Measure the temperature of the crucible with an optical pyrometer.

Make a blank determination by lowering the temperature of the crucible to 1650°C. and collecting the gas evolved during a period corresponding to the time the sample is to be heated (20 to 30 minutes).

Close all mercury cutoffs. Set the timer for the desired time interval, and open cutoff C_2. Lower the mercury in the Toepler pump below the bulb. Maintain the mercury in the McLeod gage above the side arm to the expansion bulbs but below the inlet from the Toepler pump. Pump gas evolved from the furnace and crucible assembly through pumps DP_1 and DP_2 into the Toepler pump. At the end of the collection period, close cutoff C_2 and open C_1. Transfer the gas collected in the Toepler pump to the McLeod gage measuring system by manual operation of the Toepler pump, until the amount of gas measured in the McLeod capillary shows no further increase. Measure the amount of gas collected by reading the mercury level in the McLeod capillary (from which reading the PV product is calculated). Analyze the gas for carbon monoxide, hydrogen, and nitrogen as described in the following paragraph.

Adjust the mercury cutoffs to open all reagents to vacuum. Bake out the reagents under vacuum. The copper oxide temperature should be 325°C., and that of the magnesium perchlorate 240°C. Place a Dewar flask containing liquid nitrogen to cover trap J before the analysis is begun. Transfer the gas collected in the Toepler bulb to the measuring (McLeod) bulb and determine the PV product of the combined carbon monoxide, hydrogen, and nitrogen. Lower the mercury in the gas-measuring bulb below the cutoff. Open cutoffs C_7 and C_4 to permit the gas to be pumped into the analytical system. Check the McLeod reading after a few minutes to be sure all gas has been pumped out, and then raise the mercury level in the McLeod gage to just above the cutoff level. Close cutoff C_7. Open cutoff C_{11} to permit the gas to circulate through the copper oxide tube, the magnesium perchlorate trap, and the trap cooled with liquid nitrogen.

Circulate the gas for 10 minutes or more.   Close cutoff C_4 and lower the mercury in the Toepler pump to just below the cutoff point.   With the cutoffs in these positions, pump the residual nitrogen into the Toepler bulb.   After 10 minutes, transfer this nitrogen into the McLeod bulb in the usual manner, and measure the PV product of the nitrogen.   Allow the nitrogen to remain in the McLeod gage.   Lower the mercury level in the Toepler pump below the side arm.   Remove the liquid nitrogen–filled flask from the trap, J, thereby releasing carbon dioxide from the trap. Allow 5 to 10 minutes for the carbon dioxide to collect in the Toepler pump.   Transfer the gas into the McLeod gage as before, and measure the PV product of the combined carbon dioxide and nitrogen.   The operation is now completed.   The analytical system is exhausted by opening cutoffs C_{10}, C_{11}, and C_{12} to prepare to run the sample.

The magnesium perchlorate can be kept in a baked-out condition by maintenance at 250°C. during overnight periods with the system under vacuum.   Activation or replacement of the copper oxide is necessary at intervals.   It can be activated by repeated reductions with hydrogen followed by an oxidation and a vacuum bake.

The fusion of the sample is carried out by the same procedure at the same temperature and length of time as the blank.   Turn off the power to the furnace, and allow the furnace to cool 200 to 300°C.   Introduce the sample by moving it by means of a magnet until it drops down the vertical tube into the crucible.   Again turn on the induction heater, and continue the fusion for 20 to 30 minutes at 1650°C.   Completeness of removal of gas from the sample is readily confirmed by successive readings of PV product during the collection period.   Should an abnormally long time period be necessary, a blank correction for a corresponding time must be made.   Collect the gas as in the case of the blank.

After the gas is collected from the sample, raise cutoff C_2, lower cutoff C_1, and allow the furnace to exhaust to the main evacuation line until the next sample is dropped.

Transfer the gas collected in the Toepler pump to the McLeod gage, compress into the capillary pipet, and measure the PV product.   If more gas is collected than can be measured in the capillary pipet, allow it to expand into expansion bulb H_1 or H_2 or both by lowering the mercury in the McLeod gage below the side-arm level.   Since the total volume of the system, including expansion bulbs, McLeod gage, and connecting tubing, has been previously calibrated, the PV product of the gas may be determined.

The difference between the sum of the PV products for carbon dioxide and nitrogen and the original PV product of the combined carbon monoxide, nitrogen, and hydrogen represents the PV product of water vapor, which is also equivalent to the PV product of hydrogen.

Measure the gas evolved as a result of the fusion in units of PV (milliliter-millimeters). In each case correct the amount of gas collected from the sample for the blank determination on the apparatus.

Hydrogen (converted to H_2O and measured as H_2O by difference)

$$\% \text{ H} = \frac{\text{ml.-mm. } (25°C.) \times 0.1084 \times 100}{\text{wt. of sample } (\gamma)}$$

Oxygen (converted to CO and measured as CO_2)

$$\% \text{ O} = \frac{\text{ml.-mm. } (25°C.) \times 0.86 \times 100}{\text{wt. of sample } (\gamma)}$$

Nitrogen (measured as N_2)

$$\% \text{ N} = \frac{\text{ml.-mm. } (25°C.) \times 1.51 \times 100}{\text{wt. of sample } (\gamma)}$$

C. HOT EXTRACTION METHOD

The hot extraction method is based on the diffusion of hydrogen from the solid specimen heated in vacuum. The method is applicable to all metals that hold hydrogen in solution or in combination as relatively un-

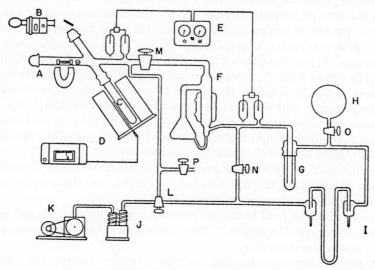

Fig. 7. Diagram of hot extraction apparatus (11).

stable compounds. As the extracted gas is virtually pure hydrogen, it may be measured directly, although in some procedures it is passed through a palladium alloy filter to isolate the hydrogen from contaminating gases before measurement.

Apparatus for the determination of hydrogen by the hot extraction method can be essentially the same as for the vacuum fusion method; it may be considerably simplified because the required temperature is much lower, there is no gettering problem, and hydrogen, in most cases, is the only gas evolved. For steel, the temperature is held just below the transformation temperature for austenite, and the hydrogen is allowed to diffuse out of the specimen held in vacuum. A commonly used temperature range is 600 to 650°C.

Fig. 7 is a schematic illustration of hot extraction apparatus (11). The following procedure is typical and may be varied as to detail and apparatus used.

Procedure

Prepare specimens in the same way as for the combustion or vacuum fusion method. Load samples into specimen-holding arm A. Open all stopcocks except P. Set stopcock L to exhaust the gas collection system. Start pumps J and K, and turn on furnace D. When the furnace reaches temperature, close stopcocks N and O, and check the system for leaks by noting the rate of pressure increase in the gas collection volume with the auxiliary volume H sealed off by stopcock O. The rate should be very small. After obtaining a satisfactory blank, push a sample from the holding arm, A, into the furnace tube, C, and allow the hydrogen to diffuse out. The Pirani gage, E, gives a continuous indication of pressure during evolution of the hydrogen. If a large volume of hydrogen is liberated, open stopcock O, and use the auxiliary gas collection volume, H. The extraction operation requires a minimum of 10 to 15 minutes and may require an hour, depending on the weight and dimensions of the specimen. After extraction is complete, read the final pressure.

Knowledge of the hydrogen pressure (corrected for blank), the temperature of collection, the volume of gas collected, and the sample weight permits calculation of the percentage of hydrogen.

After reading the final hydrogen pressure, open stopcock N, and pump out the accumulated hydrogen. Then close N, drop the next sample into C, and repeat the procedure.

The temperature of extraction may be varied. Temperatures in the range of 600 to 1100°C. are most commonly used.

D. MISCELLANEOUS METHODS

There are a number of special purpose methods for determining hydrogen. The "pickle lag" test is commonly used in production of tin plate. In this test, a coupon of known area is exposed to acid of a standard strength at a carefully controlled temperature, and the gas evolution is measured over a specified time interval. The time lag before hydrogen evolution begins has an empirical, though not well-understood, relation to the corrosion resistance of the tin plate subsequently produced from the black plate.

Pickling inhibitors may be evaluated on the basis of their efficiency in preventing evolution of hydrogen by acid attack.

For measuring the solubility of hydrogen in metals, the method originally described by Sieverts (9), with modifications of his original apparatus, is most generally used.

The hydrogen content of gases may be determined in special cases, after conversion to water, by measurement of the dew point, by measurement of the heat of reaction with a desiccant, or by the change in color of cobaltous cyanide indicator paper. It can be determined by passing the gas through a dehydrating agent and measuring the gain in weight. The desiccant must be chosen so that it does not react with or absorb the gas.

Elemental hydrogen can be determined in binary mixtures, or in a mixture of two or more other gases with nearly the same thermal conductivities, different from that of hydrogen, by relating the thermal conductivity of the mixture, at known temperature and pressure, to the amount of hydrogen. A table or calibration curve must be prepared under identical conditions by using mixtures of known composition.

The determination of deuterium in gaseous hydrogen may be made by mass spectrometry or thermal conductivity measurement directly or by gas chromatography after separation.

After conversion of deuterium to water, the mass or infrared spectrometer may be used. Measurement of the difference in density or refractive index of a mixture of deuterium oxide in hydrogen oxide will enable the deuterium content to be estimated.

The concentration of hydrogen dissolved in water may be measured by use of thermal conductivity after extraction into a closed system. Air may be used as the extractant and carrier gas (4b).

X. SUMMARY

Analysis for hydrogen is most frequently required for organic materials. A discussion of this subject will be given in a separate chapter. Analysis for water also will be considered separately.

For hydrogen determination in other materials, including metals, three methods are in general use, namely, direct combustion, vacuum fusion, and hot extraction.

The reviews published in *Analytical Chemistry* (theory and practice are covered in alternate years) give comprehensive up-to-date coverage of improvements in techniques and methods.

REFERENCES

1. *A.S.T.M. Methods for Chemical Analysis of Metals*, American Society for Testing Materials, Philadelphia, 1956.
2. Bebbington, W. P., and V. R. Thayer, *Chem. Eng. Progr.*, **55**, 70 (1959).
3. Epstein, H., J. Chipman, and N. J. Grant, *J. Metals*, **9**, 598 (1957).
4. Kirk, R. E., and D. F. Othmer, *Encyclopedia of Chemical Technology*, Vol. 7, Interscience, New York–London, 1951.
4a. Pray, H. A., C. E. Schweickert, and B. H. Minnich, *Ind. Eng. Chem.*, **44**, 1146 (1952).
4b. Robertson, R. H., and D. B. Conklin, *Bettis Technical Review WAPD-BT-16*, Office of Technical Services, Department of Commerce, Washington, D. C.
5. Rundle, R. E., *J. Am. Chem. Soc.*, **73**, 4172 (1951).
6. Sax, N. I., *Dangerous Properties of Industrial Materials*, Reinhold, New York, 1957.
7. Shull, C. G., E. O. Wollan, G. A. Morton, and W. L. Davidson, *Phys. Rev.*, **72**, 842 (1948).
8. Sidgwick, N. V., *The Chemical Elements and Their Compounds*, Vol. I, Clarendon, Oxford, 1950.
9. Sieverts, A., *Z. physik. Chem.*, **77**, 591 (1911).
10. Smith, D. P., L. W. Eastwood, D. J. Carney, and C. E. Sims, *Gases in Metals*, American Society for Metals, Cleveland, Ohio, 1953, p. 102.
11. Young, R K., and D. W. Cleaves, *Anal. Chem.*, **28**, 372 (1956).

WATER

By John Mitchell, Jr., *E. I. du Pont de Nemours & Company, Inc., Wilmington, Delaware*

Contents

Contents (*continued*)

Contents (*continued*)

Contents (*contents*)

I. INTRODUCTION

Reliable methods for the detection and quantitative determination of water are needed in essentially all industrial process work involving either synthetic or natural products, in biochemistry, in meteorology, and in many fundamental studies of structure and kinetics of reaction. Water enters directly or indirectly into practically all chemical reactions. It can be a primary reactant, as in the hydrolysis of amides and nitriles to form acids, or a principal product, as in the synthesis of esters from alcohols and acids or the dehydration of alcohols to form olefins. Water often serves as the medium in which reactions take place. Traces of water can control the courses of some reactions and in some polymerization processes may even act as a telomer. In many acid streams, small amounts of water introduce serious corrosion problems. For example, anhydrous hydrochloric acid can be handled in many metal, glass, plastic, and ceramic systems. When small quantities of moisture are present in the acid, however, severe restrictions are placed on materials of construction.

It is not surprising, therefore, that extensive research has been maintained for years on the development of suitable analyses for water in all concentrations in a variety of materials. Literally thousands of publications have appeared during the last 30 years describing new and modified methods with emphasis on applications. Many of these methods have proved to be broadly applicable to a wide variety of materials. Others have been restricted to specific applications.

Deuterium oxide (heavy water) and more recently tritium oxide have become increasingly important in tracer studies. Their use in the fields of explosives and nuclear power has been highly publicized. In addition, deuterium has been of great value in molecular structure investigations through the use of deuterium-tagged compounds during syntheses of complex materials or through exchange reactions. Normal water (protium oxide) in some substances has been estimated by exchange with deuterium or tritium oxide.

Natural water contains measurable concentrations of both deuterium and tritium, present as HDO and HTO, respectively. Deuterium levels in waters in various parts of the world have been found to lie principally in the range 0.015 to 0.016 atom %, although concentrations as low as 0.008% have been observed. Tritium concentrations have varied considerably. In sea water, for example, T/H ratios from 0.19 to 4×10^{-18} have been found, the amount decreasing with the depth at which the sample was taken. Ratios in rain water have covered the range 7 to 42×10^{-18}.

Both deuterium and tritium oxides in natural water can be concentrated by electrolysis, since the rate of discharge of H_2 is considerably more rapid than that of its isotopes. The chemical properties of deuterium and tritium oxides are very similar to those of protium oxide. The physical properties, however, differ significantly. With the nonradioactive deuterium oxide, sufficiently high concentrations often can be used to permit accurate analyses by mass and infrared spectrometry and by a variety of physical constants measurements. With the highly sensitive counters now available for radiation measurements, safe levels of the radioactive tritium oxide can be used and determined.

In this chapter a rather critical survey has been made of the most valuable techniques for the determination of water. Many already have been shown to be widely applicable; others offer the potential for uses well beyond those published in the literature. Some fundamental information is given for many of the techniques because of their relatively recent development or because background knowledge is necessary to demonstrate applications. However, no details are given for operating the numerous instruments discussed. Such information is readily available from the manufacturers and numerous physics and physical chemistry texts.

Many reviews have been published on the determination of water. Among these are the survey of methods and apparatus by Geary (111) and reviews by Klamann (177), Brissaud (31), Johnson (156), and Bennett and Hudson (17). The book *Aquametry* (219) gave references to many publications prior to 1949. The *National Nuclear Energy Series*, edited by H. C. Urey and G. M. Murphy, has presented a detailed account of many developments of the Manhattan Project during World War II. In Volume 4A, Kirshenbaum (176) described techniques developed for the measurement of physical properties of heavy water and for its analysis.

A. OCCURRENCE

Many of the physical properties of water differ considerably from what would be predicted from its low molecular weight. Its solvent power, quite apart from the property of ionizing many dissolved substances, is truly remarkable.   This property is due in large measure to the ease with which water combines with itself and with other substances.   The water molecule is nonlinear.   It may exist in stable form as solid, liquid, or gas.

1. "Free" Water

For analytical purposes water is considered "free" when it is not bound by chemical or relatively strong physical forces to other molecular species. Thus, free molecules of water are simply adsorbed on or near the surface of a solid or are not strongly associated with other molecules in solution.

Except in the gas phase, free water is rarely present as the monomer. Numerous polymers of water are known, including the dimer, trimer, and higher complex polymers formed through hydrogen bonding.   During the freezing process, depolymerization of some of the complex polymers occurs, accounting for the high latent heat of fusion of water, but the ice so formed remains polymolecular.   Even at temperatures as low as $20°K.$, several hydrogen-bonded polymers of water have been observed by infrared techniques (see Section IV-D-2).

2. Water of Hydration

Usually water in hydrated materials is referred to as *water of crystallization*.   Bonding strengths vary considerably.   Some hydrates are quite stable even at elevated temperatures; for example, hydrated zinc and nickel sulfates become anhydrous only at temperatures above $280°C.$ Others effloresce in air; for example, cyanuric acid dihydrate rather quickly becomes anhydrous in normal atmosphere.   Water is sometimes so firmly combined that the hydrate is regarded as a primary valence compound, for example, sulfuric acid, the hydrate of sulfur trioxide, and barium hydroxide, the hydrate of barium oxide.

Properties of water in crystals were reviewed by Barrer in a main Congress Lecture at the Sixteenth International Congress of Pure and Applied Chemistry (9).   He has classified the types of association as water held stoichiometrically and water held nonstoichiometrically.   The former group includes (1) hydroxyl water in acid and base hydrates such as those mentioned above and materials such as chloral hydrate in which the intramolecular bonding appears to be between hydroxyl hydrogens and chlorine atoms (63)

$$\begin{array}{ccc} & \text{Cl---HO} & \\ & | & | \\ \text{Cl—C} & & \text{C—H} \\ & | & | \\ & \text{Cl---HO} & \end{array}$$

and (2) molecular water represented by hydrates such as $ZnSO_4 \cdot 7H_2O$ and $CuSO_4 \cdot 5H_2O$. For most analytical purposes the determination of water does not include hydroxyl water but rather molecular water as such. Usually the term *water of hydration* refers to molecular water. Water held nonstoichiometrically involves substances in which (1) molecular water serves as a framework former, for example, clathrate compounds, and (2) water is not an essential framework former, for example, zeolites. In crystals where water is held nonstoichiometrically, the water is often considered "bound" and is usually thought of as that which is occluded within a crystal lattice or cell.

In a consideration of the various ways in which water is present in crystals, the clathrate compounds are unusual. The "gas hydrates" fall into this class. In ordinary ice, structural units are tetrahedra involving 5 molecules of water in which each oxygen atom is attached by hydrogen bonds to 4 other oxygen atoms. These tetrahedra are stacked together to form a cage which can accommodate other molecules. Barrer (9) described two frameworks. Type *1* is composed of 46 water molecules and has a cubic unit cell of about 12 A. Within this framework are 8 cavities having "unoccupied" diameters of 5.2 to 5.9 A. The type *2* framework contains 136 water molecules and has a unit cell of about 17.3 A; there are 24 cavities per cell with unoccupied diameters of 4.8 to 6.9 A.

TABLE I

Gas and Liquid Hydrates (Water Clathrate Compounds) (9)

Hydrate former	Boiling point, °K.	Equilibrium pressure at 0°C.
Type 1 (Gas)		
N_2O	184	10 atm.
CO_2	194	12.3 atm.
H_2S	213	0.9 atm.
Cl_2	239	252 mm.
SO_2	263	297 mm.
CH_3Br	277	187 mm.
CH_3SH	279	239 mm.
Type 2 (Liquid)		
C_3H_8	228	760 mm.
C_2H_5Cl	286	200 mm.
CH_3I	315	74 mm.
CH_2Cl_2	315	116 mm.
$CHCl_3$	334	45 mm.
$(CH_3)_2O$	248	
$(CH_3)_3CH$	261	

Gas hydrates fall into the type *1* class, and liquid hydrates, into type *2*. Examples are shown in Table I.   In both types the unit cell dimensions remain nearly constant, regardless of the hydrate former.   In the clathrate compounds the hydrate formers do not exceed 1 molecule/cavity and cannot escape without destruction of the cage.

Substances such as the crystalline zeolites represent quite a different type of structure, in which the framework does not involve water.   Molecules of water per intercrystalline cavity may exceed one.   Spacings are sufficiently large for water to pass from one cavity to another, and water may leave the lattice without affecting the framework.   Physical dimensions of cavities and windows between cages control the ease with which water can be removed from these materials.   It is interesting to note that evidence points to the fact that the so-called lower hydrates of calcium sulfate, for example, $CaSO_4 \cdot 1/2 H_2O$, are actually zeolitic adsorption complexes and that slow removal of water is associated with the small interatomic clearance in the trigonal calcium sulfate lattice (41).

Deuterates are formed in a manner similar to hydrates.   Dissociation pressures, however, are lower than those of the corresponding hydrates. Exchange of deuterium for hydrogen is used widely in studies of reaction mechanisms and molecular structure and in tracer techniques.   Both the extent and rate of exchange of D_2O for H_2O in hydrates depends upon crystal structure and accessibility of the intracrystalline regions.   Some observations of interest which throw further light on bound water were summarized by Barrer (9) as shown in Table II.   Evidence points to molecular exchange of D_2O for H_2O rather than deuterium-hydrogen atom exchange.

B. TOXICOLOGY AND INDUSTRIAL HYGIENE

Ordinary water and deuterium oxide are usually considered nontoxic. However, in a physical sense deuterium oxide behaves differently from normal water in the human body.   Heavy water should not exceed 1% of total body water, since above this level toxic effects have been observed.   Tritium compounds, on the other hand, are radioactive.   Tritium has a half life of 12.4 years, emitting soft beta rays with a maximum energy of 18.0 k.e.v. (7).

$$^3H \longrightarrow {}^3He + \beta \tag{1}$$

Tritium can be obtained as undiluted gas with an activity of about 2.63 c./cc. and as partially tritiated water having activities up to 1.0 c./g. Pure tritium oxide has an activity of about 3000 c./g. (7).

TABLE II

Deuterium-Hydrogen Exchange in Crystalline Materials Containing Water

Substance	Composition	Type[a]	Bonding	Exchange
Uranyl nitrate	$UO_2(NO_3)_2 \cdot 6H_2O$	S	Ion-dipole	Within 2 weeks
Magnesium sulfate	$MgSO_4 \cdot 7H_2O$	S	Ion-dipole	None in 3 months at near respective transformation temperatures
Copper sulfate	$[Cu(H_2O)_4 \cdot SO_4(H_2O)]$	S	Coordinate bond	
Potassium alum	$Al_2(SO_4)_3K_2SO_4 \cdot 24H_2O$	S	Ion-dipole	In range 55–75°C.
Kaolinite	$Al_2O(OH)_4 \cdot 2SiO_2{}^{b}$	S	Hydroxyl water	None up to 200°C.
Halloysite	$Al_2O_3 \cdot 2SiO_2 \cdot H_2O$	N	Molecular water (ion-dipole) with some hydroxyl water	60% at room temperature; 82% at 200°C.
Attapulgite	$Mg_5(Si_4O_{10})_2(OH)_6 \cdot {\sim}4H_2O^{c}$	N	Principally molecular water	Nearly complete
Montmorillonite	$(Mg,Ca)O \cdot Al_2O_3 \cdot 5SiO_2 \cdot {\sim}6H_2O$	N	Molecular water (ion-dipole)	93%
Chabazite	$(Ca,Na_2)Al_2(SiO_3)_4 \cdot {\sim}6H_2O$	N	Molecular water (ion-dipole)	ca. 100%
Faujasite	$(Na_2Ca)O \cdot Al_2O_3 \cdot 5SiO_2 \cdot {\sim}10H_2O^{d}$	N	Molecular water (ion-dipole)	ca. 100%

[a] S, stoichiometric; N, nonstoichiometric.

[b] Indicated composition based on report of R. H. S. Robertson, G. W. Brindley, and R. C. MacKenzie, *Am. Mineralogist*, **39**, 118 (1954).

[c] From paper by I. D. Sedletskii, *Doklady Akad. Nauk S. S. S. R.*, **89**, 339 (1953).

[d] Indicated composition based on paper by R. M. Barrer, W. Buser, and W. F. Grütter, *Helv. Chim. Acta*, **39**, 518 (1956).

Barker (7) summarized toxicity data based on information available prior to 1956. The external hazard from tritium gas as HT or T_2 is not great because of the relatively low energy of the emitted beta particles. Internal hazards from tritium gas are reduced owing to limited absorption through the skin or by lung tissue. However, HTO and T_2O are readily absorbed into the body, passing directly through the skin presumably by exchange with normal water.

The maximum permissible amount of tritium in the body is 10 mc. when the effective half life is about 15 days. According to calculations, 8 c. of tritium in the body will deliver 400 r.e.p. in the first 15 days if no effort is made to increase water turnover (LD_{50} for humans is 450 r.e.p.).

The principal danger in using systems involving the gas is from inhalation of a relatively high concentration if a leak should develop. One breath of air 10% saturated with tritium oxide at 25°C. is equivalent to about 6 c.

TABLE III

Physical Constants of Normal and Heavy Water

Property	H_2O	D_2O
Molecular weight	18.016	20.03382[a]
Density, $\frac{20°}{4}$	0.99823	1.1054
Specific gravity, $\frac{25°}{25}$	1.00000	1.10775
Maximum density, g./ml.	1.00000	1.10602
	(at 3.98°C.)	(at 11.22°C.)
Melting point, °C.	0.00	3.80
Boiling point, °C.	100.0	101.4
Critical temperature, °C.	374.2	371.5
Critical pressure, atm.	218.5	218.6
Critical density, g./ml.	0.325	0.363
Heat of vaporization, ΔH, cal.		
at 3.8°C.	10,702	11,109
at 100°C.	9,719	9,927
Heat of fusion, cal./mole	1,436	1,515
Refractive index, n, at 20°C.		
at 5893 A.	1.333000	1.328300
at 5461 A.	1.334472	1.32964
Molar refraction, R, at 20°C.		
at 5893 A.	3.712	3.679
at 5461 A.	3.692	3.727
Dielectric constant, at 25°C.	78.54	78.25
Ionization constant, at 25°C.	1×10^{-14}	1.95×10^{-15}
Diamagnetic susceptibility, at 20°C.	-0.7200×10^{-6}	-0.64665×10^{-6}
Velocity of sound,[b] m./sec.	1,496	1,398

[a] On physical scale; 20.02836 on chemical scale using $^{16}O/^{18}O/^{17}O$ ratio of 506:1:0.204
[b] With frequency of 4,950 kc.

(curies) and may deliver up to 300 r.e.p. to the body. The maximum permissible concentrations of HTO or T_2O for continuous exposure are 7 $\times$ 10^{-5} $\mu c./cc.$ in air and 5 $\times$ 10^{-1} $\mu c./ml.$ in water. The maximum permissible single intake is about 10 mc. Nonoccupational levels are 10% of these values.

II. PHYSICAL PROPERTIES OF HYDROGEN OXIDES

Physical constants of pure H_2O and pure D_2O were reported by Kirshenbaum (176). Some of these constants are given in Table III.

Only limited data have been reported for tritium oxide. Tritium has a mass of 3.0151, and tritium oxide a molecular weight of 22.0302. On the basis of the vapor pressures of ordinary water and deuterium oxide, tritium oxide would be expected to have an appreciably higher boiling point than the latter. Price (254) reported data on vapor pressures of ordinary water and HTO based on studies of tritiated water (Table IV).

TABLE IV
Vapor Pressures of Normal and Tritiated Water (254)

	Vapor pressure, mm. Hg		
t, °C.	HTO/H_2O	H_2O	HTO
25.70	0.77	24.76	19.07
27.84	0.81	28.05	22.72
39.98	0.84	55.27	46.43
55.02	0.88	118.04	104.47
75.60	0.89	296.3	265.2

III. QUALITATIVE METHODS

Many tests have been proposed for the detection of water. Most are semiquantitative and, therefore, provide an estimate of amount. Several are actually simplified versions of quantitative procedures.

Determination of deuterium and tritium oxides is discussed in Sections V and VI of this chapter. In both cases qualitative tests are closely related to quantitative methods of analysis.

A. DETECTION OF WATER

1. Chemical and Colorimetric Tests

a. COBALTOUS SALTS

Cobaltous chloride and bromide are probably the most widely used reagents for detecting water. Distinct changes in color occur as the anhydrous salts become hydrated (see Section IV-D-1). These compounds serve as visual indicators for estimating water vapor in the air and for determining the effective capacity of drying agents, such as calcium sulfate. Paper impregnated with anhydrous salt has been used for (1) testing such materials as halogenated refrigerants, gasoline, and other poor solvents for water (182) and (2) indicating rates of evaporation of water from liquids or through monolayers, for example, cetyl alcohol, on a quiescent water surface (225). A few drops of 5% anhydrous cobaltous chloride in dry acetone added to a sample of aqueous acetone provided a rapid and simple estimate of water in the range 0 to 10% (16).

b. LEAD TETRAACETATE

A 3% solution of lead tetraacetate in anhydrous benzene was used for detecting water in a variety of organic liquids (248). As little as 5 p.p.m. of water gave a brown color, whereas larger quantities led to precipitation of lead dioxide (see equation (30), Section IV-A-7).

c. DIPICRYLAMINE

Traces of water have been detected with a 1% solution of dipicrylamine in anhydrous dioxane. An orange color is formed in the presence of water (39). A drop of this reagent suspended above solids identified water evolved by gentle heating.

d. ALUMINUM SULFIDE

Aluminum sulfide reacts with water, leading to the formation of hydrogen sulfide.

$$Al_2S_3 + 6H_2O \longrightarrow 3H_2S + 2Al(OH)_3 \qquad (2)$$

Semiquantitative analyses have been made by absorbing the hydrogen sulfide in cadmium acetate solution and determining the precipitated cadmium sulfide iodometrically (24).

e. MAGNESIUM ETHOXIDE

Precipitation of magnesium hydroxide from the reaction

$$Mg(OC_2H_5)_2 + 2H_2O \longrightarrow Mg(OH)_2 + 2C_2H_5OH \qquad (3)$$

affords a convenient test for water in organic solvents (202). Magnesium alkoxides have been used for the preparation of anhydrous alcohols.

Aluminum ethoxide reacts in the same manner (see equation (38), Section IV-B-5).

f. OTHER CHEMICAL REAGENTS

Traces of water in solids, including water of hydration, have been detected by (1) the formation of a yellow color on heating the sample dispersed in paraffin oil containing K_2PbI_4, (2) the visual evolution of acetylene by reaction with calcium carbide in arachis oil (see Section IV-A-4), or (3) the formation of an intense red color on warming the sample in paraffin oil containing phosphorus pentoxide and bromocresol purple (97). The nearly colorless anhydrous copper sulfate forms the greenish blue pentahydrate in the presence of water.

2. Chromatographic Tests

Several paper chromatographic procedures have provided rapid estimates of water in specific materials. From 0.1 to 5% water in alcohol was estimated by adsorption on paper impregnated with iron sulfate and potassium ferricyanide (306). The paper was prepared by dipping strips in 3% aqueous iron sulfate solution and then 1% ferricyanide solution, with about $1/8$ inch space between the two bands. After drying, the test paper was stored in a desiccator until ready for use. A dried strip was dipped in the sample of alcohol until the iron sulfate band was just above the liquid. Diffusion of water carried salt into the ferricyanide band. The extent and intensity of the resulting blue color could be used for semi-quantitative analyses after suitable calibrations were made with standards.

When a few drops of a sample of aqueous alcohol were placed on filter paper and pressed between photographic plates, water entered the gelatin, forming a gray spot with a black border (300).

A sensitive hygrophotographic test was described based on the effect of light and moisture on photographic emulsions impregnated with the double iodide of silver and mercury. The yellow emulsion turned black in the light but became yellow again in the presence of water (299).

3. Physical Tests

Simple physical tests for water have been employed on a variety of non-volatile materials. Some substances can be heated, and water detected by allowing the vapors to condense on a cool surface. Estimates of water in wet fibrous materials and textiles have been made by pressing the sample and collecting the water in a calibrated vessel. Water in powdered materials has been estimated by measuring the increase in volume of an added water-miscible material after centrifugation.

Cloud point methods, as described in Section IV-F-1, have been used widely in qualitative tests for water in liquids and solids.

4. Instrumental Tests

In polarographic studies Vlček (336) observed that hydrogen ions were discharged at a more positive potential in acetonitrile as solvent than in water. With increasing concentrations of water in acetonitrile, the hydrogen ion reduction wave shifted rapidly to more negative potentials.

Spectroscopic methods can be used in rapid qualitative tests for water. The 1.9 μ band in the infrared is nearly specific for water. In the absence of alcohols and amines, hydroxyl group infrared absorption bands also can be used, as discussed in Section IV-D-2. Nuclear magnetic resonance and vacuum ultraviolet spectroscopy as well as other instrumental procedures described in Section IV-D may serve as convenient, rapid methods for the identification of water.

B. IDENTIFICATION OF HYDRATES

Crystalline hydrates usually can be identified by x-ray diffraction and visual microscopy. Powder diffraction patterns are characteristic for each crystalline species and often permit detection and semiquantitative analyses for hydrates in mixtures. Extensive reference data have been compiled by the American Society for Testing Materials and are available on standard cards. Summary data are given in the *Index to the X-Ray Powder Data File* (2). X-ray data also appear regularly in *Analytical Chemistry* and other journals. For details of the powder diffraction technique, the reader is referred to books such as *X-Ray Diffraction Procedures* (179). Optical crystallographic constants as determined with the petrographical microscope and crystal habit behavior as determined by fusion methods afford identification of many hydrates. Details of the techniques are given in several well-known texts on microscopy and fusion methods in chemical microscopy.

Shifts in infrared and nuclear magnetic resonance spectra often provide direct evidence of bound water (see Sections IV-D-2 and IV-D-3).

Transitions measured by differential thermal analysis and thermogravimetry serve to identify hydrates and often to determine the amount in mixtures (see Section IV-G-4).

IV. DETERMINATION OF WATER

A. CHEMICAL METHODS

1. Karl Fischer Reagent

The most widely applicable method for determining water is based on titration with the Karl Fischer reagent (KFR). Since its discovery in

1935 (96), the reagent has been applied successfully to analyses of an increasing number of materials. The nearly specific nature of this reagent, together with the rapidity with which analyses can be performed, has led to literally hundreds of applications. Many of the reported studies have presented an inaccurate picture of the method, often because of inadequate recognition of safeguards required during its use and neglect of interferences which must be provided for. Effective use of the reagent requires a thorough understanding of its potential and limitations.

In this chapter it is impractical to give a detailed discussion of the reagent and its applications. Rather, stress will be placed on the nature of the reagent, preferred procedures for its use, and the more general applications. For further details the reader is referred to *Aquametry* (219) and the numerous reviews that have appeared in the literature since 1948.

a. REACTIONS

Karl Fischer reagent is composed of iodine, sulfur dioxide, pyridine, and usually methanol. Reaction with water involves the two-step reaction,

$$C_5H_5N \cdot I_2 + C_5H_5N \cdot SO_2 + C_5H_5N + H_2O \longrightarrow$$

$$2C_5H_5N \cdot HI + C_5H_5N \cdot SO_3 \quad (4a)$$

$$C_5H_5N \cdot SO_3 + CH_3OH \longrightarrow C_5H_5N(H)SO_4CH_3 \quad (4b)$$

It is apparent that only reaction (4a) involves water, whereas reaction (4b) completes reaction of the intermediate, the pyridine sulfur trioxide complex.

The stoichiometric requirements are established by equations (4a) and (4b). Normally, however, an excess of sulfur dioxide, pyridine, and methanol or other hydroxyl-containing compound is used, and hence the effective strength of the reagent is established by the iodine concentration. For example, the most widely used reagent is prepared as a methanolic solution containing other components in the ratio of $1I_2 : 3SO_2 : 10C_5H_5N$.

For macro titrations the reagent usually is prepared at a concentration equivalent to 3 mg. or more of water per milliliter of reagent. At this level freshly prepared methanolic reagent is relatively unstable owing to a variety of parasitic side reactions involving iodine (219). Reaction rate is greatest during the first few days after preparation. Consequently, it has become common practice to allow the active reagent to stand in a closed or desiccant-protected system for a day or two prior to use. Then the equivalent concentration, determined by titration of a standard of known water content, need be determined only once or twice per day.

The rate of side reactions is dependent on iodine concentration. At a level equivalent to 1 mg. or less of water per milliliter, the reagent is quite stable.

Many variations in preparation of the reagent have been proposed to minimize the extent of degradative side reactions. Stable stock solutions of iodine and pyridine in methanol have been prepared, the sulfur dioxide being added a day or two before use (219). A two-reagent scheme has been recommended in which the sample dissolved in pyridine-methanol containing sulfur dioxide is titrated with iodine in methanol (154). Provided the iodine in methanol solution is adequately protected against moisture, the iodine concentration need be checked only occasionally (278) No significant side reactions have been observed in cases where rapid direct titrations were made, that is, where no free iodine remained in the solution. In a variation of the two-reagent titration, Johansson suggested that the end product HI (see equation (4a)) be determined via bromine oxidation.

$$HI + 3Br_2 + 3H_2O \longrightarrow HIO_3 + 6HBr \tag{5a}$$

$$HIO_3 + 5KI + 5HCl \longrightarrow 3I_2 + 3H_2O + 5KCl \tag{5b}$$

Iodine thus formed was determined by titration with standardized sodium thiosulfate.

In studies designed to improve the stability of the reagent, several materials have been tried as replacements for methanol. By far the most promising was methyl Cellosolve, use of which was proposed by Peters and Jungnickel (249). Blomgren and Jenner (23) found that the methanolic reagent could be stabilized by adjusting the iodide concentration so that the I^-/I_2 ratio was about 3.2 for a reagent containing about 1.2 and 3.5 moles/liter of sulfur dioxide and pyridine, respectively. Also, use of salts of weak organic acids in place of pyridine have been reported to help stabilize the reagent (324).

Substitution of bromine for iodine in the Karl Fischer reagent has led to an active reagent. Belcher and West (15) delivered a measured amount of sample to an excess of reagent (Br_2 plus SO_2 in $CHCl_3$), finally back-titrating with a standard solution of water in pyridine. The reaction appeared analogous to that of the iodine-containing reagent. However, alcohols as well as water reacted.

b. TITRATION PROCEDURES

Both visual and electrometric titration procedures can be used with the Karl Fischer reagent. For macroanalyses either procedure may be applicable. For micro titrations, however, the electrometric technique is better suited.

KFR is, in effect, a powerful desiccant.   In all procedures, sample and reagent must be carefully protected from moisture in the atmosphere. This precaution is ordinarily observed by using either closed titration flasks for the sample or flasks with narrow necks, such as volumetric flasks. Breathing tubes containing active desiccants are necessary for protecting the reagent during storage and delivery and desirable for protecting the sample.   Further details are given in *Aquametry* (219) and in the discussion to follow.

With the exception of the coulometric method, all titration procedures require that the KFR be standardized against a known weight of water. Usually this standardization is performed most conveniently by titration of finely divided sodium tartrate dihydrate (230).   Other methods of standardization employ methanol containing a known amount of water or water weighed directly into the titration flask.

(1) Visual Titration

The visual titration requires only simple apparatus; volumetric flasks are satisfactory.   The reagent acts as its own indicator.   The sample solution remains canary yellow as long as water is present, changing to chromate yellow near the end point and finally to the brown color of unused iodine.   The first appearance of the brown color serves as the end point (219).   As an aid in detecting the end point, a permanent standard of about $0.01N$ iodine in methanol may be used.   For reagent having a concentration equivalent to less than 2 mg. of water per milliliter, addition of a few drops of methylene blue in pyridine solution often helps in distinguishing the end point (94).   The color change is from blue to blue-green.

The visual titration method is best suited for use with colorless or lightly colored solutions.   Where feasible, the sample should be in solution.   With practice the end point can be determined with a reproducibility of 0.2 ml. of reagent, equivalent to about 0.5 mg. of water.   In most cases this error is not significant for samples containing 1% or more of water.   For example, with 3 mg./ml. reagent the error due to a spread of 0.3 ml. in titer on 10 g. of sample containing 1.00% water amounts to only 0.01%.   Analysis of 75 to 100 g. samples of adipic acid dissolved in 250 ml. of pretitrated 1:1 pyridine-methanol gave an average of 0.0639% with a standard deviation of 0.0004% (218).   Approximately 500 g. samples of liquid butadiene were titrated directly at 0°C. with a precision of better than 1 p.p.m. (218).

These results indicate the optimum that can be expected in the visual titration.   It is apparent that large samples are required for determinations of parts per million levels of water.

(2) Electrometric Titration

Significant improvements in sensitivity and precision are obtained by electrometric titration. The "dead-stop" technique (99,164), employing platinum electrodes, has been used most often. Numerous commercial instruments based on this principle are available. In its simplest form, as indicated in Fig. 1, apparatus requirements are a battery, variable resistor, galvanometer or microammeter, and platinum electrodes (154,219). A potential is applied across the electrodes to just balance the system, that is, to the point where the galvanometer is not deflected. During titration, as long as water is present, the anode is depolarized, and the cathode polarized. At the end point, the small amount of iodine depolarizes the cathode, resulting in a surge of current.

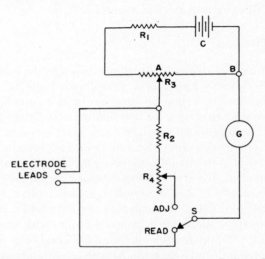

Fig. 1. Electrical circuit for direct dead-stop end point: C, dry cell, 1.5 v.; G, galvanometer (Leeds & Northrup No. 2330-C) or microammeter; R_1, resistor, wire-wound, 9000 ohms; R_2, resistor, wire-wound, 1500 ohms; R_3, potentiometer, 1000 ohms; R_4, resistor, 400 ohms, variable; S, switch, single pole, double throw.

The dead-stop technique is applicable for macro or micro titrations by manual or automatic methods. Johansson (155), for example, devised a simple micro method. A hypodermic syringe was used to contain the reagent, which was delivered by means of a worm gear drive. The motor was connected to the electrodes so that at the end point the motor instantly stopped. The volume of KFR delivered was read from the calibrated screw system. A major advance in instrumentation was made by Frediani (101), who devised a nearly foolproof automatic apparatus with an all-glass volume-measuring system. An adjustable electrical timer formed a part of the circuitry and provided an automatic means for differentiating between true and transient end points. The timer could be set for periods up to 60 seconds. Reagent was delivered until the end point was apparently reached. If the end point did not hold for the preset time interval, additional reagent would be delivered automatically. For general use an end point stable for 30 seconds was recommended (101).

Numerous other variations in circuitry for the dead-stop end point have been proposed, including use of electromagnetic switches, compact amplifiers, and an acoustic end point indicator (116).

The reproducibility of titration by the dead-stop method is less than 0.1 ml. of reagent, equivalent to less than 0.3 mg. of water. Consequently, considerably smaller samples than those necessary in the visual procedure are required to achieve the same precision in analyses.

For microanalyses, Bastin, Siegel, and Bullock (10) recommended use of an amperometric plot to determine the end point for titration with the methyl Cellosolve–modified KFR (249). Results on several milligram quantities of a variety of samples indicated a standard deviation of about 1% or 3 γ when less than 300 γ of water was titrated. Duplicate analyses of only 1 ml. samples of benzene containing 0.0359% water gave results of 0.0361 and 0.0354%.

Determination of water by coulometrically generated KFR has been demonstrated successfully in both manually controlled and automatic titrations (171,214). Iodine was generated with nearly 100% current efficiency according to the reaction

$$2I^- \longrightarrow I_2 + 2e \tag{6}$$

iodide ions being furnished by "spent" KFR (see equation (4a)). The stoichiometry of the reaction corresponds to 1 mole of iodine per mole of water, equivalent to 10.71 coulombs of generating current per milligram of water. The method was particularly appropriate for determining small quantities of water in strong amines; the amines, such as 1,2-diaminopropane, were neutralized with salicylic acid in ethylene glycol prior to analysis. The method was best suited for analysis of liquids. In titrations of 1 ml. samples, as little as 50 γ of water was determined in 1,2-diaminopropane, and 5 γ in other classes of materials. The absolute standard deviation was about 2 γ of water.

Potentiometric titrations also have been used (see reference 219).

(3) Photometric Titration

Eberius (76) described apparatus for the photometric determination of the end point.   Uniform light was passed through a thermostat containing the titration vessel and received by a photoelectric cell whose response was transmitted to a galvanometer.   The galvanometer deflection was plotted against the volume of KFR during titration of the sample.   A change of as much as 700 mm. was observed over a range of about 1 ml. of reagent as the titration passed through the end point.

The technique was suitable for use with clear, lightly colored solutions.

c. Titration Vessels

Many types of flasks have been recommended.   The protection necessary against contamination by atmospheric moisture depends on the titration procedure and the time required for analysis.   For the visual titration, vessels with narrow necks, such as volumetric flasks, often can be used.

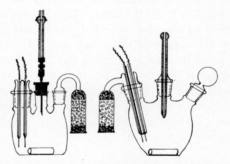

Fig. 2. Titration vessels for dead-stop end point.

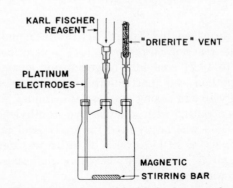

Fig. 3. Small sealed vessel assembly for dead-stop end point (352).

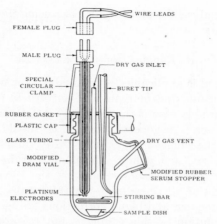

Fig. 4. Cell assembly for micro amperometric procedure (10)

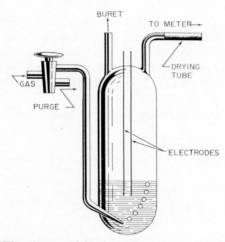

Fig. 5. Titration vessel for determining water in gases (157).

For the more sensitive electrometric methods, a completely protected system is required.

Suitable titration vessels are shown in Figs. 2 and 3 (352) and in *Aquametry* (219). For the amperometric procedure the cell assembly shown in Fig. 4 was recommended (10). Normally the KFR is delivered into the sample to be analyzed, and, therefore, active reagent is not present until after the end point has been reached. In some cases it is desirable to titrate the sample into a measured volume of KFR. Jones (157) described this approach in analyses for moisture in gases using the assembly shown in Fig. 5.

d. APPLICATIONS, LIMITATIONS

The KFR method is applicable to the analysis for water in all types of materials, both organic and inorganic. Contrary to some reports in the literature, with suitable care it can be used for determining from about 1 p.p.m. to pure water. In general, the sample should be dissolved in an inert solvent, and the whole or an aliquot titrated directly with KFR to the electrometric or visual end point. Methanol, pyridine, and dioxane are suitable solvents. For optimum sensitivity the solvent should be pre-titrated before addition of the sample. By this means, water in the solvent and the flask is removed, and blank corrections are rendered unnecessary. Often complete solution of the sample is not required. Finely divided solids dispersed in methanol are analyzed reliably if the water is not too tightly bound.

Direct titration of the sample usually gives total water, that is, free plus hydrated water. When a suitable water-miscible liquid can be found in which the sample is insoluble, free water can be determined. In this case the sample is extracted with the liquid, and the liquid then titrated; for example, dioxane will extract free water from many hydrated inorganic materials.

Since the KFR method is applicable to the determination of water in

TABLE V

Noninterfering Organic Compounds, KFR Method

Class	Examples
Acids	Carboxylic acids, hydroxy acids, amino acids, sulfonic acids
Alcohols	Monoalcohols, polyhydric alcohols, phenols
Esters	Normal carboxylic esters, ortho esters, carbamates, lactones, esters of inorganic acids
Stable carbonyl compounds	Sugars, formaldehyde, benzil, benzoin, chloral
Acetals and ethers	Methylal, diethyl ether
Hydrocarbons	Saturated and unsaturated aliphatic and aromatic hydrocarbons
Anhydrides and acyl halides	Acetic anhydride, benzoyl chloride
Peroxides	Hydroperoxides, dialkyl peroxides
Nitrogen compounds	Amines, amides
Halides	Alkyl chlorides
Sulfur compounds	Sulfides, thiocyanates, thioesters, xanthates, dithio-carbamates

many classes of organic and inorganic compounds, it seems appropriate to tabulate classes rather than individual compounds. Table V lists classes of organic compounds which do not interfere with the method, together with examples. Usually methanol is a suitable solvent. For the highest accuracy the stronger acids, anhydrides, and acyl halides are best dissolved in a pyridine-methanol solvent, which minimizes esterification. Hydroperoxides react selectively with the sulfur dioxide of KFR and, hence, do not interfere.

$$ROOH + SO_2 \longrightarrow RHSO_4 \qquad (7)$$

Strong amines react exothermally and are best titrated in acetic acid solution. Further details are given in *Aquametry* for organic and inorganic materials (219). Xanthates should be dispersed in chloroform (218).

Interfering organic materials are summarized in Table VI. Active aldehydes and ketones react with methanol in the KFR.

$$RCHO + 2CH_3OH \longrightarrow RCH(OCH_3)_2 + H_2O \qquad (8)$$

Their presence is indicated by a rapidly fading end point. Often use of pyridine as solvent reduces the rate of acetal formation, permitting reliable analyses (218). For highest accuracy, however, reaction with hydrogen

TABLE VI
Interfering Organic Compounds, KFR Method

Substance	Nature of interference	Modification
Active carbonyl compounds	Acetal formation	Cyanohydrin reaction
Ascorbic acid	Quantitative oxidation by iodine	
Quinone	Quantitative reduction by HI	
Mercaptans	Quantitative oxidation by iodine	BF$_3$-catalyzed addition to olefin
Diacyl peroxides	Reduction by HI	
Dimethylolurea	Condensation	Titration at $-40°C$.

cyanide prior to titration with KFR is recommended (219); the carbonyl compounds are converted to the inert cyanohydrins. Ascorbic acid (vitamin C) is oxidized to dehydroascorbic acid, and quinone is reduced to hydroquinone. Mercaptans are oxidized rapidly.

$$RSH + I_2 \longrightarrow RSSR + 2HI \qquad (9)$$

Their interference can be eliminated by an addition reaction with olefins prior to titration with KFR (219). However, when the concentrations

TABLE VII

Noninterfering Inorganic Compounds, KFR Method

Class	Examples
Salts of organic acids	$Na(CH_3)SO_4$, $Ba(OOCCH_3)_2$, $K_2C_2O_4$, $UO_2(OOCCH_3)_2$, $Na_2C_4H_4O_6$, $Na_3C_6H_5O_7$
Salts of inorganic acids	$NH_4H_2PO_4$, $CaCl_2$, $NaHSO_4$, Na_2SO_4, KF, NH_4NO_3, $MgSO_4$, $Na_2S_2O_4$, $KSCN$, $FeSO_4$, $Al_2(SO_4)_3 \cdot K_2SO_4$. $CaHPO_4$, NaI, $CaCO_3$, $CaCl_2$, FeF_3, $UO_2(NO_3)_2$
Acid oxides	SiO_2, Al_2O_3
Inorganic acids and anhydrides	SO_2, HI, HCl, HF, HNO_3, HCN, H_2SO_4, HSO_3NH_2
Hydroperoxides	Selective reaction with SO_2 of KFR

of these compounds are known and the amount of water in the sample is appreciable, correction for the interfering compounds can be applied to the KFR titer.

Noninterfering inorganic compounds are listed in Table VII. Usually total water is determined on titration of the sample dissolved or dispersed in methanol. The strong mineral acids should be dissolved in pyridine or pyridine-dioxane solution to minimize reaction with the methanol of KFR. Water in fuming nitric acid has been determined in pyridine-dimethylformamide solution (221).

Several inorganic substances interfere in direct KFR titrations, as noted in Table VIII. Metal hydroxides, oxides, carbonates, and bicarbonates react quantitatively in a manner analogous to that of water (217). Free

TABLE VIII

Interfering Inorganic Compounds, KFR Method

Substance	Nature of interference
Metal hydroxides and oxides	Quantitative reaction with KFR
Carbonates and bicarbonates	Quantitative reaction with KFR
Aluminum acetate, basic	Apparently incomplete reaction
Ammonia	Reaction with iodine
Boric acid and oxides	Quantitative esterification by methanol of KFR
Chromates and dichromates	Variable reaction
Cobalt amine complexes	Variable reaction
Cupric chloride and sulfate	Quantitative reduction by HI
Ferric chloride	Quantitative reaction with KFR
Hydrogen and sodium sulfide	Variable reaction
Hydroxylamine	Partial reaction with KFR
Phosphomolybdic acid	Apparently incomplete reaction
Silanols (R_3SiOH)	Quantitative reaction with KFR
Sodium thiosulfate	Quantitative reaction with iodine
Stannous chloride	Quantitative reaction with KFR
Zirconyl chloride	Apparently incomplete reaction

water in sodium hydroxide has been separated by azeotropic distillation with xylene, followed by titration of the distillate with KFR (307). Water in sodium bicarbonate has been extracted with dry methanol, and a correction applied for the small amount of base removed (106). In both of these cases use of dioxane would appear more desirable. Dioxane forms a homogeneous binary with water (b.p. 87.8°C., 18 wt. % H₂O). Benzene-ethanol, which forms a homogeneous ternary with water (b.p. 80.2°C., 7.4 wt. % H₂O, 18.5% C₂H₅OH), was used by Rush and Kilbank (271) to remove water from pigmented GR-S rubber stock. The distillate was titrated with KFR.

Ammonia forms nitrogen iodide on direct titration with KFR. Addition of excess acetic acid prior to titration eliminates this interference (219). Hydroxylamine can be converted to the inert sulfamate by treatment with spent KFR or sulfur dioxide in pyridine (219). Total water in chelates involving cobalt and ammonia usually is not determined quantitatively. In compounds of the type $[Co(NH_3)_5H_2O]Cl_3$, water in the inner sphere apparently is not titrated (219,354). Where water is bonded in compounds such as $[Co(NH_3)_5H_2O]_2(SO_4)_3 \cdot 3H_2O$, water in the outer sphere is determined (354). Silanols react quantitatively with KFR apparently by the reaction (114).

$$R_3SiOH + I_2 + SO_2 + 2CH_3OH \longrightarrow$$
$$R_3SiOCH_3 + 2HI + CH_3HSO_4 \quad (10)$$

Further details on the nature of the interference by inorganic compounds are given in reference 219.

Applications of the KFR method to commercial materials and natural products can be predicted in many cases from the known behavior of individual components. Table IX summarizes pertinent information on several materials that have been successfully analyzed for water. *Aquametry* (219) and *Wasserbestimmung mit Karl-Fischer Lösung* (76) have been given as references for some products; usually these sources have quoted other references acknowledged in the texts.

Specific products within some of the categories listed in Table IX contain compounds that interfere on direct titration with KFR, for example, some drugs, explosives, paints, minerals, and soils. Usually extraction at room or elevated temperature or distillation has been found suitable for separation of water from these products. Since many of the interfering compound reactions with KFR are quantitative, suitable corrections often can be applied to the direct KFR result when the concentrations of the reactive compounds are known.

A procedure for the KFR method is given in Section VII.

TABLE IX

Applications of KFR Method to Commercial Materials and Natural Products

Material	Range, % H_2O	Sample size	Conditions	Precision, %	Ref.
Blood, plasma	77–93	20–50 mg.	Methanol solution	0.2	(54,64)
Body tissues, cell materials	56–80	100–250 mg.	Methanol dispersion	0.2	(54,64,88)
Drugs	0.1–several	mg.–g.	Methanol solution or extraction	0.01–0.1	(61,76,85,219, 223)
Explosives	0.1–several	mg.–g.	Methanol solution or extraction; ethyl acetate–methanol extraction; pyridine–methanol extraction; ether–methanol extraction	0.001–0.1	(61,76,218,219, 268)
Fats, waxes	0.1–several	mg.–g.	Methanol solution; chloroform solution	0.001–0.2	(61,76,219)
Foods, fresh	20–75	100–500 mg.	Methanol solution or extraction	0.2	(76,219)
Foods, dehydrated	1–20	1–10 g.	Methanol extraction at room temperature or reflux	0.02–0.3	(61,76,219,277)
Lecithin	0.1–1	5 g.	Chloroform–methanol solution	0.4, relative	(32)
Leather	10–20	0.2–1 g.	Methanol extraction at room temperature or reflux	0.1–0.2	(76)
Minerals	Several	mg.–g.	Distillation of water, followed by titration	0.1	(76,218,219,270)
Naval stores	0.02–0.9	g.	Methanol solution or extraction; pyridine solution	0.002–0.05	(76,219)
Oils	0.01–1	20–40 g.	Methanol extraction from decalin solution; methanol solution or extraction; petroleum ether extraction	0.001–0.1	(219)

Material				Method	References
Paints, lacquers	0.02–5	0.002–0.1	1–50 g.	Pyridine extraction or dispersion; methanol extraction; dioxane extraction	(76,219)
Paper, pulp	3–10	0.05–0.1	1–3 g.	Methanol extraction	(76,154,219)
Petroleum products, gases	p.p.m.	0.1 p.p.m.	30 ft.³	Methanol solution or extraction; ethylene glycol extraction	(30,157,219)
liquids	p.p.m.–1	10–20, relative	2–100 g.	Methanol solution or extraction; ethylene glycol extraction; pyridine solution; chloroform-methanol solution	(76,131,214,219,252,302)
solids	0.02–0.1	0.001	100 g.	Distillation of toluene-water binary, followed by titration; toluene solution	(219,237,260,261)
Plastics, resins	0.1–12	0.01–0.2	1–10 g.	Methanol extraction at room temperature or reflux; distillation of water, followed by titration; diethylene glycol solution	(10,61,76,138,218,219,352)
Proteins	6–14	0.1	0.3–0.5 g.	Methanol extraction	(208,219)
Rubber, synthetic	0.04–0.5		15 g.	Distillation of benzene-ethanol-water ternary	(271)
Soaps, detergents	0.4–3	0.05–0.2	1–20 g.	Methanol extraction; distillation of xylene-water binary, followed by titration	(52,72,219)
Starches	9–14	0.05–1	0.3–1 g.	Methanol extraction at room temperature	(77,209,219)
Sugars	1–60	0.002–0.2	0.3–10 g.	Methanol solution or extraction	(61,76,219)
Textiles	6–10	0.05–0.1	1 g.	Methanol extraction at room temperature	(76,219)
Wood	7–45	0.1	0.02–2 g.	Methanol extraction at room temperature or reflux	(219)

2. Acetyl Chloride and Other Acyl Halides

a. REACTIONS, METHODS

Acetyl chloride is easily hydrolyzed. Because of its low boiling point (52°C.), however, this compound must be combined with a suitable substance to reduce its vapor pressure. Smith and Bryant (301) developed a simple procedure using pyridine to combine with the reagent and acidic products. The acetylpyridinium chloride reacted rapidly with water.

$$C_5H_5N \cdot CH_3COCl + H_2O \longrightarrow C_5H_5N \cdot HCl + CH_3COOH \quad (11a)$$

An excess of reagent was used. After hydrolysis was complete, usually several minutes at room temperature, the excess acetyl chloride was removed by reaction with dry alcohol.

$$C_5H_5N \cdot CH_3COCl + ROH \longrightarrow C_5H_5N \cdot HCl + CH_3COOR \quad (11b)$$

The difference in acidity between the sample and a blank, as determined by titration with standardized caustic, was equivalent mole for mole to water present in the sample. Procedural details are given in Section VII.

With analyses of known samples, Smith and Bryant (301) found that recoveries were consistently 97 to 98% of theory. They recommended that observed results be corrected to the stoichiometric values by dividing by the factor 0.975. A precision of 1% was obtained on samples containing 50 mg. or more of water. With $1.5M$ acetyl chloride and $0.5N$ base, as little as 2 mg. of water, equivalent to 0.02% on a 10 g. sample, could be detected.

In applying the procedure to fats, Kaufmann and Funke (168) used 0.2 to $0.5M$ acetyl chloride in carbon tetrachloride. Excess reagent was allowed to react with aniline.

$$C_5H_5N \cdot CH_3COCl + C_6H_5 \cdot NH_2 \longrightarrow$$

$$C_5H_5N \cdot HCl + C_6H_5 \cdot NHCOCH_3 \quad (12)$$

Several other acyl chlorides have been studied as reagents for water in the micro dry combustion method for carbon and hydrogen. A suitable compound could be used in a titrimetric method for water evolved instead of in the conventional gravimetric procedure. Belcher, Thompson, and West (14) investigated some substances and chose succinyl chloride (m.p., 17°C.; b.p., 192°C. at 760 mm.) as the most likely candidate among those tried. This compound was found to be readily available and relatively stable and to have only a slight vapor pressure at 60°C., the optimum temperature for the analysis. With a large excess of the chloride, 2 moles of hydrochloric acid were recovered per mole of water, according to the reaction

$$(CH_2COCl)_2 + H_2O \longrightarrow (CH_2CO)_2O + 2HCl \qquad (13)$$

In carrying out an analysis, a tube containing succinyl chloride was substituted for the usual solid desiccant in the dry combustion train. Hydrochloric acid evolved was absorbed in an aqueous scrubber and titrated with $0.05N$ sodium borate. The blank varied from 0.60 to 1.50 ml. but was reproducible for each lot of reagent used.

Cinnamoyl chloride also has been used for determining small amounts of water in gases (326) and in microanalysis (197). Lindner (197) carried out the reaction at 65 to 70°C., using a stream of air to remove the hydrochloric acid at rates up to 1 liter/hour. With at least a $10M$ excess of chloride over water (for example, 1 g. of reagent for 11 mg. of water), the reaction corresponded to that of succinyl chloride, equation (13). With a smaller excess, however, some cinnamic acid, rather than the anhydride, was formed.

$$C_6H_5CH{=}CHCOCl + H_2O \longrightarrow C_6H_5CH{=}CHCOOH + HCl \quad (14)$$

Aluminum chloride reacts with water vapor at 450°C. in a manner analogous to that of the acyl chlorides (93).

$$2AlCl_3 + 3H_2O \longrightarrow Al_2O_3 + 6HCl \qquad (15)$$

A method based on this reaction was used successfully in analyses for water in gaseous hydrogenation products at elevated temperatures. After reaction was complete, the gas was condensed, and the hydrochloric acid determined by acidimetric titration.

b. APPLICATIONS, LIMITATIONS

The acetyl chloride procedure has been applied to the determination of water in a wide variety of organic materials. Examples are shown in Table X.

Most fatty acids do not interfere; they, of course, are titrated with the standardized base, and the titer must be corrected accordingly. Formic acid, however, interferes since it is dehydrated by the reagent. Easily hydrolyzed esters, such as the lower formates, are partially saponified in the general method employing aqueous caustic. This interference is eliminated by use of sodium methylate in dry alcohol as titrating agent. Strong tertiary amines like triethylamine and appreciable quantities of aldehydes interfere with the phenolphthalein end point.

TABLE X
Determination of Water by Acetyl Chloride Method

Material	Level, % H_2O	Ref.
Acids (except formic)	>0.2	(301)
Amines, primary and secondary	>0.2	(301)
Amines, tertiary	>0.02	(301)
Ethylene glycol	>0.5	(301)
Glycerol	>0.5	(301)
Methanol	>0.5	(301)
Alcohols, other	>0.2	(301)
Esters (except C_1–C_3 formates)	>0.02	(301)
Ethers	>0.02	(301)
Fats and Oils	>0.02	(168,200)
Hydrocarbons	>0.02	(301)
Hydrocarbon gases	p.p.m.	(193)
Ketones	>0.02	(301)
Sulfonated oils	>0.02	(91)

Colored materials that interfere with the visual end point may be titrated potentiometrically. For analysis of colored or highly acidic fats, waxes and oils, however, Loury and Piquard (200) used azeotropic distillation with toluene to separate the water (see Section IV-C-1.) They analyzed the distillate by the acetyl chloride method, using $0.5N$ KOH in ethanol for the acidimetric titration.

Small amounts of alcohols and primary and secondary amines do not interfere beyond using up part of the acetyl chloride reagent. As much as 1 g. of these materials usually can be tolerated.

Since ketones do not interfere, compounds such as acetone can be used to extract moisture from solids or gases (193). High results have been reported for tars (27).

3. Acetic Anhydride and Other Anhydrides

a. REACTIONS, METHODS

Acid anhydrides are hydrolyzed to the free acids.

$$(RCO)_2O + H_2O \longrightarrow 2RCOOH \tag{16}$$

Their rate of hydrolysis is considerably slower than that of corresponding acyl chlorides. For example, in the absence of a catalyst about 12 hours at 110°C. was required to affect complete hydrolysis of benzoic anhydride (266).

Acetic anhydride has been the most widely used anhydride for determining water. In order to accelerate hydrolysis, a number of relatively strong acids have been used as catalysts, including 2,4-dinitrobenzenesulfonic acid (319), fluoroboric acid (323), perchloric acid (62,122,319), and sulfuric acid (147).

(1) Acidimetric Titration

The most popular titrimetric methods are based on reaction of the water in the sample with excess reagent. The excess anhydride has been determined by titration with sodium methylate to the thymol blue end point (319).

$$RCOOH + NaOCH_3 \longrightarrow CH_3COONa + CH_3OH \qquad (17a)$$

$$(CH_3CO)_2O + NaOCH_3 \longrightarrow CH_3COONa + CH_3COOCH_3 \qquad (17b)$$

The difference in titer between the sample and a blank containing the same amount of anhydride is a measure of water in the sample.

Alternatively, aniline has been employed.

$$(CH_3CO)_2O + C_6H_5NH_2 \longrightarrow C_6H_5NHCOCH_3 + CH_3COOH \qquad (18)$$

The acid formed can be titrated with sodium hydroxide (220). A known amount of aniline can be added, and the excess titrated with $0.1N$ perchloric acid in glacial acetic acid to the methyl violet end point (62). Triethanolamine in ethanol also has been used to react with excess anhydride (323).

(2) Conductometric Titration

This technique was applied to determinations of water in fuming nitric acid (147). The sample was placed in a cell containing anhydrous acetic acid with catalytic amounts of sulfuric acid and titrated with acetic anhydride in acetic acid. The equivalence point was indicated by a sharp break in a plot of specific conductance vs. volume of titrant added.

(3) Polarimetry

Toennies and Elliott (319) found that polarimetry offered a novel means for estimating water in acetic acid. Hydrolysis was effected in the presence of perchloric acid as catalyst. Excess anhydride was allowed to dehydrate d-camphoric acid.

$$(CH_3CO)_2O + C_8H_{14}(COOH)_2 \longrightarrow 2CH_3COOH + C_8H_{14}(CO)_2O \qquad (19)$$

The change in optical rotation of a known quantity of camphoric acid was a measure of the excess anhydride.

(4) Thermal Techniques

Probably the most important anhydride methods have been based on the heat evolved during hydrolysis of acetic anhydride. Of particular interest are the two procedures of Greathouse, Janssen, and Haydel (122). In the first procedure, sample and acetic anhydride are mixed, the initial result being a significant decrease in temperature. (Hydrolysis in the absence of a catalyst is quite slow.) The lowest temperature reached is recorded, and perchloric acid catalyst is added immediately. The maximum temperature is noted, and the quantity of water in the sample is determined from a calibration curve relating amount of water to temperature rise. Procedural details are given in Section VII.

In the other procedure, a known amount of acetic anhydride (excess) and catalyst are added carefully to the sample in a Dewar flask. After hydrolysis is complete and the solution cooled to room temperature, excess anhydride is determined by careful titration with water–acetic acid reagent. Addition of 0.5 to 1 ml. increments is continued until no further temperature rise is noted. The amount of water in the sample is related to anhydride used up, as measured by the difference between anhydride originally added and excess anhydride determined by the titration.

The former thermometric procedure would appear to be the more reliable since it represents a direct approach. For both methods calibration curves were prepared from data obtained by analysis of known samples containing from 0.19 to 4.44 g. of water per liter of acetic acid. These analyses were checked by direct titration with Karl Fischer reagent (see Section IV-A-1).

(5) Ultraviolet Spectrophotometry

Acetic anhydride absorbs appreciably at 252 mμ. Bruckenstein (37), in a variation of the hydrolysis reaction, measured excess anhydride at this wavelength in a sensitive method for determining small amounts of water in acetic acid. A measured amount (excess) of acetic anhydride was added to a few milliliters of sample. Absorbance was determined before and after heating for 1.5 hours at 110°C. The decrease in absorbance was proportional to anhydride which had reacted and, hence, to water originally present in the sample. As a check on instrument stability and reproducibility, a known amount of water could be added to the sample plus reagent after the first heating, and the procedure repeated. Five successive analyses of a sample containing 15 p.p.m. of water agreed within 5% (37). Further details on this procedure are given in Section VII.

b. Applications, Limitations

With few exceptions, the anhydride methods have been applied to determinations of water in acetic acid. However, they are more broadly applicable, as indicated in Table XI.

TABLE XI
Applications of Anhydride Methods

Substance	Range, % H₂O	Method	Ref.
Acetic acid	0.1–several	Acidimetric	(62)
	0.1–0.6	Polarimetric	(319)
	0.8–3.2	Thermometric	(122)
	0–100 p.p.m.	Ultraviolet	(37)
Inert organic compounds	0.1–several	Acidimetric	(323)
Nitric acid	0.01–5	Conductometric	(147)
Starch, cotton	0.2–several	Distillation or extraction-acidimetric	(220)

The acidimetric methods are of limited value. They are more time-consuming than many other procedures and offer no advantages in precision and accuracy (usually about 1% relative, 0.1 to 0.2% absolute) or freedom from interferences. For a relatively narrow range of water content, the thermometric procedures are rapid and simple. In particular, the method based on direct temperature rise shows potential for automatic process stream as well as batch analysis. Although the thermometric methods presumably have been used only for acetic acid samples, they should be equally suitable for determining water in many other acids and inert materials. In each case, of course, empirical calibration would be necessary.

Although the ultraviolet spectrophotometric method has been applied only to acetic acid, it should be applicable to the determination of small amounts of water in other acids and compounds that do not react with acetic anhydride. Only a few milliliters of sample are required.

All of the anhydride procedures are subject to interference in varying degrees from formic acid, acetone, aldehydes, and excessive amounts of alcohols and primary or secondary amines. Further details are given in Section IV-A-2, which describes similar interferences for the acyl halides.

4. Calcium Carbide

a. Reactions, Methods

Calcium carbide, like most carbides of alkali metals, can be regarded as a salt of acetylene in which both hydrogen atoms are replaced by the metal.

All carbides of this group of metals give acetylene on hydrolysis; for example,

$$CaC_2 + 2H_2O \longrightarrow Ca(OH)_2 + C_2H_2 \tag{20}$$

The rapidity with which the carbides react with water has made them attractive as reagents for its determination. Calcium carbide has been used most often for this purpose. This compound combines the desirable features of high reactivity, ready availability, low cost, and relative ease of handling.

Several procedures have been employed for measuring the extent of reaction. Most are based on determining the acetylene (1) manometrically (178,227,281), (2) volumetrically (118,227,351), (3) by combustion-measuring flame intensity (48) or oxygen consumption (226), (4) by gas chromatography (12), or (5) as cuprous acetylide determined gravimetrically after ignition to cupric oxide (24), titrimetrically after reduction of ferrisulfate to ferrosulfate and titration with permanganate (24), or colorimetrically (24,137). Loss in weight of the carbide sample mixture also has formed the basis for a convenient, rapid means of analysis (95,240,291,348).

Simple procedures based on manometric and loss-in-weight measurements have been used widely for determination of several per cent water. Colorimetric methods offer the potential for estimating fractions of a milligram of water in gases.

(1) Manometric Technique

Analyses have been made in compact closed apparatus consisting of either heavy-walled glassware (227) or a small steel pressure flask (178,281). Acetylene released from reaction of water with carbide is determined from the increase in pressure measured by an attached manometer or gage. Procedural details are given in Section VII.

(2) Loss in Weight

Loss in weight has been suitable in rapid analyses for water using simple equipment. In typical procedures the finely divided sample was placed in a tared open glass vessel. A known weight of calcium carbide, through 35 mesh and on 60 mesh sieves, was added, and the mixture was stirred, with heating to 100°C. if necessary. After reaction was completed, the flask, at room temperature, was weighed again. Loss in weight was calculated to per cent moisture (291,348).

(3) Colorimetry

Colorimetric determination of cuprous acetylide has been used to a limited extent. Boller (24) passed the gas stream containing water vapor through a tube containing calcium carbide at 180 to 200°C. (Water was stripped from solids by means of an inert gas, for example, nitrogen or hydrogen.) The acetylene produced was carried through ammoniacal cupric sulfate to form the red-colored cuprous acetylide. Prior addition of gelatin and alcohol to the ammoniacal copper salt solution aided in dispersing the cuprous salt (137). The color was compared to dye standards or ruby glass.

b. Applications, Limitations

According to equation (20), stoichiometric reaction would form 1 mole (26.04 g.) of acetylene for every 2 moles (36.03 g.) of water. That is, each gram of acetylene found would represent 1.38 g. of water. In practice the reaction is seldom quantitative, and, hence, the relationships must be established empirically for each lot of calcium carbide used. This can be done conveniently by use of a known compound such as ammonium oxalate monohydrate (118). For specific applications, however, it is preferable to use a control sample for which the water content has been established by an independent reliable method (216).

Time and temperature of reaction must be established for each type of material analyzed. Localized high concentrations of water must be avoided to control this vigorous reaction. Samples, such as corn, containing high percentages of water are preferably dispersed in anhydrous salt or other finely divided inert solid before addition of the carbide (348).

Materials containing substances that react with calcium carbide to form acetylene cannot be analyzed. For example, methanol reacts as follows (177):

$$CaC_2 + 2CH_3OH \longrightarrow Ca(OCH_3)_2 + C_2H_2 \qquad (21)$$

Probably other alcohols behave similarly. Also, substances that react with or absorb acetylene must be absent. Materials with which the method has been used are listed in Table XII.

The manometric method offers some advantages over other carbide procedures. Simple, compact apparatus can be designed for field use The method is best suited for analyses of samples containing relatively high percentages of water.

Little use has been made of the colorimetric method, and, currently, more reliable techniques offer broader applicability. However, for special

TABLE XII
Applications of Calcium Carbide Method

Material	Range, % H_2O	Method	Ref.
Cheese	10–30	Gravimetric	(291)
	10–70	Manometric	(281)
Corn	60–80	Gravimetric	(348)
Flour		Gravimetric	(95)
		Manometric	(22,281)
Foodstuffs		Manometric	(281)
		Volumetric	(118)
Grain	12–14	Gravimetric	(240)
		Manometric	(203,281)
Gravel	1–2	Manometric	(281)
Gravel	1–2	Manometric	(281)
Hydrates	5–10	Manometric	(181)
Hydrocarbon gases	0.1–1	Colorimetric	(24,137)
		Volumetric	(227)
Sand	5–12	Manometric	(281)
Soils	9–30	Manometric	(58,281)
Solid fuels	1–2	Colorimetric	(24)
		Volumetric	(227)
Solvents	10–100 p.p.m.	Gas chromatography	(12)

cases modern photometric techniques may provide sensitive analyses. With the visual colorimetric method (24,137) as little as 0.03 mg. of water was detected, and the accuracy was 0.05 mg. for samples containing about 2 mg. of water (137).

5. Calcium Hydride and Other Hydrides

a. CALCIUM HYDRIDE

Calcium hydride reacts rapidly with water according to the equation

$$CaH_2 + 2H_2O \longrightarrow 2H_2 + Ca(OH)_2 \tag{22}$$

On a stoichiometric basis 1 ml. of hydrogen gas at S.T.P. would be equivalent to 0.804 mg. of water. However, Perryman (247) found that deviations from theory were significant and recommended that the method be calibrated with distilled water. For example, he found a mean equivalent of 0.841 ± 0.007 mg. of water per milliliter of gas from results of 10 determinations of 20 mg. amounts of water in 0.1 ml. portions of anhydrous dioxane.

(1) Volumetric Method

Measurement of the volume of hydrogen released has been used most often for the analysis of liquid samples. Thus, Perryman (247) measured the volume of hydrogen evolved from the reaction of calcium hydride with 0.5 ml. of dioxane solution of the sample containing up to 25 mg. of water. Constant gas volume usually was obtained in 40 to 60 minutes at room temperature. A precision of 0.3 to 0.4% was observed in analyses of samples containing from 10 to 90% water.

Solids were extracted with dioxane, and a portion of the extract was used in the analysis. Extraction with pyridine was suitable for removing free water from several hydrated salts (78,298).

(2) Thermometric Method

Measurement of the heat of reaction of calcium hydride with water has formed the basis of a rapid, sensitive method for moisture in gases. Harris and Nash (135) developed a simple apparatus using thermistors for measuring the temperature rise. A precision of 0.0005 vol. % water was indicated in analyses of inert gases containing 0.003 to 0.1% moisture (135). In the 0.1 to 0.6% range, the precision was 0.05% (8). Procedural details are given in Section VII.

The method was calibrated with known mixtures. Unfortunately, the activity of calcium hydride has been observed to change from lot to lot (195). For maximum precision, therefore, the heat of reaction of each new batch of hydride should be checked with standards.

(3) Thermal Conductivity Method

For the determination of moisture in nitrogen, Linde and Rogers (195) investigated thermal conductivity measurements of hydrogen liberated from calcium hydride. Observations were made after reaction at room temperature, 100, 150, 235 and 290°C. Best reproducibility of results was obtained at 235°C. for moisture in nitrogen in the 200 to 2000 p.p.m. range.

b. LITHIUM ALUMINUM HYDRIDE

This hydride has found limited application in determinations of water. The reaction usually is expressed by the equation

$$LiAlH_4 + 4H_2O \longrightarrow 4H_2 + LiOH + Al(OH)_3 \qquad (23)$$

However, current evidence indicates that reaction (23) occurs only in the presence of excess water (89). When the hydride is in excess, the H_2/H_2O mole ratio has been found to be 1.4:1.6 rather than 1.0:1.0 as provided in equation (23). Baker and MacNevin (6) suggested two likely reactions based on (1) dehydration of $Al(OH)_3$, giving a net reaction,

$$6LiAlH_4 + 15H_2O \longrightarrow 6LiOH + 3Al_2O_3 + 24H_2 \qquad (24)$$

or (2) amphoteric reaction of $Al(OH)_3$,

$$2LiAlH_4 + 5H_2O \longrightarrow LiOH + LiH(AlO_2)_2 + 8H_2 \qquad (25)$$

In both equations (24) and (25) the H_2/H_2O ratio equals 1.6.

This procedure is not considered highly precise. However, results showing a precision of 0.005% were found with samples containing about 0.1% water (6).

c. APPLICATIONS, LIMITATIONS

The calcium hydride method has been used for the analysis of a variety of materials. Some applications are shown in Table XIII for samples containing from parts per million to about 90% water.

TABLE XIII
Applications of Calcium Hydride Method

Material	Range, % H_2O	Method	Ref.
Ammonium nitrate	0.1–0.6	Thermometric[a]	(81)
Blood	79–80	Volumetric	(247)
Blood serum	75–90	Volumetric	(78,247)
Carbon dioxide	0.01–0.06	Thermometric	(135)
Foods, dehydrated	2.4–4.6	Volumetric[b]	(247)
Hydrocarbon gases	0.01–0.1	Thermometric	(135)
Hydrogen	0.03–0.06	Thermometric	(135)
Nitrogen	0.02–0.2	Thermal conductivity	(195)
Oxygen	0.003–0.1	Thermometric	(135)
Polyorganosiloxanes	0.1–10 p.p.m.	Volumetric	(309)
Salts, hydrated		Volumetric[b]	(298)
Sodium chloride solution	77	Volumetric	(247)
Urea solution	48–88	Volumetric	(247)

[a] After removal of water in a nitrogen stream.
[b] After extraction with dioxane or pyridine.

The hydride procedures are not specific for water. Calcium hydride reacts with alcohols (96,195,245,247), acetone and probably other methyl ketones (96), ammonia (195), and other compounds containing active hydrogen. Ethanol, for example, reacts essentially quantitatively,

$$CaH_2 + 2C_2H_5OH \longrightarrow 2H_2 + Ca(OC_2H_5)_2 \qquad (26)$$

Lipoidal substances, such as fats, may interfere (247). Lithium aluminum hydride reacts with all compounds containing active hydrogen, releasing hydrogen gas. Actually procedures have been developed for determining alcohols, phenols, esters, aldehydes, ketones, amines, and amides (142).

These interferences seriously restrict the applicability of the hydride methods. Where applicable, however, the calcium hydride reaction in particular serves as the basis for a rapid and simple method of analysis. Usually only 10 to 15 minutes is required for a determination.

6. Magnesium Nitride

a. REACTIONS, METHODS

Dietrich and Conrad (70) demonstrated the utility of this reagent for determining water in alcohol power fuels. The analysis, carried out in a Kjeldahl apparatus, was based on titration of ammonia formed in the reaction.

$$Mg_3N_2 + 6H_2O \longrightarrow 3Mg(OH)_2 + 2NH_3 \qquad (27)$$

(1) Titrimetry

Roth and Schultz (267) adapted the method for determinations of moisture in gases and solids. An inert dry gas, such as nitrogen, was used to carry water vapor into a tube containing the nitride dispersed on glass wool at 80 to 90°C. Evidence was presented that in this temperature range some water was retained by the magnesium hydroxide, probably as $Mg(OH)_2 \cdot 0.5H_2O$, with production of low results (251). This difficulty was eliminated by maintaining the reaction tube at 100°C. In these titrimetric procedures the ammonia was absorbed in standardized sulfuric acid. Excess acid was determined by titration with standard base.

(2) Conductometry

For control purposes the ammonia has been absorbed in $0.1M$ boric acid. The electrical conductivity of the resulting solution of the ammonium salt was measured and compared with that of the boric acid solution alone (243).

(3) Colorimetry

Colorimetric determination of the ammonia also has been used for determining low concentrations of moisture in gases. Using Nessler's reagent, Šingliar and Zubák (297) reported a limit of detection of $5 \times 10^{-5}\%$ water. Absorbance was measured at 470 mμ.

b. APPLICATIONS, LIMITATIONS

Unlike the calcium carbide and hydride methods, the magnesium nitride procedure is unaffected by ethanol. Methanol in relatively large concentrations interferes.

$$Mg_3N_2 + 6CH_3OH \longrightarrow 3Mg(OH)(OCH_3) + NH_3 + N(CH_3)_3 \quad (28)$$

Klamann (177) observed that this reaction does not occur in methanol-ethanol mixtures if the sample contains less than 60% methanol.

Materials that release ammonia or other volatile bases or acids under conditions of the analysis interfere. Carbon dioxide in moderate amounts does not interfere. However, relatively high levels of water and carbon dioxide lead to formation of ammonium carbonate, which will remain in the reaction tube (251).

The titrimetric procedure has been used for determinations of water in alcohol power fuels (70), motor fuels (252), natural gas (251), ethanol (252), and benzene (252). Both the electrical conductivity (243) and colorimetric (297) procedures have been employed for analyses of gases.

7. Other Chemical Methods

The Grignard reagent has been used with materials in which water is the only compound containing active hydrogen.

$$CH_3MgI + H_2O \longrightarrow CH_4 + MgI(OH) \quad (29)$$

Usually the methane formed is measured volumetrically. The method gave nearly quantitative results for determining several per cent water in oil (188), charcoal, clay and cornstarch (314), and inorganic hydrates (181).

Lead dioxide is precipitated on reaction of water with lead tetraacetate.

$$Pb(OOCCH_3)_4 + 2H_2O \longrightarrow PbO_2 + 4CH_3COOH \quad (30)$$

In a reported method the oxide was recovered, dispersed in acetone, and treated with sodium acetate–potassium iodide reagent. The liberated iodine was determined by titration with standardized sodium thiosulfate (248).

In special cases (*1*) hydrogen was measured after reaction of water with sodium (120),

$$2Na + 2H_2O \longrightarrow 2NaOH + H_2 \tag{31}$$

(*2*) ammonia was titrated after treatment of water with sodamide (267),

$$NaNH_2 + H_2O \longrightarrow NaOH + NH_3 \tag{32}$$

(*3*) hydrochloric acid was titrated after reaction of water with α-naphthoxydichlorophosphine (198), its oxide (184), or α-naphthyldichlorophosphine (196),

$$C_{10}H_7OPCl_2 + 2H_2O \longrightarrow C_{10}H_7OP(OH)_2 + 2HCl \tag{33}$$

$$C_{10}H_7OPOCl_2 + 2H_2O \longrightarrow C_{10}H_7OPO(OH)_2 + 2HCl \tag{34}$$

$$C_{10}H_7POCl_2 + 2H_2O \longrightarrow C_{10}H_7PO(OH)_2 + 2HCl \tag{35}$$

and (*4*) water in alcohol was determined by a two-step sodium-ester method,

$$Na + H_2O \longrightarrow NaOH + \tfrac{1}{2}H_2 \tag{36a}$$

$$Na + ROH \longrightarrow NaOR + \tfrac{1}{2}H_2 \tag{36b}$$

$$NaOH + CH_3COOC_2H_5 \longrightarrow CH_3COONa + C_2H_5OH \tag{36c}$$

After reaction of the sample with sodium, one portion of the solution was titrated for total base. A second portion was treated with excess ethyl acetate to remove sodium hydroxide and permit specific titration of the sodium alkoxide. The net titer was a measure of sodium hydroxide, equivalent to water originally present in the sample (130).

B. GRAVIMETRIC METHODS

Thermal methods for removal of moisture are probably the oldest techniques for determining water in nonvolatile materials. Usually they are based on gravimetric procedures in which (*1*) loss in weight is measured at atmospheric or reduced pressure or (*2*) increase in weight is determined after absorption of moisture by a desiccant.

1. Oven Drying

a. Types

Where applicable, direct oven drying at 1 atm. provides a simple, though often time-consuming, method of analysis for water. The sample is placed in an oven and dried to constant weight at 100 to 105°C. or other suitable temperature. In most cases it is allowed to cool to room temperature in a desiccator prior to weighing. Total loss in weight is taken as a measure of water content of the sample.

The drying ovens are usually heated electrically, and every effort is made to attain uniform temperature within them. Infrared units for localized heating have found wide application, also. Both electrical and infrared heaters have been used in ovens with built-in balances for rapid routine analyses of many stable solid materials.

Since analysis for water by oven drying is based on weight loss, the sample must be thermally stable and obviously must not contain significant quantities of other volatile components. Conditions must be established for each type of material to assure reproducible results.

Difficulties with thermal decomposition of the sample often are minimized by drying at reduced pressure. A number of vacuum ovens are available which operate at pressures from about 1 mm. up to 760 mm. Hg and at temperatures from ambient to well over 100°C.

Removal of moisture from the sample requires that the partial pressure of moisture in the vapor phase be lower than that of water in the sample. For efficient drying, therefore, some movement of the air over the sample is desirable. Many ovens are equipped with fans providing forced draft to assure a continuous supply of fresh dry air.

In practice, conditions for drying a particular material usually have been established empirically. For natural products and biological materials, minimum conditions for drying in a vacuum oven or by desiccation (see Section IV-B-2) have been established by plotting weight loss vs. time at constant temperature and pressure. The water content is calculated after the weight loss has remained essentially constant for a significant period of time. With many materials the sample continues to lose weight, the loss usually decreasing greatly in rate after several hours. Consequently, it often is difficult to establish by oven drying alone whether decomposition of the sample is contributing to weight loss. Several investigators have made extensive studies to learn whether water in natural products can be determined accurately. Sair and Fetzer (272) used as a standard for ground corn the value obtained from vacuum drying at 40°C. for 340 hours. Other portions of the same sample were dried at 100°C. *in vacuo* for varying lengths of time. After 2 hours at this temperature, the result was nearly equal to that of the standard. After 4 hours, however, decomposition apparently had occurred. Makower and co-workers (204) obtained nearly constant weight loss for cabbage and onions by drying samples in a vacuum oven at 60°C. for at least 60 hours. Shorter times at higher temperatures were assumed reliable when results approximated those of the standards. Thus conditions had to be established rigidly for each substance examined.

An often overlooked significant source of error is the absorption of moisture by the dried sample during cooling in the desiccator.   Many anhydrous samples are better desiccants than the drying agents contained in desiccators.   In addition, since the rate of removal of water from the atmosphere in a desiccator may be quite slow, the drying agent may absorb very little moisture during the short time usually allowed for cooling of the dried sample to room temperature.   Consequently, special precautions should be taken to prevent the introduction of water vapor when the desiccator is opened.

Thus the choice of desiccant becomes important in high-precision work. Relative efficiencies of drying agents have been studied in considerable detail.   Results reported in the *International Critical Tables* (151) and by Bower (26) often have been quoted.   Data for the most commonly used agents, given in Table XIV, are based on residual water per liter of air.

TABLE XIV
Relative Efficiencies of Drying Agents

| | Residual water, mg./liter of air | |
Substance	Bower (26) (30.5°C.)	I.C.T. (151) (25°C.)
Liquid air or N_2 (cooling to -190°C.)		1.6×10^{-23}
P_2O_5		$<2 \times 10^{-5}$
BaO	6.5×10^{-4}	
$Mg(ClO_4)_2$, anhyd.	2×10^{-3}	$<5 \times 10^{-4}$
CaO	3×10^{-3}	0.2
$CaSO_4$, anhyd.	5×10^{-3}	
Al_2O_3	5×10^{-3}	3×10^{-3}
H_2SO_4, anhyd.		3×10^{-3}
Silica gel	0.03	
$Mg(ClO_4)_2 \cdot 3H_2O$	0.03	$<2 \times 10^{-3}$
$CaCl_2$, anhyd.	0.36	0.36
$CaCl_2$, gran.	1.5	0.14–1.25
H_2SO_4, concd.		0.3
$CuSO_4$, anhyd.	2.8	1.4

In both cases metered volumes of moist air were passed through the agents, and the amounts of air remaining were measured.   The two sets of results are not strictly comparable since different flow rates probably were used. Bower (26) passed 1 to 5 liters of air per hour through U tubes packed with the drying agent at 30.5°C.   Phosphorus pentoxide served as a final absorber, and, hence, Bower's results were dependent on its efficiency for removing water.

These experiments, however, did not correspond to conditions in a static system such as those usually encountered in a desiccator. Booth and McIntyre (25) found that 1.5 to 2 hours was required to remove moisture from air in a desiccator. The type of drying agent appeared to have little effect, and, consequently, these authors concluded that the particular desiccant used made little difference. This reasoning does not apply in all cases. An additional factor to be considered is the activity of drying agent compared to that of dry sample. Belcher and Mort (13) demonstrated that oven-dried coal was a better desiccant than calcium chloride, silica gel, alumina, sulfuric acid, or potassium bisulfite. These authors found that simply cooling the dried coal in a tightly covered petri dish on an aluminum plate gave better precision than cooling in a desiccator over the drying agents studied. Similar observations were made by King (173), who found that oven-dried flour continued to absorb moisture from calcium chloride, sulfuric acid, or powdered pumice for periods at least up to 20 hours. He found that lumps of calcium carbide placed below and around the sample in a desiccator were satisfactory. This drying agent would be suitable only for inert systems involving very small amounts of water since it reacts with water to release acetylene (see equation (20), Section IV-A-4).

In general, phosphorus pentoxide, barium oxide, or magnesium perchlorate appear to be the most practical drying agents. In all these cases the surface of the agent must be kept reasonably clean of reaction product—phosphoric acid, barium hydroxide, or trihydrate, respectively.

b. APPLICATIONS

Oven drying procedures have been applied to determinations of water in many nonvolatile materials. The classes of materials listed below have been studied extensively.

Drying at atmospheric pressure		Drying in vacuum
Clay	Malt	Dairy products
Coal	Meat products	Drugs
Dairy products	Refractor materials	Emulsions
Drugs	Sand, stoney	Fruits, vegetables
Fats, waxes	Soaps	Glue
Fertilizers	Sugar	Grains
Flour	Textiles	Meat products
Grains	Tobacco	Natural products
Leather	Wood, paper	Sugar
		Tobacco

c. LIMITATIONS

Since conventional oven drying methods measure weight loss, several errors may be introduced by volatile components other than water, decomposition or oxidation of the sample, or incomplete removal of water. Any substance having significant vapor pressure at the temperature used for drying will, of course, contribute to weight loss. A material whose vapor pressure is relatively low, for example, a few millimeters, will be lost as long as its partial pressure in the gas phase is less than its vapor pressure in the sample. This situation becomes more serious as the time for drying is increased. Some materials normally considered "high boilers" may be lost through sublimation. Oxalic acid, for example, may sublime at temperatures above 100°C.

Thermal decomposition is one of the most frequent sources of error. The products may include water or other volatile material, which will contribute to weight loss. This error may become excessive in drying of many natural products, particularly at temperatures of 100°C. or higher. Many polyhydric and polycarboxylic compounds are subject to both dehydration and decarboxylation. Thus dibasic acids may dehydrate to the anhydrides or lose carbon dioxide. These decompositions usually occur at or just above the melting points of the original compounds. Oxidation may occur in materials containing active double bonds or groups subject to ready oxidation. Many of the natural oils, for example, linseed oil, may be affected in this way. Contrary to most other interferences, oxidation is likely to lead to an increase in weight of the dry sample resulting in low values for moisture calculated from weight loss.

Complete removal of water from complex materials or from hydrates often requires considerable energy. Surface moisture usually can be removed with relative ease, but water "bound" within crystal lattices or simply occluded within a solid structure presents complications. Complete volatilization may be quite slow since diffusion often becomes controlling. Hydrates may be formed through direct molecular association, hydrogen bonding, or other forces. For complete dehydration, some hydrates require temperatures well above those usually employed in oven drying. For example, Chihara and Seki (46) observed the following sequence in dehydration of nickel sulfate heptahydrate by differential thermal analysis:

$$NiSO_4 \cdot 7H_2O \xrightarrow[-H_2O]{43.6°C.} NiSO_4 \cdot 6H_2O \xrightarrow[-2H_2O]{111-115°C.}$$

$$NiSO_4 \cdot 4H_2O \xrightarrow[-3_2HO]{134-140°C.} NiSO_4 \cdot H_2O \xrightarrow[-H_2O]{280°C.} NiSO_4$$

Under the conditions of this analysis, the materials were, in effect, in an open system; consequently, existing phases were not usually in the equilibrium state. A similar situation would exist in oven drying.

Adequate temperatures and plots of weight loss vs. time are essential parts of all investigations and are designed to assess the reliability of data and to establish the conditions for reliable data. Curves which rise sharply and then level off with time usually, but not always, indicate that oven drying may be suitable for determining water. The sample must, of course, be free of other low-boiling components. Low results may be obtained if part of the water is tightly bound or present as a hydrate that is relatively stable at the operating temperature. Curves which continue to rise with time may be due to one or more of several factors, for example, occluded water that diffuses slowly through the solid sample, slow dehydration of water of crystallization, or decomposition. When establishing a procedure, it is advisable to examine the vapors evolved from the sample to determine whether products other than water are evolved. Vavruch (328) used this approach in assessing oven drying at 102 to 105°C. for determining water in sugar products. He found that only water was evolved from refined sugar, whereas water and carbon dioxide were evolved from raw sugar and molasses.

Some of these factors are illustrated in Fig. 6, which gives weight loss data for leather and for some hydrated salts. In the upper family of curves, weight loss is plotted vs. time for sole leather at various temperatures (163). Kanagy and Charles (163) obtained these data from analyses in a Brabender drier. They collected similar information for a variety of leathers and concluded that results at 60°C. tended to be low, whereas those after 6 hours at 80°C. appeared reasonably reliable. At 100°C. and above, two decompositions were apparent: first, a slow decomposition contributing to the slight rise up to 6 hours, followed by a more marked decomposition rate beyond this time. Extrapolation of the 100°C. curve to zero time appeared to give the most reliable results. These curves are typical of materials subject to (1) slow decomposition or (2) slow vaporization of a relatively high-boiling component.

The curves in the lower section of Fig. 6 illustrate problems encountered with samples containing certain hydrated salts. Hill, Caro, and Kumagai (144) determined weight loss on a variety of fertilizer ingredients using oven drying at 130 and 100°C., air flow at 60°C., and vacuum desiccation at room temperature. The two latter methods were unsatisfactory. The higher temperatures could be used safely for some materials. However, as shown in Fig. 6, magnesium hydrogen phosphate trihydrate (38.4% water present) and calcium sulfate dihydrate (20.93% water calculated) were only

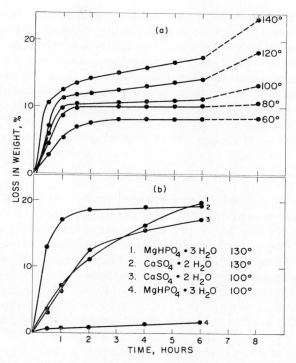

Fig. 6. Weight loss data for (a) sole leather and (b) some hydrated salts (163).

partially dehydrated after 6 hours' heating. After 20 hours at 130°C., the calcium sulfate had lost 18.84% in weight. Transition temperatures for $CaSO_4 \cdot 2H_2O$ are 128°C. to the so-called hemihydrate and 163°C. to the anhydrous salt.

For thermally unstable materials, the vacuum oven method has been investigated thoroughly. In many cases, such as dehydrated vegetables, decomposition continues to represent a critical problem. Makower, Chastain, and Nielsen (204) made an extensive study of vacuum oven drying of several dehydrated vegetables. In all cases decomposition was evident at temperatures above 60°C. and pressures of 5 mm. Hg or less. These authors chose conditions for each material which would give results comparable with those of a primary reference method (several months over anhydrous magnesium perchlorate in a vacuum desiccator). Thus drying times for a few dehydrated vegetables were chosen as follows: (1) carrots, 29 to 35 hours at 70°C.; (2) potatoes, 43 to 67 hours at 70°C.; (3) cabbage, 22 to 40 hours at 60°C.; and (4) onions, 15 to 45 hours at 60°C.

The above examples were chosen to illustrate the types of problems that must be considered in applying oven drying procedures. The composition of each system to be analyzed must be known, and conditions chosen to provide reliable data. Usually a reference method will be necessary. Willits (349) recommended the following conditions for oven drying: "using diminished pressure to minimize time of diffusion of deep-seated moisture; using properly desiccated air to sweep the water vapor from the drying chamber; and heating the specimen at a temperature as close as possible to that at which the rate of thermal decomposition becomes appreciable."

2. Desiccation

Desiccation at atmospheric or reduced pressure, normally at room temperature, has been used for many materials that are thermally unstable at higher temperatures. This method, like oven drying, usually is based on weight loss. The weighed sample in a suitable container is placed in a desiccator over a drying agent. The desiccant continuously absorbs moisture from the air above the sample, and, hence, water will continue to diffuse into the atmosphere until equilibrium has been achieved. The container with the sample is removed periodically, tightly stoppered, and weighed. After constant weight loss has been reached, the sample is assumed to be anhydrous.

The amount of water removed from the sample is dependent on the efficiency of the drying agent employed. Reference to data in Table XIV indicates that such commonly used desiccants as calcium chloride and concentrated sulfuric acid are relatively inefficient. Phosphorus pentoxide, barium monoxide, and magnesium perchlorate are considerably better as long as a fresh surface is maintained.

With few exceptions, desiccation is a lengthy procedure, often requiring weeks and even months for the sample to achieve constant weight (204, 205). Consequently, the procedure is seldom employed for routine analyses. However, because of the relatively mild conditions, results by this method often serve as reference standards on which more rapid procedures are calibrated. In some cases the rate of water removal can be increased by use of infrared lamps, electrical heaters, or built-in circulating fans.

A number of factors often are overlooked in applying the desiccation procedures. Materials having vapor pressures of only a few millimeters of mercury at room temperature may be evolved in significant quantity during the lengthy time required for analysis. Diffusion of moisture may be sufficiently slow that differences in weight may be considered due to experimental error. Water of hydration and tightly bound water may not be evolved. For most purposes the method should be considered only for determining surface moisture on solid materials. Curves of weight loss vs. time often show sharp changes in slope after surface or loosely bound water has been evolved, as, for example, with many dyes and metal oxides.

3. Freeze Drying (Lyophilization)

This technique has been used widely by biochemists for the nondestructive drying of small samples of tissue, cells, and so forth. Large-scale applications include desiccation of blood plasma, penicillin, fruits, and fruit juices.

The method is particularly valuable for handling relatively unstable materials, since the water is removed at low temperatures. Even at temperatures below 0°C., water will be removed from the sample by sublimation as long as the partial pressure of moisture in the gas phase over the sample is less than the vapor pressure of water in the sample. During the freezing process, the specimen may swell, making easier the diffusion of water to the outer surface.

Usually the drying operation proceeds in two stages. In the first, most of the water, as ice, is sublimed from the frozen sample in a high-vacuum system. The temperature usually is kept well below 0°C. In the second stage, the nearly dry product is dried at a higher temperature, depending on stability, in order to attain a minimum weight level in the shortest time. Removal of water vapor under high vacuum must be efficient to maintain low vapor pressure in the system. Three methods employed are condensation and refreezing at a temperature below that of the sample, absorption on a desiccant, and direct pumping. General principles with emphasis on industrial applications have been described by Flosdorf (98).

Application of the process was illustrated by Makower and Nielsen (205) in a procedure for determining water in dehydrated vegetables. Weighed samples were first saturated with water to swell the particles, and the slurry was frozen and cooled to about −70°C. The frozen sample was transferred to a lyophilization apparatus, where it was dried overnight to a water level of 2 to 3%. Tappel (311) described a simple apparatus for this purpose which satisfied theoretical requirements with a condenser temperature below −40°C., a short clear vapor path, low pressure, and rapid heat input (for example, from an infrared lamp) into the sample to provide for vaporization of ice at the maximum rate. Lyophilization apparatus also is available commercially.

Makower and Nielsen (205) found that lyophilization greatly accelerated the drying rate through swelling of the particles, with little shrinkage on

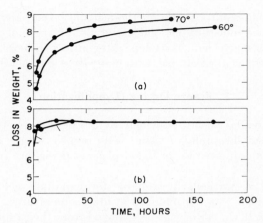

Fig. 7. Drying curves of sweet potatoes at 60 and 70°C. (205): (*a*) not lyophilized; (*b*) lyophilized.

subsequent drying, and an increase in the porosity, due to leaching of soluble materials, such as sugars, from within the tissue.

Final drying was made by vacuum oven at 60 to 70°C. or by vacuum desiccation over magnesium perchlorate at room temperature. Without prior freeze drying, dehydrated vegetables continued to lose weight even after more than 100 hours. After freeze drying, some vegetables attained constant weight relatively quickly. Fig. 7 shows drying curves of sweet potatoes at 60 and 70°C. With the freeze-dried samples, constant weight was attained in 38 and 22 hours at 60 and 70°C., respectively. Results of 8.3% weight loss at 70°C. and 8.2% at 60°C. compared favorably with results of 8.2% after 4 days' vacuum desiccation at room temperature. Similar observations were made with beets and white potatoes. With carrots, however, results of vacuum oven drying at 60°C. appeared satisfactory, being about 0.3% higher than those of vacuum desiccation for about 50 days at room temperature.

Conditions vary for efficient and nondestructive removal of water from different substances. Like other thermal methods, procedural details must be established empirically for each type of material to be analyzed.

4. Absorption

A variation in drying procedure has employed absorption of evolved moisture by a drying agent. Previously dried air, nitrogen, or other inert gas is passed over the sample at elevated temperature through a tared absorption tube, usually containing magnesium perchlorate or phosphorus pentoxide. At the end of the analysis, the absorption tube is weighed, and the increase in weight is a measure of water in the sample. The procedure, in effect, is similar to the conventional dry combustion procedures for carbon and hydrogen.

This technique is more nearly specific than methods based on weight loss. However, it is subject to the same types of errors. Other volatile constituents may be absorbed by the drying agent. Water formed during thermal decomposition of the sample will lead to proportionately high results.

Often the method has proved to be more accurate and precise than weight loss procedures for determining low concentrations of water in solids, particularly where large samples are used. It has also been suitable for determining water in certain gases and relatively nonvolatile liquids. Thus moisture was measured in fluorocarbon gases by passing the sample directly through an absorption tube containing phosphorus pentoxide (244).

Free and combined water were determined in white lead by a combination of desiccation and absorption methods (325). The free water was determined by desiccation over phosphorus pentoxide at room temperature. For the estimation of combined water, dry carbon dioxide–free air was passed through the gently heated sample, and evolved moisture was absorbed on calcium chloride or silica gel.

Absorption methods have been applied to determinations of moisture in alkali metal hydroxides, rocks, beryllium carbide, coal and coke, soil, concrete, ores, oils, nitrogen oxides, and foods.

5. Miscellaneous Gravimetric Methods

Several other gravimetric procedures have been described for determining water in specific materials. The first two presented in this section show promise for wider application.

In addition to their use in colorimetric methods (see Section IV-D-1), cobaltous salts have been employed in gravimetric procedures. For example, Gardiner and Keyte (107) used cobaltous bromide for determining free and bonded water in refined nearly dry sugars. For determination of free water, the sugar crystals were ground under dry chloroform in a specially designed vessel. The chloroform was separated, and anhydrous cobaltous bromide in chloroform was added. The precipitated hydrate was recovered, washed, dried, and weighed as the anhydrous salt. For determination of total water, an excess of standardized cobaltous bromide reagent was agitated with the finely ground sample under chloroform. Under these conditions the bromide was found to react with bound water *in situ*. Unused bromide was separated by filtration, and the amount determined gravimetrically. The difference between the amount of cobaltous bromide added to the sugar in chloroform mixture and that remaining after reaction was reported to be equivalent to total water in the sample (107).

The authors indicated that the crystals must be ground to a specific surface of 3500 cm.^{2}/g. to expose all bonded water. The method was not absolute, requiring standardization by water in the presence of dry sucrose powder having a specific surface area of 3500 cm.^{2}/g.

Water in bromine has been determined by passing dry sulfur dioxide into a carbon tetrachloride solution of the bromine (229). The reaction,

$$2H_2O + Br_2 + SO_2 \longrightarrow H_2SO_4 + 2HBr \tag{37}$$

leads to formation of sulfuric acid, which is determined gravimetrically as barium sulfate after volatilization of excess bromine. (Note the similarity to the Karl Fischer reagent reaction, Section IV-A-1.) Water concentrations as low as 0.01% were determined in 400 to 500 g. samples.

Water in some organic compounds was estimated by gravimetric determination of aluminum hydroxide (dehydrated and weighed as the oxide) after reaction with aluminum ethoxide (140).

$$Al(OC_2H_5)_3 + 3H_2O \longrightarrow Al(OH)_3 + 3C_2H_5OH \tag{38}$$

For determining several per cent water in alcohol, Adickes (1) added sodium ethoxide and ethyl formate.

$$C_2H_5ONa + HCOOC_2H_5 + H_2O \longrightarrow HCOONa + 2C_2H_5OH \tag{39}$$

The insoluble sodium formate was removed by filtration and determined gravimetrically.

A modification of the Penfield method (180a,243a) was used by Shapiro and Brannock (282) in a rapid estimation of water in silicate rocks. Water was expelled from the heated sample and absorbed on tared filter paper, after which the paper was reweighed. Details of the modified method, together with notes on the original, are given in Section VII.

C. SEPARATION METHODS

These methods usually involve such techniques as distillation, extraction, and chromatography. Although direct fractional distillation of water has been used in special cases, results are usually only semiquantitative. Of much wider applicability is azeotropic distillation of binary or ternary compositions of which one component is water. Extraction as a direct method of analysis has been restricted to estimations of surface water on nonporous solids. With such materials, increase in volume of the extracting water-miscible liquid has served as a measure of water content.   From the general standpoint, extraction more often provides a convenient and reliable means for separating water from a substance that would interfere in direct analysis.   In this case, the extract is analyzed for water. Numerous examples of this approach are given in sections of this chapter dealing with chemical, photometric, physical, and electrical methods of analysis for water.   A few applications of chromatographic methods are described.   Up to the present time, little use has been made of chromatography for quantitative analysis.   Displacement methods are discussed in Section IV-F-3.

1. Distillation

Removal of water by distillation with a liquid carrier long has been used as a method of analysis for water in many solid materials, greases, and other high-boiling substances.   Usually the carrier is a water-immiscible liquid which forms an azeotrope with water or which boils above 100°C. and, therefore, acts as a carrier for water.   The vapors are allowed to condense and collect in a graduated receiver, where the volume of water can be measured.

a. TYPES

Only relatively simple distillation apparatus is required, since efficient fractionation normally is unnecessary.   However, design of the condenser and the receiver are quite important.   Since the heterogeneous condensate consists of organic and water phases, there must be no significant holdup of water in the condenser or the line to the receiver.   To conserve the organic carrier and reduce the time for analysis, a decanting type of receiver, which allows the condensed organic phase to return to the distillation flask, has been recommended.   Fetzer (87) reviewed several types of apparatus, the most satisfactory of which were variations of the original Dean-Stark equipment (65).   These designs still were unsatisfactory for high-precision analyses owing to (1) the tendency for water droplets to adhere to various parts of the apparatus, (2) relatively poor precision in reading the volume of water, and (3) occasional lack of sharp separation between the organic liquid and water.   Tryon (321) largely overcame these difficulties by coating the inside of the apparatus with a silicone polymer and using an accurately calibrated narrow tube for measuring the volume of water recovered.   Gentle suction provided by an aspirator was used to draw the water into the tube. Barr and Yarwood (8) modified Tryon's apparatus for more efficient operation.   Their equipment is shown in Fig. 8.   An upward-sloping outflow

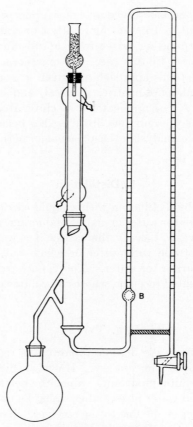

Fig. 8. Distillation apparatus (8).

tube, similar to that used by Tryon, speeded the distillation process by diverting into the receiver droplets of condensed water which in conventional equipment would flow back into the flask.   The measuring tube was made from 8 mm. tubing and graduated in 2 mm. divisions over the two 50 cm. lengths.   An internal diameter up to 4 mm. was satisfactory; a 2 mm. bore tube gave a total capacity of 5 ml. providing an accuracy of ±0.003 ml. in measurement of the volume.   The bulb B, ca. 4 mm. I.D., served to unite disconnected segments of water.   Droplets collected in the bulb where they remained until joined by the rest of the aqueous layer.   With this apparatus the error in determining water rarely exceeded 0.027 g., so that reliable analyses could be made on stable materials containing as little as 0.5 g. of water.   Further details are given in Section VII.

Of the many organic liquids recommended as carriers, benzene, toluene, and xylene are the most widely used. Other carriers that have been used include petroleum fractions in the turpentine and gasoline range and mineral oil. Several carrier liquids are listed in Table XV, together with their boiling points and densities (186), azeotrope (148) data, and solubility (280) data; the compounds are grouped as those lighter than water and those heavier than water. The actual choice of carrier depends on

TABLE XV
Liquid Carriers in Distillation Methods for Water

Carrier			Azeotrope		Solubility of H_2O in carrier at ca. 25°C., g./100 g.
Compound	b.p., °C.	d^a	b.p., °C.	% H_2O	
Benzene	80.2	0.88	69.25	8.8	0.05
Toluene	110.7	0.86	84.1	19.6	0.05
n-Butanol	117.8	0.81	92.4	38	20.3[c]
Xylene	ca. 140	0.86			0.04
Heptane	98.5	0.68	80.0[b]		0.015
Isooctane	99.2	0.69			0.014
Tetralin	194	0.87			0.04[d]
Decalin	185	0.87			0.03[d]
Chloroform	61.2	1.49	56.1	2.5	0.10[d]
Carbon tetrachloride	76.8	1.59	66.0	4.1	0.01
Tetrachloroethylene	120.8	1.63			0.03[d]
Tetrachloroethane	146.4	1.60			0.11[d]
o-Dichlorobenzene	179.5	1.30			0.03[d]

[a] Density at about 25°C.

[b] M. Lecat, *Tables Azeotropes*, Chez L'Anteur, Brussels, 1949.

[c] Solubility of n-butanol in water = 7.3 g./100 g. at 25°C.

[d] Data obtained in the author's laboratory based on titration with Karl Fischer reagent (see Section IV-A-1).

several factors, such as thorough wetting of the sample, density of the sample, adequate heat transfer, chemical inertness, and flammability problems. Most of the lighter-than-water liquids are highly inflammable. Varying degrees of toxicity are involved, also, and adequate ventilation must be provided.

The type of receiver will differ, of course, with the two types of liquid. For the lighter-than-water liquids, a calibrated tube of sufficient volume to contain all of the water has been sealed at the bottom of the conventional receiver. Only a single meniscus need be read to determine its volume. For the chlorinated liquids, the calibrated tube has been located above a suitable volume that provides for the organic layer, and two meniscuses must be read (87).

TABLE XVI

Applications of Distillation Method

Material	Carrier	Ref.[a]
Antifreeze compositions	n-Butanol	(160)
Bleaching powders	o-Dichlorobenzene	(117)
Blood	Toluene	
Camphor	Toluene, xylene	
Cellulose products	Petroleum fractions, toluene	
Cereals	Petroleum fractions, toluene	
Cheese	Benzene, petroleum ether	
Coal	Benzene, toluene, xylene	
Cosmetics	Toluene	
Creams	Tetralin, decalin, chloroform	(239)
Dynamite	Carbon tetrachloride	
Egg albumin	Benzene	
Fats, oils	Benzene, toluene, xylene, heptane, gasoline, paraffin	
Felt	Toluene	(8)
Foods	Toluene, xylene, isooctane, petroleum fractions, chloroform, bromobenzene, tetrachloroethylene	(87,236)
Fruits	Tetrachloroethylene	(255)
Fur	Toluene	(8)
Glycol, glycerol	n-Butanol	(160)
Grain	Benzene, toluene, mineral oil	
Grease	Xylene	
Hops	Turpentine, toluene	
Leather	Toluene	
Molasses	Benzene, xylene	
Oil seeds	Heptane	
Paper	Toluene	(311)
Petroleum products	Benzene, xylene	
Polyhydroxy compounds	Chloroform, n-butanol	(160;239)
Salts, inorganic	Benzene, xylene	(134)
Shellac	Toluene	(8)
Soap	Benzene, xylene, petroleum ether	
Soil	Toluene, xylene	
Spices	Benzene, toluene, xylene, kerosene	
Sugars	Benzene, toluene, xylene	
Syrups	Toluene	
Textiles, wool	Toluene, carbon tetrachloride	(8,189)
Tobacco	Toluene	
Rubber	Toluene	(321)

[a] Unless otherwise noted, original references are given in the review by Fetzer (87).

b. Applications

Many heat- and air-sensitive materials are analyzed for water more reliably by distillation than by oven drying. Since a large volume of organic liquid is used, the sample is diluted and protected by the inert atmosphere. Typical applications are given in Table XVI.

Overbeek and Mossel (236) reported that an accuracy of 0.1% could be attained in analyses of some foods. Iso-octane (b.p. 99.2°C.) was recommended as carrier to ensure that removal of water was complete within 8 hours and that decomposition was negligible. Determinations of water in glycol, glycerol, and antifreeze compositions could not be made with toluene or xylene because of the formation of the ternary, hydrocarbon-water-glycol (see page 126). Jordon and Hatch (160) used n-butanol as carrier for determining from 1 to 95% water in these materials. Since butanol is quite soluble in water (see Table XV), the alcohol was salted out with anhydrous potassium carbonate. Results indicated a maximum error of 0.5 ml. (160). With a 100 ml. sample containing 10% water, this would amount to about 0.5% absolute error. Analyses in Tryon's apparatus of rubber containing about 1% water gave a reproducible recovery of 96% with a standard deviation of 0.023% (4). When corrected for the low recovery, results compared favorably with those of a Karl Fischer reagent titration method (see Section IV-A-1).

Harel and Talmi (134) used separate distillations with benzene and xylene for determining, respectively, free and total water in gypsum. These workers recovered added free water from 10 g. samples of $CaSO_4 \cdot 2H_2O$ within 35 minutes with benzene. Total water (free water plus water of hydration) was recovered in 35 minutes with xylene. High results for free water were obtained from $CaH_4(PO_4)_2 \cdot H_2O$ owing to the presence of phosphoric acid. The error was minimized by addition of anhydrous calcium carbonate.

Several investigators have combined distillation with chemical analysis of the distillate to eliminate interferences; examples of such procedures are those for the determination of water in colored or acidic waxes by the acetyl chloride method (200) (see Section IV-A-2) and in alkali hydroxides and certain greases by the Karl Fischer reagent titration method (260,261) (see Section IV-A-1). The same approach can be used in correcting for other components distilled with the carrier. Chemical or other suitable analysis of the distillate also permits the use of carriers that form homogeneous binaries or ternaries with the water in the sample. The obvious advantages include (1) elimination of holdup of water in the distillation column, encountered when heterogeneous azeotropes are employed, (2) wider choice of carrier, and (3) use of azeotropes containing considerably higher concentrations of water than the hydrocarbon and halide systems, for example, dioxane, ethanol, and n-butanol.

c. Limitations

The distillation method usually is limited to analyses for water in non-volatile, heat-stable materials. In practice the carrier is chosen that will remove water within a few hours with no more than slight decomposition of the sample. (Decomposition of carbohydrates in fruits during distillation with tetrachloroethylene was reduced by the addition of calcium carbonate to the distillation flask (239).) In special cases vacuum distillation, like vacuum oven drying, may be desirable as a means for lowering the boiling point of the sample plus carrier.

Before the routine application of the distillation procedure to new systems, the composition of the distillate always should be analyzed to ensure that unexpected substances are not present. Other water-soluble components of the sample having appreciable vapor pressures at the temperature of the boiling liquid may interfere. These materials will distil at least in part and will probably add to the volume of the water layer in the receiver. Even a material having a vapor pressure of only a few millimeters may be carried over mechanically in significant quantity during the few hours' distillation. Glycerol, for example, interferes even when chloroform is used as carrier (239), and propylene glycol (231) interferes when toluene or xylene is used. Actually, inclusion of a third component in the distillate may be due to a ternary azeotrope. Any compound that forms a binary or pseudobinary with water and with the carrier can be expected to form a ternary. Examples include these: benzene-ethanol-water, b.p. 64.9°C., 7.4% water; carbon tetrachloride–methyl ethyl ketone–water, b.p. 65.7°C., 3.0% water; xylene-phenol-water (148); toluene- or xylene-glycol-water (160). When the presence of such compounds is known, corrections for their contributions to the aqueous layer often can be made by refractive index measurements (239).

In the conventional Dean-Stark–type apparatus finely divided solids may be blown out of the flask as soon as the mixture begins to boil. For materials such as slaked lime, Billitzer (20) modified the apparatus so that the sample was in contact only with vapors of the carrier.

2. Chromatography

Typical qualitative paper chromatographic tests were described in Section III-A-2. After proper calibration of each system to be analyzed, these tests may provide quantitative data.

Direct separation and analysis by gas-liquid or gas-solid chromatography usually leads to broad peaks for water with significant "tailing." Consequently, there may be considerable loss of precision and accuracy as compared to analyses for other compounds. Bayer (12) devised a prereactor in which the water reacted with calcium carbide, releasing acetylene (see equation (20), Section IV-A-4). The acetylene was separated sharply by passage through a dinonyl phthalate on Sterchamol column and measured by thermal conductivity. By this means 10 p.p.m. of water was detected. Menapace and co-workers (213) applied the same reaction to analyses of acetylene (from reaction of water and calcium carbide), ethylene, carbon dioxide, and ethane mixtures. Separations were made on a 30 to 60 mesh silica gel column at 80°C.

Cain and Stevens (38b) found that an 18 inch column containing 30% Carbowax 1500 on C-22 firebrick at 80 to 90°C. gave satisfactory separation of water-hydrazine mixtures by gas chromatography. (Longer columns were impractical.) Components in impure hydrazine were eluted in this order: ammonia, N,N-dimethylhydrazine, water, hydrazine. Analyses of samples containing from 0.5 to 1.6% water showed an average deviation for a single determination of 0.05% with an estimated accuracy of 0.07%.

D. PHOTOMETRIC METHODS, SPECTROSCOPY

Most of these instrumental procedures are particularly well suited for rapid determinations of low concentrations of water. Usually only relatively small samples are required. Techniques, such as infrared and nuclear magnetic resonance spectroscopy, often permit differentiation between free and bound water, or water of hydration. Through proper design of equipment, analyzers can be provided for batch or continuous analysis of process streams. Several instruments for this purpose are available commercially.

1. Colorimetric Methods

a. COBALTOUS CHLORIDE AND BROMIDE

Most colorimetric methods have been based on the use of cobaltous salts, normally the chloride or the bromide. The salts are used widely as relative humidity indicators and, actually, have been applied for estimating evaporation rates from aqueous systems (225).

The anhydrous chloride is pale blue, progressing through violet, purple, and magenta to red-brown for the di-, tri-, tetra- and hexahydrates, respectively (166). The anhydrous bromide, on the other hand, is brilliant green, and the hexahydrate, red.   Often the color of the undissociated material is quite different from that of the ionized form.   If the salt contains water, however, the color approximates that of the ions, for, on dissociation in water, hydrates are formed of the radicals capable of combining with water.

The cobalt salts may also combine with a variety of other materials, each of which can affect the absorption maxima in solution.   These include certain amines, alcohols, ketones, and tetrahydrofuran.   Consequently, for maximum accuracy, any colorimetric method for water must be calibrated in the particular system in which the analysis is to be made and may be reliable only when the concentrations of all components other than water remain essentially constant.

Katzin and co-workers (166,167) studied extensively the absorption of a variety of solvates with cobaltous chloride.   Typical data are summarized in Table XVII.

TABLE XVII
Absorption Maxima for Cobalt Complexes (166,167)

		Absorption maxima, mμ		
Absorbing form^a	Color	Determined by Cl/Co ratio	Dependent on molecular addenda X^{b,c}	
$Co(H_2O)_6^{+2}$	Salmon pink		510	
CoX_4Cl_2	Rose to magenta		524–540	
CoX_2Cl_2	Blue	575	610–615, 640, 665	(1)
			615, 655–660	(2)
			625–630, 675	(3)
$CoXCl_3^-$	Blue	595	630, 665	(1)
			[625], [640], 675	(2)
			[630], 685	(3)
$CoCl_4^{-2d}$	Blue		[615], 625, [640], 670, 700	(4)
			615, 625, 635, 665, 695	(5)

^{a} X represents water, alcohol, etc.   See footnote b.
^{b} (1) X = pyridine or quinoline;   (2) X = alcohols;   (3) X = acetone or tetrahydrofuran;   (4) acetone or tetrahydrofuran with LiCl;   (5) acetone with HCl.
^{c} Bracketed wavelengths indicate small or poorly defined peaks.
^{d} Solutions containing excess chloride as LiCl or HCl.

Procedures have been devised for the colorimetric determination of water in solids, liquids, and gases.   For solids, a suitable insoluble water-miscible liquid usually is employed to extract water, and the colorimetric measurement made on the extract. Gases may be scrubbed with a liquid, for example, an alcohol.

Ferguson and Coulter (86) studied a number of variables in an attempt to devise a general method of analysis. With cobalt chloride in absolute ethanol used as reagent, an absorption maximum occurred at 671 mμ. A plot of log per cent transmittance vs. cobalt concentration gave a curved line, although, between 100 and 400 p.p.m. of cobalt, Beer's law was nearly obeyed. Optimum concentration was 300 p.p.m. of cobalt for the range 2 to 10 mg. of water per milliliter. With temperatures from 20 to 30°C., the

TABLE XVIII

Comparison of Results of Cobaltous Chloride and
Karl Fischer Reagent Methods (86)

Material	Water found, %	
	Cobaltous chloride	Karl Fischer reagent
Bauxite	7.55	7.54
Cereal	0.25	0.27
Sawdust	8.50	8.40
Soybean mash	6.78	6.84

transmittance changed reversibly about 1%/degree, decreasing with increase in temperature. Recommended procedural details are given in Section VII. Analytical data for water extracted from solid materials are given in Table XVIII. The results compare favorably with those obtained by Karl Fischer reagent titration (see Section IV-A-1).

b. OTHER COLORIMETRIC PROCEDURES

A colorimetric dichromate–sulfuric acid reaction was used for determining relatively large percentages of water in some natural products. The depth of the yellowish green color after oxidation of the organic matter was proportional to the water content. Measurements were made at about 660 mμ, and the amounts of water estimated from a standard reference curve (294).

The solubility and, therefore, the color intensity of potassium dichromate in aqueous ethanol were found to vary with water concentration. For this determination, Meditsch (212) added excess dichromate and acetic acid to the sample. Absorbances of solutions, determined at 520 mμ, were found to follow Beer's law at least in the range 5 to 30% water. A relative accuracy of 1 to 2% was reported.

The intensity of the blue color formed on shaking grain with a mixture of sodium chloride, ferric alum, and potassium ferricyanide was related to water content (67).

Application of the near ultraviolet absorption of acetic anhydride in a sensitive method for determining water is described in Section IV-A-3.

Reference to a colorimetric method employing the calcium carbide reaction is given in Section IV-A-4.

2. Infrared Spectrophotometry

The infrared region of the spectrum provides the basis for sensitive, nearly specific methods for determining water in many solids, liquids, and gases.   Infrared procedures are particularly appropriate for small concentrations of water in relatively small samples.   They are nondestructive, permitting recovery of the sample.

Both the fundamental and near infrared regions contain absorption bands suitable for determining water.   Actual choice of the analytical wavelength depends on the system in which water is to be determined. Calcium fluoride prisms with cells containing calcium fluoride windows are generally recommended for use in the fundamental region.   Water, of course attacks the commonly used sodium chloride units.   Quartz or glass cells often can be employed in the near infrared region.

a. ABSORPTION BANDS

The 2.5 to 6 μ region of the infrared spectrum has been studied extensively.   In this area the wavelength for maximum absorption is affected by hydrogen bonding between water molecules or between water and other polar molecules.   The nature and the extent of bonding are influenced by the concentration of water and the type of system in which the measurement is made.

Assignments for monomeric and polymeric forms of water were established in high-resolution studies made by Van Thiel, Becker, and Pimentel (327).   Frequencies were determined by a matrix isolation technique in solid nitrogen at 20°K.   Bands at 3725 and 3627 cm.$^{-1}$ shown by the monomer were attributed to symmetric and antisymmetric OH stretching vibrations.   From studies of absorption by the dimer at 3691 and 3546 cm.$^{-1}$, the investigators concluded that this polymer has a cyclic structure rather than the open or bifurcated structure usually proposed.   Table XIX gives wavelength data and type of vibration for each of the species.   Also included is comparable information on water vapor, 0.1M water in dioxane, and 0.0075M water in carbon tetrachloride (123).

TABLE XIX
Infrared Absorption by Water in the 2.6 to 6.5 Micron Region

Species	Type	Wavelength of max. absorption	
		μ	cm.$^{-1}$
Monomer in vapor phase	O—H stretching	2.66	3756
		2.74	3652
	H—O—H bending	6.27	1595
Monomer	O—H stretching	2.68	3725
		2.76	3627
	H—O—H bending	6.25	1600
Dimer	O—H stretching	2.71	3691
		2.82	3546
	H—O—H bending	6.17	1620
Trimer and higher polymers	O—H stretching	2.85	3510
		2.98	3355
		3.02	3318
		3.11	3222
	H—O—H bending	6.12	1633
Water in dioxane, bonded	O—H stretching	2.79	3580
		2.85	3510
	H—O—H bending	6.11	1638
Monomer in CCl₄	O—H stretching	2.70	3705
		2.77	3614

The data in Table XIX show that absorption maxima for the OH stretching vibrations from monomer to polymers of water shift toward lower frequencies. For HOH bending vibrations, however, the shift is toward higher frequencies. In polar systems, hydrogen bonding is likely to be strong between water and solvent molecules. The dioxane system illustrates such a case. In dilute solution in many nonpolar solvents, such as carbon tetrachloride, the water may be free unless intramolecular hydrogen bonding has occurred. The free hydroxyl groups usually give sharp bands, whereas bonded groups show broad strong absorptions at lower frequencies. The magnitude of the frequency shift is related to the strength of the hydrogen bond. Greinacker, Luttke, and Mecke (123) presented details on absorption of water in a variety of polar and nonpolar solvents.

Spectra of H_2O, HDO, and D_2O in the bending region in rare gases at 20 and 4.2°K. are much more complex than those in solid nitrogen at 20°K. and have been attributed to rotation of the water molecules in the rare gas matrixes (42). Internuclear distances in crystalline neon, argon, krypton, and xenon are 3.22, 3.83, 4.02, and 4.40 A., respectively. From spatial considerations alone, water could enter these structures interstitially. On the other hand, crystalline nitrogen at temperatures below 32°K. has an internuclear distance of only 1.06 A., insufficient for rotation of water in the matrix.

The near infrared between about 0.7 and 2 μ is particularly important for quantitative analyses. Overtone and combination bands are observed in this region, and the stronger combination bands are essentially specific for water. Curcio and Petty (59) investigated the region with high-resolution apparatus and found five relatively prominent bands for liquid water at 20°C. Wavelength data with absorption coefficients are given in Table XX, together with band data on water in dioxane and carbon tetrachloride (123). The intensities of these bands are considerably less than those in the fundamental region above 2 μ. Cell lengths of several centimeters can be used for the weaker bands below 1 μ, compared to fractions of a millimeter for bands above 1.5 μ.

The sharpening of bands of water in solution as compared to water alone is illustrated in Fig. 9. The spectra shown are for various thicknesses of

TABLE XX
Near Infrared Absorption by Water

Wavelength of max. absorption		Path length, cm.	Absorption coeff., α, at max. absorption, cm.$^{-1}$	Vibration type
μ	cm.$^{-1}$			
0.76	13200	12.97	0.026	Overtone
0.97	10300	1.99	0.46	Overtone
1.19	8400	0.99	1.05	Combination
1.45	6900	0.09	26.0	Overtone
1.94	5160	0.02	114.0	Combination

Wavelengths of Maximum Absorption for Water in Dioxane and Carbon Tetrachloride

0.1M H$_2$O in dioxane		0.0075M H$_2$O in CCl$_4$	
μ	cm.$^{-1}$	μ	cm.$^{-1}$
0.73	13625		
0.76	13220		
0.94	10666		
0.97	10340	0.95	10493
0.98	10230		
1.16	8630		
1.41	7073	1.37	7290
1.46	6865	1.39	7181
		1.46	6840
1.91	5237	1.89	5292

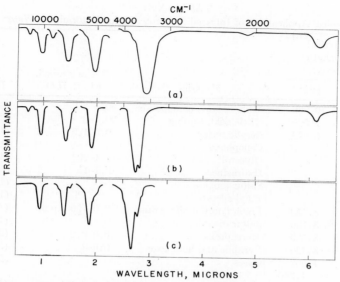

Fig. 9. Infrared spectra of water (*a*) alone and in (*b*) dioxane and (*c*) carbon tetrachloride solutions.

water: alone, $0.0075M$ (free) in carbon tetrachloride, and $0.1M$ (bonded) in dioxane for the region from about 0.6 to 6 μ (ca. 15,000 to 1500 cm.$^{-1}$) (123).

b. APPLICATIONS, LIMITATIONS

The intensities of absorption bands are proportional to concentration. In a system free of interferences, any one of several wavelengths may be calibrated for quantitative analysis. The choice depends on the concentration range of the water to be determined and the nature of the sample. Actually, most of the absorption bands are not specific for the water molecule. Absorption by hydroxyl groups in other compounds and other strongly absorbing groups may be coincidental with that by water or cause such serious overlapping that certain bands will be inapplicable. Each system to be analyzed should be examined carefully before choice is made of the most suitable analytical wavelength. Known mixtures should be analyzed over the expected concentration range of the water. From this information, reliable absorptivities or calibration curves usually can be made. In some cases of intermolecular hydrogen bonding, a band associated with the nonaqueous component often is enhanced in proportion to the concentration of water.

TABLE XXI

Typical Applications of Infrared Spectroscopy for Determining Water

Analytical wavelength, approx.		Material	Range studied, wt. % H_2O	Ref.
μ	cm.$^{-1}$			
1	10,000	Misc. organic compounds	0.1–>1	(330)
1.423	7,025	Nitric acid, fuming	0.1–6	(346)
1.9	5,260	Acrylic resins	0.0–1.2	(158)
1.9		Cellophane		(146)
1.9		Glycerol	1–20	(43)
1.9		Hydrazines	0.1–15	(55)
1.9		Sulfur dioxide		(146)
1.9		Vinyl acetate		(146)
2.67	3,750	Freon fluorine refrigerants	0.0–100 p.p.m.	(18,68)
2.7	3,700	Sulfur dioxide		(165)
2.8	3,570	Mercaptans	0.0–0.2	(207)
2.92	3,420	Pyridine and homologs	0.0–3	(57)
5.5–7.5	1,800–1,350	Gases		(201)
5.8–6.3	1,700–1,600	Propane gas	0.0–> 13 p.p.m.	(105)
6.1	1,640	Chlorine, liquid	p.p.m.	(256)

Typical applications are shown in Table XXI. Explanations for the choice of the particular wavelength illustrate the ways in which a method is developed and the nature of interferences.

Vendt (330) found that the absorption band in the near infrared at about 1 μ was suitable for determining water in liquids such as acetone, acetic acid, acetic anhydride, methanol, ethanol, glycerol, and pyridine. A special filter was used to isolate the desired wavelength, and a silver sulfide photoelectric element was employed. Water content was read from a series of standard curves prepared from data obtained in analyses of known mixtures. The same technique was used for estimating water up to saturation in compounds such as butanol, ethyl acetate, ether, benzene, toluene, and chloroform.

The band at 1.423 μ was found to be nearly specific for water in fuming nitric acid (346). A correction was necessary for the self-dissociation of the acid as influenced by the quantity of nitrogen dioxide present. Empirical relations were established for two ranges of dioxide:

$$\% \ H_2O = (4.74 \times absorbance) - 0.58 \quad \text{for up to 10\% } N_2O_4$$

$$\% \ H_2O = (5.00 \times absorbance) - 0.67 \quad \text{for 12 to 17\% } N_2O_4$$

The reliability of the method was dependent on the accuracy with which the wavelength was established. An error of 0.006 μ was equivalent to about 0.3% water at the 5% level.

The nearly specific absorption band at about 1.9 μ has been used for determining water in a variety of substances. Jones (158) found a linear relationship in acrylic resins between extinction coefficient and per cent water in the range 0 to 1.2% water. At higher levels, the relationship was nonlinear. A precision of about 0.05% was observed. In analyses of glycerol, Chapman and Nacey (43) found that the absorption band at 1.9 μ was clearly separated from that at 2.1 μ arising from hydroxyl groups in the glycerol. A linear relationship was observed between per cent water and absorbance in samples containing from 1 to 20% water. Results for water in refined and crude glycerol compared favorably with values found by Karl Fischer reagent titration (see Section IV-A-1). The standard deviation was about 0.06%. Usually the 1.9 μ absorption band is most likely to be free of interference from overlapping absorption by other groups. However, several per cent methanol and ethanol were found to interfere; for example, 5% methanol or 5% ethanol in dimethylhydrazine gave the same absorbance as 0.11% or 0.03% water, respectively (55).

Most of the relatively strong bands for water in the near infrared are subject to interference by hydroxyl and amine groups. In the 2.5 to 3 μ region all hydroxyl and some amine groups absorb. In the 2.6 to 2.7 μ region, many hydrogen-containing compounds may interfere unless suitable compensation is provided. These interferences include alcohols, alkyl esters, hydrocarbons, and chloroform (18). Benning, Ebert, and Irwin (18) determined parts per million water in Freon fluorine refrigerants. A brass cell with quartz windows was used to handle liquefied samples under pressure. In the range 0 to 10 p.p.m. water, the accuracy was about 1 p.p.m. Water in oil-contaminated Freon 12 refrigerant was calculated from the difference between the absorbances at 2.67 and 2.34 μ. The former represented the sum of water and water equivalent of the oil, and the latter, the oil itself (68). As little as 0.002% water was determined in 0.1 ml. samples of pyridine by means of the absorbance of the 2.92 μ (3420 cm.$^{-1}$) band due to water bonded with the nitrogen atom of the base (57).

Absorption in the 6 μ region has formed the basis for analyses of certain materials such as gaseous mixtures containing oxygen, hydrogen, carbon monoxide, carbon dioxide, methane, propane, and ammonia (201). In a special application, Pross (256) reported that liquid chlorine was essentially transparent to infrared radiation up to about 8.5 μ (1180 cm.$^{-1}$). He used a 5 cm. tantalum-clad steel pressure cell fitted with calcium fluoride windows for the sample and a calcium fluoride prism in the spectrophotometer.

The absorbance measured at 6.1 μ (1640 cm.$^{-1}$) was better suited for analyses than that at 2.7 μ (3700 cm.$^{-1}$), since measurements at the latter wavelength required correction for carbon dioxide. However, carbonyl and carbon-to-carbon double bonds would interfere at 6.1 μ. Other groups that could interfere in the 6 μ region include amine and amide.

3. Nuclear Magnetic Resonance Spectroscopy

Nuclear magnetic resonance (NMR) is based on absorption or emission of energy when nuclei oscillate between spin or Zeeman quantum levels. Differences in local magnetic fields, magnetic moments, and nuclear spins cause variations in the separation of these energy levels which are observed experimentally in the NMR spectrum.

a. PROTON RESONANCE

If a substance containing nuclei having a magnetic moment, μ, and a spin, I, is placed in a homogeneous magnetic field, H, any nucleus may occupy one of $(2I + 1)$ Zeeman levels. For hydrogen nuclei (protons), I equals $1/2$; hence only two Zeeman levels are available. These correspond to a parallel and an antiparallel orientation of the proton magnetic moment with the applied magnetic field. The energy difference between these levels may be expressed by

$$E = \mu H - (-\mu H) = 2\mu H \tag{40}$$

By placing an alternating field at right angles to the applied magnetic field, H, at the precession frequency of the nucleus, a resonance absorption of energy will occur. The expression for the measured resonance frequency, ω (or f), is

$$\omega = 2\mu H/h = \gamma H \tag{41}$$

where h is Planck's constant, and the gyromagnetic ratio, $2\mu/h$, may be expressed as the constant γ. The magnetic moment of the proton is 1.4×10^{-23} erg/g. Thus, in a magnetic field of 10 k gauss, ω equals 42.6 Mc., a frequency readily achieved by means of standard radio-frequency techniques.

Actually, the nucleus exists in a magnetic field arising not only from that applied but also from neighboring nuclei. Consequently, equation (41) might be written more correctly as

$$\omega = \gamma (H + H_{loc.}) \tag{42}$$

where H is the external or applied field, and $H_{loc.}$ is the field arising from other nuclei.

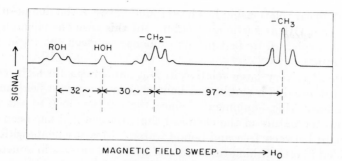

Fig. 10. Proton resonance spectrum of 5% water in ethanol.

In studies involving liquid water, nuclear magnetic resonance has been practiced in two areas, which may be described as "high-resolution" and "low-resolution" fields, respectively. The former has provided a means for differentiating protons associated with different groups. The actual spectrum obtained, however, depends on the system being examined and is influenced to a considerable extent by hydrogen bonding and by proton exchange reactions. For example, the spectrum of 5% water in ethanol obtained with a 40 Mc. spectrometer exhibits well-separated lines for the proton resonances, as shown in Fig. 10. Thus, in this case, each "type" of proton has a characteristic resonance frequency, and differences are referred to as chemical shifts. No measurable changes in chemical shift are observed in ethanol mixtures containing up to about 20% water (342). At higher water concentrations, fast proton exchange occurs until at a molar ratio of about 1:1, corresponding to 27 wt. % water, the ethanol OH and water OH lines coalesce. The total hydroxyl resonance line apparently remains in a constant position at higher water concentrations (342). Consequently, the high-resolution technique provides positive information for identification and estimation of up to about 20% water in ethanol, according to observations with a 40 Mc. spectrometer at a d.c. magnetic field of 9500 gauss (342). Similar behavior has been observed for water in tributyl phosphate (224). At a level of 1.7% water, the water line is located clearly between the methyl and methylene group signals. At near saturation, 6.2% water, the water proton signal shifts to lower field strength and coincides with one line of the methylene proton quartet.

Acetic acid–water mixtures in all concentrations show only two lines from high-resolution equipment, due to proton resonances of the methyl group and the combined water plus carboxyl group (129). The latter line is located between the normal positions of the carboxyl and water proton resonances, and its exact position depends on the concentration of water.   A linear relationship has been found between the line position and mole per cent OH as acetic acid (129).   In this case the single hydroxyl line can be explained by fast proton exchange between the water and the carboxyl group.

Because H is very large relative to $H_{loc.}$, apparatus for high-resolution NMR must provide a stable and homogeneous magnetic field and high-precision measuring equipment.   Since the environment of the protons determines the nature of the chemical shift, the method has been used to differentiate between free and bound water.   Measurements with 40 Mc. NMR aided in establishing the nature of hydrated cations in aqueous solutions (5,293).   Also, relative strengths of hydrogen bonding in water, water-acetone, and water–dimethyl sulfoxide were determined by the proton resonance shifts of the OH proton in the water molecule (73).   The order of increasing strength of the hydrogen bonds was $>$CO- - -HO, $>$SO- - -HO, HO- - -HO.   The proton resonance appeared to shift to lower fields as hydrogen bonding was increased.

In solids or viscous liquids, $H_{loc.}$ ceases to have discrete values.   In these cases, the nucleus is relatively rigid and is capable of only restricted movement, limiting the influence of neighboring nuclei.   The resulting spectrum is quite broad compared to the relatively sharp signals from the protons of water and other liquids of low viscosity.

Up to the present time, practically all investigations concerned with the quantitative determination of water have been made on simpler and, therefore, considerably cheaper equipment than that necessary for high-resolution NMR spectroscopy.   A permanent magnet, a fixed-frequency probe, and a detector have been employed.   Shaw, Elsken, and Kunsman (290) used a fixed magnetic field, H, of 6.3 kgauss where ω, therefore, was about 27 Mc.   Rubin (269) described an instrument with H of 1.75 kgauss where ω was approximately 7.45 Mc.

With these low-resolution instruments, there has been no distinction between proton signals from water and those from other hydrogen-containing substances in the liquid phase.   However, as shown in the absorption curve of Fig. 11, there is a sharp signal from the liquid, water, superimposed on the broad signal from a solid. H_0 represents the strength of the applied magnetic field.   The derivative curve in Fig. 11 was obtained directly by applying a square-wave current to the modulation coils in the radio-frequency assembly (269,290), and the absorption curve by graphical integration.   One of two measurements, the peak-to-peak amplitude, D, and possibly the line width, δf, could be used to determine water content

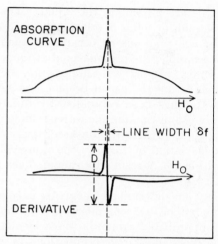

Fig. 11. Proton absorption and first derivative curves for liquid water on a solid (290).

(290). The former would appear to be the more reliable since small differences in water content have a greater affect on peak to peak amplitude than on line width.   However, in limited ranges where marked changes in line width are observed, δf could have advantages; the actual quantity of sample used, the packing of the sample, and the control of the spectrometer would not be as critical as with measurements based on D.

Sample sizes have varied with the type of material and with the apparatus employed.   In all cases the precision has been largely dependent on the reproducibility of packing of the sample.   Shaw, Elsken, and Kunsman (290) used 1 g. samples of starch and pectin packed in 1 cm. tubes and 15 g. of potato or apple in 2.5 cm. tubes.

Plots of D vs. water content determined by an independent method usually have given a straight line above a few per cent water with rather sharp curving below this level.   These plots have served as calibration curves.

b. Applications, Limitations

Low-resolution NMR has provided a rapid, nondestructive method of analysis for water in a variety of solid materials.   Usually 1 to 2 minutes is required for analysis.   In effect, the method determines protons in the liquid phase and, therefore, is likely to give a total value for protons in solution.   Before application of the method to the determination of water in any new material, it is necessary to ascertain whether other hydrogen-containing compounds are present in the liquid. These might be either other low-viscosity liquids or solids in solution. Often suitable corrections can be made for the contributions by other constituents. In certain oil-water mixtures, for example, the proton signal at room temperature could represent oil plus water. At reduced temperature, for example, $-20°C.$, the water would freeze, and the signal become due solely to oil. Under these conditions, water has been estimated by difference. For apples, Elsken and Kunsman (79) estimated the water-soluble portion, principally sugars, and corrected the NMR results accordingly. Corrected results showed a standard deviation of 1.3% in the range 82.6 to 86.1% water and usually were within 1% of results by vacuum oven drying (see Section IV-B-1).

NMR spectroscopy has determined free water in solids. Water that is tightly bound, owing either to strong adsorption or molecular association, as water of hydration, probably cannot be found by this method. Typical applications of the technique to determinations of water are given in Table XXII.

TABLE XXII
Analytical Data for Water by NMR Spectroscopy

Material	Sample size, g.	Optimum range for water detn., %	Precision, %	Ref.
Candy	8–40	3–25	0.2	(52a)
Chicle		6–24		(53)
Corn syrup		13–25		(53)
Cotton		10–17		(269)
Egg albumin	1	7–17	0.2	(288)
Paperboard pulp		7–20[a]		(269)
Pectin	1	7–20	0.2	(290)
Potato	15	20–85	2	(290)
	10	8–16	1	(79)
Starch	1	7–20	0.2	(290)
	40	8–16[a]	0.1	(269)
Starch suspensions		63–92	2	(289)
Sucrose	10	20–90	2	(79)
Vegetables	10	80–92	2	(79)
Wood		7–20[a]		(269)

[a] Upper limit not established; higher value was maximum reported.

4. Mass Spectrometry

Although mass spectrometry is not often considered for the quantitative determination of water, the technique is capable of giving fairly reliable results over a wide concentration range. Its particular value is in estimating water as part of the complete analysis of complex mixtures of gases or liquids. Only small samples are required, about 0.1 cc. of gas at S.T.P. or a few microliters of liquid. These requirements can be reduced even further by sealing off the ballast volume in the mass spectrometer's inlet system; gas samples as small as 1 μl. can then be analyzed.

Electron bombardment of water molecules produces a mass spectrum consisting primarily of the mass 18 peak due to $H^{16}OH^+$ ions, commonly referred to as the parent mass (of water). Actually, many ions are produced by direct bombardment and by secondary collisons of some of these ions with neutral molecules. Washburn, Berry, and Hall (340) reported the following ions, exclusive of deuterium and tritium: H^+, $^{16}O^+$, $^{16}OH^+$, $^{17}O^+$, $H^{16}OH^+$, $^{17}OH^+$, ^{18}O, $H^{17}OH^+$, $^{18}OH^+$, $H^{18}OH^+$. More complete details are given in Section V-A. In the range of masses 16, 17, and 18, the relative intensities are 2.3, 24.5, and 100.0, respectively (313). Calculations based on mass 18 are best suited for determining water. Usually, contributions to this mass by other compounds are relatively small.

TABLE XXIII
Determination of Water by Mass Spectrometry

Mixture	Water, mole %		Ref.
	Calcd.	Found	
Ethanol, diethyl ether, ethyl *tert*-butyl ether, water	14.8	13.3, 13.8	(313)
n-, *sec*-, *tert*-, and isobutanols, water	66.4	66.1	(113)
Methanol, ethanol, methyl ethyl ketone, water	44.8	44.3	(113)
	59.0	58.4	(113)
Ethanol, acetone, propionaldehyde, isopropyl ether, water	15.7	16.4, 15.6, 16.2	(113)
Ethanol, *n*-butanol, acetone, water	99.44	99.46, 99.55, 99.48[a]	(113)
	99.86	99.88, 99.87, 99.88[a]	(113)
Nitrogen dioxide, water	41.0	39.7	(102)
Ketones, aldehydes, alcohols, water	5.0[b]	5.9, 5.5, 6.0, 8.0, 5.8[b]	(315)
	5.0[b]	4.7–5.1[b]	(315)
	20.8	19.0–20.8[b]	(315)

[a] Calculated by difference after analysis for organic compounds.

[b] Calculated as volume %.

Water is adsorbed to a serious extent on the walls of the mass spectrometer inlet system. Similar effects are observed with the low members of most homologous series of polar organic compounds, the lowest member being the most strongly adsorbed. Errors from this source are minimized by careful conditioning of the instrument, by use of a heated inlet system, and by reduction of the volume of the inlet system (69,113,313). The sorption problem may lead to a variable background limiting the lower level for which reliable analyses for water can be made. Usually an accuracy and precision of about 0.2% absolute or 1% relative error, whichever is the larger, can be expected.

Table XXIII shows results reported for water calculated as part of the complete analysis of the mixtures noted in the first column.

5. Vacuum Ultraviolet, Glow Discharge, Miscellaneous Methods

Water vapor shows no appreciable absorption in the ultraviolet above 185 mμ. Below this wavelength, however, there are regions of continuous absorption between 180 and 130 mμ and a group of relatively intense bands between 125 and 105 mμ (109). In the vacuum ultraviolet region, bands at 122 and 112 mμ have been considered best suited for the detection and estimation of water vapor. The band at 122 mμ appears to be diffuse and structureless, and in practice the absorption coefficient (500 cm.$^{-1}$ at S.T.P.) is independent of pressure. The 112 mμ band possesses rotational structure, and, consequently, the absorption coefficient (600 cm.$^{-1}$ at S.T.P.) is pressure-sensitive (109).

Garton, Webb, and Wildy (109) chose the 122 mμ band because of its freedom from pressure effects and because of its proximity to the nearly monochromatic 121.6 mμ line conveniently enhanced by electrodeless discharge in hydrogen. Their apparatus consisted basically of (1) a silica lamp containing hydrogen at low pressure excited by means of a radiofrequency oscillator at a frequency of 16 to 20 Mc./second; (2) absorption tubes, 1, 42, and 82 cm. long, having lithium fluoride windows (transparent down to 105 mμ); and (3) a photomultiplier and recorder. The light was allowed to pass down one of the absorption tubes containing the gaseous sample. The decrease in intensity of the radiation was found to be due to absorption by the 122 mμ band of water. Calibration with nitrogen samples containing known amounts of water gave a linear relation between concentration and cell response in the ranges 0 to 10 p.p.m. and 10 to 700 p.p.m. With the 82 cm. absorption tube, as little as 0.1 p.p.m. of moisture could be detected in hydrogen, nitrogen, and other inert gases.

Determinations of 1 to 10 p.p.m. water in nitrogen gave a standard deviation varying from 0.23 at the lowest level to 1.96 at the 10 p.p.m.

level. Oxygen and carbon dioxide absorbed slightly at 121.6 mμ; the limits of detection were 10 p.p.m. water in oxygen and 100 p.p.m. in carbon dioxide. In order to achieve this sensitivity, other substances that absorb in the 150 to 105 mμ region, such as methane and hydrogen sulfide, must be absent.

In other spectroscopic methods as little as 5 p.p.m. water in organic vapors has been determined by measurement of the hydroxyl band at 3064 A. in the glow discharge (274). Similar applications in analyses of deuterium oxide–water mixtures are given in Section V-C. Residual moisture in air in vacuum drying equipment has been estimated by glow potential (145).

Continuous determination of moisture in paper and rayon pulp has been made by corona discharge (180) and microwave spectroscopy (353), respectively.

E. NEUTRON SCATTERING AND OTHER RADIOCHEMICAL METHODS

During investigation of methods for the direct determination of water in soil, Gardner and Kirkham (108) considered radiochemical techniques involving alpha, beta, and gamma rays and neutrons. Gamma rays had been used for measurement of water equivalent of a snow pack (112). In this case gamma radiation of known intensity was applied to the pack; that passing through was measured and related to water content.

Successful use of gamma rays for the determination of moisture in soil was considered unlikely since solid components of the soil also would be expected to absorb the radiation (108). The ranges of alpha and beta rays were believed to be too short to be practical. The use of neutrons, however, showed considerable promise. Hydrogen was known to reduce the speed of fast neutrons more effectively than any other common element. Therefore, in the absence of significant amounts of other hydrogen-containing compounds, neutron scattering would be expected to serve as a measure of moisture in soil.

1. Neutron Scattering

Gardner and Kirkham (108) devised a compact unit containing a mixture of polonium and beryllium as a fast neutron source. This combination, having a half life of 140 days and a strength of about 10^4 neutrons/second, was placed in a small metal cylinder. A slow neutron counter containing boron trifluoride was located on top of, and concentric with, the fast neutron source. The counter was operated at 3050 v. Pulses from the counter were amplified and recorded. Analyses were made after lowering the neutron source and counter into a hole drilled in the soil.

Tests on fine mineral soils indicated that the results were not affected by the nature of the soil as long as they were expressed on a volume basis. The unit was best suited for determining moisture in the several per cent range with a precision of about 2%. To minimize sampling and counting errors, at least 1000 counts were usually taken. For moisture contents below 1%, about 1.5 hours were required to obtain the needed counts. The method was calibrated against oven-dried samples (108). When used on the mineral soils, the method seemed to be unaffected by temperature, texture, composition, compaction, or concentration of the soil solution.

Since, in effect, hydrogen is determined by the method, organic matter or other hydrogen-containing material will interfere. Soils high in humus content, for example, contain several per cent organic substances. As long as the amount of interfering material is known accurately, a suitable correction can be applied to the apparent water value.

Gardner and Kirkham (108) foresaw field applications in which measurements could be made by placing appropriate equipment on the surface of the soil. Spinks and co-workers (242,304) further extended the technique for nondestructive estimations of water in soil and in concrete. In one system, neutrons from a radium-beryllium source slowed down by water were captured by ^{115}In to give the beta-active isotope, ^{116}In, having a half life of 45 minutes (304). In this case, neutron scattering would be expected to produce beta activity dependent on water content. Usually, however, improved boron trifluoride counters appeared better suited for measuring slow neutrons directly in both soils (283) and concrete (242).

2. Beta and Gamma Ray Counting

In other applications, use of beta and gamma rays has been successful. Friedman, Zisman, and Sullivan (103) employed beta rays for determining water continuously in fuels. A source was placed on one side of the line carrying the fuel. Rays passing through a radiation-permeable plug on the opposite side were measured with a Geiger-Müller counter.

Gamma radiation was utilized in the Bendix nuclear density gage, designed for measuring water in cement slurries passing through pipes (217). Cesium-137 served as a source. The beta rays emitted by the cesium were absorbed in the pipe carrying the slurry. The gamma rays, on the other hand, having considerably greater penetrating power, passed through the two thicknesses of pipe plus the slurry and were detected in an ionization chamber. This method was based on the fact that different densities of materials reduce nuclear radiation intensity by different amounts. In this system the intensity of the rays passing through the flowing slurry was related to density or specific gravity. By suitable calibration the percentage of water or solids could be recorded. In the 30 to 40% water range, the accuracy was reported to be ±0.2% when a 12 second time constant was used or ±0.3% with a 6 second time constant (217).

Use of tritium in an exchange method for determining water in small quantities of hydrocarbons is discussed in Section VI-B.

F. PHYSICAL METHODS

1. Turbidity

Turbidity or cloud point has been used in several applications. Once a system has been established, this method serves as a rapid and simple analysis for water in certain liquids. Conditions and calibration for each system must be established individually. In most cases the method has been applied to the determination of water in organic liquids in which water is only slightly soluble, such as aniline and furfural. Three variations in technique have been employed: (1) titration to turbidity with a reagent that is soluble in the organic material but not in water; (2) addition of a measured amount of water until turbidity develops; and (3) direct reduction in the temperature of the sample until the system becomes turbid.

Direct titration to turbidity often leads to variable results. A considerable improvement has been realized by adding a suitable oil phase, heating until the solution becomes clear, and allowing the solution to cool until the cloud point has developed. For determining water in aniline, Seaman, Norton, and Hugonet (279) found that a mixture of cottonseed oil and heavy mineral oil, for example, Nujol, offered advantages over the previously recommended rapeseed oil. In making an analysis, 3.5 ml. of cottonseed oil–mineral oil mixture (5:1) was added to 20 ml. of aniline. The mixture was warmed in a water bath until the opaque emulsion was essentially clear. The mixture was removed from the bath immediately and allowed to cool spontaneously. The temperature at which the cloud point formed was recorded to the nearest 0.05°C. Precision and accuracy were reported to be about 0.01% in the range 0.0 to 4% water (279). A similar procedure was used for determining water in furfural with hexanol–cottonseed oil as additive (127).

Samples soluble in ethanol have been analyzed by titration with xylene (136). A linear relationship was found between water content of the sample and the amount of xylene required to cause turbidity. The method was also suitable for determining water in some solids when only water was removed during extraction with ethanol.

Titration of the sample, containing an added component of limited solubility in water, with water was used for the lower alcohols and ketones (305). A compound such as camphor or furfural was added to the sample, and the solution was titrated with water at constant temperature until the appearance of turbidity. Through the use of suitable controls, an accuracy of 2% was reported for water in alcohol or acetone.

For the determination of water in styrene (185) or mercaptans (207), the cloud point was measured directly on the cooled sample.

Where applicable, the turbidity or cloud point methods have proved to be rapid and simple. Most of the procedures reported are based on visual observation. Sensitivity probably could be improved by photometric detection of the cloud point. In one case, for example, moisture in inert gases was determined with a sensitivity of 10 to 250 mg./m.[3]. The gas was passed over oleum, and the opacity of the aerosol formed was measured photometrically (44).

2. Density, Refractive Index

Density or specific gravity and refractive index measurements have been used for a variety of liquids and inert solids. Such techniques are suitable for binary liquid solutions or for liquids in which only variation in the water content will affect the measurements. Many alcohols have been analyzed by these means.

Solids, such as coal, coke, and soil, have been analyzed indirectly. The wet inert sample is shaken with a water-miscible liquid, and the density or refractive index of the separated liquid determined. The change in the physical constant is related to water content, assuming that no other substances are extracted from the solid sample.

3. Displacement

Approximate procedures based on Archimedes' principle have served as convenient and simple field tests for estimating water in wet gravel, soil, and concrete aggregates.

The density of the dried solid must be known. A weighed or measured volume of the wet sample is placed in a suitable vessel. Variations in the procedure have included (1) use of a graduated vessel containing a known volume of water and measurement of the final total volume, (2) volumetric addition of water to a given volume, or (3) displacement by siphoning into a graduated cylinder (210). The buoyancy effect has been used in field

testing, also.   In this case, the moist material was first weighed in air and
then while immersed in water (175).

Better precision has been attained by direct specific gravity measurements.   Batson and Hogan (11), for example, used this approach for rapid
determination of water in starch containing 15 to 50% water.   Analysis
was based on the difference between the weight of 100 g. of starch diluted
to 500 ml. with water and that of 500 ml. of water alone at constant temperature.   When the density of the starch (1.633 for sweet potato starch)
was known, the percentage of water could be calculated.   An accuracy of
0.5% was reported as compared with vacuum oven drying data.

4. Vapor Pressure

Direct and indirect methods for measuring vapor pressure have been
used for analysis of a variety of gases and solids.   Usually the gaseous
sample is drawn into an evacuated flask.   The vapor pressure is measured
manometrically before and after removal of the water.   The water may
be removed by freezing or preferably by absorption in a suitable desiccant,
for example, phosphorus pentoxide (334) or sulfuric acid (159).

For determining water in sugar, Hill and Dobbs (143) placed the sample,
in a sealed ampule, in a flask which was then evacuated.   The ampule
was broken, and the sample heated.   Moisture evolved was condensed in a
second evacuated flask of known volume.   The condensate was allowed to
evaporate, and the vapor pressure measured.   Provision was made in the
apparatus for grinding the sugar, which in effect gave a means for estimating surface water and total water.   The condensation step permitted
compensation for adsorbed gases released with water during heating of the
sugar.   This compensation, of course, required accurate measurements of
vapor pressure over the condensed water and of the vapors after evaporation
of the water.

A simpler apparatus was used by Vincent and Bristol (333) in a rapid
method for determining moisture in dehydrated foods and other solids.
The sample was placed in a flask and attached to a simple vacuum bench.
Air was evacuated, after which the system was allowed to equilibrate.   The
difference in pressure, as measured on a manometer, before and after
freezing out water vapor was equivalent to the vapor pressure of water over
the sample.

In analyses for moisture in hydrocarbon gases, Evans and Davenport
(82) determined pressure differential after exposure of the sample to
lithium chloride.

Direct measurement of steam volume was applied successfully in a field
kit for estimating water in nylon resins (310).   The sample was placed in a

hypodermic syringe and heated. Displacement of the plunger of the syringe was related directly to water content. Sample size was 0.3 g. for samples containing 1 to 10% water and 2.5 g. for 0.1 to 1% moisture. Temperatures of 240 and 200°C. were used for nylons 66 and 610, respectively. A precision (95% confidence limit) of 0.07% was found for samples containing 0.1 to 1% water, and a precision of 0.7% for samples in the range 1 to 10% water. Analyses of 10 g. samples containing 0.2 to 0.3% water gave a precision of 0.04%.

Volumetric methods also can be employed. A known volume of gas is taken into a buret. After condensation of the water, the volume is re-measured. The change in volume is related to water content of the sample. Velling (329) used a steam-jacketed buret. After sampling, the steam was replaced by water at about 0°C., and contraction in the gas volume due to condensation was noted.

5. Dew Point

The dew point of a gas is the temperature at which dew begins to form, that is, the temperature at which the gas becomes saturated with moisture. Analyses usually have been based on the temperature at which moisture begins to condense onto a cool surface. To facilitate observation, a thin mirror or other highly polished surface has been employed. Provision is made for controlled cooling or heating to permit alternating adjustments to slightly above and below the dew point. A thermocouple or other suitable temperature-measuring device attached to the surface has served to determine the temperature. The dew point has been observed visually (66) or, more reliably, photometrically (337).

Ilfeld (149) described an automatic apparatus for recording the dew point over the temperature range from ambient to about −68°C. (−90°F.). He provided a table for converting dew point temperatures to moisture content for air and other inert gases in the range −73 to 43°C. (−100 to 110°F.).

Dew point methods have been used successfully for determining moisture in air, nitrogen, hydrogen, oxygen, carbon monoxide, carbon dioxide, methane, etc. Many corrosive gases attack the metal surfaces. Compounds other than water may condense on the mirror, obscuring the dew point. These include heavy hydrocarbons, ammonia, etc.

6. Hygrometry

Relative humidities of air are commonly determined by the dry and wet bulb psychrometer. In its simplest form the psychrometer consists of two thermometers; the bulb of one is left bare while the other is covered by a moistened cotton or cloth wick. Relationships have been derived from the two temperatures found after swinging the thermometers, the wet bulb temperature depending on the evaporation of water from the wet surface (344).

$$p = p' - AP(t - t') \qquad (43)$$

where p is the partial pressure of water vapor in mm. Hg at the dry bulb temperature, $t°C.$; p' is the saturation pressure of water vapor in mm. Hg at the wet bulb temperature, $t'°C.$; A is the psychrometer constant, which for air equals $6.60 \times 10^{-4} (1 + 0.00115 t')$; and P is the total pressure in mm. Hg. The constant A is derived from the relation $C_p/\sigma\lambda$, where C_p is specific heat, σ is specific gravity of water vapor relative to dry air, and λ is heat of vaporization (29).

In English units pressures are expressed in inches of Hg at degrees Fahrenheit, and A for air is $3.67 \times 10^{-4}[1 + 0.00064(t' - 32)](344)$.

Relative humidity, RH, is determined from the relation

$$RH = (P/P_s) \times 100 \qquad (44)$$

where P_s is the saturation pressure of water vapor at the dry bulb temperature.

The psychrometric equation (43) also can be applied for determining the partial pressure of water in other gases. The constant A, however, depends on the properties of the particular gas being analyzed. Values of A for several mono-, di-, tri-, and higher-atomic gases were determined by Brauckhoff (29) and, when converted to the same basis as that for air, gave the figures shown in Table XXIV.

TABLE XXIV
Psychrometer Constants[a] for Gases

Gas	Constant, $A'(\times 10^{-4})$	Gas	Constant, $A'(\times 10^{-4})$
He	4.8	CO	6.6
A	4.8	H_2S	8.4
Air	6.60	CO_2	8.4
O_2	6.60	N_2O	8.8
N_2	6.60	NH_3	8.5
H_2	6.5	SO_2	9.5
Cl_2	8.4	CH_4	8.0
HI	6.7	C_2H_6	11.8

[a] Metric system, $A = A'(1 + 0.00115t')$.

Factors affecting the precision and accuracy of the dry and wet bulb method include (1) accuracy of the thermometers, (2) speed of air past the wet bulb, (3) radiation, (4) size, shape, material, and wetting of the wick, (5) relative positions of the two thermometers, and (6) temperature and purity of the water used to wet the wick.   Wexler and Brombacher (344) discussed each of these factors in some detail.   Ordinarily standardized equipment is used in the so-called sling psychrometer.   The psychrometer constant is a function of the velocity of ventilation across the wet bulb thermometer.   It reaches a minimum value at a certain velocity and remains constant at higher levels.   For most mercury-in-glass thermometers with bulbs having diameters of 0.25 inch or less, the minimum rate of ventilation is 900 feet/minute.

Tables and charts are widely available for converting dry and wet bulb thermometer readings and air pressure to relative humidity, vapor pressure, or dew point of air (see reference 344).

Special psychrometers have been developed in which the thermometers are stationary, ventilation being provided by fans or blowers.   Thermocouples, resistance, and bimetallic elements have been used in place of the mercury-in-glass thermometers (344).

The psychrometric technique is used widely in meteorology and in the air-conditioning and refrigerating industries.

The hair hygrometer, often called *hygroscope*, provides a simple means for determining relative humidities in confined areas (344).   This compact instrument is commonly made from a bundle of human hairs kept under tension with a simple lever system connecting their mid-point with a pointer or recorder.   Changes in humidity cause variations in the tension which are indicated directly on the pointer or recording accessory.   The hair hygrometer can be used over a wide range of temperature but is most reliable above 0°C.   A reliability of about 3% in relative humidity at room temperature has been reported when sufficient time is allowed for attaining equilibrium (344).   Other elements have been tried in place of human hair, but up to the present time none has been as satisfactory.

Among the applications of the hygroscope are determination of relative humidity in areas surrounding air-conditioning and refrigeration equipment and estimation of the water content of trees.   In one example, a small hole was bored into the tree, and moisture in the air within this small volume was determined with a hair hygroscope (3).   Other applications include rapid estimates of water in gases and of equilibrium humidity over viscous liquids, such as oils, and solids, including wood, foods, and textiles.

Several other methods are described in this chapter for determining the moisture content of air or other gas at equilibrium with its surroundings.

7. Sonic Techniques

The velocity of sound is dependent on the medium through which it passes. In many uniform solids, sound waves may be influenced by the concentration of water. Brough and Puleston (34) used this principle for estimating water in moving webs of paper, cloth, etc. Sound waves were developed on one side of the web by means of an electric audio-frequency generator and loud speaker. Signals were received and recorded on the other side via a microphone and amplifier. Improvements in the design of sonic analyzers were made by Martin and Mounfield (206).

Ultrasonic velocity measurements have been used for determining bound water in aqueous solutions of electrolytes and nonelectrolytes. In solutions of electrolytes the water molecules bound to the electrolyte ions are compressed to a small degree owing to the strong electric field of the ions. The degree of hydration of the ions has been determined by adiabatic compressibility measurements based on ultrasonic velocity data (241). Shiio, Ogawa, and Yoshihashi (292) proposed a more general approach to include bound water in nonelectrolytes such as sugars. The authors defined bound water as that which is hydrogen-bonded to the solute and the amount of bound water as that which is dehydrated when a precipitating agent is added to the precipitation point. Equations were derived relating volumes with adiabatic compressibilities of solution, solvent, solute, and bound water calculated from ultrasonic velocity measurements.

Aqueous solutions of sugars were titrated with ethanol to the precipitation point. It was assumed that addition of this precipitating agent led to a gradual decrease in hydration until at the precipitation point hydration became zero. The amount of hydration was determined from volume, concentration, and compressibility data for the original aqueous solution and the alcohol-water solution at the precipitation point.

Experimental results were obtained on aqueous solutions of glucose, maltose, and dextrin at 20°C. Ultrasonic velocities were measured by an interferometer with an X-cut crystal having a resonance frequency of 1 Mc. The amount of bound water was found to be 0.43, 0.23, and 0.40 cc./g. for glucose, maltose, and dextrin, respectively. For glucose the results indicated that 1 mole of water was bound to each free —OH group. For maltose, however, the lower result indicated a decrease in free —OH groups due to intramolecular hydrogen bonding.

8. Miscellaneous Physical Techniques

A variety of specialized physical techniques has been used for determination of water in specific systems. These include methods for determination of moisture in (1) soil in relation to soil moisture tension as measured with a tensiometer (259); (2) solids by the rate at which high-frequency mechanical oscillations are transmitted through the material (100,338); (3) flexible gelatin capsules by measurements of deformation under stress (232); (4) phenol by cryoscopy (253); (5) cellulose by extraction with trichloroacetic acid and determination of the freezing point depression (215); (6) beet pulp by application of pressure to the wet sample mixed with molasses and measurement of the volume (56); (7) grains based on the extent of penetration by a stainless steel blade (92); (8) wet solids by centrifugation (264); (9) ammonium nitrate by measurement of the boiling point at reduced pressure (356); (10) certain liquids by measurement of viscosity (137); (11) gases by critical flow based on differences in entrance pressures between two nozzles and on absolute pressure and temperature of the gas (347); and (12) gases by rate of diffusion based on density difference relative to saturated air (263) or rate of diffusion through a semipermeable membrane (124).

G. THERMAL METHODS

Many thermal techniques have been used for determining moisture in gases, liquids, and solids.   Those based on thermogravimetry and differential thermal analysis may also discriminate between free and "bound" water and water of hydration.   Both of these techniques indicate transitions and often with polyhydrated materials will indicate stepwise changes to lower levels of hydration; see Section IV-B-I-C.

1. Thermal Conductivity

Several variations in technique have been employed in applying thermal conductivity measurements to determinations of water, usually in gases. Since the rate at which heat is conducted depends on composition, change in thermal conductivity is proportional to water content, provided other components in a mixture remain essentially constant.

The method has been used for years for measuring the relative humidity of air.   Actually, with some binary mixtures maxima occur when the thermal conductivities of the two components are nearly equal.   This applies to binary mixtures of moisture with air, nitrogen, oxygen, and probably with carbon monoxide, acetylene, ethylene, and ethane (45).   For these gases restrictions are placed on the range in which the method is applicable.   For example, the method is unsuited for determining 12 to 47 vol. % water vapor in air.   However, the method is reliable below and above this concentration range.

Cherry (45) developed an apparatus for determining moisture in air, nitrogen, oxygen, and probably other gases. Thermal conductivities of water vapor in air could be used for analyses of compositions containing from 0.16 to 12.3 vol. % and above 47.4 vol. % water. The method was relative, requiring calibration by an independent procedure. Where applicable, it was rapid and easily adapted to recording and control. In any system the presence of an additional component could introduce significant errors. Cherry (45) studied the effects of 13 contaminants on determinations of water vapor in air. These were reported in terms of concentration change from a calibrated value which would cause an error of 0.1 vol. % in the result. They varied from a change of 0.005 vol. % for hydrogen to 4.8% for ethylene. For any known system differential compensating arrangements could be made to increase the tolerance. By this means the hydrogen content could be increased to 5 vol. %.

The method has been used in indirect analyses for water in liquids and solids. Dry gas was allowed to equilibrate with the sample, after which the thermal conductivity of the gas was measured (126).

Direct thermal conductivity measurements have been used for determining water in soils and other porous materials. Equipment has included (1) two heated wires imbedded in the soil forming two elements of a Wheatstone bridge in which changes in heat transfer were measured (169,286) and (2) a heated metallic plate (49). In the latter case the cooling rate of the plate, as measured on a galvanometer, was found to depend on moisture content.

2. Heat of Vaporization

Advantage has been taken of the heat of vaporization of water for direct and indirect methods of analysis. Kinsella (174) devised apparatus based on this principle for determining moisture in gas, particularly air. The gas was passed over heated metal cylinders on which the temperature was measured by means of suitably located thermocouples. The cooling effect due to evaporation of water was related to water content.

3. Heat of Reaction or Solution

The heat of reaction or solution often has been related to water content. Application to determining water in acetic acid through hydrolysis of acetic anhydride was discussed in Section IV-A-3. With similar apparatus, advantage has been taken of the heat of dilution of sulfuric acid. In one example, concentrated sulfuric acid was added to coal in a Dewar flask, and the maximum temperature rise noted (121). The relationship between temperature rise and water content varied with the type of coal. An accuracy of about 5% was reported.

This same technique should be applicable to other materials which are inert toward concentrated sulfuric acid.

Partially hydrated materials have been analyzed by measurement of the heat of hydration (250). Estimations of moisture in some solids have been based on specific heat data (273). Relative humidities of air have been measured on the basis of the temperature rise accompanying exposure of dry cotton to moist air (322).

4. Thermogravimetry

The thermobalance offers a convenient means for determining water of hydration (75). With this equipment, weight loss can be measured as a function of time and temperature. During thermogravimetric studies of complex mixtures of anhydrous and hydrated salts, Griffith (125) found that in many cases he could determine not only total water but also the amount of water in each phase.

At any fixed temperature, a mixture of anhydrous and hydrated salts exhibits a definite dissociation pressure. As vapor is removed, the hydrate maintains the same dissociation pressure until that phase is converted to a lower hydrate. Hence through proper control of temperature and heating rate the various phases within a polyhydrate may be determined. When sodium tetraborate decahydrate was heated from room temperature to 500°C., the step from $Na_2B_4O_7 \cdot 10H_2O$ to $Na_2B_4O_7 \cdot 5H_2O$ was clearly evident. All of the water was gradually lost over a period of 8 hours (125).

The thermogravimetric method requires a knowledge of the system to be analyzed. Mixtures of hydrates of different salts can behave differently from each hydrate alone. For example, the pyrolysis curve from a mixture of $Na_2B_4O_7 \cdot 10H_2O$ and $Na_4P_2O_7 \cdot 10H_2O$ differed from those of the tetraborate and pyrophosphate alone (125). A break in the curve was observed, but this did not correspond to $Na_2B_4O_7 \cdot 5H_2O$. Rather the tetraborate lost water continuously up to 9 moles at a maximum temperature of 165°C. At temperatures as high as 500°C., only a part of the tenth mole of water was lost in 8 hours. The $Na_2P_2O_7 \cdot 10H_2O$ alone was rendered anhydrous at 100°C. Thermogravimetric studies of soils and clays usually gave results between those obtained by Karl Fischer reagent titration and conventional oven drying (276).

Once proper conditions are established, the technique may provide a reliable means for establishing the particular hydrate and the total water in hydrated substances. Further information of the thermal behavior of some hydrates is given in Section IV-B-1.

H. ELECTRICAL METHODS

Water has unique electrical properties which can be used to advantage in a variety of fairly specific and rapid methods for its determination. Pure water, of course, is a poor conductor of electricity. Water has a very high dielectric constant, well above that of most liquids, which accounts for the great ionization of salts, acids, and bases in aqueous systems. A variety of instruments has been developed for the determination of water in many solids, liquids, and gases. These usually are small, compact units suitable for use in the field for measurement of conductivity, capacitance, or dielectric constant.

1. Dielectric Techniques

Included in the category of dielectric methods are measurements for dielectric constant, dielectric loss, and often capacitance. Direct determination of dielectric constant is usually the most reliable because of the high constant for water, ca. 80, as compared to most other materials. Paper, for example, has a dielectric constant of about 2.5. Many instruments which presumably determine the constant basically measure the capacitance of a condenser using the sample as the dielectric. In these cases the capacitance of a condenser filled with the sample is compared with that of the same condenser when empty. The capacitance of a parallel plate condenser is proportional to the area of the plates and the dielectric constant of the sample between the plates and inversely proportional to the distance between the plates. Consequently, results usually depend on the thickness and density of the sample as well as water content.

Under ideal conditions the dielectric constant of a binary mixture, ϵ_m, can be calculated from the linear relation

$$\epsilon_m = \epsilon_1 p_1 + \epsilon_2 p_2 \tag{45}$$

where p_1 and p_2 are the relative concentrations of each component. In this case $p_1 + p_2 = 1$, and p_2 can be expressed as $1 - p_1$. A substance containing 1% water would then have a calculated ϵ_m of $0.8 + \epsilon_2$ or $\Delta\epsilon = \epsilon_m - \epsilon_2 = 0.8$ ($\epsilon_1 p_1 = 80 \times 0.01$, and $\epsilon_2 p_2 = \epsilon_2 \times 0.99 \approx 1$). Theoretically, therefore, the presence of 1% water in any substance will lead to an increase in dielectric constant of the substance by 0.8 unit. Oehme (233) found, however, that most systems did not behave ideally and, hence, calibration curves would be required for each system to be analyzed. This is illustrated in Fig. 12, which shows the effect of increasing concentrations of water on the dielectric constants of methanol, dioxane, and octanol at

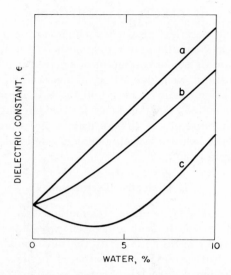

Fig. 12. Effect of water on the dielectric constants of (*a*) methanol, (*b*) dioxane, and (*c*) octanol (233).

constant temperature.   Only the methanol-water system showed a linear relationship.   In the figure, for illustrative purposes, the three organic compounds are expressed in terms of identical dielectric constants.   Actually they differ considerably.   Thus, ϵ = 2.3 and 33.8 for dioxane and methanol, respectively (233).   Deviations from theory appear to be associated with decreased precision of measurement as the dielectric constant of the substance increases and with the nature of the molecular association in solution.

Oehme (233) applied high-frequency techniques for dielectric measurements, using a single-stage quartz oscillator with a working frequency of 7 Mc./second.   Probably the most rapid measurement was that of the grid

TABLE XXV

Temperature Coefficients of the Dielectric Constant of Acetic Acid
Containing Various Amounts of Water (233)

Water, %	$d\epsilon/dT$
0.05	$+1.23 \times 10^{-2}$
0.12	$+0.69 \times 10^{-2}$
0.52	0.00
0.52	Negative

current. However, if damping due to the sample varied widely, measurements by the grid current method could be in serious error.

For some materials, for example, the lower fatty acids, analyses have been based on the temperature coefficient, $d\epsilon/dT$ (233). Data for acetic acid are given in Table XXV.

The dielectric methods have been applied to determinations of water in liquids and solids. The sample is placed in a suitable measuring cell, the instrument is tuned, and a reading is taken. Equipment and type of measurement have varied with the nature of the material to be analyzed. Oehme (233) applied variations of the grid current method to determinations of certain levels of water in alcohols, acids, uniform emulsions, powders, cellulose, tobacco, and ceramics. For determining water directly in leather, Kremen (183) used an oscillator circuit operating at about 11 Mc./second. With the measuring condenser, C_m, empty, the tuning condenser, C_t, was adjusted to give a minimum reading on the tuning meter. Insertion of the sample between the plates of C_m required a reduction in C_t proportional to the water content. Calibration curves were required for various thickness ranges. For calf leather an accuracy of about 3% (as compared to oven drying) was observed in the optimum range of 15 to 50% water.

Dielectric measurements also have been used for determining water in paper, textiles (211), powders (128), meat products (222), and salts (233).

Analysis of extracts from solids often has been preferable to direct analysis, particularly on materials which are difficult to pack uniformly or on which the water may be distributed unevenly. Dioxane is one of the most useful extraction solvents because of its low dielectric constant and complete miscibility with water. Oehme (233) set the following restrictions on the use of dioxane for most dielectric constant measurements: (1) the dioxane must not dissolve any material other than water; (2) the water must be extracted completely from the solid; and (3) the volume used should be selected so that the dioxane will contain no more than 1% water. This final restriction is made to assure minimum extraction of electrolytes. In some cases, for example, aminocaprolactam, the substance is completely soluble in dioxane. Satisfactory analyses were made on samples containing up to 1% water after proper calibration curves had been prepared (233). For extraction of some materials, for example, meats, a mixture of dioxane and ethylene glycol has been found superior to dioxane alone (222).

In some instances dielectric loss angle measurements may be superior to dielectric constant measurements. For a given frequency, ω, the loss angle, δ, can be calculated from the relation

$$\tan \delta = k\sigma/\omega\epsilon \tag{46}$$

where k is a constant (1.13×10^{13}), and σ is the conductivity. With the method of grid current maximum, tan δ also can be calculated from the effective capacity and the damping of the measuring cell containing the sample (233). For determinations of small amounts of water (up to 1%) in C_1 to C_5 alcohols, Oehme (233) reported that dielectric loss angle measurements were more reliable than dielectric constant measurements. However, small amounts of impurities interfered seriously in the loss angle method.

2. Conductivity, Resistance

Among the electrical techniques, those based on conductivity measurements are probably the most widely used. Applications to solids, liquids, and gases require that (1) an electrolyte be present and (2) components other than water in the sample be essentially nonconducting materials. Under these conditions, when electrodes at a fixed potential are placed in the sample, the current is proportional to the water content. Analyses are made either directly on a measured amount of the sample or indirectly on an inert water-miscible liquid used to extract water from the sample. The former method requires rather simple compact apparatus and is well suited for rapid analyses of solid materials containing several per cent water. Each system must be calibrated, however, since the physical form and density of the material affect the results. Instruments have been described for the direct determination of water in grains, paper, textiles, plastics, tobacco, sand, concrete mix, wood, leather, soils, and oil. The indirect approach, using an inert liquid, gives more versatility provided the water can be extracted reproducibly. Acetone, methanol, and ethanol have been used as extractants. Oxalic acid, sodium chloride, and lower fatty acids are typical of electrolytes which have been added when necessary. Indirect methods have been used in analyses for moisture in gases and soils (133).

Electrical conductivity measurements of solid or liquid absorbents can be used directly or indirectly for determining water in gases. Thus lithium salts have been employed for measuring the relative humidity of gases above 5%. A mixture of sulfuric and phosphoric acids has been a suitable absorbent in rapid determinations of low concentrations of water in small samples (341). Weaver and co-workers (341) actually measured water content by balancing pressure (designated *comparison pressure*) between a standard and the unknown until the electrical resistances were equal. Hence a pressure gage actually served as the measuring instrument, and the approximate water content, W, was calculated from the relation

$$W = CP_w/P_x = SP_cP_w/P_sP_x \qquad (47)$$

where C is the water content of the standard at the comparison pressure; P_w is the absolute pressure at which the water content of the unknown is desired; P_c is the comparison pressure at which the electrical resistance of the standard is balanced with the electrical resistance produced by the unknown at pressure P_x; and P_s is the pressure at which the standard contains a known concentration of water vapor, S.

In determining moisture in compressed gases, it has been convenient to use as the standard air, oxygen, or nitrogen saturated at about 35 atm. and expanded to 1 atm. Where the water content of the unknown is desired at 1 atm., equation (47) reduces to

$$W_x = S/P_s P_x \qquad (48)$$

where S is the concentration of water in a vapor space in equilibrium with liquid water. S and W may be expressed in weight per unit volume, relative humidity, or other desired unit.

Actually, these equations assume that all components, including water vapor, behave as ideal gases. Hence, ideally in cases where a dry, inert gas is used to equilibrate with a liquid or solid sample, the mass of water vapor in equilibrium with liquid water is independent of the presence of other gases. Deviations from ideality, of course, are common and are best explained on the basis of fugacity, that is, the tendency for a substance to escape from one phase into another. For best accuracy the relation between fugacity and pressure must be established by experiment, and equation (47) modified to account for deviations from ideality. Necessary constants for oxygen, air, and nitrogen are essentially the same, and the more exact relation is

$$W_x = S[P_c P_w(1 - 1.9 \times 10^{-4}P_c + 1.4 \times 10^{-8}P_c{}^2)]/[P_s P_x(1 - 1.9 \times$$
$$10^{-4}P_s + 1.4 \times 10^{-8}P_s{}^2)(1 - 1.9 \times 10^{-4}P_x + 1.4 \times 10^{-8}P_x{}^2)] \quad (49)$$

A hand computer in the form of a circular slide rule was developed to assist in handling this calculation (341).

Where data on changing concentrations of water vapor are desired, it may be impractical to make separate pressure adjustments. The electrical resistance measurements can be employed, usually by interpolation between values determined by pressure readings.

The method also can be used for determining water in liquids and solids by employing a dry inert gas to elute the water. Alternatively, the water content of air in equilibrium with a liquid sample may serve as a measure of water in the sample. This approach was reliable for ether but not for alcohol. The procedure has been applied to determination of water in gases, such as air, oxygen, nitrogen, and natural gas.   Equipment is available from commercial sources.

Fig. 13 shows a convenient arrangement of the detector for determining water vapor in equilibrium with a liquid (341).   In practice a glass tube A, having openings at the bottom F and one side G, is dipped into the liquid. (For small samples capillary tubes with flared tops can be used.)   The detector D is connected as shown in the figure.   Block B and spring C

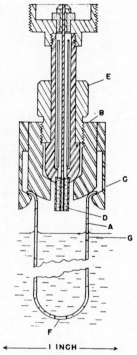

←——————— I INCH ———————→

Fig. 13. Detector for determining water vapor in equilibrium with a liquid (341).

provide a tight fit with the top of the tube, and nut E serves as a rigid connector for the detector.   Only a fraction of a cubic centimeter of space is necessary for measuring relative humidities in a static system.   The evolution of water during dehydration of less than 1 g. samples of silica gel at elevated temperatures and the diffusion of moisture through small membranes were followed successfully (341).

The method has proved particularly sensitive for determining water in liquids in which its solubility is limited, such as hydrocarbons, ethers,

and ketones.   It has been less reliable for water-miscible substances such
as alcohols and mineral acids.   Since the quantitative significance of the
fugacity in terms of water content differs for each liquid, application to
each system must be established empirically.   Water in solids has been
determined after extraction into a suitable liquid.   The sensitivity of
measurement, that is, the change in concentration of water vapor that can
be observed with the instrument, approaches 0.3 γ/liter or 0.1%, whichever
is greater.

Dielectric methods usually are not well suited to analyses of samples in
which the conductivity increases markedly with increase in water content.
This behavior is particularly critical in samples containing relatively high
concentrations of electrolytes.   In these cases high-frequency systems may
be used for conductivity measurements.   Jensen and co-workers (153)
used this approach in analyses for water in sodium chloride and ammonium
nitrate.   A dioxane-methanol solution was used to extract the moisture
for analysis in a 9.45 Mc./second unit.   A precision of 0.02% was found
for water contents in the range 0.3 to 2.5%.   Binary mixtures of water in
several alcohols were analyzed successfully (343).   At the 1% water level,
the precision and accuracy were about 0.05% and 0.2%, respectively.

3. Electrolysis

Of the electrical methods available for determining water in gases, that
utilizing electrolysis probably is the most versatile.   Keidel (170) devised
a unique system based on quantitative absorption of water in a suitable
hygroscopic material followed by electrolysis of the water to oxygen and

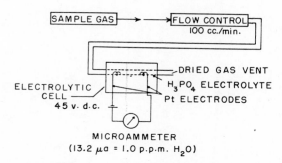

Fig. 14. Schematic diagram of electrolytic water analyzer (170).

hydrogen.   The electrolysis current serves as a direct indication of water
content.   The technique is particularly appropriate for continuous deter-

TABLE XXVI

Recommended Methods for Determining Water

Substances	Method	Procedure type	Optimum level, % H_2O	Typical interferences	Page
Air, inert gases	CaH_2	Thermometric	p.p.m.	Compounds containing active hydrogen	105
	Dew point	Temperature measurement	p.p.m.	Ammonia, corrosive materials	148
	Electrical	Conductivity	p.p.m.		158
		Electrolysis	p.p.m.	Ammonia	161
	Hygrometry	Temperature measurement	p.p.m.		148
	Infrared	Spectrophotometric	0.16–12.3,	Alcohols, amines	130
	Thermal conductivity		>47.4 vol. %	Hydrocarbons	152
	Vacuum ultraviolet	Spectroscopic	p.p.m.	Oxygen-containing compounds	142
Dairy products	CaC_2	Manometric	10–70	Alcohols	102
	Electrical	Dielectric constant	Several		155
		Conductivity	Several	High concentrations of electrolytes	158
	KFR	Volumetric	1–>90		82
	Oven drying	Gravimetric	0.1–several	Volatile and thermally unstable materials	109
Drugs	KFR	Volumetric	0.1–several	Inorganic hydroxides, oxides, carbonates, bicarbonates	82
	Lyophilization	Gravimetric	Several	Volatile compounds	117
	Oven drying	Gravimetric	0.1–several	Volatile and thermally unstable materials	109
Foods	CaC_2	Manometric	Several	Alcohols	102
	$CoCl_2$	Colorimetric	0.1–1	Colored materials	127
	Desiccation	Gravimetric	Several	Volatile compounds	116
	Distillation	Azeotropic	Several	Volatile and thermally unstable materials	121

			Range	Application	
	Electrical	Dielectric constant	Several		155
	KFR	Volumetric	1–75	Ascorbic acid, inorganic hydroxides, oxides, carbonates, bicarbonates	82
	Lyophilization	Gravimetric	Several	Volatile compounds	117
	Oven drying	Gravimetric	0.1–several	Volatile and thermally unstable compounds	109
	NMR	Spectroscopic	5–90	Hydrogen-containing compounds in solution	136
Inorganic compounds	$CoCl_2$	Colorimetric	0.1–1	Colored compounds	127
	Distillation	Azeotropic	Several	Volatile and thermally unstable materials	121
	Infrared	Spectrophotometric	0.1–several	Hydroxides	130
	KFR	Volumetric	p.p.m.–>90	Hydroxides, oxides, carbonates, bicarbonates	82
Chlorine	Infrared	Spectrophotometric	0.1–several		130
Organic compounds	Infrared	Spectrophotometric	p.p.m.–several	Alcohols, amines	130
	KFR	Volumetric	p.p.m.–>90	Aldehydes, ketones, mercaptans, diacyl peroxides	82
Acetic acid	$(CH_3CO)_2O$	Thermometric	0.8–3.2		100
		Ultraviolet	0–100 p.p.m.	Formic acid, peroxides	100
Ketones	CH_3COCl	Volumetric	0.00–several		96
Paints, lacquers	Distillation	Azeotropic	0.1–several	Volatile and thermally unstable materials	121
Petroleum products	KFR	Volumetric	0.02–several	Inorganic hydroxides and oxides	82
Gases	CaH_2	Thermometric	p.p.m.	Compounds containing active hydrogen	105
	Dew point	Temperature measurement	p.p.m.		148
		Conductivity	p.p.m.	Corrosive materials	158
	Electrical	Electrolysis	p.p.m.		161

(continued)

TABLE XXVI (*continued*)

Substance	Method	Procedure type	Optimum level, % H_2O	Typical interferences	Page
Liquids	Infrared	Spectrophotometric	p.p.m.–1	Alcohols, amines	130
	KFR	Volumetric	p.p.m.–1	Aldehydes, ketones, mercaptans	82
	Beta radiation	Continuous	Several		144
	CaC_2	Gas chromatography	10–100 p.p.m.	Alcohols	126
	Infrared	Spectrophotometric	p.p.m.–1		130
	KFR	Volumetric	p.p.m.–1	Aldehydes, ketones, mercaptans	82
Solids	Distillation	Azeotropic	0.1–several	Volatile and thermally unstable materials	121
Plastics	KFR	Volumetric	0.02–several	Aldehydes, ketones, mercaptans	82
	Distillation	Azeotropic	Several	Volatile and thermally unstable materials	121
	Electrical	Conductivity	Several	High concentrations of electrolytes	158
		Dielectric constant	0.1–1	Alcohols	155
	Infrared	Spectrophotometric	0.1–several	Alcohols, amines	130
	KFR	Volumetric	0.01–several	Aldehydes, ketones, mercaptans, inorganic oxides	82
	Vapor pressure	Physical	0.1–several	Volatile materials	147
Sand, soil, gravel, etc.	CaC_2	Manometric	1–30	Alcohols	102
	Displacement	Physical	Several		146
	Gamma radiation	Continuous radiochemical	30–40		144
	Modified Penfield	Gravimetric	Several	Sulfur and ferrous compounds	120
	Neutron scattering	Radiochemical	1–several	Hydrogen-containing materials	143
	Oven drying	Gravimetric	Several	Volatile and thermally unstable materials	109
Soaps, detergents	Distillation	Azeotropic	0.5–several	Volatile and thermally unstable materials	121
	KFR	Volumetric	0.1–several	Inorganic hydroxides	82

Material	Method	Technique	Range	Limitations / Interferences	Ref.
Starches	Distillation	Azeotropic	Several	Volatile and thermally unstable materials	121
	KFR	Volumetric	0.1–several		82
	NMR	Spectroscopic	8–>90	Hydrogen-containing compounds in solution	136
	Oven drying	Gravimetric	0.1–several	Volatile and thermally unstable materials	109
Sugars	Distillation	Azeotropic	Several		121
	KFR	Volumetric	0.01–several	Volatile and thermally unstable materials	82
	Oven drying	Gravimetric	0.1–several	Volatile and thermally unstable materials	109
Textiles	Distillation	Azeotropic	Several	Volatile and thermally unstable materials	121
	Electrical	Dielectric constant	Several	Alcohols	155
	Hygrometry	Temperature measurement	Several		148
	KFR	Volumetric	0.05–several	Inorganic oxides	82
	Oven drying	Gravimetric	0.1–several	Volatile and thermally unstable materials	109
Tobacco	Distillation	Azeotropic	Several		121
	Electrical	Conductivity	Several	High concentrations of electrolytes	158
Wood, paper	Electrical	Dielectric constant	Several		155
	CoCl₂	Colorimetric	0.1–1	Colored substances	127
	Electrical	Conductivity	Several	High concentrations of electrolytes	158
	Hygrometry	Dielectric constant	Several		155
		Temperature measurement	Several		148
	KFR	Volumetric	Several		82
	NMR	Spectroscopic	5–>20	Hydrogen-containing compounds in solution	136
	Oven drying	Gravimetric	Several		109

mination of from less than 1 to 1000 p.p.m. water in gases.   It also can be used as a batch analyzer.

Analysis is accomplished in a special cell which combines absorption with electrolysis.   The absorbent is distributed as a thin viscous film in contact with two platinum electrodes which may be coiled inside a tube of Teflon TFE fluorocarbon resin.   Water vapor in the gas flowing through the cell is absorbed by the hygroscopic electrolyte.   The absorbed water is quantitatively electrolyzed at the electrodes by application of a d.c. voltage greater than the decomposition potential of water.   According to Faraday's law, the electrolysis of 0.5 g.-mole of water requires 96,500 coulombs.   The electrolysis current is proportional to the number of moles of water absorbed per unit time.   This not only provides a continuous measure of water concentration but also maintains the film in an active condition.   Usually a flow rate of 100 cc. of gas per minute is suitable.   Under these conditions the electrolysis current is 13.2 μa./p.p.m. by volume.   A schematic diagram is shown in Fig. 14.

The choice of absorbing material is critical.   Requirements include (1) ability to remove very small quantities of water from a flowing gas stream; (2) stability in the electrical system—that is, current flow from application of the d.c. potential must result only from electrolysis of water; and (3) inertness toward other components in the gas stream (170).   Partially hydrated phosphorous pentoxide has been found to be satisfactory, particularly for low concentrations of water.

The method has been applied successfully to determinations of water in a variety of gases, including air, nitrogen, hydrogen, carbon dioxide, argon, helium, hydrocarbons, and Freon fluorinated hydrocarbon refrigerants and propellants.   Successful applications also have been made to analyses for water in many liquids.   Materials boiling below 100°C. often can be handled as vapors.   Others in which water is only slightly soluble have been analyzed indirectly by sparging with a stream of dry, inert gas such as air or nitrogen.

Compounds which interfere include hydrogen fluoride, ammonia and other basic materials, and high concentrations of alcohols or acetone.   The basic materials react with the phosphoric acid electrolyte.   In many cases, potassium carbonate or hydroxide can be substituted for the phosphorus pentoxide absorbent in analyses for several hundred parts per million water in the presence of volatile bases.

Units based on electrolysis are available from several commercial sources. Usually at least 1 liter of gas sample is required for an analysis.   A maximum error of 5% in the reading has been achieved easily with commercially available components.

4. Friction Coefficient, Electrostatic Charge

The friction coefficient between carbon brushes and a rotating metal rod was found to depend on the formation of an adsorbed layer on the carbon surface and the partial pressure of water vapor in a variety of gases. Perlick and Perlick (246) devised a method based on this principle for determining water in nitrogen, oxygen, argon, carbon dioxide, and several organic vapors, including acetylene. The method was applicable to water contents over the range 0.05 to 5 mg. of water per cubic meter of gas.

Continuous analyses for water in textiles were made by an electrostatic method (295). The cloth was first grounded to remove the charge and then passed over rollers; the charge developed was measured and related to water content.

I. RECOMMENDED METHODS

Table XXVI summarizes suitable methods for the quantitative determination of water in inorganic and organic compounds and in a variety of commercial materials. The most widely applicable methods are azeotropic distillation, electrical measurements, Karl Fischer reagent (KFR) titration, infrared spectrophotometry, and oven drying.

V. DETERMINATION OF DEUTERIUM OXIDE

Prior to 1950 emphasis was placed on the development and application of the mass spectrometer for analyses of deuterium–protium oxide mixtures. Since that time, infrared spectrophotometric techniques have become increasingly important. In the discussion to follow, emphasis will be placed on general procedure and applications. For details of instrumentation the reader is referred to the *National Nuclear Energy Series* and the many other reference works now available.

A. MASS SPECTROMETRY

Both indirect and direct methods have been employed for the isotopic analysis of water. Usually the former approach has provided better precision and accuracy over the entire range from pure normal water to pure heavy water.

1. Indirect Methods

Indirect methods have involved gas analysis after (1) decomposition of water to form protium and deuterium, (2) equilibration of the sample with gaseous hydrogen or deuterium, or (3) conversion to volatile hydrogen-containing organic compounds.

a. Decomposition

Decomposition methods have utilized reduction by zinc, decomposition over a tungsten filament, or electrolysis. All have required essentially complete conversion to avoid fractionation of the isotopes. Of these, the zinc method has offered a number of advantages. The apparatus is relatively simple, and reduction is fairly rapid. Several analyses can be made without changing any part of the apparatus. Sample size may vary from several grams to a few milligrams. Often unpurified water samples can be used (176).

Reduction has been effected in a vacuum bench over pure granulated zinc at 400 to 410°C. The hydrogen gas, as it formed, was transferred by Toepler pump into a receiver at $-78°$C., where it was sampled for mass spectrometer analysis (176). Dubbs (74) found that a dry ice trap and the Toepler pump could be eliminated in a simplified, compact apparatus consisting essentially of a tube, in which the liquid sample was reduced, attached directly to a gas-sampling tube. Samples of 0.01 ml. or less were used. For routine analyses Chinard and Enns (47) further simplified the apparatus, using individual small sealed tubes for carrying out the reduction and permitting direct transfer of a portion of the gas directly into the mass spectrometer inlet system.

In the tungsten filament procedure, the sample in the vapor phase has been decomposed over a 1000 w. coiled tungsten filament projection lamp (176). During reduction, oxide is formed and may introduce errors by adsorbing hydrogen or by acting as an exchange catalyst.

Although electrolysis requires relatively simple apparatus, reaction must be complete to avoid large errors in the determination of deuterium. However, the technique also releases the oxygen isotopes and therefore provides a means for complete analysis of water. Errors due to incomplete hydrolysis are more serious in determining H/D ratios than in measuring $^{16}O/^{18}O$ ratios (176). Even after 99.7% electrolysis of samples containing very small concentrations of deuterium, errors up to about 15% may be observed in determining the hydrogen isotopes. As little as 90% electrolysis, on the other hand, leads to less than 1% error in the oxygen isotope analysis (176).

b. Equilibration

Either protium or deuterium is used in the equilibration method, depending on their relative concentrations in the sample. The technique is capable of providing accurate analyses; water containing 0.0140 mole % deuterium has been analyzed with an accuracy of 0.0002 mole % (176).

For analysis of water of low deuterium content (0.01 to about 3 mole % D), the sample and platinum oxide catalyst are placed in a special equilibration flask. The water is frozen in dry ice, and air is removed by vacuum pump. Outgassing of the sample is completed by alternate thawing and freezing, with evacuation after the freezing step. Then protium is admitted to a pressure of about 1 atm. After equilibration is complete (several hours), the gas phase is analyzed by the mass spectrometer, protected by a dry ice or liquid nitrogen trap for removing water vapor from the gas. Mole % D is calculated from the relation

$$\frac{50K'_1(HD)/H_2}{1 + K'_1(HD)/H_2}$$

where K'_1 is the equilibrium constant for the reaction

$$H_2O(l) + HD(g) \rightleftharpoons HDO(l) + H_2(g) \tag{50}$$

At 25°C., $K'_1 = 3.87$ (176). Equation (50) applies only to water of low deuterium content, where the concentration of D_2O is insignificant. For very low levels of deuterium the calculation reduces to $50K'_1(HD)/H_2$.

Equilibration is made with deuterium gas with samples containing high levels of deuterium oxide (<3 mole % protium) following the reaction

$$HDO(l) + D_2(g) \rightleftharpoons D_2O(l) + HD(g) \tag{51}$$

Mole % D is calculated from the relation

$$\frac{100\{1 + 0.5[(HD)/D_2](1/K'_4)\}}{1 + [(HD)/D_2](1/K'_4)}$$

where the constant, K'_4, is 3.33 (176).

A deuterium gas exchange method was used for determining water (or its equivalent as hydroxyl) in oxide catalysts (192). After contact for 16 hours at 300 to 500°C., a gas sample was analyzed with the mass spectrometer. Data on alumina and silica compared favorably with loss on ignition at about 1200°C.

c. ANALYSIS OF PROTIUM-DEUTERIUM MIXTURES

Ions produced in the mass spectrometer from mixtures of hydrogen and deuterium range in mass from 1 to 6, with the relative intensities varying with concentration (176).

Mass	1	2	2	3	3	4	4	5	6
Ion	H^+	H_2^+	D^+	H_3^+	DH^+	D_2^+	H_2D^+	HD_2^+	D_3^+

In gas of low deuterium content the HD to H_2 ratio is obtained from masses 2 and 3. In this case the D^+ contribution to mass 2 is negligible, and the contribution of H_3^+ to mass 3 can be eliminated by a simple ion-pressure plot. For deuterium gas low in protium, masses 3 and 4 are employed, whereas for intermediate ranges, masses 2, 3, and 4 must be compared.

Direct calculations for water over a broad range of deuterium contents involve several equilibria, and the computation becomes quite complex. In addition, factors such as memory and water vapor effects, spectrometer discriminations, and sample size must be considered. The calculations are simplified by use of a comparative method (176). In this case, mass ratios of a standard and the sample are compared directly, and deuterium content is calculated from the relation

$$\frac{(\text{Mass 3/mass 2})_{\text{sample}}}{(\text{Mass 3/mass 2})_{\text{standard}}} \times \text{deuterium content of standard}$$

Results by several methods are given in Table XXVII. Products of reaction from the methods noted in the first three columns were analyzed by mass spectrometry. Comparative data in the final column were obtained by direct methods.

TABLE XXVII
Analytical Data for Deuterium in Water (176)
(Results are expressed in mole % deuterium.)

Tungsten decomposition	Zinc reduction	Equilibration	Other method
0.065		0.061	
0.661[a]			0.650[b]
		1.67[c]	1.661[b]
	0.0145	0.0147	
0.026	0.025		
0.176	0.173		
		0.839[d]	0.835[b]
		3.54	3.54[b]
		99.26	99.32[e]
		99.73	99.83[e]

[a] 0.654 standard.

[b] Falling drop method (see Section V-D-3).

[c] 1.665 standard.

[d] Average of 26 analyses with average deviation $\Sigma d/n = 0.011$, where d is the deviation from the mean.

[e] Specific gravity method (see Section V-D-1).

A variation of the comparison method was suggested in mass spectrometer analyses for deuterium in natural waters (50). Standards were prepared from mixtures of natural water and pure D_2O, giving different known excesses, ΔC, above the unknown concentration, C_0, of deuterium in the water. The relation $\Delta C/C_0$ was determined directly by mass spectrometry since

$$(HD/H_2)_{standard}/(HD/H_2)_{natural} = 1 + (\Delta C/C_0) \qquad (52)$$

A plot of $\Delta C/C_0$ vs. ΔC gave a straight line passing through the origin in which the reciprocal of the slope equalled C_0. A sample of water from the Thames River analyzed $0.0152 \pm 0.0003\%$ D.

d. Conversion to Organic Compounds

Organometallic compounds have been used for conversion of deuterated water to gaseous hydrocarbons. Thus Orchin, Wender, and Friedel (235) employed the Grignard reaction, for example,

$$2CH_3MgI + 2HDO \longrightarrow$$

$$CH_4 + CH_3D + MgI(OH) + MgI(OD) \qquad (53a)$$
$$2CH_3MgI + MgI(OH) + MgI(OD) \longrightarrow$$

$$CH_4 + CH_3D + 2MgO \cdot MgI_2 \qquad (53b)$$

$$4CH_3MgI + 2HDO \longrightarrow 2CH_4 + 2CH_3D + 2MgO \cdot MgI_2 \qquad (53c)$$

Actually less than the theoretical 2 moles of methane ($CH_4 + CH_3D$) was recovered per mole of HDO, but the reaction was reproducible. The low results were probably due to incomplete conversion during the second stage of the reaction. Evidence for this conclusion was obtained in studies of the Grignard reaction with tritium oxide, where radioactivity was measureable in the residue after separation of the tritiomethane (see Section VI-A-2). Similar results were observed for the reaction of normal water (see Section IV-A-7).

Analyses were based on the ratio of the parent mass 17 for CH_3D to that of mass 16 for CH_4. As little as 10 to 20 mg. samples were analyzed in the range of 1 to 15% deuterium oxide with an absolute precision of about 0.16 mole % D.

Friedman and Irsa (104) recommended conversion to ethane by reaction with diethylzinc, for example,

$$(C_2H_5)_2Zn + HDO \longrightarrow C_2H_6 + C_2H_5D + ZnO \qquad (54)$$

Analyses were based on relative intensities of the parent masses 31 for C_2H_5D and 30 for C_2H_6. This procedure also was used for analyses of about 10 mg. samples in the optimum range 0.5 to 1.0% deuterium. The lower limit was restricted owing to interference by the natural ^{13}C isotope, and the upper limit depended primarily on the pattern stability and quality of the deuterium oxide used for calibration purposes. Samples containing as much as 95% D_2O required a spectrum precision of 0.1% for 2% accuracy.

These methods, like those described previously, require complete conversion to eliminate fractionation effects. For routine analyses the zinc reduction method appears best.

2. Direct Methods

Mixtures of protium and deuterium oxides involve the equilibrium

$$H_2O + D_2O \rightleftharpoons 2HDO \tag{55}$$

Complete analysis with the mass spectrometer must account for each of these species. Masses of potential analytical value are 17, 18, 19, and 20. Theoretically, mass 17 is due to OH^+ ions produced by fragmentation and ionization of H_2O and HDO; mass 18, by HOH^+ and $^{16}OD^+$; and masses 19 and 20, by HDO^+ and D_2O^+, respectively. Actually oxygen isotopes contribute in some measure to these peaks: $^{17}O^+$, $^{17}OH^+$, ^{18}O, $H^{17}OH^+$, ^{17}OD, $^{18}OH^+$, $H_3{}^{16}O^+$, $H^{17}OD^+$, $H^{18}OH^+$, $^{18}OD^+$, $H_2D^{16}O^+$, and $H_3{}^{17}O^+$ (340). Thomas (315) found that the abundance of mass 19 varied almost linearly with the amount of D_2O added to H_2O standards. In the range 0 to 5% D_2O, there was no correlation between mass 20 and per cent D_2O. In the range 5 to 10% D_2O, mass 20 was greater, as expected from the equilibrium. The maximum abundance of mass 19 resulted from a 1:1 mixture of H_2O and D_2O.

Direct analyses by mass spectrometry have been subject to serious errors caused by adsorption of water on the glass inlet system, leading to marked "memory effects" due both to elution and to atom exchange. These errors have been minimized by repeated flushing with the sample to be analyzed before making a determination. By comparing the relative abundances of mass 19 for HDO^+ and mass 18 for HOH^+ from a 90° sector-type mass spectrometer, Thomas (315) found an accuracy of 0.2% absolute in the range 0.2 to 1% D_2O and about 0.3% accuracy in the range 1 to 10% D_2O.

Washburn and co-workers (340) obtained improved accuracy in direct analyses by using a 158 or 180° mass spectrometer after carefully adjusting the repeller voltage, electron current, and sample pressure. At low deuterium levels (ca. 0.015 atom %), differences as low as 0.0006 atom % could be measured after reduction in the formation of spurious m/e 19 ions, probably due to H_3O^+. This measurement was accomplished by means of an ion source in a high magnetic field with about five times the normal voltage applied to the ion-repelling electrode. In the range of 3 to 10% D, the accuracy was 0.2 to 0.3%. With nearly pure D_2O, ratios of mass 19:20 peaks were measured with relatively high accuracy. All of these analyses required comparison with standard samples and repeated flushing of the inlet system of the mass spectrometer with the sample before actual recording of the mass ratios.

B. INFRARED SPECTROPHOTOMETRY

Development of infrared methods for the determination of normal water–heavy water mixtures has accelerated in the last few years. For the most part, direct analyses have been reliable, with suitable absorptions in both the conventional and near-infrared regions. Spectra of nearly pure deuterium oxide in dry dioxane and carbon tetrachloride, respectively, for the sodium chloride region are shown in Fig. 15. These spectra were obtained in a double-beam instrument, with the solvent alone used for compensation. Prominent bands in dioxane are the D—O—D bending vibrations at 8.33 μ (1200 cm.$^{-1}$) and the doublet of D_2O stretching at 3.70 and 3.88 μ (2705 and 2575 cm.$^{-1}$). Also evident are the H—O—D stretching vibrations at 2.82 μ (3547 cm.$^{-1}$) and 3.76 μ (2660 cm.$^{-1}$), the latter appearing as a shoulder on the D_2O stretching absorption bands. The spectrum of the

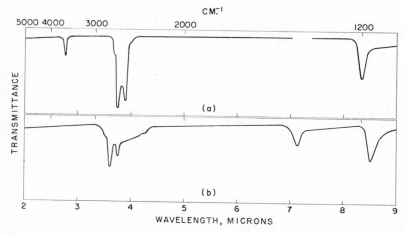

Fig. 15. Infrared spectra of deuterium oxide in (a) dioxane and (b) carbon tetrachloride.

carbon tetrachloride shows absorption due to D_2O bending at 8.48 μ (1179 cm.$^{-1}$) and D_2O stretching at 3.64 and 3.79 μ (2750 and 2640 cm.$^{-1}$), together with that at 7.15 μ (1398 cm.$^{-1}$) due to HOD bending. The intensity of the H—O—D stretching vibration at 2.82 μ was too low to show absorption in carbon tetrachloride. (Compare with Fig. 9, the spectra of normal water in these solvents.)

The actual choice of wavelength depends on the relative concentrations of deuterium and hydrogen because of mutual interferences among the H_2O, HDO, and D_2O vibrations. The most useful bands are those shown in Fig. 15, together with the unbonded HOD stretching vibration at 3.72 μ (2690 cm.$^{-1}$). In Fig. 15 this absorption was obscured by the D_2O stretching bands. These bands can shift slightly, depending on the system and strength of bonding (132).

Gaunt (110) studied a broad range of deuterium concentrations and proposed measurements at differing wavelengths depending on concentration and, hence, predominating species in the equilibrium $H_2O + D_2O \rightleftharpoons 2HDO$. Through use of the equilibrium constant for the reaction $(HOD)^2/(H_2O)$-(D_2O) of 3.80 at 25°C., predominating species in any concentration range could be calculated. For all practical purposes the following relationships were found to apply: (1) at about 99% D_2O, the water consists of D_2O and HDO; (2) in the 50% range, the HDO concentration remains essentially constant; (3) at the 97% H_2O level, the composition is about 94.4% H_2O, 0.1% D_2O, and 5.5% HDO; and (4) at above 97% H_2O, the solution is H_2O and HDO. Recommended wavelengths with results are shown in Table XXVIII. In order to achieve the indicated precision and accuracy, special conditions were established for the analyses. Calibrations were made with carefully prepared standards. For the 99 to 100% D_2O range,

TABLE XXVIII

Determination of Deuterium by Infrared Spectrophotometry (110)

Range, wt. % D_2O	Absorption band		Results, wt. % D_2O	
		μ	Found[a]	Known
99–100[b]	H—O—D	2.95	99.801 ± 0.003(5)	99.799[c]
50	O—H	1.445	51.73 ± 0.06(10)	51.74[d]
0–3	O—D	3.98	3.236 ± 0.004(5)	3.237
			0.216 ± 0.002(5)	0.217
			0.0368 ± 0.0008(7)	0.0367

[a] Figures in parentheses represent numbers of individual determinations.

[b] The 1.66 μ band of H—O—D also has been used for determining >96% D_2O with an indicated accuracy of 0.1% (190).

[c] By mass spectrometer analysis.

[d] By direct weighing of H_2O and D_2O.

0.25 mm. silica cells were used in a spectrophotometer equipped with a lithium fluoride prism set at 2.95 μ, a lead sulfide detector, and an 800 cycles/second amplifier and set at a slit width of 0.14 mm. Soda glass having a strong absorption band at 2.95 μ was used as a reference standard. For the 50% range, the weak 1.445 μ combination band for water was chosen because of its freedom from overlapping HDO and D_2O bands. Consequently, 5 mm. glass cells could be used with either a double- or single-beam instrument. At the 3% D_2O level, neither the 1.66 or 2.95 μ bands of HDO could be used, owing to interference from H_2O. However, the band at 3.98 μ was essentially free of interference. Quantitative results were obtained with 0.07 mm. cells having synthetic sapphire or calcium fluoride windows in a single-beam spectrophotometer equipped with a thermocouple and a 10 cycles/second amplifier. Below 3% D_2O, larger cells were used, for example, 0.19 mm. at the 0.2% level and 0.25 mm. in the natural range. Otherwise, conditions were the same as those used at 3% D_2O.

Berglund-Larsson (19) recommended conditions differing from those of Gaunt (110) for analyses in the range 0 to 1.5% D_2O. He used a 0.05 mm. cell in a single-beam instrument set at 3.98 μ and a slit width of 0.05 mm. Using data from standards prepared by mixing D_2O and H_2O, he obtained a linear calibration curve following the relation $\log (I_0/I) = 0.3174C - 0.0034$, where C is the concentration of D_2O in weight per cent. A correction was made for naturally occurring D_2O in distilled water, assuming a concentration of 0.0163%. Beer's law was obeyed in this range, and the H—O—D absorption band at 3.98 μ was well separated from other bands. The mean error of a single determination was calculated to be ± 0.006 wt. %.

Through prior dilution with H_2O of samples containing more than 3% D_2O, the 3.98 μ band was used indirectly for the whole range (318). With a 0.05 mm. calcium fluoride cell, the 3.98 μ band was suitable for analyses of D_2O–H_2O mixtures from the combustion of deuterium-containing organic compounds (320).

As in the mass spectrometric procedures, conversion to organic compounds also has been of value in some cases. Brown and Bernstein (36) used the Grignard reaction (methylmagnesium iodide) to convert deuterated water to methane and methyl deuteride (see equation (53)). The methyl deuteride was measured at 4.54 μ (2204 cm.$^{-1}$) in a 10 cm. cell.

C. SPECTROSCOPY

The intensities of the D_α or D_β lines have served as a convenient means for determining deuterium or deuterium oxide in the vapor phase. Comparison with the H_α or H_β lines has given a rapid method for obtaining H/D ratios.

Broida and Morowitz (33) applied this technique for determining total water (H_2O) in materials. The sample was mixed with heavy water, usually containing about 99% D_2O. Comparison was made of the D_2O/H_2O ratio of the resulting solution with that of the solvent. The liquid was placed in a system which was evacuated to 0.3 to 1.0 mm. Hg to remove air. Vapors were carried through an electrodeless discharge tube excited by radio-frequency energy in the range of 100 to 10,000 Mc. Under these conditions the molecules dissociated into H and OH, D and OD. The H/D ratio was determined by measuring the ratio of the H_β line at 4861 A. to the D_β line at 4860.0 A. on a recording spectrometer. The fraction by weight, f, of H_2O in the sample was calculated to a first approximation from the relation

$$f = (R - r)V/(1 + R)M \qquad (56)$$

where r is the molar ratio of H_2O to D_2O in the solvent alone; R is the final molar ratio in the solution; V is milliliters of solvent; and M is grams of sample. This approximation, which is accurate to about 0.4%, assumes that the partial molar volumes of protium oxide and deuterium oxide are the same and the density of water at room temperature is 1.000.

Broida and Morowitz (33) reported that 0.1% accuracy could be obtained in a total analysis time of about 1 hour whereas 3% accuracy was feasible in 7 minutes. Examples were given for the determination of water in the pentahydrates of copper sulfate and sodium thiosulfate, results of which are shown in Table XXIX. The procedure appears broadly applicable for determining total water.

TABLE XXIX
Spectroscopic Determination of Water of Hydration (33)

| Hydrate | Wt. of sample, g. (M) | Vol. of solvent, ml. (V) | H/D ratio | | Wt. fraction H_2O | |
			In solvent (r)	In solution (R)	Found (f)	Calcd.
$CuSO_4 \cdot 5H_2O$	0.770	1.00	0.011	0.286	0.354	0.361
$Na_2S_2O_3 \cdot 5H_2O$	0.648	1.00	0.011	0.249	0.364	0.363
$Na_2S_2O_3 \cdot 5H_2O$	0.779	1.00	0.011	0.289	0.353	0.363

Dontsov and Striganov (71) used a similar approach for the analysis of hydrogen oxide–deuterium oxide mixtures based on measurement of the H_α and D_α lines at 6562.8 A. and 6261.0 A., respectively. Intensities were compared with those of standards covering the range 2 to 80% D_2O. Relative errors reported were 4% at the lower levels and 0.6% at the 48% D_2O level.

Oganov and Striganov (234) extended their photographic method to cover the range 0.7 to 97% hydrogen in deuterium. An autocollimating three-prism glass spectrograph was used having dispersion in the 6500 A. region of 9.5 A./mm. The light was excited by an electrodeless discharge from an oscillator with a frequency of 10 Mc./second. For hydrogen-deuterium mixtures the H_α line was preferred because it was considerably more intense than the H_γ line and, unlike H_β, was free of interfe·ence from molecular bands. However, there was some restriction in this region due to limitations in dispersion of the instrument. Calibrations were made by analysis of known mixtures prepared from normal water and 99.5% deuterium oxide.

D. DENSITY

Normal and heavy water differ in density by about 10%. Consequently, with suitably precise techniques, the density serves as the basis for a convenient analysis. The most important methods for determining density employ the pycnometer and the float and falling drop techniques.

Accurate determination of density or specific gravity, like other physical constant measurements, requires pure water, and samples usually must be purified before analysis. Correction must be made for contributions by ^{17}O and ^{18}O isotopes which in natural waters may be in higher concentration than deuterium.

1. Pycnometer Methods

Properly designed pycnometers for highly precise density measurements have provided accurate analyses of the complete range of protium-deuterium oxide mixtures. Kirshenbaum and co-workers (176) used Reischauer-type pycnometers with an additional bent side arm. Both graduated arms were 0.05 mm. I.D. The calibrated pycnometer was filled without contamination by drawing the sample through the bent side arm, with the aid of a siphon, by applying gentle suction at the opening of the straight arm. The filled pycnometer (free of air bubbles) was capped and placed in a water bath kept constant to a few thousandths of a degree. After the sample reached constant temperature, the positions of the menisci in the two arms of the pycnometer were read, and the weight was determined against a tare on a balance having a sensitivity and reproducibility of about 0.05 mg. Buoyancy corrections were applied, and the density or specific gravity was calculated with fifth decimal place accuracy.

Complete details of the calculation and correction for ^{18}O content were given by Kirshenbaum (176).   Improvements in the technique, including mass spectrometer analysis for ^{18}O, were reported by Bryant (38).

Kirshenbaum (176) also discussed the differential method of Washburn and Smith (339) which employed two single capillary stem pycnometers of essentially the same size, shape, and weight.   In a determination, one pycnometer was filled with sample, and the other with a water standard. After the weighing step was completed, the sample and standard were reversed, and the measurement was repeated.   With 50 ml. pycnometers having capillary stem diameters of 1 mm., differences in density of 1 γ/ml. could be measured by using a thermostat controlled to $\pm0.01°C$., making the capillary height reading to 0.1 mm., and weighing to 0.03 mg.   The differential pynometer procedure compensates for several variables which affect the single-unit method.   Thus (1) dry weights of the pycnometers are unnecessary, (2) effects of varying humidity are balanced, (3) effects of barometric and hydrostatic pressures are balanced, (4) the temperature of the thermostat need not be known accurately, and (5) the correction for air buoyancy applies only to small differences in the capillary volumes (176).

The differential procedure was applied to measurements over the range 1 to 99 atom % deuterium, with an average deviation of ±0.02 atom % (296).   For maximum accuracy the sample was compared with a standard having about the same deuterium content.   Otherwise, a nearly pure deuterium oxide standard was used for the 75 to 100% D range, distilled normal water for 0 to 25%, and an intermediate standard for the 25 to 75% range.

2. Float Methods

The familiar flotation procedure employing a float of known density has been shown to be applicable for analyses over a broad range of deuterium contents.   Control of one of several variables can be used to obtain "floating equilibrium," that is, the position in which the submerged float neither rises nor falls in the liquid and, hence, where the densities of float and liquid are the same.   The condition can be achieved by (1) addition of known weights to a float less dense than the liquid, (2) measured addition of a liquid of known density, (3) adjustment of the temperature of the solution until the density of the liquid matches that of the float, (4) adjustment of the pressure above the liquid, or (5) electromagnetic means.   The last three methods have been employed most widely by workers using the flotation technique (176).

In the temperature adjustment procedure, a fused quartz float has been recommended (176). Quartz combines the desirable properties of low thermal expansion, elasticity, strength, and stability. In making an analysis, the sample of water is distilled directly into a scrupulously clean test tube. The clean float, previously calibrated by standards, is inserted, and the tube placed in a double-tank bath. The outer tank, which contains the heater and thermoregulator, is stirred vigorously, while the inner tank remains stationary. By this means a temperature difference of about $0.0003°C$. can be measured with a Mueller bridge and platinum resistance thermometer. At $25°C$., the temperature difference is equivalent to a difference of $0.078 \gamma/ml$. in density (176).

Adjustment of the temperature to the point at which the float is motionless is a slow and painstaking process. This condition can be improved by plotting the temperature within about $0.1°C$. vs. the velocity of the float on either side of the point of no motion and interpolating (80). This method is not absolute; it measures the difference between flotation temperatures of unknown and known. An absolute density may be determined by conversion of the temperature difference to density difference and measurement of the absolute density or deuterium content of the known (176).

An accuracy of $±0.0002$ atom % D was reported after purification of the sample by distillation under nitrogen (285). Somewhat less stringent requirements were employed by Spaepen (303) for determining small concentrations of D_2O in H_2O. The sample tube was kept in a thermostat and the temperature measured to $±0.001°C$. with a Beckmann thermometer. The rate of motion of the float was found to be a linear function of temperature as long as it did not exceed 0.04 mm./second. An accuracy of 0.002% was reported for samples containing about 0.04% D_2O.

The equilibrium temperature technique was used by Viallard and Marchetti (332) in an exchange method for determining water in solids such as synthetic rubber, polymethyl methacrylate, and cellulose.

The pressure float procedure is based on measurement of the pressure at which a float remains exactly balanced. In this, like the temperature adjustment procedure, a comparison is made between unknown and standard (176).

Equipment for the magnetic float method has included a permanent magnet sealed in the bottom of the float and an electromagnet placed beneath the bath. The difference in density between sample and known is calculated from the exact voltage required to prevent the float from rising (176). The magnetic float method has been used for determining the deuterium content of beer and malt and the water of crystallization of alum. Only 1 ml. of liquid was needed for determinations of small concentrations of D_2O to within 0.004% (335).

3. Falling Drop Methods

The density of a liquid can be determined by measuring the time required for a single drop of known size to fall a fixed distance through an inert, immiscible liquid of known density. For use with water, o-fluorotoluene has been recommended (172) as well as diphenylmethane for the range 5 to 27 atom % D and a mixture of diphenylmethane and 1-chloronaphthalene for 20 to 100% D (284).

To a first approximation, the density can be calculated from Stokes' law. There is some variation, however, and the true density has been measured most readily by comparison with standards. Then mole per cent D in a sample may be calculated from the relation

$$D = A + K[(1/t_1) - (1/t_2)] \tag{57}$$

where A is the D content of the standard, K is a function of the D content of the sample, and t_1 and t_2 are falling drop times of sample and standard, respectively.

A variety of special micropipets have been designed for delivering the sample (176).

The falling drop method has given reliable analyses of small samples (less than 0.1 ml.). It has been of particular value to biochemists studying biological fluids (199,275). Ljunggren (199) compared the deuterium oxide and phenazone methods for estimating total body water. An accuracy of

TABLE XXX

Comparison of Methods for Determining Deuterium in Water (176)

(Results are expressed in mole % deuterium.)

Float	Falling drop	Equili- bration	Mass spectrometry	Calcd. from dilution
0.071		0.069		
1.46		1.48		
0.0105 ± 0.0003			0.0105	
0.0096			0.0080 ± 0.00005	
0.3459	0.339			0.3459
5.4002[a]	5.395			5.3981
	0.756		0.74	
	3.994		4.08	

[a] Diluted to 0.5 mole % for analysis.

0.0017% D was claimed for the former as determined by the graduated tube method using a white spirit–bromobenzene mixture. He concluded that the D_2O method probably gives high values because of exchange of deuterium with labile hydrogens whereas the phenazone method gives low values owing to protein bonding of the reagent.

A comparison of various methods for determining low concentrations of heavy water in normal water is given in Table XXX (176).

E. REFRACTIVE INDEX

The refractive indexes of D_2O and H_2O differ significantly in the third decimal place; for example, at 20°C. and 5791 A., $n_{H_2O} - n_{D_2O} = 0.00474$ (176). With pure samples this difference is sufficient for the analysis of mixtures. Correction must be made for ^{18}O content; the molar refraction of $H_2{}^{18}O$ is higher than that of both $H_2{}^{16}O$ and $D_2{}^{16}O$ (176).

Direct measurement on a conventional refractometer has not been suitable for high-precision work. Temperature control to 0.01°C. is necessary for an accuracy of one unit in the sixth decimal place (176).

Interferometric procedures have been preferred for high-accuracy measurements. In this case, of course, comparison is made between the refraction of the sample and that of a standard of nearly the same composition (176).

More recently the phase contrast refractometer was used for determining D_2O in all concentrations with an accuracy of about 0.002 mole % D_2O (150). The Riken interferometer was applied for analyses over the range 0 to 6% D_2O with a sensitivity of 0.05 mole % (228).

F. OTHER TECHNIQUES

1. Freezing Point Method

Cziki and Fodor (60) and Reaser and Burch (258) found that the freezing point of deuterium oxide–hydrogen oxide mixtures varied linearly over the range 0°C. for H_2O to 3.80°C. for D_2O. Supercooling presented no problem in the range 0.8 to 2.9°C. The former authors used a calibration curve obtained with standards on which the D_2O contents were determined by density. An absolute accuracy of 0.13% D_2O was observed when temperatures were measured to 0.005°C. In the range 0 to 2% D_2O in H_2O an accuracy of 0.05% was observed with the Fiske osmometer (Fiske Associates, Boston, Mass.) (258). A standard error (deviation from theoretical) was reported of 0.014% and 0.019% for the ranges 0 to 2% and 0 to 5% D_2O, respectively (258).

2. Effusion Method

The rate of effusion of hydrogen-deuterium mixtures was used in analyses for deuterium in water (191).   The vaporized sample of deuterated water was passed over uranium metal turnings at 500°C.   Conversion to an equilibrium mixture of H_2, HD, and D_2 was quantitative, and impurities were removed by the uranium.   A small portion of the gas (a few hundredths of a cubic centimeter of gas at S.T.P. was sufficient) was forced through a fixed orifice.   Effusion of the gas or pressure change was measured by a microammeter in a Wheatstone bridge circuit containing a matched pair of thermistors placed on either side of the orifice.   The effusion time was recorded on an electric timer between two preselected pressures.   At pressures of 200 μ or less, straight line plots were obtained from the log of the meter reading vs. time, the slopes of which varied inversely as the square root of the density.   Calibrations were made from standards prepared by mixing weighed amounts of normal and heavy water and following the reduction-effusion procedure.   A linear plot was obtained of effusion time vs. per cent hydrogen.   Essentially the same curve resulted from known mixtures of hydrogen and deuterium (191).

3. Other Methods

Thermal conductivity measurements, based on differences in the specific heats of the gases H_2, HD, and D_2, have been used.   One mole % or more of deuterium was determined in 2 to 3 mm.[3] of gas with an accuracy of 0.1 mole % (84).   Analysis of water was made by determining the difference in thermal conductivity between vapors of H_2O and vapors of D_2O in equilibrium with the corresponding ices (51).   Because its thermal conductivity is greater than that of H_2, HD has been recommended for analysis after reaction of deuterated water with CaH_2 (4a).

Other methods have included measurements of viscosity and differences in potential between hydrogen and deuterium electrodes (3).

Vapor pressure differences were found to be sufficient for some analyses (194,257).

VI. DETERMINATION OF TRITIUM OXIDE

In normal water tritium is essentially all in the form of THO.   For use in tracer studies only very low concentrations, which are measured by sensitive counting techniques, are necessary.   For many biological studies tritium is replacing deuterium as a tracer.   Actually deuterium can be used in only a relatively narrow range between the highest concentration which can be administered safely and the lowest concentration which can be measured reliably (317).

The low energy level precludes the use of conventional end window Geiger counters. Counting of thick samples in windowless counters is inefficient. Most methods have been based on transfer of the tritium as a gas into an ionization chamber where the disintegration rate is measured by radiation-induced ionization of the gas. The process is recorded as discrete pulses by a counting tube. By proper choice of field strength and circuitry, counting can be made in the Geiger or proportional region or as total ionization collected within a fixed period of time. Recent advances in scintillation counting offers another important approach for direct analysis of solutions.

Most of the procedures based on gas analysis employ chemical reactions similar to those used for conversion of deuterium oxide to gaseous products.

A. INDIRECT METHODS

1. Decomposition

Tritiated water may be reduced to hydrogen over a variety of metals.

$$THO + H_2O + 2M \rightarrow TH + H_2 + 2MO \qquad (58)$$

where M may be magnesium (331), magnesium amalgam (141,308), zinc (35,350), or calcium (83,139). Typical experimental technique can be illustrated by reaction with magnesium amalgam, as recommended by Swain, Kreiter, and Sheppard (308) and described in Section VII.

Apparatus normally applied to ^{14}C determinations (350) is used satisfactorily for the ion current measurement. In this case the chamber consists of a gas-tight conducting shell having an insulated electrode. Ions of a given sign produced by radiation in the gas are collected on the electrode by applying sufficiently low potential so that multiplication of ions does not occur. The rate of ion collection is measured by a vibrating-reed electrometer (238) or a Lauritzen electroscope (141). By means of the vibrating-reed electrometer, the activity can be determined by measuring the rate of charge of a condenser or the voltage drop across a high-precision resistor.

Wilzbach, Van Dyken, and Kaplan (350) established the precision of the tritium assay in the ion current range of 10^{-15} to 10^{-9} amp. Standards of tritiated water were reduced over zinc at about 375°C. The gas was transferred to the ionization chamber and adjusted to atmospheric pressure with methane. Ion currents were measured with a vibrating-reed electrometer. Results are given in Table XXXI. With a measuring time of 1 hour and 25 disintegrations/second, a standard error of 1.3% was observed.

TABLE XXXI

Proportionality of Ion Current to Disintegration Rate (350)

Relative concn. of T	Measured ion current, (amp. $\times 10^{-16}$)/ mg. of H_2O	Time per measurement, minutes	Error,[a] %	Relative current per disintegration
1×10^6	1.734×10^6	5	0.35	1
0.980×10^4	1.720×10^4	5	0.35	1.012
0.949×10^2	1.663×10^2	15	1.03	1.010
9.50	16.63	25	0.22	1.010
1.049	1.824	50	2.61	1.003

[a] Standard error of single determination.

The method was suitable for assay over at least a 10^{-8}-fold range of tritium activities.

Swain and co-workers (308) reported a similar precision based on analyses of standards prepared by dilution of tritiated water having an activity of 77 μc./ml.   As little as 10^{-4} μc./mmole was detected.

For biological studies Fallot and co-workers (83) used azeotropic distillation with toluene to isolate tritiated water from other matter.   About 2.5 ml. of sample ($\approx$ ca. 1550 cc. of hydrogen) was reduced by calcium metal, and the gases were transferred to an ionization chamber.   The memory effect was studied by carrying out three conversions in the same flask, with samples having activities of 0.5 μc./ml., 0.1 μc./ml., and 0.1 μc./ml., respectively.   Recoveries were 0.49, 0.09, and 0.09 μc./ml., respectively.   The limit of detection was at a level of 0.01 μc./ml. of water (83,139).

With a quartz ionization chamber attached to a Lauritzen electroscope, as little as 10^{-4} μc. of tritium was determined quantitatively in 10 mmoles of hydrogen (141).

Measurements in the Geiger region also have been used successfully. Brown and Grummitt (35) used the Geiger-Müller counter in determining the tritium content of natural waters.   The THO in 100 to 2000 ml. samples of rain and sea water was concentrated 2000 to 20,000 times by electrolysis and then reduced over zinc at 375°C.   The resulting hydrogen was passed through a liquid nitrogen trap to remove condensable impurities into the Geiger counter with 6 cc. of argon and 5 cc. of ethylene.   The natural deuterium in water was used as a tracer during the electrolysis.   The concentration was calculated from the relation

$$t/t_0 = (d/d_0)^{\alpha/\beta}$$

where d_0, d, t_0, and t were initial and final moles of D and T, respectively, and α and β were the separation factors of D and T, respectively, from H. In natural waters α/β was about 0.5. The T/H ratio in sea waters varied from 0.19 to 4×10^{-18}, and in rain water, from 7 to 42×10^{-18}.

Viallard and co-workers (331) found that the Geiger counter method would detect 10^{-14} g.-atom amounts of tritium per mole.

2. Conversion to Organic Compounds

Typical products formed by reaction of tritium oxide with organometallic compounds are tritiobutane (115), tritioacetylene (90,317), and tritiomethane (262,345).

Glascock (115) studied extensively the Grignard reaction, using n-butylmagnesium bromide as reagent (see equation (53) for similar reaction with CH_3MgI). Purification of the butane was accomplished by condensation in a liquid air bath. Vaporization at dry ice temperature was used to free the butane (vapor pressure ca. 13 mm. at $-78°C.$) from less volatile components. The precision of the method was established by analyses of known samples prepared by dilution of radioactive water containing about $2 \mu c./ml.$ The specific activity of the butane was proportional to dilution, indicating that at these levels no isotopic separation occurred. Results are given in Table XXXII. The Grignard reagent could be used only once, possibly owing to contamination from exchange of hydrogen in a new sample with residual tritium in the magnesium compound, $Mg(OT)Br$.

TABLE XXXII
Precision of Butane-Geiger Method (115)

Water sample (% stock)	Butane assayed, cc.	Activity, counts/minute	Specific activity, counts/minute/ml.		Error, %
			Obs.	Calcd.	
10	8.85	1353	153	153	0
20	3.70	1152	312	306	+2.0
40	2.59	1554	600	612	−2.0
60	1.005⎱ 0.860⎰	908⎱ 802⎰	915	918	−0.33
80	0.805	972	1210	1224	−1.7
100	0.645	987	1530		

Methylmagnesium iodide also has been used as reagent. Robinson (262) employed a proportional counting chamber for measuring activity of the tritiomethane, which he felt had the advantages of convenience, absence of memory effects, linearity of response, and good precision. He made a simultaneous comparison of the use of deuterium and tritium as tracers in determining body water in dogs. By the tritium tracer technique, he obtained values of 9.39 ± 0.10 kg. of total body water compared to 9.56 ± 0.10 kg. by the deuterium tracer method with mass spectrometer analysis.

The rapid reaction of water with impure aluminum carbide also has been used for preparing methane.

$$Al_4C_3 + 3HTO + 9H_2O \longrightarrow 3CH_3T + 4Al(OH)_3 \qquad (59)$$

In this case, the result was impure methane, containing small amounts of oxygen, hydrogen, ammonia, hydrogen sulfide, and unsaturated hydrocarbons (345). Partial purification was achieved by condensation of some impurities at $-78°C$. The impure methane, although unsatisfactory for measurements in the Geiger region, was suitable for the proportional region. With a 2 inch lead screen and methane at 40 cm. Hg pressure, the background of the counter was 1.7 counts/second. Consequently, samples having activities as low as 1 count/second could be estimated; the assay of water having a specific activity of 1.5×10^{-6} μc. per milligram of hydrogen was possible. At a pressure of 20 cm. Hg, a reproducibility in measurement of 2 to 3% was reported (345).

Conversion to acetylene by reaction with calcium carbide was reported.

$$CaC_2 + HTO + H_2O \longrightarrow HC{\equiv}CT + Ca(OH)_2 \qquad (60)$$

The tritioacetylene was assayed with a vibrating-reed electrometer (90, 317). Under some conditions, the ratio of the H found was about 3% low owing to isotopic depletion during the reaction of water with the carbide (90).

B. DIRECT METHODS

1. Exchange

Direct measurement of beta particles has been used in some cases, for example, for a 1.5 cm. layer of water in front of a Geiger tube of the end window type (119). For determining tritium in air, the sample has been drawn through an ionization gage coupled through an electrometer to an amplifier where results can be continuously recorded (287).

More reliable results have been reported through use of an organic compound acting as an exchange medium. Most commonly employed compounds include methanol (40), ethanol (21,161), or acetone (28) in dilution with argon, usually as a 1:9 mixture. Bradley and Bush (28) found that under normal conditions alcohols were restricted to use at a vapor pressure

of water only slightly above that corresponding to saturation at 20°C.
and preferably based on saturation at 0°C. These workers recommended
acetone in slightly alkaline solution, which has a significantly higher vapor
pressure at 0°C. Using the Geiger region with a plateau at 2500 v. and a
125 ml. counter, they reported the following comparative data.

Sample	Counts/minute
Background (unscreened)	140
Ethanol	190
Methanol	228
Acetone with 0.1N NaOH for 12 hours	750

The exchange reaction with acetone was slow in neutral solution. In
alkaline solution the exchange presumably occurred via keto-enol tauto-
merism, involving a mesomeric anion.

$$CH_3—C—CH_3$$
$$\overset{\|}{O}$$

alk. acid

$$CH_3—C—CH_2{}^-$$
$$\overset{\|}{O}$$
$$+ H^+$$

$$CH_3—C{=}CH_2$$
$$\overset{|}{OH}$$

alk. acid

$$CH_3—C{=}CH_2$$
$$\overset{|}{O}{}^-$$
$$+ H^+$$

Taylor and co-workers (21,161) used tritium in a novel method for determining the solubility of water in hydrocarbons. Tritium concentrated to a
level of about 10^{-12} mole per mole of deuterium oxide was used; it was
present primarily as TDO. After equilibration with the hydrocarbon, the
radioactive water was absorbed by calcium oxide. Hydrocarbon was removed by vacuum distillation, and the tritium extracted for counting
through an exchange reaction with ethanol vapor. Activity was measured
by a Geiger-Müller counter after adjustment of the pressure with argon.
Through application of known relative solubility data, the results were
calculated in terms of normal water. Results were reported for solubilities
of water in benzene (0.030 g. per 100 g. at 10°C. and 0.054 g. per 100 g. at
26°C.), cyclohexane (0.010 g. per 100 g. at 20°C.), and 13 other C_4 to C_8
saturated and unsaturated aliphatic hydrocarbons. This procedure required only small amounts of sample.

Water in hydrocarbons (38a) and halogenated oil (40a) was determined
by exchanged with tritium. After equilibrium was attained, activity was
measured with a scintillation counter.

Solid phase counting has given rapid assays with about 15% accuracy. Jenkins (152) used ammonium chloride as the hydrogen-containing solid on which the exchange reaction was effected, giving NH_3TCl. Activity of the solid was determined with a Geiger-Müller counter.

2. Liquid Scintillation Counting

Liquid scintillation counting is becoming increasingly useful for analyses of tritiated water. Kallmann and Furst (162) demonstrated the scintillation effect due to excitation by high-energy radiation. They found that with pure liquids the excitation energy from alpha and gamma radiation was mainly quenched. However, if small amounts of suitable foreign organic molecules were present in solution, the excited energy would be transported to the dissolved molecules, where the fluorescent emission could be measured. As little as 1 g./liter of the solute was found to increase the light emission of a solvent by a factor of a least 35. A large number of potential scintillators were evaluated.

Rosenthal and Anger (265) found that as little as $4.3 \times 10^{-4} \mu c$. of tritium could be measured. Their apparatus was the same as that used for ^{14}C assays. The basic components were a photomultiplier tube, preamplifier, and scale. A light shield was attached to the phototube to permit introduction of the glass vial containing the samples and scintillator solution. Phototube and preamplifier were placed in a deep-freeze unit for operation at reduced temperature. In making an analysis, 1 ml. of a 5% solution of the sample in absolute ethanol was mixed with 3 ml. of xylene containing 5 g./liter of terphenyl plus 0.015 g./liter of diphenylhexatriene.

Rosenthal and Anger (265) listed the following advantages of the liquid scintillation technique over the ionization chamber method; (1) combustion of samples is unnecessary; (2) the sample is handled in the liquid phase, so that gas-sampling problems are eliminated; (3) memory effects are eliminated; (4) more samples can be handled; and (5) the background counting rate is much more stable.

Precautions and limitations include these: (1) color of the scintillation solution cannot be altered by the sample; (2) no scintillator "poisons" can be tolerated; and (3) the sample should be precooled and kept in the dark before counting.

For samples of low activity, degassing by ultrasonic means was found to enhance greatly the light output (355). The scintillator was 4.0 g. of 2.5-diphenyloxazole (PPO) plus 0.1 g. of 1,4-di-[2-(5-phenyloxazolyl)]-benzene (POPOP) per liter of toluene. The POPOP served as a wavelength shifter. A minimum amount of ethanol was used to solubilize the sample of tritiated water in the scintillator solution.

Langham and co-workers (187) gave detailed procedures for determining tritium used as tracer in the studies of water metabolism, fluid balance, and water transfer in biological fluids. The scintillation solution contained PPO, naphthalene, and POPOP in 1,4-dioxane solution. Use of dioxane in place of toluene provided a water-soluble system, eliminating the need for ethanol as solubilizing agent. Their procedure for analysis of human blood serum is given in Section VII.

For human blood serum, trichloroacetic acid was added to decolorize yellow pigments while simultaneously precipitating serum proteins. Trichloroacetic acid was found to have a quenching effect; consequently, it was necessary that sample, standard, and blank contain equal amounts of the acid. Turbidity had to be avoided; it could develop from transfer of some of the precipitated protein to the counting bottle or from freezing of the samples.

Use of trichloroacetic acid was unnecessary for rat serum. Decolorization of urine by charcoal was satisfactory. Mean recovery values were 97% or more with an error of less than 3%.

The technique was tested on a human subject. A fasted, normal man was given 800 ml. of water containing 3 mc. of HTO. Analysis of blood and urine samples showed that both reached their peaks in tritium activity within 20 minutes after ingestion of the HTO. Apparently HTO was in equilibrium with all body fluids within 90 minutes. From these data, the total body water in this particular case was estimated at 58% of body weight.

3. Spectroscopy

Spectroscopic analyses also are feasible. For protium-tritium mixtures, the H_α and T_α lines are well resolved. For protium-deuterium-tritium mixtures in a spectrograph having a dispersion in the 6500 A. region of 9.5 A./mm., however, the D_α and T_α lines overlapped. Use of an instrument

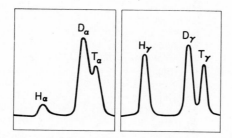

Fig. 16. Microphotometer traces of H_α and H_γ lines (234).

with a resolution of 2.8 A./mm. gave essentially complete isotopic line resolution for H_α, D_α, and T_α (234). This situation is illustrated in Fig. 16, which shows copies of the microphotometer traces of the photographic plates (see also Section V-C).

VII. RECOMMENDED LABORATORY PROCEDURES

The procedures detailed in this section are among the most widely used methods for determining water. In all cases further information on procedural steps can be obtained in the references cited. Although, up to the present time, a few techniques have been used only for analyses of specific substances, the principles involved suggest much broader applicability.

Variations in procedure may be necessary for determining water in specific materials. Occasionally certain of the more limited methods already discussed will be better suited for a particular system. Reference to the general discussion in this chapter is desirable in these cases.

Procedural steps for other important methods cannot be described conveniently in brief form. Many of these involve operation of a commercial instrument for which complete operating instructions are usually supplied by the manufacturer. Included in this category are techniques involving infrared and nuclear magnetic resonance spectroscopy and electrical measurements. No general procedure can be given for such widely used methods as oven drying and desiccation. Conditions must be established empirically for each type of material to be analyzed.

Specific comments on each of the procedures discussed in this section follow.

	Method	Type	Procedure written for use on
A.	KFR	Titrimetric	Solutions, adsorbed water on solids
B.	CH_3COCl	Titrimetric	Solutions
C.	$(CH_3CO)_2O$	Thermometric	Acetic acid
D.	$(CH_3CO)_2O$	Spectrophotometric	Acetic acid
E.	CaC_2	Manometric	Solids, viscous liquids
F.	CaH_2	Thermometric	Gases
G.	Modified Penfield	Gravimetric	Silicate rocks
H.	Distillation	Azeotropic, carrier $d < 1$	Nonvolatile substances
I.	$CoCl_2$	Colorimetric	Solids insoluble in ethanol
J.	Reduction	Mass spectrometric	Deuterated water
K.	Reduction	Counting	Tritiated water
L.	Grignard reaction	Counting	Tritiated water
M.	Direct	Liquid scintillation counting	Human blood serum

A. KARL FISCHER REAGENT METHOD (219)

About 50 to 100 ml. of dry methanol or other suitable inert solvent or dispersing agent is added to the titration flask. (A 250 ml. volumetric flask is suitable for the visual titration; a special flask is desirable for electrometric titration.) The solvent is titrated to the end point with Karl Fischer reagent ($\approx$ 3 to 3.5 mg. of H_2O per milliliter of KFR). The sample, containing up to 150 mg. of water, is added, and the resulting solution again titrated to the same end point. The second titer is equivalent to water contained in the sample.

The KFR is conveniently standardized by titration of 1 to 1.5 g. (accurately weighed) of finely ground sodium tartrate dihydrate dispersed in 50 ml. of "pretitrated" methanol.

B. ACETYL CHLORIDE METHOD (301)

Precisely 10 ml. of $1.5M$ acetyl chloride in purified dioxane is transferred to a 250 ml. glass-stoppered volumetric flask. The flask is stoppered and placed in a container filled with a slurry of finely divided ice; then 2 ml. of dry pyridine ($<0.1\%$ H_2O) is added slowly. The flask is stoppered and shaken with a swirling motion until a smooth paste of acetylpyridinium chloride is formed (the reagent is no longer volatile). The sample, containing up to 10 mmoles of water, is added, and the mixture shaken. After at least 2 minutes at room temperature, 1 ml. of dry methanol ($<0.05\%$ H_2O) is added, and the mixture is shaken vigorously to decompose the major portion of unused reagent. After an additional 5 minutes, 25 ml. of the dry methanol is added, and the homogeneous solution is titrated with $0.3N$ aqueous sodium hydroxide. The net difference in acidity between the sample and a blank, after correction for free acidity in the sample, is equivalent mole for mole to water originally present.

C. ACETIC ANHYDRIDE THERMOMETRIC METHOD (122)

A 300 ml. sample, containing up to about 1.5 g. of water, and 100 ml. of acetic anhydride (both at about 1°C. above ambient temperature) are placed in a Dewar flask. The liquids are carefully mixed, and the lowest temperature reached is recorded to the nearest 0.01°C. by means of a thermometer. Then while the solution is being stirred, 8 ml. of catalyst solution is added (1:20 dilution of 60% perchloric acid in acetic acid plus a calculated amount of acetic anhydride for stoichiometric reaction with all water in both acids). The maximum temperature is recorded. The net increase in temperature is proportional to water in the sample. Water content is read from a graph prepared by analyses of standards.

D. ACETIC ANHYDRIDE ULTRAVIOLET SPECTROPHOTOMETRIC METHOD (37)

Six ml. of sample, containing up to 0.05 mmole (0.9 mg.) of water is placed in a 2 cm. quartz cell with ground-glass stoppers, and the absorbance is measured at 252 mμ. By means of an ultramicroburet, 14 μl. (0.148 mmole) of acetic anhydride is added, and the absorbance is measured vs. acetic acid immediately and again after heating for 90 minutes at 110°C. The difference in absorbance corresponds to the acetic anhydride used up during hydrolysis of water in the sample. Then 10 μl. (0.0555 mmole) of water is added, and the heating step repeated. The change in absorbance before and after heating corresponds to the amount of anhydride which reacted with the added water. Water in the original sample is calculated by ratios.

For routine purposes the net change in absorption after reaction of anhydride with water in the sample can be used for analysis. In this case absorbances are calculated from analyses of knowns. However, because of the large slit widths required, periodic checks of the method should be made by addition of a known amount of water as indicated above.

E. CALCIUM CARBIDE MANOMETRIC METHOD (178,281)

The sample, containing up to 2 g. of water, is placed in a small steel pressure flask. A thin-walled glass ampule containing about 5 g. of finely divided calcium carbide and two steel balls are added. The flask is closed with an airtight cap fitted with a pressure gage. The flask is shaken vigorously with a sideways motion to break the ampule and distribute the carbide throughout the sample. After 5 to 10 minutes, depending on the type of sample, the pressure is measured.

The apparatus is calibrated by analysis of standards prepared from the same type of material as the unknown.

F. CALCIUM HYDRIDE THERMOMETRIC METHOD (135)

The apparatus consists of a 25 cm. length of 16 mm. glass tubing drawn to a constriction of about 9 mm. at the mid-point. Side tubes near each end of the tube serve as inlet and outlet for the gas sample. Most of the tube is enclosed in a silvered vacuum jacket with the exposed ends protected from drafts by a two-layer wrapping of sheet asbestos. With the tube in an upright position, about 1 g. of finely divided calcium hydride (ca. 1 mm. particles) contained in 50 mesh platinum gauze in the form of a cup is placed in the tube to rest on the shoulders of the constriction. Western Electric 17A thermistors, having a resistance of about 1000 ohms, are placed in each end of the tube and supported at a distance of about 3 cm.

from either side of the calcium hydride. The thermistors are connected to a circuit consisting of a decade resistance box, a 1000 ohm fixed resistance, and a galvanometer having a resistance of 10.27 ohms and a sensitivity of 0.002 μa./mm. scale deflection.

The sample of gas is passed upward through the tube at a rate of 1.3 liters/minute. The change in temperature of the gas resulting from the reaction of moisture with the hydride causes a differential between the two thermistors which is proportional to moisture content. The adjustment of the variable resistance necessary to bring the bridge circuit into balance therefore is a function of moisture concentration.

The apparatus is calibrated by analysis of gases containing known amounts of water. There is evidence that different batches of calcium hydride may vary in reactivity, and so check standardization by one or two standards is required with each new lot a reagent (195).

G. MODIFIED PENFIELD METHOD (282)

One g. of powdered sample is weighed into an 18 × 150 mm. borosilicate-glass test tube, care being taken that all of the sample collects at the bottom of the tube. (Use of a funnel is desirable for delivering the sample.) Into an 18 × 65 mm. test tube (weighing tube) is placed, with the aid of forceps, a 5 cm. square piece of filter paper rolled into a cylinder. The tube is stoppered and weighed accurately. Then the paper cylinder is transferred rapidly to the upper part of the tube containing the sample (ignition tube), after which the tube is closed with a one-hole rubber stopper. A 5 × 7.5 cm. piece of wet filter paper is placed around the outside of the upper part of the tube. The tube is placed in a horizontal position, and the closed end is heated with a Meker burner, gently at first and then at full heat for 5 minutes. At the end of this time, the flame is carefully moved up the tube to the filter paper to drive forward any water which may have condensed on the sides of the tube. After the tube has cooled, the stopper is removed, and the paper cylinder is rotated around the inside of the tube. Then the paper is quickly transferred to the weighing tube and reweighed. The increase in weight is equivalent to water absorbed by the paper. An empirical correction is applied for the small amount of water lost: for 20 mg. or less of water absorbed, the weight is increased by 10%; for >20 mg., the weight is increased by 2 mg.

The result obtained represents total water in the sample. Combined water may be calculated by subtracting the value for hygroscopic water obtained by drying 1 g. of powdered sample to constant weight at 105 to 110°C. (180a).

For rocks containing appreciable quantities of sulfur, 3 g. of anhydrous sodium tungstate is intimately mixed with the sample (282).   For minerals which lose combined water only at high temperatures ($>1000°C$.), use of a flux such as lead chromate and lead oxide is recommended (180a). The lead chromate also has been used with samples containing ferrous iron to prevent the reduction of water by ferrous oxide (180a).

In the original Penfield method (180a,243a) a 150 to 200 $\times$ 5 to 6 mm. test tube is used, preferably with a bulb blown at the closed end and also near the mid-point of the tube.   Wet cloth or paper is placed around the middle bulb, extending a few cm. toward the open end of the tube.   After all condensed water has been driven into the middle bulb, the hot flame is placed midway between the bulbs, and the upper portion of the tube is drawn off and rounded.   After cooling, the moist cloth is removed, the outside of the tube is wiped dry, and the tube is weighed.   Then the tube is dried and reweighed.   The decrease in weight is a measure of total water in the sample.

H. AZEOTROPIC DISTILLATION METHOD (8)

New apparatus (see Fig. 8) is conditioned and coated with silicone as follows.   The inner glass surface is cleaned with dichromate–sulfuric acid solution, rinsed with distilled water, and treated for an hour with alcoholic potassium hydroxide.   This treatment is followed by successive washes with alcohol, concentrated nitric acid, and distilled water.   Then steam is passed through the apparatus for 3 hours, followed by filtered air for drying. The apparatus is filled with a solution of 2 to 3% silicone fluid in carbon tetrachloride.   After 30 minutes, the fluid is drained, and the unit is dried at 110°C. to remove the solvent and then baked at 250 to 275°C. for 2 hours.   To ensure a uniform coating, the silicone treatment is repeated.   If the apparatus is rinsed after each distillation with toluene containing a little silicone grease, the surface remains intact for months.

In preparing for a distillation the flask is first replaced by a cap, and the apparatus is filled with dry toluene introduced at the top of the condenser. With the aid of a rubber suction bulb attached to the tip of the stopcock, the toluene is drawn through the siphon tube until it is filled.   The stopcock is closed.

The distillation flask containing sample and dry toluene is connected to the apparatus.   Heat is applied and adjusted so that the rate of condensation is about 1 drop/second.   Water collects in the bottom of the trap while excess toluene returns to the flask.   When water no longer is condensed, the stopcock is partially opened until the water reaches the bulb at the base of the graduated upright leg of the measuring tube.   Then the stopcock is opened fully until the water is carried over into the descending leg of the measuring tube.   The stopcock is closed, and the volume of water measured.

For successive routine analyses the condenser need only be sprayed with dry toluene.   When not in use, the apparatus should be kept filled with dry toluene containing a little silicone grease.

I. COBALTOUS CHLORIDE COLORIMETRIC METHOD (86)

The sample, weighing 1 to 5 g., is placed in a flask containing 50 ml. of absolute ethanol.   The mixture is shaken vigorously for 5 to 10 minutes, after which the suspended material is allowed to settle.   An aliquot of the clear supernatant liquid is transferred to a 50 ml. volumetric flask, and cobaltous chloride in absolute ethanol reagent is added to provide 300 p.p.m. (ca. 15 mg.) Co^{+2} in 50 ml. of final solution.   The flask is filled to the mark with absolute ethanol, the temperature adjusted to $25 \pm 0.1°C$., and the absorbance measured against absolute ethanol at 671 mμ.   The amount of water is determined by reference to a standard curve obtained from analysis of known solutions of water in ethanol.

J. REDUCTION METHOD FOR DEUTERATED WATER (47)

The sample tube is prepared from about a 15 cm. length of 10 mm. I.D. borosilicate-glass tubing.   One end is drawn down to a thin-walled capillary protected with a guard tube; at about 5 cm. from the other end, the tube is drawn down to a constriction of about 3 mm. I.D.   A plug of glass wool is placed in the tube at the capillary end, followed by about 2 g. of zinc dust. Then the tube is heated overnight in a drying oven at 120°C. and allowed to cool in a desiccator over $CaCl_2$.

The tube is connected with vacuum tubing through a three-way stopcock to a vacuum pump with alternate connection to a calcium chloride tube.   With the stopcock turned to connect the sample tube to the desiccant, the tube is gently warmed to drive off residual moisture.   The sample tube is allowed to cool to about 50°C., and is then disconnected.   About 0.01 ml. of sample is introduced quickly, with a pipet which has been dried previously in the same way as the sample tube, and the sample tube is again connected to the vacuum assembly.   The sample is frozen by dry ice applied to the outside of the tube, the system is evacuated, and the tube is sealed at the constriction.   The tube is inserted in a protective brass tube and placed in an oven at $400 \pm 10°C$. for 30 minutes.   At the end of this time, the tube is allowed to cool, preferably in the oven, and the glass tube is then connected to the mass spectrometer, which is provided with a simple magnet arrangement for breaking the capillary tip of the tube, thus introducing directly the whole sample.

This method is well suited for multiple routine analyses.   About 1 hour is required to prepare 20 samples for heating at 400°C.   The brass tubes serve as shields to contain tubes in case of explosion.

K. REDUCTION METHOD FOR TRITIATED WATER (308)

From 13 to 18 mg. (0.7 to 1 mmole) of sample is placed in a thin-walled borosilicate-glass ampule having a break tip.   The ampule is sealed and placed in a bomb constructed from 10 mm. borosilicate-glass tubing with a break tip on one end.   About 0.3 g. each of granular magnesium and mercury are added, and the bomb is evacuated to a pressure of about 0.05 mm. Hg.   After sealing, the bomb is shaken to break the ampule, and the contents are mixed and then heated at 400 to 410°C. for 1 to 2 hours.   At the end of this time, the bomb is connected to a vacuum bench which contains an ionization chamber evacuated to a pressure of about 0.01 mm. Hg. The gas is transferred to the ionization chamber by means of a Toepler pump.   The pressure is adjusted to 1 atm. with hydrogen, methane, or propane (308,350), and the activity is measured.

L. GRIGNARD REACTION METHOD FOR TRITIATED WATER (115)

About 1.5 ml. of a $2N$ solution of n-butylmagnesium bromide in ethyl ether is placed in a tube connected to a vacuum bench, and the ether is pumped off.   About 10 mg. of the sample of radioactive water is added, and the mixture is heated for 1 hour at 120°C.   (A yield of 90 to 95% of tritiobutane is obtained.)   The vapors at liquid oxygen or nitrogen temperature are carried into a trap, where the butane condenses and more-volatile components are evolved.   A measured sample of the purified gas (from 10 μl. to 10 cc.) is removed after the temperature of the trap has been raised to −78°C.   The sample is transferred to a Geiger counter, the pressure adjusted if necessary to 14 cm. with inactive butane, and the activity measured.

M. LIQUID SCINTILLATION COUNTING METHOD FOR HUMAN BLOOD SERUM (187)

One ml. of fresh serum, containing HTO, is mixed thoroughly with 2 ml. of 10% aqueous trichloroacetic acid.   After precipitation of the serum protein, the sample is centrifuged.   One ml. of the clear supernatant liquid is pipetted into a Kimble Opticlear 10 dram vial containing 24 ml. of scintillation solution (7 g. of PPO, 50 g. of naphthalene, and 0.05 g. of POPOP in 1 liter of 1,4-dioxane).   The vial is closed with a polyethylene stopper and allowed to stand in the dark for 1 hour at 2 to 3°C. before counting.

A standard containing a known amount of tritium activity and a blank are prepared as solutions containing 1 part of water to 2 parts of 10% trichloroacetic acid solution. One ml. aliquots are mixed with 24 ml. of scintillation solution and treated as described.

REFERENCES

1. Adickes, F., *Ber.*, **63**, 2753 (1930).
2. *Am. Soc. Testing Materials ASTM Spec. Tech. Publ.* No. 48-H, 1959.
3. Anon., *Holztechnik*, **28**, 202 (1948); through *Brit Abstr.*, **1949**, C221.
4. Anon., *Rubber Age* (*N. Y.*), **69**, 54 (1951).
5. Axtmann, R. C., *J. Chem. Phys.*, **30**, 340 (1959).
6. Baker, B. B., Jr., and W. M. MacNevin, *Anal. Chem.*, **22**, 364 (1950).
7. Barker, R. F., *Isotopics*, **32**, 10 (Jan., 1956).
8. Barr, T., and J. I. Yarwood, *Chem. & Ind.* (*London*), **1957**, 803.
9. Barrer, R. M., *Intern. Congr. Pure and Appl. Chem., 16th Congr., Exp. Suppl.* No. 7, 113 (1957).
10. Bastin, E. L., H. Siegel, and A. B. Bullock, *Anal. Chem.*, **31**, 467 (1959).
11. Batson, D. M., and J. T. Hogan, *Anal. Chem.*, **31**, 718 (1949).
12. Bayer, E., *Angew. Chem.*, **69**, 732 (1957).
13. Belcher, R., and R. A. Mort, *J. Appl. Chem.* (*London*), **1**, 204 (1951).
14. Belcher, R., J. H. Thompson, and T. S. West, *Anal. Chim. Acta*, **19**, 148 (1958).
15. Belcher, R., and T. S. West, *J. Chem. Soc.*, **1953**, 1772.
16. Bender, A. E., M. Burnham, and D. S. Miller, *Chem. & Ind.* (*London*), **1953**, 293.
17. Bennett, A., and J. R. Hudson, *J. Inst. Brewing*, **60**, 29 (1954).
18. Benning, A. F., A. A. Ebert, and C. F. Irwin, *Anal. Chem.*, **19**, 867 (1947).
19. Berglund-Larsson, U., *Acta Chem. Scand.*, **10**, 701 (1956).
20. Billitzer, A. W., *Anal. Chem.*, **25**, 533 (1953).
21. Black, C., G. G. Joris, and H. S. Taylor, *J. Chem. Phys.*, **16**, 537 (1948).
22. Blish, M. J., and B. D. Hites, *Cereal Chem.*, **7**(2), 99 (1930).
23. Blomgren, E., and H. Jenner, Brit. Pat. 722,983 (1955); Can. Pat. 558,861 (1958); U. S. Pat. 2,780,601 (1957).
24. Boller, W., *Chemiker-Ztg.*, **50**, 537 (1926).
25. Booth, H. S., and L. McIntyre, *Ind. Eng. Chem., Anal. Ed.*, **8**, 148 (1936).
26. Bower, J. H., *J. Research Natl. Bur. Standards*, **12**, 241 (1934).
27. Braae, B., *IVA*, **18**, 230 (1947); through *Chem. Abstr.*, **42**, 5212 (1948).
28. Bradley, J. E. S., and D. J. Bush, *Intern. U. Appl. Radiation and Isotopes*, **1**, 233 (1956).
29. Brauckhoff, H., *Arch. tech. Messen*, Lfg. 152, T17 (1947).
30. Brickell, W. F., *Petrol. Engr.*, **24**, D-58 (1952).
31. Brissaud, M. L., *Chim. anal.*, **33**, 159 (1951).
32. Brobst, K. M., *Anal. Chem.*, **20**, 939 (1948).
33. Broida, H. P., and H. J. Morowitz, U. S. Pat. 2,708,387 (1955).
34. Brough, A. F., and P. R. Puleston, Brit. Pat. 468,005 (1937).
35. Brown, R. M., and W. E. Grummitt, *Can. J. Chem.*, **34**, 320 (1956).
36. Brown, T. L., and R. B. Bernstein, *Anal. Chem.*, **23**, 673 (1951).
37. Bruckenstein, S., *Anal. Chem.*, **28**, 1920 (1956).
38. Bryant, F. J., *Atomic Energy Research Establ.* (*Gt. Brit.*), Rept. C/R 1927 (1956).
38a. Caddock, B. D., and P. L. Davies, *Nature*, **184**, 2011 (1959).

38b. Cain, E. F. C., and M. R. Stevens, Paper presented at 2nd International Symposium on Gas Chromatography, sponsored by ISA, Michigan State Univ., East Lansing, Mich., June, 1959.

39. Caldas, A., *Chemist Analyst*, **43**, 100 (1954).

40. Cameron, J. F., *Nature*, **176**, 1264 (1955).

40a. Cameron, J. F., I. S. Boyce, and R. M. Glaister, *Brit. J. Appl. Phys.*, **10**, 463 (1959).

41. Caspari, W. A., *Proc. Roy. Soc. (London)*, **A155**, 41 (1936).

42. Catalino, E., and D. E. Milligan, *J. Chem. Phys.*, **30**, 45 (1959).

43. Chapman, D., and J. F. Nacey, *Analyst*, **83**, 377 (1958)

44. Cherrier, C., L. Verot, and R. Wagner, *Spectrochim. Acta*, **6**, 87 (1953).

45. Cherry, R. H., *Anal. Chem.*, **20**, 958 (1948).

46. Chihara, H., and S. Seki, *Bull. Chem. Soc. Japan*, **26**, 88 (1953).

47. Chinard, F. P., and T. Enns, *Anal. Chem.*, **25**, 1413 (1953).

48. Chopin, M., U. S. Pat. 2,281,182 (1942).

49. Chudnovskiǐ, A. F., *Zhur. Tekh. Fiz.*, **24**, 2190 (1954); through *Chem. Abstr.*, **50**, 3141 (1956).

50. Clarke, G. R., W. H. Denton, and P. Reynolds, *Nature*, **174**, 469 (1954).

51. Cleno, G. R., and G. A. Swan, *J. Chem. Soc.*, **1942**, 370.

52. Compton, J. W., and L. M. Liggett, *J. Am. Oil Chemists' Soc.*, **28**, 81 (1951).

52a. Conway, T. F., R. F. Cohee, and R. J. Smith, *Food Processing*, 32 (June, 1957).

53. Conway, T. F., and R. J. Smith, *Electronics, Eng. Ed.*, **31**, 51 (1958).

54. Cook, S. F., C. F. Cramer, and K. Kenyon, *Science*, **115**, 353 (1952).

55. Cordes, H. F., and C. W. Tait, *Anal. Chem.*, **29**, 485 (1957).

56. Cotton, R. H., W. A. Harris, L. P. Orleans, and G. Rorabaugh, *Anal. Chem.*, **24**, 1498 (1952).

57. Coulson, E. A., J. L. Hales, and E. F. G. Herington, *J. Chem. Soc.*, **1951**, 2125.

58. Croney, D., and J. C. Jacobs, *Rds. & Rd. Constr.*, **29**, 191 (1951); through *Brit. Abstr., BI*, **1951**, 930.

59. Curcio, J. A., and C. C. Petty, *J. Opt. Soc. Am.*, **41**, 302 (1951).

60. Cziki, K., and P. Fodor, *Magyar Kém. Folybóirat*, **63**, 95 (1957); through *Anal. Abstr.*, **5**, #354 (1958).

61. Dalbert, R., and J. Tranchant, *Chim. & ind. (Paris)*, **61**, 457 (1949).

62. Das, M. N., *J. Indian Chem. Soc.*, **34**, 248 (1957); through *Anal. Abstr.*, **5**, #560 (1958).

63. Davies, M. M., *Trans. Faraday Soc.*, **36**, 333, 1114 (1940).

64. Davis, F. E., K. Kenyon, and J. Kirk, *Science*, **118**, 276 (1953).

65. Dean, E. W., and D. D. Stark, *Ind. Eng. Chem.*, **12**, 486 (1920).

66. Deaton, W. M., and E. M. Frost, Jr., *U. S. Bur. Mines Rept. Invest.* No. 3399 (1938).

67. Dexter, S. T., *Mich. State Univ. Agr. Exp. Sta. Quart. Bull.*, **30**, 422 (1948).

68. Diamond, W. J., *Appl. Spectroscopy*, **12**, 10 (1958).

69. Dibeler, V. H., in J. Mitchell, Jr., I. M. Kolthoff, E. S. Proskauer, and A. Weissberger, *Organic Analysis*, Vol. III, Interscience, New York–London, 1956, pp. 387 ff.

70. Dietrich, K. R., and C. Conrad, *Angew. Chem.*, **44**, 532 (1931).

71. Dontsov, Yu. P., and A. R. Striganov, *Zhur. Anal. Khim.*, **12**, 5 (1957); through *Anal. Abstr.*, **5**, #355 (1958).

72. Draper, A. L., and W. O. Milligan, *Texas J. Sci.*, **1950**, No. 2, 209.

73. Drinkard, W., and D. Kivelson, *J. Phys. Chem.*, **62**, 1494 (1958).
74. Dubbs, C. A., *Anal. Chem.*, **25**, 828 (1953).
75. Duval, C., *Inorganic Thermogravimetric Analysis*, Elsevier, Amsterdam–Houston–London–New York, 1953.
76. Eberius, E., *Wasserbestimmung mit Karl-Fischer Lösgung*, Verlag Chemie, Weinheim, 1954.
77. Eberius, E., and W. Kempf, *Stärke*, **4**, 77 (1957); through *Anal. Abstr.*, **5**, #1360 (1957).
78. Elitzur, A. G., *Biochimia*, **16**, 81 (1951); through *Brit. Abstr.*, *AIII*, **1952**, 21; *Zavodskaya Lab.*, **12**, 794 (1946); through *Chem. Abstr.*, **41**, 3713 (1947).
79. Elsken, R. H., and C. H. Kunsman, *J. Assoc. Offic. Agr. Chemists*, **39**, 434 (1956).
80. Emeleus, H. J., F. W. James, A. King, T. G. Pearson, R. H. Purcell, and H. V. A. Briscoe, *J. Chem. Soc.*, **1937**, 1207.
81. Engelbrecht, R. M., and S. Drexler, *Anal. Chem.*, **29**, 1100 (1957).
82. Evans, R. N., and J. E. Davenport, *Ind. Eng. Chem.*, *Anal. Ed.*, **14**, 732 (1942).
83. Fallot, P., A. Aeberhardt, and J. Masson, *Intern. J. Appl. Radiation and Isotopes*, **1**, 237 (1957).
84. Farkas, A., *Orthohydrogen, Parahydrogen, and Heavy Hydrogen*, Cambridge Univ. Press, London, 1935.
85. *Federal Register*, **13**, 4186 (1948); through *Chem. Abstr.*, **42**, 9080 (1948).
86. Ferguson, B. L., and N. M. Coulter, *Proc. Indiana Acad. Sci.*, **63**, 124 (1953).
87. Fetzer, W. R., *Anal. Chem.*, **23**, 1062 (1951).
88. Fiechter, A., and U. Vetsch, *Experientia*, **13**, 72 (1957); through *Anal. Abstr.*, **5**, #3548 (1958).
89. Finholt, A. E., A. C. Bond, Jr., and H. I. Schlesinger, *J. Am. Chem. Soc.*, **69**, 1199 (1947).
90. Finkelstein, A., and H. Lesimple, *J. Nuclear Energy*, **2**, 101 (1955).
91. Finken, H., and H. Hölters, *Fette u. Seifen*, **46**, 70 (1939).
92. Finn-Kelcey, P. G., Brit. Pat. 731,826 (1952); through *Anal. Abstr.*, **2**, #3250 (1955).
93. Fischbeck, K., and E. Eckert, *Z. anal. Chem.*, **112**, 305 (1938).
94. Fischer, E., *Angew. Chem.*, **64**, 592 (1952).
95. Fischer, E. A., and J. Thomlinson, *J. Soc. Chem. Ind. (London)*, **51**, 355 (1932).
96. Fischer, K., *Angew. Chem.*, **48**, 394 (1935).
97. Fischer, R., *Mikrochemie ver. Mikrochim. Acta*, **31**, 296 (1949).
98. Flosdorf, E. W., *Freeze-Drying*, Reinhold, New York, 1949.
99. Foulk, C. W., and A. T. Bawden, *J. Am. Chem. Soc.*, **48**, 2045 (1926).
100. Foxboro Co., Foxboro, Mass., Brit. Pat. 444,056 (1936).
101. Frediani, H. A., *Anal. Chem.*, **24**, 1126 (1952).
102. Friedel, A. R., A. G. Sharkey, Jr., and C. R. Humbert, *Anal. Chem.*, **25**, 1314 (1953).
103. Friedman, H., W. A. Zisman, and M. V. Sullivan, U. S. Pat. 2,487,797 (1949).
104. Friedman, L., and A. P. Irsa, *Anal. Chem.*, **24**, 876 (1952).
105. Gallaway, W. S., *Oil Gas J.*, **47**(28), 279 (1948).
106. Gard, L. N., and R. C. Butler, *Anal. Chem.*, **26**, 1367 (1954).
107. Gardiner, S. D., and H. J. Keyte, *Analyst*, **83**, 150 (1958).
108. Gardner, W., and D. Kirkham, *Soil Sci.*, **73**, 391 (1952).
109. Garton, W. R. S., M. S. W. Webb, and P. C. Wildy, *J. Sci. Instrum.*, **34**, 496 (1957).
110. Gaunt, J., *Analyst*, **79**, 580 (1954); *Spectrochim. Acta*, **8**, 57 (1956).

111. Geary, P. J., *Brit. Sci. Instr. Research Assoc. Rept.* M. 24 (1956).
112. Gerdel, R. W., B. L. Hansen, and W. C. Cassidy, *Trans. Am. Geophys. Union*, **31**, 449 (1950).
113. Gifford, A. P., S. M. Rock, and D. J. Comoford, *Anal. Chem.*, **21**, 1026 (1949).
114. Gilman, H., and L. S. Miller, *J. Am. Chem. Soc.*, **73**, 2367 (1951).
115. Glascock, R. F., *Nucleonics*, **9**, No. 5, 28 (1951); *Nature*, **168**, 121 (1951); *Biochem. J.*, **52**, 699 (1952); *Atomics, Eng. and Technol.*, **6**, 329, 343, 363 (1955).
116. Glastonbury, H. A., *Analyst*, **78**, 682 (1953).
117. Goldenson, J., and C. E. Dauner, *Anal. Chem.*, **20**, 359 (1948).
118. Gorbach, G., and A. Jurinka, *Mikrochemie ver. Mikrochim. Acta*, **34**, 174 (1949).
119. Gracheva, E. G., and S. G. Khusainova, *Atomnaya Energ.*, **2**(1), 70 (1957); through *Anal. Abstr.*, **5**, #1778 (1958).
120. Graefe, E., *Petroleum*, **1**, 813 (1906).
121. Gray, V. R., and P. F. Whelan, *Chem. & Ind. (London)*, **1955**, 126.
122. Greathouse, L. H., H. J. Janssen, and C. H. Haydel, *Anal. Chem.*, **28**, 357 (1956).
123. Greinacher, E., W. Luttke, and R. Mecke, *Z. Electrochem.*, **59**, 23 (1955).
124. Greinacher, H., *Helv. Phys. Acta*, **17**, 437 (1944); through *Chem. Abstr.*, **40**, 5606 (1946).
125. Griffith, E. J., *Anal. Chem.*, **29**, 198 (1957).
126. Griis, H., Ger. Pat. 648,275 (1937).
127. Griswold, J., M. E. Klecka, and R. V. O. West, Jr., *Ind. Eng. Chem., Anal. Ed.*, **18**, 696 (1946).
128. Gur'yanova, E. N., *Zavodskaya Lab.*, **13**, 163 (1947).
129. Gutowsky, H. S., and A. Saika, *J. Chem. Phys.*, **21**, 1688 (1953).
130. Gyngell, E. S., M. A. Phillips, and E. L. Smith, *Ind. Chemist*, **21**, 526 (1945).
131. Hagethorn, N. E. M., *Chem. Weekblad*, **46**, 919 (1950).
132. Halverson, F., *Revs. Modern Phys.*, **19**, 87 (1947).
133. Hancock, C. K., and C. M. Hudgins, Jr., *Anal. Chem.*, **26**, 1738 (1954).
134. Harel, S., and A. Talmi, *Anal. Chem.*, **29**, 1694 (1957).
135. Harris, F. E., and L. K. Nash, *Anal. Chem.*, **23**, 736 (1951).
136. Harth, O., W. Kreienberg, and D. Mertz, *Klin. Wochschr.*, **31**, 905 (1953); through *Anal. Abstr.*, **1**, #1332 (1954).
137. Hartley, H., and H. R. Raikes, *J. Chem. Soc.*, **127**, 524 (1925).
138. Haslam, J., and M. Glasper, *Analyst*, **77**, 413 (1952).
139. Healey, J. W., and L. C. Schwendiman, *Radiation Research*, **4**, 278 (1956); through *Anal. Abstr.*, **4**, #3235 (1957).
140. Henle, F., *Ber.*, **53**, 719 (1920).
141. Henriques, F. C., Jr., and C. Margnetti, *Anal. Chem.*, **18**, 420 (1946).
142. Higuchi, T., in J. Mitchell, Jr., I. M. Kolthoff, E. S. Proskauer, and A. Weissberger, *Organic Analysis*, Vol. II, Interscience, New York–London, 1954, pp. 123 ff.
143. Hill, S., and A. G. R. Dobbs, *Analyst*, **83**, 143 (1958).
144. Hill, W. L., J. H. Caro, and R. Kumagai, *J. Assoc. Offic. Agr. Chemists*, **34**, 641 (1951).
145. Hinzpeter, A., and W. Meyer, *Z. angew. Phys.*, **3**, 216 (1951); through *Chem. Abstr.* **46**, 4283 (1952).
146. Hoffmann, K., and L. Fischer, *Chem. Ing. Tech.*, **27**, 604 (1955).
147. Hoover, T. B., and A. W. Hutchison, *Anal. Chem.*, **29**, 518 (1957).
148. Horsley, L. H., *Anal. Chem.*, **19**, 508 (1947).
149. Ilfeld, R. M., *Anal. Chem.*, **23**, 1086 (1951).

150. Inglestam, E., E. Djurle, and L. Johansson, *J. Opt. Soc. Am.*, **44**, 472 (1954).
151. *International Critical Tables*, Vol. 3, McGraw-Hill, New York, 1928, p. 385.
152. Jenkins, W. A., *Anal. Chem.*, **25**, 1477 (1953).
153. Jensen, F. W., M. J. Kelly, and M. B. Burton, Jr., *Anal. Chem.*, **26**, 1716 (1954).
154. Johansson, A., *Svensk Papperstidn.*, **50**, 124 (1947).
155. Johansson, A., *Acta Chem. Scand.*, **3**, 1058 (1949).
156. Johnson, A. S., *Chem. & Ind. (London)*, **1949**, 511.
157. Jones, A. G., *Analyst*, **76**, 5 (1951).
158. Jones, E. R. S., *J. Sci. Instr.*, **30**, 132 (1953).
159. Jones, F. R., *J. Appl. Chem. (London)*, **1**, S144 (1951).
160. Jordan, C. B., and V. O. Hatch, *Anal. Chem.*, **22**, 177 (1950).
161. Joris, G. G., and H. S. Taylor, *J. Chem. Phys.*, **16**, 45 (1948).
162. Kallmann, H., and M. Furst, *Phys. Rev.*, **79**, 857 (1950); **81**, 853 (1951).
163. Kanagy, J. R., and A. M. Charles, *J. Am. Leather Chemists' Assoc.*, **43**, 274 (1948).
164. Kao, S. S., and Hsu, K. H., *Acta Chim. Sinica*, **24**, 1 (1958); through *Anal. Abstr.*, **5**, #4400 (1958).
165. Karasek, F. W., and E. C. Miller, *Ind. Eng. Chem.*, **46**, 1374 (1954).
166. Katzin, L. I., and J. R. Farraro, *J. Am. Chem. Soc.*, **74**, 2752 (1952).
167. Katzin, L. I., and E. Gebert, *J. Am. Chem. Soc.*, **72**, 5464 (1950).
168. Kaufmann, H. P., and S. Funke, *Fette u. Seifen*, **44**, 386 (1937).
169. Kawada, S., and S. Uchida, *Rept. Inst. Sci. Technol. Univ. Tokyo*, **5**, 241 (1951); through *Chem. Abstr.*, **46**, 5899 (1952).
170. Keidel, F. A., U. S. Pat. 2,830,945 (1958); *Anal. Chem.*, **31**, 2043 (1959).
171. Kelley, M. T., R. W. Stelzner, W. R. Laing, and D. J. Fisher, *Anal. Chem.*, **31**, 220 (1959).
172. Keston, A. S., D. Rittenberg, and R. Schoenheimer, *J. Biol. Chem.*, **122**, 227 (1937).
173. King, J., *Analyst*, **77**, 8 (1952).
174. Kinsella, J., U. S. Pat. 2,642,737 (1953).
175. Kirkham, R. H. H., *Civil Eng. Public Works Rev.*, **50**(591), 979 (1955); through *Eng. Ind.*, **1955**, 212.
176. Kirshenbaum, I., *Natl. Nuclear Energy Ser.*, *Div. III*, **4-A** (1951). (This series is published under the auspices of the U. S. Atomic Energy Commission.)
177. Klamann, D., *Osterr. Chemiker-Ztg.*, **54**, 165 (1953).
178. Klockmann, R., *Chemiker-Ztg.*, **76**, 706 (1952).
179. Klug, H. P., and L. E. Alexander, *X-Ray Diffraction Procedures*, Wiley, New York–London, 1954.
180. Kobayashi, R., F. Motoyama, and S. Nishikata, *J. Inst. Elec. Engrs. (Japan)*, **73**, 728 (1953); through ref. 111.
180a. Kolthoff, I. M., and E. B. Sandell, *Textbook of Qualitative Inorganic Analysis*, 3rd ed., Macmillan, New York, 1952, p. 717.
181. Koshkin, N. V., and N. M. Shreĭner, *Trudy Leningr ad. Tekhnol. Inst. Pishchevoĭ Prom.*, **13**, 161 (1956); through *Anal. Abstr.*, **5**, #388 (1958).
182. Krause, W. O., U. S. Pat. 2,836,974 (1958).
183. Kremen, S. S., *J. Am. Leather Chemists' Assoc.*, **44**, 774 (1949).
184. Kunz, P., *Ber.*, **27**, 2559 (1894).
185. Lane, W. H., *Ind. Eng. Chem., Anal. Ed.*, **18**, 295 (1946).
186. Lange, N. A., *Handbook of Chemistry*, Handbook Publishers, Sandusky, Ohio, 1956.
187. Langham, W. H., W. J. Eversole, F. N. Hayes, and T. T. Trujillo, *J. Lab. Clin. Med.*, **47**, 819 (1956).

188. Larson, R. G., *Ind. Eng. Chem., Anal. Ed.*, **10**, 195 (1938).
189. LeCompte, G. C., and H. H. Lipp, *Am. Dyestuff Reptr.*, **38**, 484, 512 (1949); through *Brit. Abstr., C*, **1949**, 396.
190. Lecomte, J., M. Ceccaldi, and E. Roth, *J. chim. phys.*, **50**, 166 (1953).
191. Lee, D. A., *Anal. Chem.*, **30**, 1296 (1958).
192. Lee, J. K., and S. W. Weller, *Anal. Chem.*, **30**, 1057 (1958).
193. Levin, H., K. Uhrig, and F. M. Roberts, *Anal. Chem.*, **17**, 212 (1945).
194. Lewis, G. N., and R. T. MacDonald, *J. Am. Chem. Soc.*, **55**, 3057 (1933).
195. Linde, H. W., and L. B. Rogers, *Anal. Chem.*, **30**, 1250 (1958).
196. Lindner, J,. *Z. Anal. Chem.*, **66**, 305 (1925).
197. Lindner, J., *Mikrochemie ver. Mikrochim. Acta*, **32**, 133 (1944).
198. Lindner, J., and G. Zienert, *Mikrochemie ver. Mikrochim. Acta*, **31**, 254 (1943).
199. Ljunggren, H., *Acta Physiol. Scand.*, **33**, 69 (1955).
200. Loury, M., and J. Piquard, *Oléagineux*, **2**, 560 (1947); through *Chem. Abstr.*, **42**, 359 (1948).
201. Luft, K. F., and R. Guerin, *Chim. anal.*, **37**, 100 (1955).
202. Lund, H., and J. Bjerrum, *Ber.*, **64**, 210 (1931).
203. Magee, A. I., and W. Kalbfleisch, *Sci. Agr.*, **32**, 117 (1952); through *Brit. Abstr., BIII*, **1952**, 463.
204. Makower, B., S. H. Chastain, and E. Nielsen, *Ind. Eng. Chem.*, **38**, 725 (1946).
205. Makower, B., and E. Nielsen, *Anal. Chem.*, **20**, 856 (1948).
206. Martin, A. E., and D. Mounfield, U. S. Pat. 2,874,564 (1959).
207. Matsuyama, G., *Anal. Chem.*, **29**, 196 (1957).
208. McComb, E. A., *Anal. Chem.*, **20**, 1219 (1948).
209. McComb, E. A., *J. Assoc. Offic. Agr. Chemists*, **33**, 1021 (1950).
210. McIntosh, J. D., *Cement & Concrete Assoc.*, Res. Note Rp. 6 (1951); through *Brit. Abstr., C*, **1953**, 62.
211. McMaster, E. A., *Textile World*, **98**, 141, 201 (1948); through *Brit. Abstr.*, C **1949**, 40.
212. Meditsch, J. O., *Chemist Analyst*, **45**, 49 (1956).
213. Menapace, H. R., G. Kyryacos, and C. E. Boord, Division of Analytical Chemistry, 132nd Meeting, ACS, New York, Sept., 1957.
214. Meyer, A. S., Jr., and C. M. Boyd, *Anal. Chem.*, **31**, 215 (1959).
215. Milone, M., and E. Grandis, *Ann. chim. appl.*, **29**, 130 (1939); through *Chem. Abstr.*, **33**, 9656 (1939).
216. Minczewski, J., and J. Tromszczýnski, *Przemysł Chem.*, **11**, 147 (1955); through *Anal. Abstr.*, **3**, #1622 (1956).
217. Minneapolis-Honeywell Regulator Co., *Instrumentation Data Sheet*, No. 1, 1 (Oct. 1957).
218. Mitchell, J., Jr., *Anal. Chem.*, **23**, 1069 (1951).
219. Mitchell, J., Jr., and D. M. Smith, *Aquametry*, Interscience, New York–London, 1948.
220. Mitra, N. C., and K. Venkataraman, *Current Sci. (India)*, **5**, 199 (1936); *J. Soc. Chem. Ind.*, **57**, 306 (1938).
221. Moberg, M. L., W. P. Knight, and H. M. Kindsvater, *Anal. Chem.*, **28**, 412 (1956).
222. Möhler, K., and K. Slevogt, *Fette u. Seifen* **56**, 46 (1954).
223. Mulder, G. J. and J. A. C. van Pinxteren, *Pharm.Weekblad*, **91**, (2), 33 (1956).
224. Murray, B. B., and R. C. Axtmann, *Anal. Chem.*, **31**, 450 (1959).
225. Mysels, K. J., *Science*, **129**, 96 (1959).

226. Naklonov, V. A., Russ. Pat. 52,306 (1937).
227. Naklonov, V. A., Zavodskaya Lab., 6, 187 (1937); Chem. Abstr., 32, 3933 (1938).
228. Namba, S., Rev. Sci. Instr., 27, 872 (1956).
229. Nebbia, L., and B. Pagani, Chim. e ind. (Milan), 39, 5 (1957); through Chem. Abstr., 51, 14479 (1957).
230. Neuss, J. D., M. G. O'brien, and H. A. Frediani, Anal. Chem., 23, 1332 (1951).
231. Newburger, S. H., J. Assoc. Offic. Agr. Chemists, 30, 683 (1947).
232. Notton, H. E. E., Pharm. J., 161, 250 (1948).
233. Oehme, F., Angew. Chem., 68, 457 (1956).
234. Oganov, M. N., and A. R. Striganov, Spectrochim. Acta, 13, 139 (1958).
235. Orchin, M., I. Wender, and R. A. Friedel, Anal. Chem., 21, 1072 (1949).
236. Overbeek, J. T. G., and D. A. A. Mossel, Rec. trav. chim., 70, 63 (1951).
237. Ozaki, T., Japan Analyst, 4, 11 (1955); through Anal. Abstr., 2, #2483 (1955).
238. Palevsky, H., R. K. Swank, and R. Grenchik, Rev. Sci. Instr., 18, 298 (1947).
239. Palfray, L., S. Sabetay, and G. Libmann-Métayer, Inds. parfum., 2, 325 (1947); through Chem. Abstr., 42, 3908 (1948).
240. Parks, R. Q., U. S. Pat. 2,362,396 (1944).
241. Pasynskiï, A., Acta Physicochim. U. R. S. S., 8. 385 (1938); J. Phys. Chem. (U. S. S. R.), 20 981 (1946).
242. Pawliw, J., and J. W. T. Spinks, Can. J. Technol., 34 503 (1957).
243. Peck, J., S. Zedek, and M. Wittová, Chem. průmysl, 5(5), 219 (1955); through Anal. Abstr., 4, #809 (1957).
243a. Penfield, S. L., Am. J. Sci., (3)48, 30 (1894).
244. Pennington, W. A., Anal. Chem., 21, 766 (1949).
245. Perkin, F. M., and L. Pratt, J. Chem. Soc., 95, 159 (1909).
246. Perlick, A., and R. Perlick, Kältetechnik, 6, 271 (1954); through Anal. Abstr., 2, #1380 (1955).
247. Perryman, P. W., Analyst, 70, 45 (1945).
248. Pesez, M., Bull. soc. chim. France, 15, 1108 (1948).
249. Peters, E. D., and J. L. Jungnickel, Anal. Chem., 27, 450 (1955).
250. Pflug, H., Chemiker-Ztg., 51, 717 (1918).
251. Pipparelli, E., and A. Simonetti, Ann. chim. appl., 33, 3 (1943); through Brit. Abstr., C, 1949, 97.
252. Pleeth, S. J. W., J. Inst. Petrol., 36, 345 (1950).
253. Pollack, L. R., Anal. Chem., 19, 241 (1947).
254. Price, A. H., Nature, 181, 262 (1958).
255. Pritzker, J., and R. Jungkunz, Mitt. Gebiete Lebensm. u. Hyg., 43, 499 (1952); through Brit. Abstr., C, 1953, 285.
256. Pross, A. W., Can. J. Chem., 32, 956 (1954).
257. Puddington, I. E., Can. J. Research, 27B, 1 (1949).
258. Reaser, P. B., and G. E. Burch, Science, 128, 415 (1958).
259. Richards, L. A., Soil Sci., 68, 95 (1949).
260. Roark, J. N., and R. Y. Meelheim, Anal. Chem., 25, 348 (1953).
261. Roberts, F. M., and H. Levin, Anal. Chem., 21, 1553 (1949).
262. Robinson, C. V., Rev. Sci. Instr., 22, 353 (1951).
263. Romberg, A., and L. W. Blau, J. Opt. Soc. Am., 13, 717 (1926).
264. Rosenthal, Chemiker-Ztg., 33, 1259 (1909).
265. Rosenthal, D. J., and H. O. Anger, Rev. Sci. Instr., 25, 670 (1954).
266. Ross, J., J. Soc. Chem. Ind., 51, 121 (1932).

267. Roth, F., and A. Schultz, *Brennstoff-Chem.*, **20**, 317 (1939).
268. Roy, A. and J. A. Mabon, *J. Appl. Chem. (London)*, **1**, Suppl. 1, S1 (1951).
269. Rubin, H., *ISA Journal*, **5**, 64 (1958).
270. Rulfs, C. L., *Mikrochemie ver. Mikrochim. Acta*, **33**, 338 (1948).
271. Rush, I. C., and S. C. Kilbank, *Ind. Eng. Chem.*, **41**, 167 (1949).
272. Sair, L., and W. R. Fetzer, *Cereal Chem.*, **19**, 633 (1942).
273. Sandomirskiĭ, M. G., *Zavodskaya Lab.*, **22**, 75 (1956); through *Chem. Abstr.*, **50**, 8366 (1956).
274. Sauter, E., *Z. Naturforsch.*, *Pt. a*, **3a**, 392 (1948); through *Brit. Abstr.*, *C*, **1949**, 369; through *Chem. Abstr.*, **43**, 3316 (1949).
275. Schloerb, P. R., B. J. Friis-Hansen, I. S. Edelman, B. Sheldon, and F. D. Moore, *J. Lab. Clin. Med.*, **37**, 653 (1951); through *Brit. Abstr.*, *C*, **1951**, 377.
276. Schnitzer, M., J. R. Wright, and I. Hoffman, *Anal. Chem.*, **31**, 440 (1959).
277. Schroeder, C. W., and J. H. Nair, *Anal. Chem.*, **20**, 452 (1948).
278. Seaman, W., W. H. McComas, Jr., and G. A. Allen, *Anal. Chem.*, **21**, 510 (1949).
279. Seaman, W., A. R. Norton, and J. J. Hugonet, *Ind. Eng. Chem.*, *Anal. Ed.*, **15**, 322 (1943).
280. Seidell, A., *Solubilities of Organic Compounds*, Suppl. to 3rd ed., Van Nostrand, New York, 1952.
281. Serger, H., *Chemiker-Ztg.*, **78**, 681 (1954).
282. Shapiro, L., and W. W. Brannock, *Anal. Chem.*, **27**, 560 (1955).
283. Sharpe, J., *Brit. J. Appl. Phys.*, **4**, 93 (1953).
284. Shatenshteĭn, A. I., E. A. Yakovleva, E. N. Gladkova, S. F. Suzdal'tseva, and N. P. Antipova, *Zhur. Anal. Khim.*, **12**(1), 115 (1957); through *Anal. Abstr.*, **5**, #353 (1958).
285. Shatenshteĭn, A. I., and E. N. Zvyagintseva, *Zhur. Anal. Khim.*, **12**(4), 516 (1957); through *Anal. Abstr.*, **5**, #1111 (1958).
286. Shaw, B. and L. D. Baver, *J. Am. Soc. Agron.*, **31**, 886 (1939); through *Chem. Abstr.*, **34**, 566 (1940).
287. Shaw, D. F., *J. Sci. Instr.*, **32**, 178 (1955).
288. Shaw, T. M., and R. H. Elsken, *J. Chem. Phys.*, **21**, 565 (1953).
289. Shaw, T. M., and R. H. Elsken, *Anal. Chem.*, **27**, 1983 (1955).
290. Shaw, T. M., R. H. Elsken, and C. H. Kunsman, *J. Assoc. Offic. Agr. Chemists*, **36**, 1070 (1953).
291. Shemin, E. R., and J. W. Wagner, *Food Inds.*, **19**, 1230 (1947).
292. Shiio, H., T. Ogawa, and H. Yoshihashi, *J. Am. Chem. Soc.*, **77**, 4980 (1955).
293. Shoolery, J. N., and B. J. Alder, *J. Chem. Phys.*, **23**, 805 (1955).
294. Siddappa, G. S. and D. P. Das, *Current Sci. (India)*, **23**, 157 (1954); through *Anal. Abstr.*, **1**, #3085 (1954).
295. Siegenheim, M., Brit. Pat. 491,604 (1938); U. S. Pat. 2,189,352 (1940).
296. Silverman, L., and W. Bradshaw, *Anal. Chim. Acta*, **10**, 68 (1954).
297. Šingliar, M., and J. Zubák, *Chem. průmysl*, **6**, 426 (1956); through *Anal. Abstr.*, **4**, #3556 (1957).
298. Sirotenko, A. A., *Mikrochim. Acta*, **5-6**, 917 (1955).
299. Sivadjian, J., *Anal. Chim. Acta*, **9**, 70 (1953).
300. Sivadjian, J., *Compt. rend.*, **238**(6), 678 (1954).
301. Smith, D. M., and W. M. D. Bryant, *J. Am. Chem. Soc.*, **57**, 841 (1935).
302. Sneed, R. W., R. W. Altman, and J. C. Mosteller, *Anal. Chem.*, **26**, 1018 (1954).
303. Spaepen, J., *Tech.-Wetenschap. Tijdschr.*, **25**, 12 (1956); through *Anal. Abstr.*, **4**, #3234 (1957).

304. Spinks, J. W. T., D. A. Lane, and B. B. Torchinsky, *Can. J. Technol.*, **29**, 371 (1951).
305. Spiridonova, S. I., *J. Appl. Chem.* (*U. S. S. R.*), **19**, 966 (1946); through *Brit. Abstr.*, *C*, **1949**, 182.
306. Stringer, J. E. C., *Nature*, **167**, 1071 (1951).
307. Suter, H. R., *Ind. Eng. Chem., Anal. Ed.*, **19**, 326 (1947).
308. Swain, C. G., V. P. Kreiter, and W. A. Sheppard, *Anal. Chem.*, **27**, 1157 (1955).
309. Syavtsillo, S. V., B. E. Berezovskaya, N. I. Grinkevich, and O. V. Kloptsova, *Zhur. Anal. Khim.*, **11**, 463 (1956); through *Anal. Abstr.*, **4**, #1578 (1957).
310. Symons, N. K. J., and E. C. McKannan, *Anal. Chem.*, **31**, 1990 (1959).
311. Tappel, A. L., *Anal. Chem.*, **26**, 1671 (1954).
312. T.A.P.P.I. Chemical Methods Committee, *Tappi*, 36, 137A (1953).
313. Taylor, R. C., R. A. Brown, W. S. Young, and C. E. Headington, *Anal. Chem.*, **20**, 396 (1948).
314. Terent'ev, A. P., D. G. Kadaner, and Y. K. Kopchenova, *J. Gen. Chem. U. S. S. R.* (*Eng. Transl.*), **17**, 913 (1947); through *Chem. Abstr.*, **42**, 1527 (1948).
315. Thomas, B. W., *Anal. Chem.*, **22**, 1476 (1950).
316. Thomas, B. W., and W. D. Seyfried, *Anal. Chem.*, **21**, 1022 (1949).
317. Thomson, R. C., *J. Biol. Chem.*, **197**, 81 (1952).
318. Thornton, V., and F. E. Condon, *Anal. Chem.*, **22**, 690 (1950).
319. Toennies, G., and M. Elliott, *J. Am. Chem. Soc.*, **57**, 2136 (1935); **59**, 902 (1937).
320. Trenner, N. R., B. H. Arison, and R. W. Walker, *Appl. Spectroscopy*, **7**, 166 (1953); *Anal. Chem.*, **28**, 530 (1956).
321. Tryon, M., *J. Research Natl. Bur. Standards*, **45**, 362 (1950).
322. Tyndall, A. M., and A. P. Chattock, *Proc. Phys. Soc.* (*London*), **34**, 72 (1921–2).
323. Valentin, F. H. H., *J. S. African Chem. Inst.*, **2**, 59 (1949); through *Chem. Abstr.*, **44**, 2892 (1950); *Brit. Abstr.*, C, **1950**, 512.
324. Van der Meulen, J. H., Brit. Pat. 728,947 (1955).
325. Van Loon, J., *Verfkroniek*, **17**, 2, 14 (1944); through *Chem. Abstr.*, **42**, 6131 (1948).
326. van Niewenburg, C. J., *Chem. Weekblad*, **34**, 217 (1937).
327. Van Thiel, M., E. D. Becker, and G. C. Pimentel, *J. Chem. Phys.*, **27**, 486 (1957).
328. Vavruch, I., *Listy cukrovar.*, **64**, 153 (1948); through *Chem. Abstr.*, **42**, 4376 (1948).
329. Velling, G., *Brennstoff-Chem.*, **34**, 199 (1953).
330. Vendt, V. P., *Doklady Akad. Nauk S. S. S. R.*, **73**, 689 (1950); through *Chem. Abstr.*, **44**, 10596 (1950).
331. Viallard, R., M. Corval, B. Dreyfus-Alain, M. Grenon, and J. Herrmann, *Chim anal.*, **36**, 102 (1954).
332. Viallard, R., and A. Marchetti, *Chim. anal.*, **36**, 214 (1954).
333. Vincent, J. F., and K. E. Bristol, *Ind. Eng. Chem., Anal. Ed.*, **17**, 465 (1945).
334. Vincent, R. S., *J. Sci. Instr.*, **29**, 155 (1952).
335. Vinkanovič, V., and B. Pavlovič, *Rec. trav. inst. recherches structure matière* (*Belgrade*), **1**, 103 (1952); through *Brit. Abstr.*, C, **1953**, 105.
336. Vlček, A. A., *Chem. listy*, **48**, 1741 (1954); **49**, 28 (1955); through *Chem. Abstr.*, **49**, 5158 (1955).
337. von Ripka, L., *Chem. Ing. Tech.*, **26**, 440 (1954).
338. Warren, A., Ger. Pat. 670,261 (1939).
339. Washburn, E. W., and E. R. Smith, *J. Research Natl. Bur. Standards*, **12**, 305 (1934).
340. Washburn, H. W., C. E. Berry, and L. G. Hall, *Anal. Chem.*, **25**, 130 (1953).
341. Weaver, E. R., E. E. Hughes, and A. W. Diniak, *J. Research Natl. Bur. Standards*, **60**, 489 (1958).

342. Weinberg, I., and J. R. Zimmerman, *J. Chem. Phys.*, **23**, 748 (1955).
343. West, P. W., P. Senise, and T. S. Burkhalter, *Anal. Chem.*, **24**, 1250 (1952).
344. Wexler, A., and W. G. Brombacher, *Natl. Bur. Standards (U. S.) Circ. No.* 512 (1951).
345. White, D. F., I. G. Campbell, and P. R. Payne, *Nature*, **166**, 628 (1950).
346. White, L., Jr., and W. J. Barrett, *Anal. Chem.*, **28**, 1538 (1956).
347. Wildhack, W. A., *Rev. Sci. Instr.*, **21**, 25 (1950).
348. Williams, K. T., E. A. McComb, and B. L. Washauer, *Foods Inds.*, **22**, 458 (1950).
349. Willits, C. O., *Anal. Chem.*, **23**, 1058 (1951).
350. Wilzbach, K. E., A. R. Van Dyken, and L. Kaplan, *Anal. Chem.*, **26**, 880 (1954).
351. Winogradow, L., *Przemsył Chem.*, **31**, 569 (1952); through *Chem. Abstr.*, **47**, 8585 (1953).
352. Yakubik, M. G., *J. Chem. Educ.*, **35**, 5 (1958).
353. Yasukawa, A., *J. Soc. Instr. Technol., Japan*, **6**, 386 (1956); through ref. 111.
354. Zemlyakova, E. P , *J. Gen. Chem. U. S. S. R. (Engl. Transl.)*, **26**, 2993 (1956).
355. Ziegler, C. A., D. J. Chleck, and J. Brinkerhoff, *Anal. Chem.*, **29**, 1774 (1957).
356. Zil'berman, D. E., *Zavodskaya Lab.*, **11**, 108 (1945); through *Chem. Abstr.*, **39**, 4025 (1945).

THE INERT GASES (GROUP 0)

By Gerhard A. Cook, *Linde Company, Division of Union Carbide Corporation, Tonawanda, New York*

Contents

Contents (*continued*)

Contents (*continued*)

Contents *(continued)*

I. INTRODUCTION

Although great strides have been made in all branches of analytical chemistry during the last 10 years, the changes in the principal methods used for the analytical determination of inert gases have been among the most revolutionary. Of the two chief techniques in use today, one (gas chromatography) is not mentioned at all in the section on noble gases (published in 1949) of the *Handbuch der Analytischen Chemie* (65); the other (mass spectrometry) is given less than a page (65f) and is recommended only for difficultly analyzable isotopic mixtures.

Since the inert gases are not chemically active in the usual sense of the word, it has always been necessary to rely on physical methods to separate them and to determine their concentration; the new methods are faster and more convenient than most of those used earlier. The principles of mass spectrometry were first experimentally demonstrated in 1910 (8), and of gas chromatography in 1941 (88,100a), but the extensive utilization of these techniques was brought about only recently by the appearance on the market of convenient and reliable laboratory instruments. The techniques of gas chromatography are especially valuable since the cost of the required instrumentation is relatively low.

The gases covered in this chapter are variously known as the *inert gases*, the *noble gases*, the *rare gases*, the *helium group gases*, and the *group 0 gases*. The term *rare gases* is now a misnomer with respect to helium and argon. Helium is separated from natural gas and used in the United States on a large scale. Argon is present to the extent of almost 1% in air and is now shipped as a highly pure liquid in railroad tank cars and in tank trucks.

The inert gases are all chemical elements; see Table I.

The symbol A has in the past been used in the United States and England for argon. In 1957 the Commission on Inorganic Nomenclature of the International Union of Pure and Applied Chemistry adopted the symbol Ar (6). In favor of adopting Ar is the general desirability of two-letter symbols for the elements, and the possible confusion of A with the abbreviation of Angstrom units and with A used in a series A, B, C, etc. On the other hand, Ar now is used to represent aryl. Recently (24) the Chemical

TABLE I
The Inert Gases

Name	Symbol	Atomic number	1957 International atomic weight (121)
Helium	He	2	4.003
Neon	Ne	10	20.183
Argon	Ar	18	39.944
Krypton	Kr	36	83.80
Xenon	Xe	54	131.30
Radon	Rn	86	222

Abstracts Service of the American Chemical Society decided henceforth to use the symbol Ar, and the other journals published by the American Chemical Society will probably do the same.

This chapter includes the methods for commercial analysis of inert gases and their mixtures; there is no separate chapter on the inert gases in Part III of this Treatise. Since the analytical chemistry of radon is covered in another chapter along with that of some of the other radioactive elements, it is included in the present chapter only incidentally.

In writing this chapter, most attention has been paid to the literature published after January 1, 1937. For reviews of the older literature see references 65 and 114.

II. GENERAL INFORMATION

A. OCCURRENCE

1. In Nature

Helium occurs to the extent of 5.24 p.p.m. in air; thus any country having large air-processing plants will always be able to produce enough helium for cryogenic and other vital research purposes. The United States is blessed with large quantities of natural gas containing 1% or more helium; at least one well has given gas containing almost 9% helium (1e). The supply of helium in the United States is at present limited only by the capacity of the helium-separating plants. Limited quantities of helium-containing natural gas have also been discovered in Canada, in South Africa, and in the Soviet Union.

Helium occurs to a variable extent occluded in uranium and thorium minerals, especially in monazite (a mineral containing thorium and the rare earths). The principal sources of monazite are in India and Brazil, but some is found in the United States.   Helium also occurs in gases of volcanic origin and in some gases from hot springs.

The commercial source of neon, argon, krypton, and xenon is the earth's atmosphere (Table II).   These gases, along with oxygen and nitrogen, are separated and purified, as needed, in factories in which air is liquefied and fractionally distilled.

TABLE II

Concentration of the Inert Gases in the Earth's Atmosphere

Gas	P.p.m. by volume in dry air	Ref.
Argon	9340 ± 10	(38)
Neon	18.18 ± 0.04	(38)
Helium	5.239 ± 0.004	(38)
Krypton	1.14 ± 0.01	(41)
Xenon	0.086 ± 0.001	(41)
Radon	6×10^{-14a}	(96)

[a] This is the average concentration of radon near the surface of the earth.   The concentration decreases with increasing height.

Of general interest, but not of immediate use on earth, is the fact that the inert gases also occur in the stars and in other heavenly bodies.   Helium, in fact, was discovered spectroscopically in 1868 in the sun before it was found on earth.

2. As Impurities

The chief impurity in commercial oxygen is argon.   This condition arises from the fact that most oxygen is produced by the fractional distillation of liquid air and that the boiling point of argon is closer to that of oxygen than to that of nitrogen.

The inert gases also occur to some extent as impurities in nitrogen and other gases, usually in low concentration and usually harmless for the uses to which the gases are to be put.

B. ISOTOPES

A list of the stable isotopes of the inert gases and their natural isotopic abundance in the earth's atmosphere is given in Table III, and a list of the radioactive isotopes having half lives greater than 2 hours in Table IV. The only natural radioisotope listed in Table IV is radon-222, which is the daughter of radium-226.   For additional information on isotopes, both

TABLE III
Stable Isotopes of the Inert Gases

Element	Mass number of isotope	Natural isotopic abundance in air, mole %
Helium	3	0.00013
	4	100.0
Neon	20	90.92
	21	0.26
	22	8.82
Argon	36	0.337
	38	0.063
	40	99.600
Krypton	78	0.35
	80	2.27
	82	11.56
	83	11.55
	84	56.90
	86	17.37
Xenon	124	0.096
	126	0.090
	128	1.919
	129	26.44
	130	4.08
	131	21.18
	132	26.89
	134	10.44
	136	8.87
Radon	No stable isotope	

stable and radioactive, see reference 51. Reference 77 gives data on radioactive isotopes.

C. PRODUCTION, HANDLING, AND TRANSPORTATION

Helium is produced from natural gas by removing moisture, carbon dioxide, and hydrogen sulfide, cooling until substantially all the gases except helium are liquefied, and purifying the uncondensed gas (21). On a large scale, helium is stored and shipped as a gas under pressure in steel cylinders and spheres. As a result of the development of better insulation and handling techniques, small quantities of helium have recently been transported in liquid form, and within the next few years helium will probably be shipped as a liquid in tank trucks and railroad tank cars.

TABLE IV

Radioactive Isotopes of the Inert Elements with
Half Lives Greater than 2 Hours

Element	Mass number of isotope[a]	Approximate half life	Mode of decay[b]
Helium	None		
Neon	None		
Argon	37	35 days	EC
	39	265 yr.	β^-
	42	3.5 yr.	β^-
Krypton	79	34 hrs.	EC and β^+
	81	2.1×10^5 yr.	EC
	85m	4.5 hrs.	β^- and IT
	85	9.4 yr.	β^-
	88	2.8 hrs.	β^-
Xenon	122	20 hrs.	EC
	123	2 hrs.	β^+ and EC
	125	19 hrs.	EC
	127	30 days	EC
	129m	8 days	IT
	131m	12 days	IT
	133	5.3 days	β^-
	133m	2.2 days	IT
	135	9.1 hrs.	β^-
	137	3.6 mo.	β^-
Radon	210	2.4 hrs.	α and EC
	211	16 hrs.	EC and α
	222	3.8 days	α

[a] The letter m represents a metastable nucleus.

[b] The modes of decay are indicated as follows: α, emission of a helium nucleus (alpha particle); β^-, emission of an electron (beta particle or negatron); β^+, emission of a positron; EC, capture of a K or L orbital electron, accompanied by emission of an x-ray photon; and IT, isomeric transition (transition from a nuclear structure of higher energy to one of lower energy, the composition of the nucleus being the same), accompanied by emission of a gamma photon.

Helium can be isolated as a by-product of the processing of monazite sand to obtain cerium, thorium, and rare earth elements. The amount of helium produced by this method is very small but may occasionally be of importance for countries not in a position to import helium from the United States or to separate it from indigenous supplies of helium-containing natural gas.

Argon, neon, krypton, and xenon are all obtained in connection with the liquefaction and distillation of liquid air. In the liquefaction of air, helium

and neon are not usually condensed and are "bled" off from above the
liquid.   The main products of air distillation are nitrogen, taken off at
the top of the column, oxygen, taken off at the bottom, and argon, taken off
in between.   Krypton and xenon are less volatile than oxygen and therefore are taken off at the bottom along with the oxygen.   After rough preliminary separations, steps are taken to recover each gas in pure form.   At
present in the United States it is not economical to produce helium from
air, but this situation will probably change when the supply of helium-
containing natural gas has been exhausted.

Fig. 1. Glass vessel equipped with break-seal. (This vessel is known to the trade as a
"rare gas bulb.")

Argon is a major product of air separation and is handled and shipped in
the same way as oxygen and nitrogen: either as a compressed gas in steel
cylinders, or as a liquid in insulated containers such as railroad tank cars
and tank trucks.

Neon, krypton, and xenon are either compressed into steel cylinders or
shipped in glass bulbs at atmospheric pressure.   The chief reason for using
the glass bulbs is to make it easy to transfer the gases into equipment such
as neon tubes and Geiger counters, in which only a little of the gas is
required.   Fig. 1 shows a typical bulb used for shipping neon and other
inert gases.   The customer inserts a piece of iron into the glass tube, seals
the tube to his manifold, and evacuates up to the break-seal.   He then
breaks the break-seal with the help of a magnet and the piece of iron, thus
releasing the inert gas to flow into his manifold.

Radon is radioactive and has a half life of less than 4 days. It is obtained by collecting and purifying the gas produced by the radioactive disintegration of radium.

D. USES

The inert gases have extensive commercial uses. Helium is used for shielded arc welding and to provide inert gas atmospheres. It is used to inflate balloons and other lighter-than-air craft. Helium-oxygen mixtures are used as breathing atmospheres for asthma patients and for men working in an atmosphere of compressed air who might otherwise get "the bends" from formation of bubbles of nitrogen in the blood. Liquid helium is employed as a temperature-regulating bath for research at very low temperatures; it has the unique property of remaining liquid (unless pressurized) all the way down to absolute zero.

Neon-filled signs are familiar to everyone.

Argon (7) is employed in large quantities as a shielding gas for the electric arc welding of aluminum, stainless steel, and other metals, to keep air away from the hot metal; as an inert atmosphere in some of the steps in the metallurgy of reactive metals like titanium; and as a filling gas for electric light bulbs and fluorescent lamps. When used as a filling gas for lamps, the argon is usually mixed with one or more other gases.

Gaseous krypton and xenon are used, often mixed with argon, as filling gases in several kinds of light sources. Xenon has possibilities as an excellent total anesthetic, but at present its high cost prevents wide use as such. Liquid xenon makes an efficient filler for "bubble chambers" in which mesons, gamma photons, and high-speed particles from radioactive sources or from ion accelerators can be detected.

The inert gases also have a variety of uses that do not require large quantities of the gases but that are a great help in instrumentation and in various kinds of scientific research. Among such uses are these: (1) as filling gas for a variety of electron tubes, such as counters for x-ray photons, electrons, and ions, and (2) as diluents for reactive gases in spectroscopy and kinetic studies.

E. TOXICOLOGY AND INDUSTRIAL HAZARDS

The only one of the inert gases which can be considered toxic is radon, and even radon is not toxic in a chemical sense; it is dangerous because of its radioactivity and the radioactivity of its nonvolatile decay products. Helium and neon have no bad physiological effects, even when inhaled in rather high concentration; their solubility in body fluids is extremely small. Xenon is soluble in fats and in blood and is a nontoxic anesthetic.

It does not, of course, replace oxygen, and the breathing of pure xenon would lead to suffocation, as would the breathing of any of the other inert gases.

It is necessary to handle cylinders of compressed gases carefully to prevent them from falling and to prevent the valves from breaking off. This point is discussed in Section IV-A-6-g.

Liquid inert gases, because of their very low temperature, should not be allowed to come in contact with the skin.

III. PROPERTIES

A. PHYSICAL PROPERTIES

Some of the physical properties of the inert gases of interest to analytical chemists are given in Table V. See also reference 63.

One property of analytical interest is the fact that the rate of diffusion of xenon and krypton at room temperature through Tygon vinyl plastic or rubber is so great (78) as to make undesirable the use of these materials in accurate analytical work on gas mixtures containing xenon and krypton. Not only is there danger of loss of gases by diffusion, but the gases tend to be stored up in the tubing and given off at a later date, contaminating new samples. The property of xenon which makes it diffuse readily into and through rubber and plastic is probably the same as that which makes it soluble in human tissues and a good anesthetic, namely, some sort of weak chemical attraction.

Helium and neon also diffuse rapidly through rubber (3a), but in this case the reason for the high rate of diffusion is more likely related to the small size of the molecules rather than to chemical attraction.

Helium diffuses through ordinary borosilicate (Pyrex) glass at a measurable rate, very slowly at room temperature (12) and faster at higher temperatures (98a). There are, however, types of laboratory glass now on the market through which the rate of helium diffusion is negligible. In a period of a few days, the error from diffusion of helium through glass at room temperature is important only when traces of helium are being determined. Given time enough, every borosilicate glass vessel will contain helium at the same partial pressure as that of helium in the air, even if there was no helium originally in the vessel (101a). An experimental determination of the diffusion coefficient has been reported (103); the value found varied from 4.4×10^{-8} cc. (S.T.P.) of helium per square centimeter of glass surface per second per atmosphere helium pressure difference for each centimeter of glass thickness at 83°C., to 2.1×10^{-6} at 353°C. These figures make it possible for anyone determining small quantities of helium to make a rough

TABLE V

Physical Properties of the Inert Elements

	Helium	Neon	Argon	Krypton	Xenon	Radon
Color	Colorless	Colorless	Colorless	Colorless	Colorless	Colorless
Color of light emitted by a discharge tube filled with gas[a]	Yellow	Red	Red or blue	Yellow-green	Blue to green	
Melting point, °C.	[b]	−248.6	−189.4	−157.2	−111.8	−71
Boiling point, °C., at 760 mm. Hg	−268.9	−246.1	−185.9	−153.4	−108.1	−62
Gas density, g./liter, at 0°C. and 760 mm. Hg	0.17850	0.90002	1.78380	3.7493	5.8971	9.73
Liquid density, g./ml. at −183.0°C.			1.3832			
at b.p.	0.125	1.207	1.3985	2.413	3.06	4.4
Vapor pressure, mm. Hg at −195.8°C.			20[c]			
at −183.0°C.			990[d]			
Viscosity of gas, μP., at 20°C. and 760 mm. Hg	196.14	313.81	222.86	249.55	227.40	229.0
Critical temperature, °C.	−267.9	−228.7	−122.3	−63.8	16.59	105
Critical pressure, atm.	2.26	26.9	48.3	54.3	57.64	62
Heat capacity (C_p), cal./g.-atom/°C., at 25°C.	4.9680	4.9680	4.9680	4.9680	4.9680	4.9680
C_p/C_v for gas (0 to 20°C.)	1.63	1.642	1.667	1.689	1.666	

Heat of fusion, kg-cal./g-atom, at m.p.		0.080	0.281	0.391	0.549	(0.776)[e]
Heat of vaporization, kg-cal./g-atom, at b.p.	0.0194	0.414	1.5575	2.158	3.020	(4.325)[e]
Velocity of sound, ft./sec., at 0°C. and 1 atm.	3182	1427	1010	699	551	
Thermal conductivity, cal./cm./cm.^{2}/°C./sec., at 0°C. and 1 atm.	33.90×10^{-5}	11.00×10^{-5}	3.920×10^{-5}	2.09×10^{-5}	1.21×10^{-5}	
Solubility in water, cc. (S.T.P.) per 1000 g. at 1 atm.						
at 0°C.	9.78	14.0	52.4	99.1	203.2	510
at 20°C.	8.61	10.5	33.6	59.4	108.1	230
at 30°C.	8.42	9.89	28.5	48.8	85.4	169
Index of refraction (sodium D line = 5893 A.) at 0°C. and 1 atm.	1.000035	1.000067	1.000284	1.000427	1.000702	
Dielectric constant at 25°C. and 1 atm.	1.0000639	1.0001229	1.0005085	1.000768	1.001238	

[a] Color depends on the type of excitation.
[b] Helium does not form a solid phase at atmospheric pressure. It solidifies at 25.05 atm. pressure and 1.0°K.
[c] Solid.
[d] Liquid.
[e] Values in parentheses are uncertain.

calculation of both the possible losses of helium from the sample and the possible contamination of the sample by helium from the air.

The excitation and ionization potentials are of interest in connection with the identification and determination of the inert gases by emission spectroscopy. Table VI lists a few values that give an idea of the electronic energy levels in inert gas atoms. The table shows that all resonance

TABLE VI

Resonance and Ionization Information

Element	Lowest resonance potentials,[a] e.v.	Resonance lines of atoms, A.	Ionization potentials, e.v.	
			First electron	Second electron
Helium	21.13	584.35 (^1P) 591.43 ($^3P_1$)	24.58	54.40
Neon	16.84	735.89 ($^1P_1$) 743.71 ($^3P_1$)	21.56	41.07
Argon	11.83	1049.22 ($^1P_1$) 1066.66 ($^3P_1$)	15.76	27.62
Krypton	9.99	1235.82 ($^3P_1$)	14.00	24.56
Xenon	8.44	1469.62 ($^3P_1$)	12.13	21.21
Radon	6.94	1786.07 ($^3P_1$)	10.75	

[a] See reference 27. The resonance potential is here defined as the energy required to raise an atom from the ground state to the lowest excited state from which it can return to the ground state by emission of radiation. The resonance lines are the spectrum lines emitted or absorbed in this or the reverse transition. When the resonance lines are doublets, the wavelengths of both components are given. The spectroscopic symbols are for the excited states.

radiation of all the inert elements is in the far ultraviolet. The lines of chief analytical interest at present (Tables VIII, IX, and X in Section VI-C) are all caused by energy transitions from one excited state of the atom to another, rather than by energy transitions involving the ground state.

None of the inert gases under ordinary conditions absorbs radiation in the visible, near ultraviolet, or infrared spectral regions. In the visible and near ultraviolet portions of the radiation spectrum, photons do not have enough energy to excite any of the inert gas atoms to even the lowest excited state (see Table VI). There is no absorption in the infrared because the gases are monatomic; there are no vibration spectra, and the moment of inertia of the atoms is too small to produce pure rotational spectra.

The inert gas atoms exhibit both line and continuous absorption in the far ultraviolet, often referred to as the "vacuum ultraviolet" because spectrographs employed in this region are usually evacuated to prevent absorption of the radiation by gases of the air. Not much information is available on the continuous absorption regions. Continuous absorption starts in argon at about 800 A. and in neon at about 575 A., extending to shorter wavelengths; at longer wavelengths than these, there is only discontinuous line absorption (15a).

B. CHEMICAL PROPERTIES

The inert gas elements constitute group 0 of the periodic table. Each of them has, for all practical purposes, only one atom per molecule. The electronic structures of the atoms are stable, and the atoms do not form strong chemical bonds, either with each other or with other atoms.

When argon, krypton, xenon, and radon are sufficiently compressed over water at 0°C., crystals of gas hydrates containing about 6 moles of water per mole of gas are formed. At 0°C. the dissociation pressures of these hydrates vary from 150 atm. for argon to 1 atm. for radon (90a). The inert gas hydrate is an example of a class of compound called a *clathrate*, in which gas atoms are trapped in crystal cages. Clathrate-type compounds with phenol and with hydroquinone have also been reported for argon, krypton, and xenon (90b). Vapors of HCl, H_2S, and CO_2 are said to form crystals with radon at low temperatures.

Ions such as He_2^+ and $(ArKr)^+$ which contain more than one inert gas nucleus are found in the gas phase in electric discharges to a slight extent, but not in sufficient concentration to be detected in ordinary analytical mass spectrometry.

The analytical determination of the inert gases utilizes their physical rather than their chemical properties.

IV. SAMPLING

The importance of adequate sampling can be briefly stated as follows: not only are the time and money spent on analyzing a sample wasted unless the composition of the sample is representative of the composition of the material being investigated, but even the most accurate analysis of an unrepresentative sample may lead to expensive mistaken conclusions. In the words of Jacobs (60a):

In order to make a correct analysis, a proper, representative, and adequate sample of the material to be analyzed must be obtained. Very likely there are as many incorrect determinations resulting from improper sampling as from the combined errors of manipulation, measurement, and calculation. An improper sample makes a subsequent analysis practically worthless. No analysis can be better than the sample nor can the chemist improve the quality of the sample.

The general principles and methods of sampling are given in Chapter 4 of Part I of this Treatise.

The most common kinds of sampling involved in inert gas analysis are those of gases and of minerals.

A. GASES AND LIQUEFIED GASES

This subject is covered in the standard books on gas analysis (36a,85a). A good recent treatment is given by Mullen (92). The information given by Kahle (65a) applies particularly to the inert gases.

1. Natural Gas

The Bureau of Mines has analyzed thousands of samples of natural gas in an extensive survey of United States helium resources. Most of these samples were collected by individuals who had no previous experience in gas sampling; the Bureau of Mines furnished them with clearly worded instructions (3b).

Gas samples for the helium survey were collected in many different types of containers, such as fruit jars, tin cans, glass bottles, several kinds of metal cylinders, toy rubber balloons, and inner tubes of automobile tires. With the exception of the rubber inner tubes and balloons, all the containers served their purpose satisfactorily, provided they did not leak. The inner tubes and balloons permitted diffusion of gases in the sample through the rubber walls of the containers; moreover, some air diffused through the rubber into the container.

"The steel sampling cylinders furnished by the Bureau of Mines were of two general types—a lightweight cylinder for samples under pressures up to 200 p.s.i., and a heavier cylinder for samples under a maximum pressure of 2,000 p.s.i. Both types were equipped with valves at each end of the cylinder, so that the cylinder could be purged before sampling" (3).

Glass bottles were filled by displacement of water, with a rubber hose to bring in the gas, and then sealed off under water to prevent contamination by air.

These sampling methods were simple but adequate for the purpose. They represent the easiest types of gas sampling.

The problem of getting a representative sample from a gas well is not serious; it is assumed that the composition of the gas coming from the well is the same from day to day. As a check on this assumption, samples may be taken on successive days.

As an alternative to using cylinders with a valve on each end, cylinders equipped with a built-in re-entrant tube, as shown in Fig. 2, may be used.

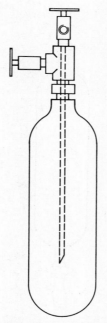

Fig. 2. Steel gas sample vessel equipped with re-entrant tube.

2. Air

In analyzing air, it is usually better to collect a separate sample at each location of interest rather than to try to get a composite sample. Records should be kept of the exact location and of the time each sample is taken.

The size of the sample required depends upon which component of the air is to be determined and what kind of analytical equipment is available. Of the components usually determined in air, only carbon dioxide is appreciably soluble in water; hence large air samples may be collected by displacement of water with very little change in composition. Any handy container can be used for this purpose, provided both the walls and the closure are gastight. However, it is easier to analyze the sample afterward in the laboratory if the container is equipped with valves, one for admitting a displacing liquid such as water and the other for withdrawing the sample.

Small air samples may be conveniently collected in standard gas-sampling tubes (Fig. 3) made of glass and fitted with a stopcock at each end. The tubes are evacuated before collection of the samples. A sample is then taken simply by opening one of the stopcocks at the desired location and closing it again when the air stops flowing in.

Fig. 3. Gas sample tube.

3. Liquid Air

In an air liquefaction plant there is usually no location at which liquid can be sampled with any assurance that the composition is the same as that of outdoor air.   This situation prevails because, from the moment the air enters the intake of the plant, its composition is changed in various ways, as by removal of carbon dioxide and water to prevent clogging of the heat exchangers.   After the air is liquefied, its composition keeps changing by evaporation, distillation, and adsorption or filtration processes.   A sample of liquid is therefore always analyzed with the knowledge that its composition represents only the composition of the liquid at the particular point in the plant where the sample was taken.

A liquefied gas may be sampled by withdrawing some of the liquid into an evacuated metal pressure vessel, usually a cylinder equipped with a pressure gage and a safety release valve and partly cooled by liquid nitrogen. Care must be exercised not to take too much of the liquid.   After the required amount of sample has entered the cylinder, the valves are closed, and the cylinder is withdrawn from the liquid nitrogen bath.   As the temperature of the cylinder rises, the gas pressure builds up.   If too large a liquid sample has been taken, the safety valve will release gas, and the gas left in the cylinder may not have the same composition as the original sample; in this event, the sample must be discarded, the cylinder re-evacuated, and a smaller sample taken.

After all the liquid has evaporated, the cylinder should be rolled or shaken or allowed to stand long enough for the gas sample to become homogeneous. Since mixing by diffusion alone in gases at elevated pressures is a very slow process, the cylinder may have to stand for several days or weeks unless something is done to hasten mixing.

Metal pressure vessels that are to be cooled to liquid nitrogen temperatures should not be made of ordinary steel, because it becomes brittle at low temperatures. Stainless steel (18% chromium, 8% nickel) or copper alloys such as Everdur can be used for these vessels. For strength to withstand pressure, the vessels should be either spherical or cylindrical. Since cylinders are usually easier to fabricate, handle, and store than spheres, most metal pressure vessels for transporting gases are cylinders.

4. Inert Gases in Glass Bulbs and Tubes

If it is known in advance that a glass bulb or glass tube containing gas is to be sampled, the best procedure is to provide the container in advance either with a stopcock or break-seal. A convenient type of break-seal is shown on the bulb in Fig. 1. There are two ways to sample a vessel equipped with a break-seal: (*1*) a piece of iron is inserted in the glass tubing surrounding the seal, the tubing is connected to the apparatus to which the sample is to be transferred, the apparatus is evacuated, and the break-seal is broken by manipulating the piece of iron externally with the help of a magnet; (*2*) a glass bead or iron pellet is inserted into the tubing, the tubing is sealed to a glass stopcock, the tubing is evacuated, the stopcock is closed, the break-seal is broken with the help of the pellet, the tube on the other side of the stopcock is sealed to the manifold, the entire apparatus is evacuated up to the stopcock, and the rare gas is then admitted to the apparatus as desired by turning the stopcock.

No break-seal or stopcock is available when the gas in an electric light bulb or in a fluorescent lamp tube is to be analyzed. If many bulbs or tubes of the same type are to be sampled, the easiest way to sample the gas is probably to use a metal vessel large enough to contain the bulb or tube. The metal vessel should be provided with a valve and with an opening wide enough to admit the glass vessel; a gasketed flange may be used to close this opening. (The gasket must not be made of a material that will contaminate or absorb the gas; soft metal gaskets are usually satisfactory.)

The glass bulb or tube is inserted into the metal vessel along with a piece of metal, and the flanged joint is closed. The vessel is evacuated through its valve, the valve is closed, and the glass bulb is broken with the help of the piece of metal. The sample is then ready for analysis.

For single samples it may not pay to construct the special vessel described in the preceding paragraph, and other methods of obtaining a gas sample may be improvised. For example, to analyze the gas contained in an ordinary electric light bulb, the center post wire may be unsoldered from the metal base, and the base carefully peeled from the glass bulb with pliers. A thick-walled rubber tube may then be slipped over the glass and connected to the analytical apparatus. The apparatus and tubing are evacuated, and the glass tip is broken off inside the rubber tubing. Similarly, a fluorescent lamp may be sampled by slipping a rubber tube of sufficiently large diameter over several inches of the glass and breaking the glass at a location well within the rubber tubing by means of a hammer. Whenever rubber tubing is used, the sample should quickly be transferred to a glass or metal container to prevent loss or contamination by diffusion.

5. Welding Atmospheres

One of the chief uses for argon and helium is to carry the arc and to keep air away while nonferrous metals, such as aluminum, are arc-welded. The sampling of the protective atmosphere during the welding is made difficult by the motion of the welding torch and by drafts in the room where the welding is being done. A composite sample would probably have very little significance. The best procedure would seem to be to do the welding in a room that is as free of drafts as possible, and to take small samples at prearranged and carefully measured locations spaced around the welding arc. The samples may be taken simply by opening one stopcock of an evacuated gas-sampling tube (Fig. 3) at each of the desired locations, carefully labeling each tube. From the analyses of the samples, a three-dimensional picture is thus obtained of the concentration of inert gas in the neighborhood of the weld.

6. Gases Dissolved in Liquids

Samples of gases dissolved in water (for example, from rain, rivers, or lakes) or other liquids may be liberated by boiling the liquid and collecting the gas evolved. More convenient are the techniques described by Shirley, Pachucki, and Lolas (73) for the determination of argon in dissolved water. In both their techniques, some of the sample is first admitted into an evacuated vessel through a three-way stopcock, the air in the tubing leading to the stopcock having been previously flushed out through the stopcock with some of the sample liquid. In one technique the sample is then shaken in the evacuated vessel to liberate the gas, and the gas is analyzed. In the other technique, some convenient gas, different from any gases dissolved in the liquid, is added to the vessel, the vessel is shaken to equilibrate the dissolved gases with the added gas, and the resulting gas mixture is then analyzed.

7. General Techniques and Precautions

a. Adaptation of the Sampling Procedure to Special Requirements

The sampling method must be suited to the purpose of the analysis. For example, if trace constituents are to be determined, it may be necessary to bake out the sampling vessel under vacuum before gathering the sample, but for most purposes this treatment is unnecessary. For sampling hot gases, as from fissures in a volcano, an evacuated vessel with a long handle and a valve that can be opened from a distance can be used (105).

b. Contamination by Air

One of the greatest difficulties in gas sampling is to avoid contamination by air. If the person doing the sampling is conscious of the problem, he can often devise methods for avoiding it. If it is impossible to avoid contamination by air, the fact is usually taken into consideration by reporting the analysis on both an "as is" and an "air-free" basis.

c. Preparation of Homogeneous Samples

Mixing of gases by diffusion alone is slow and gets slower as the temperature is lowered and the pressure raised. Samples that are not homogeneous at the time they are taken must be allowed to mix thoroughly before analysis. The same condition applies to samples prepared in the laboratory as standards for the calibration of instruments such as the mass spectrometer.

Example. If a cylinder 1 m. long is filled to 10 atm. absolute pressure (147 p.s.i. absolute) with argon, and if xenon to the extent of 1% of the quantity of argon present is added slowly through the cylinder valve, it will take about 70 hours' standing at room temperature for mixing to be 90% complete in the absence of any mixing force other than molecular diffusion. At a total pressure of only 1 atm. absolute, the time for 90% mixing by diffusion alone is about 7 hours, and at 0.1 atm., about 0.7 hour. In practice, mixing can be speeded up by adding the gases through a jet built into the cylinder, by gently cooling a spot near the top of the cylinder to set up convection currents, or by rolling or shaking the cylinder.

d. Errors Due to Flexible Tubing

Plasticized flexible tubing, such as Tygon, adds plasticizer vapors to the gas sample. Rubber is permeable to helium and should not be used as a permanent part of a gas-sampling vessel. Both Tygon and rubber are appreciably permeable to xenon and krypton.

e. Error Due to Glass Vessels

Borosilicate (Pyrex, Kimax, etc.) glass is slightly permeable to helium even at room temperature. See Section III-A.

f. Sampling of Gas Cylinders Containing Liquid

With cylinders containing both liquid and gas phases, the gas phase is sampled by being withdrawn through a valve that is well away from the liquid. The liquid phase may be sampled in one of two ways: either the cylinder is turned upside down (or tilted) so that liquid instead of gas comes out of the cylinder valve when it is opened, or the sample is withdrawn through a re-entrant tube (Fig. 2) built into the cylinder and extending below the level of the liquid in the bottom of the cylinder. In a cylinder equipped with a re-entrant tube, the pressure of the gas on the liquid forces liquid up the tube and out of the valve connected to the tube when it is opened.

g. Handling of Pressurized Gas Cylinders

Cylinders of compressed gases should be chained or otherwise secured in such a way that they cannot fall. When they have to be moved, they should be handled gently. Two-wheel trucks to which cylinders can be fastened are handy for moving heavy cylinders around in a laboratory. If cylinders must be rolled by hand in a near-vertical position, the cap should be screwed in place over the cylinder valve; cylinders should never be rolled while the cylinder valve itself is being held, as the valve might open. Once the valve opens, the cylinder can easily spin out of control and fall to the floor.

There are two chief reasons for handling cylinders of compressed gases so that they will not fall. The first is that a heavy, falling cylinder can injure the feet and legs of persons in the vicinity and can break or damage equipment. The second reason is that the cylinder valve might break off. If this happens when the cylinder is full of gas, the cylinder may "take off" like a rocket, propelled by the thrust of the escaping gas. A cylinder can thus reach a speed of 30 to 70 m.p.h. in less than a second. Actual occurrences of this type are extremely rare, but the importance of careful handling of compressed gas cylinders is evident.

B. MINERALS

Occasionally the problem of analyzing gases occluded in minerals arises. Here the general rules given in Chapter 4 of Part I of this Treatise apply. Steps should, of course, be taken to see that the sample is representative. Probably the only unusual precaution has to do with grinding the sample. During grinding, a portion of the occluded gases is released, and the finer the grinding, the more gas will be lost. Fine grinding before the vacuum fusion (or other gas liberation) step should therefore be avoided unless means are provided for catching the gas released during grinding.

V. SEPARATION AND ISOLATION

A. MICRO SEPARATIONS

When there is plenty of sample available, the separation and isolation of the inert gases is not particularly difficult; the methods are discussed in the following section. The case is quite different when very small quantities of the gases are to be isolated; for this situation, specialized micro techniques are required. In micro gas analysis, gastight apparatus containing the sample at pressures ranging from a few millimeters of mercury to much less is used, pressures being measured with sensitive gages.

The inert gases may be separated from each other on a micro scale by desorption from activated carbon at controlled temperatures. The gas fractions are introduced, one at a time, into an evacuated vessel of known volume where the pressure and temperature are measured; this procedure makes it possible to calculate the quantity of each gas present. The accuracy of such an analysis depends, of course, upon the sharpness of the separation attained in the desorption process. Paneth (97) has written an interesting review of this subject. Micro work is very specialized; the many details that, taken together, make up the required technique were developed over a period of years in a few laboratories in Europe and the United States.

B. SEPARATION OF INERT GASES FROM OTHER GASES

In carrying out qualitative and quantitative analyses of the inert gases, it is usually not necessary to isolate the individual elements. In some cases, however, it is desirable to make separations. For example, identification of neon in the mass spectrometer is difficult if both carbon dioxide and argon are in the gas sample, because the doubly charged ions of carbon dioxide and argon give mass/charge (m/e) peaks which obscure the two principal peaks of neon.   Separations of inert gases from other gases may be carried out by chemical methods.

1. Orsat Procedure

Probably the best procedure for dealing with a gas mixture of completely unknown composition is to put it through the standard Orsat apparatus (3d,36b,85b).   Some apparatus supply houses sell complete Orsats, together with reagents and directions for analyzing gases.   One general procedure is to remove, in turn, the following components:

1. Acid gases, usually carbon dioxide, in potassium hydroxide solution.

2. Oxygen in an alkaline solution of potassium pyrogallate or other oxygen absorber.

3. Unsaturated hydrocarbons in fuming sulfuric acid.

4. Carbon monoxide in cuprous chloride solution or other carbon monoxide absorber.   Alternatively, carbon monoxide may be determined along with hydrogen by passing the sample over copper oxide at about 300°C. The hydrogen is oxidized to water and determined by measuring the contraction in volume of the gas.   Carbon monoxide is oxidized to carbon dioxide, which is absorbed in potassium hydroxide solution after the volume reduction due to the oxidation of hydrogen has been measured.

5. Saturated hydrocarbons, by combustion with added oxygen, either over a heated platinum filament or in a heated bed of oxidation catalyst.

The volume of the gas is read three times in the gas buret: after the oxygen has been added; after the combustion has been completed and the resulting water vapor allowed to condense; and after the carbon dioxide has been absorbed by the potassium hydroxide solution.   From the two volume changes thus measured, the quantity and nature of the saturated hydrocarbons originally present can be estimated.

There are several possible variations in the order in which the gases are removed and in the reagents employed.   Detailed instructions for preparing the reagents are given in references 36c and 85c.   Instructions for carrying out the combustion of hydrogen and hydrocarbons are given in reference 85d.

The residue from the Orsat procedure consists of nitrogen and the inert gases.   By the time the chemist has carried out the Orsat determination, he will have a good idea of what, if anything, is in the original sample besides inert gases and nitrogen; if the residue is too small to handle conveniently, he will be in a position to decide how best to remove the bulk of the noninert gases from a larger sample of the original gas.   This removal would probably be done in apparatus especially designed for the purpose, not in an Orsat.

2. Removal of Nitrogen and Traces of Other Gases

In most cases the mixture of nitrogen and the inert gases is examined directly by the mass spectrometer, gas chromatograph, or emission spectrometer. Only if the proportion of nitrogen is high is it necessary to remove the nitrogen before trying to identify the inert gases present.

Nitrogen may be removed by titanium metal sponge at 900 to 1000°C. (29), by metallic calcium at 440 to 500°C. (65b) or at 650 to 700°C. (72, 122), by metallic barium (97a), by activated uranium (28), or by molten lithium (65c). Handy apparatus for the rapid removal of nitrogen by molten lithium heated to 420°C. has been described (83).

All the hot metals mentioned absorb oxygen as well as nitrogen. Nitrogen and all other impurities except the inert gases themselves may be removed by suitably activated uranium (28).

C. ISOLATION OF THE INDIVIDUAL ELEMENTS

1. Desorption from Activated Carbon

Isolation of the individual inert gases is not carried out as an analytical technique as often as formerly because the mass spectrometer and the gas chromatograph have made it relatively easy to analyze mixtures. However, there probably will be special cases in which it is desirable to separate the gases.

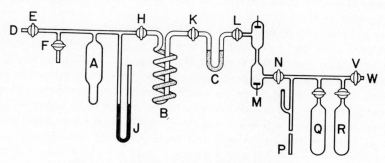

Fig. 4. Apparatus for isolating the inert gases.

Kahle (65h) describes a charcoal desorption method for the separation of all the inert gases except helium from neon and states that complete separation of each of the inert gases (except helium from neon) in a mixture of all of them may be carried out, after practice, in about 2 hours. This time may be shortened if any of the gases are known to be absent. The method depends upon the gradual replacement of less strongly adsorbed gas by more strongly adsorbed gas.   A similar method was described by Cady (19).

Apparatus similar to that suggested by Kahle is partly shown in Fig. 4. A is an empty measuring and condensation vessel. B and C are, respectively, a spiral tube and a U-tube made of glass tubing and filled with activated charcoal.   The vessel containing the sample is not shown in Fig 4; it is attached to the manifold below stopcock F.   Let us use the letter S to refer to the valve or stopcock with which the sample vessel is equipped. To carry out an analysis, stopcocks E, F, H, K, and L are opened.   With stopcocks S and N closed, vessels A, B, and C are pumped out by means of a vacuum pump connected at D.   Stopcocks E, H, K, and L are then closed, and S is opened to admit a part of the gas sample to vessel A. Then F is closed, the pressure is read on manometer J, and the temperature is recorded.   The volume of vessel A being known, the quantity of sample can readily be calculated.

Vessels A and C are then cooled by liquid nitrogen, and vessel B by a bath kept at $-110°C$.   Most of the xenon and krypton are frozen out in A; a pressure reading will give a rough preliminary idea of the combined helium, neon, and argon content of the original sample.   Stopcock H is slowly opened, and then stopcock K.   When the pressure becomes constant, stopcock L, leading to the gas discharge (Geissler) tube, M, is opened.   At first only the yellow color of the helium discharge should be seen.   A spectroscope is used to show the spectral lines being emitted by the excited gas (see Section VI-C).

Beyond stopcock N there is attached to the manifold a series of vessels, Q, R, etc. (only two of which are shown in Fig. 4), each of known volume, which are evacuated through W.   Stopcock V is then closed.   As soon as the Geissler tube is in operation, vessel Q is slowly opened to admit helium.   After a while, neon lines will appear in the spectrum, and since the method does not give a clean separation of helium from neon, the gas is allowed to continue to flow through stopcock N until argon lines first appear in the spectrum, at which time stopcock N is immediately closed. The pressure in vessel Q is read with the help of the McLeod-type gage, P, partly shown in the figure.   (If the flow of gas through N stops, that is, if the pressure read on P becomes constant before argon lines appear in the spectrum, vessel Q is closed, and vessel R is opened, etc., until all the helium and neon have passed stopcock N.)   From the volume, pressure, and temperature in vessel Q (plus R, etc., as required) the quantity of helium and neon can be calculated.   Vessels Q, R, etc., are then evacuated through W, stopcock V is closed, and stopcock N and vessel Q are opened to admit the argon.

When the gas flow becomes slow, the liquid nitrogen bath is removed from around vessel *A;* when the flow again becomes slow, the liquid nitrogen bath is gradually removed from *C.* Finally the cooling bath is gradually removed from *B.* The moment krypton lines appear in the spectrum, *N* is closed, and the argon pressure in *Q* is measured. Krypton is withdrawn next. If no xenon lines appear after *A, B,* and *C* are all at room temperature, *B* is warmed in a water bath to 100°C.; if there are still no xenon lines, *C* is also warmed to 100°C. When the xenon lines appear, *N* is closed, and the krypton pressure in *Q* is measured. Xenon is determined last.

If any of the gases are known to be absent, the above procedure can be shortened correspondingly.

Helium and neon cannot be separated quantitatively in a single-stage process. Separation is accomplished by fractional desorption from charcoal at −196°C., the temperature of boiling liquid nitrogen, using 12 to 15 stages. The theory of fractional desorption and a description of the method are given by Glückauf (37,39a).

2. Fractional Distillation

Partial separation of the inert gases can be accomplished by fractional distillation, but this procedure is usually not so convenient as the desorption process—especially if helium and neon are both present, since liquid helium or liquid hydrogen would have to be used as a refrigerant for a distillation in which neon is to be liquefied. If only argon, krypton, and xenon are to be separated, the problem of refrigeration is much simpler, and pure gases can be obtained with distilling columns that have a sufficient number of theoretical plates. When small samples are to be analyzed, distillation suffers from the drawback that in practice a mixture of inert gases cannot be completely separated into its components unless there is a substantial quantity of the least volatile component to act as a "chaser," since there is some unavoidable holdup in the column and kettle.

3. Gas Chromatography

The inert gases can be separated from each other, although mixed with the eluting gas, in a gas chromatograph.

D. SEPARATION OF ISOTOPES

Glueckauf and co-workers (39) reported a slight separation of the neon isotopes by desorption from charcoal at −196°C. From this work they concluded that there is a possibility that helium-3 may be separated from helium-4 by desorption from charcoal at the temperature of liquid hydrogen.

Fractional desorption and fractional distillation are not usually effective for the separation of isotopes, and other methods must be considered.   The most important of these other methods are multistage diffusion through semipermeable barriers (65i), repeated passage through thermal diffusion columns (65j), and ion separation in a magnetic field (115a).   The isotopes of neon and of krypton have been isolated in thermal diffusion columns by Clusius and Dickel (22).   All these methods are slow and expensive.

VI. QUALITATIVE DETECTION AND IDENTIFICATION

A. INTRODUCTION

The presence or absence in a gas mixture of one or more of the inert gases as a class is fairly easy to demonstrate with simple chemical apparatus in which all chemically active gases are removed from a gas sample (see Section V-B-2).   Any residue after such a treatment is evidence of the presence of one or more of the inert gases.

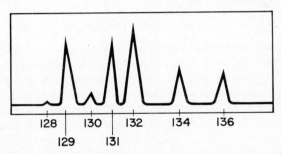

Fig. 5. Oscilloscope pattern of mass spectrum of atmospheric xenon. (Courtesy of Cincinnati Division of Bendix Aviation Corporation.)

The choice of method for the qualitative detection of the individual inert gases depends partly upon what apparatus is available to the analyst and partly upon what noninert gases are present in the sample.

Usually the mass spectrometer gives the answer most easily, but it is possible that other gases may be present that give m/e patterns interfering with the peaks used to identify the inert gases.

The emission spectrometer is good for identifying inert gases, but unless it has been calibrated with similar gas mixtures, it is difficult to get even a rough idea of the concentrations of the gases detected.

The gas chromatograph is handy for qualitative analysis if the sample is one of a series of similar samples, the composition of which is roughly known, or if the retention times of all the components are known.   Identification of components in mixtures analyzed by the gas chromatograph may be made easy by the use of a high-speed mass spectrometer (122,123) which scans the mass spectrum of the eluted mixture up to 10,000 times/ second and exhibits the mass spectrogram on an oscilloscope screen (Fig. 5).

B. MASS SPECTROMETRY

The principles of mass spectrometry are explained in Part I of this Treatise.

Available types of mass spectrometers differ greatly in the range of mass numbers covered and in resolution, sensitivity, and speed.   For detection of all the inert gases, it is necessary that good resolution be available up to about mass 222 (principal isotope of radon).   Instruments having a well-resolved range of 1 to 135 mass numbers can detect all the inert gases except radon.

Given a gas sample of completely unknown composition, one can get a quick preliminary idea of what is in it by use of the mass spectrometer. After the scan has been made, it is examined for mass/charge (m/e) peaks

TABLE VII

Principal Nonradioactive Inert Gas Ions Produced in the Mass Spectrometer
(See also Table III.)

Mass/charge (m/e) peak	Ion	Mass/charge (m/e) peak	Ion
4	He^+	64 ⎫	
20	Ne^+, Ar^{+2}	$64\frac{1}{2}$ ⎪	
21 ⎫		65 ⎪	
22 ⎭	Ne^+	$65\frac{1}{2}$ ⎬	Xe^{+2}
36 ⎫		66 ⎪	
38 ⎭	Ar^+	67 ⎪	
39	Kr^{+2}	68 ⎭	
40	Ar^+, Kr^{+2}	78 ⎫	
41 ⎫		80 ⎪	
$41\frac{1}{2}$ ⎬	Kr^{+2}	82 ⎪	Kr^+
42 ⎭		83 ⎬	
43	Kr^{+2}, Xe^{+3}	84 ⎪	
$43\frac{2}{3}$ ⎫		86 ⎭	
44 ⎪		128 ⎫	
$44\frac{2}{3}$ ⎬	Xe^{+3}	129 ⎪	
$45\frac{1}{3}$ ⎭		130 ⎪	
		131 ⎬	Xe^+
		132 ⎪	
		134 ⎪	
		136 ⎭	

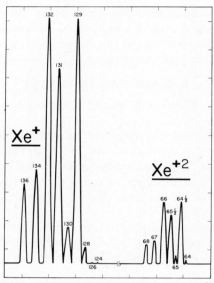

Fig. 6. Mass spectrogram of atmospheric xenon (pen recording on strip chart.)

characteristic of the inert gas isotopes.   The principal m/e peaks for the inert gases are given in Table VII; this table should be used in connection with the list of stable isotopes given in Table III.

It will be seen from Table VII that the only appreciable interferences are at m/e values of 20, 40, and 43, and of these the only serious one is at 20. In a sample containing a large amount of argon and only a small concentration of neon, the peak at 20 loses much of its value for the detection of neon. The peak at 22 may then be used for neon, if it is certain that there are no traces of impurities other than inert gases, for example, CO_2^{+2}, which could give a peak there.   If there is too little neon to produce a measurable peak at 22, argon will have to be separated from the neon; see Section V-C-1.

The contribution of Kr^{+2} to the 40 peak is very slight and can readily be corrected for, since there are several clear krypton peaks.   The peak at 43 is not of analytical importance, since both krypton and xenon have clear peaks.

In using the mass spectrometer as a tool for qualitative analysis of gas mixtures of completely unknown composition, two things should be kept in mind.

1. Hydrocarbons and other gases can give breakdown patterns containing some of the same mass peaks as those listed in Table VII for the inert

gases.   In the case of neon, krypton, and xenon, it is fairly easy to see
whether there is any interference from other gases because the natural isotopes occur in families of peaks of known ratio; see, for example, Fig. 6.
If interference is suspected, confirmatory tests may have to be made by
other methods to insure correct identification of the unknown.

2. A gas mixture of unknown composition could contain isotopes of the
inert gases with concentration ratios different from the natural abundance
ratios.   It is, however, unlikely that samples of this type would be offered
for analysis without some information as to the unusual origin of the sample.

C. EMISSION SPECTROMETRY

1. General Discussion

The principles of emission spectroscopy are explained in Part I of this
Treatise.

Spectra from gas samples may be obtained, for example, by filling a discharge tube like the one in Fig. 7 with the gas to a few mm. Hg pressure,

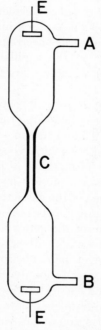

Fig. 7. Gas discharge tube: *A*, *B*, tubes through which gas flows; *C*, glass capillary; *E*.
E, electrodes.

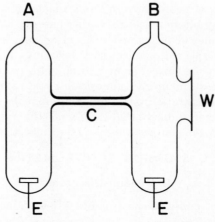

Fig. 8. Gas discharge tube, end-on type: *A*, *B*, tubes through which gas flows; *C*, glass capillary; *E*, *E*, electrodes; *W*, fused quartz window.

imposing a high voltage on the electrodes, and analyzing the emitted light. The tube shown in Fig. 7 is called a Geissler or Plücker tube. Another type (Fig. 8) is the "end-on" tube, which makes it possible to get much more light into the spectrometer or spectrograph than is possible from a Geissler tube, the discharge in the capillary being viewed through a vitreous silica (fused quartz) window. For another design of discharge tube see reference 106a.

The Geissler tube is mounted so that its capillary is opposite and parallel to the slit of the spectrometer. Discharge tubes are usually filled with the sample to pressures between 0.5 and 10 mm. Tubes equipped with sealed-in electrodes may be excited with high voltage (several thousand volts) from either an induction coil (often called a spark coil), a transformer, or a Tesla coil. When electrodes are present inside the discharge tube, they often act as "getters" for some of the gases that are present in low concentrations (2,118c). This situation may be either good or bad, depending upon circumstances. The problem of the getter action may be partly avoided by using the so-called "electrodeless" discharge, in which there are no electrodes inside the tube, but even here adsorption on the glass may occur. The electrodeless discharge may be produced by wrapping a copper coil around the discharge tube and connecting the ends of the coil to a vacuum tube oscillator to give radio-frequency power (106b). The best way of minimizing changes in composition of gas samples in discharge tubes is to keep the sample flowing through the tube all the time the spectrum is being photographed.

In trying to identify the inert gases from their emission spectra, Tables VIII, IX, and X will be of help. They give the most sensitive and intense emission lines of each gas. Also of assistance will be Harrison's monumental *MIT Wavelength Tables* of more than 100,000 spectrum lines between 10,000 A. and 2000 A. arranged in order of decreasing wavelength. By looking up the wavelengths at which lines in the spectrum of the gases are found, one can check on possible interference by other elements with the line being identified. To be sure of the presence of a specific element in a given sample, it is desirable to identify at least two lines in its emission spectrum.

TABLE VIII

Wavelengths of Emission Lines Useful for Identifying Inert Gases (47)

Gas	Sensitivity[a]	Wavelength, A.	Relative intensity
Helium	2	5875.618	1000
	3	4685.75	300
	1	3888.646	1000
Neon		6402.246	2000
		5852.488	2000
		5400.562	2000
Argon	1	8115.311	5000
	3	7503.867	700
	2	7067.217	400
	2	6965.430	400
Krypton	1	5870.9158	3000
	2	5570.2895	2000
Xenon	1	4671.226	2000
	2	4624.276	1000
	3	4500.977	500
Radon	1	7450.00	600
	2	7055.42	400
Mercury		5460.740	2000
		3654.833	200

[a] The lowest number represents the greatest sensitivity.

When known, the sensitivity is given for each spectrum line listed in Table VIII. The line having the greatest sensitivity is the last line of the element to disappear as the concentration of the emitting element becomes less and less (48a). The order of sensitivity is not necessarily the same as the order of intensity. Since observed line intensities depend greatly on the emulsions used in photographing the lines, whereas the true intensities depend on the excitation conditions in the source used, all listed intensities

TABLE IX

Wavelengths of Emission Lines Useful for Identifying Inert Gases with a Spectroscope

Gas	Pressure in discharge tube, mm. Hg	Kahle (65g)		MIT Wavelength Tables (47)	
		Wavelength, mμ	Intensity[a]	Wavelength, A.	Relative intensity[b]
Helium	4	587	5	5875.618	1000
		501.5	4	5015.675	100
		471	7	4713.143	40
		447	10	4471.477	100
		438.5	5	4387.928	30
		388	9	3888.646	1000
Neon	5	588	4	5881.895	1000
		584	4	5852.4878	2000
		575	4	5748.299	500
		594	3	5944.8342	500
		545	3	5448.508	150
		540	3	5400.562	2000
		534	3	5341.093	1000
				4715.344	1500
				4712.060	1000
		471	3	4710.058	1000
				4708.854	1200
				4704.395	1500
Argon	1.5	436	10	4363.794	80
		404.7	6	4044.418	1200
		545	5	5451.650	500
		435	5	4348.11	500
		434	5	4345.167	1000
		421.1	5	4203.43	20
Krypton	1	557	7	5570.2895	2000
		546	7	5468.17	200 ha
		436	8	4362.6423	500
		432.5	6	4319.5797	1000
		405.5	6	4057.01	300 ha
Xenon	3	466	5	4671.226	2000
		461.5	4	4624.276	1000
		420	4	4208.48	200 h
				4193.15	200 h
		404.5	6	4037.59	100
		472.5	3	4731.19	50 ha
		449.5	3	4500.977	500
		407.5	3	4078.820	100
Mercury vapor		546		5460.740	2000
		436		4358.35[c]	500
		408		4077.811[c]	150
		404		4046.561[c]	300

[a] The lowest number represents the greatest sensitivity.

[b] The letter h stands for hazy, and a for asymmetrical.

[c] Not listed by Harrison (47) as a discharge line.

should be taken merely as rough approximations (47a). The table includes lines in the ultraviolet and infrared as well as in the visible portion of the spectrum.

Table IX will give additional help in the identification of the inert gases by means of their emission spectra. This table lists the strongest lines in the visible portion of the spectrum as photographed by Kahle (65g) through a pocket spectroscope. His wavelengths could be read only to about three significant figures. To extend the usefulness of Table IX, Harrison's *MIT Wavelength Tables* (47) were searched for strong lines in the neighborhood of the wavelengths observed by Kahle, and Harrison's values for the wavelength and intensity of each of the lines thus found have been included.

The discrepancies between the intensities observed by Harrison and by Kahle are explained by the fact that the relative intensities of lines are changed by almost any alteration in the physical conditions, such as variation in voltage and type of power applied to the discharge, pressure, temperature, and presence of other gases (104a).

Mercury lines have been included in both tables because of the possible presence of mercury from a Toepler pump, a mercury vapor diffusion pump, or other sources. It is best, however, to exclude mercury vapor from the discharge tube by having the gases first pass through a small tube containing some gold leaf (118b).

2. Comments on Spectra of Individual Gases

Those who have occasion to look frequently at the discharge spectra of the inert gases soon become able to recognize the patterns of the lines. A glance tells whether the patterns obtained represent pure single gases, mixtures of just inert gases, or inert gases containing impurities. Travers (118d) gives a helpful practical discussion of the spectrometry of the inert gases. He made the following observations:

Helium. At 7 to 8 mm. pressure, with an intermittent d.c. voltage from an induction coil, the color of the glow in the discharge tube is yellow, and the 5875.9 A. line reaches its maximum intensity. On reduction of the pressure, the intensity of the 5015.6 (green) line increases, and at 1 to 2 mm. the tube emits a green light. This happens only when the gas is pure. In the presence of other gases, particularly nitrogen, the helium lines are most easily distinguished when the pressure is very low, the green 5015.6 helium line usually being the most brilliant.

Neon. The red neon lines are easily identified. The presence of helium in neon is most easily detected by the green line at 5015.6 A.

Argon. The spectrum of argon is very complex and undergoes a striking change when the nature of the discharge is altered. With an intermittent d.c. voltage (induction coil), the glow in the tube is red, and there are only a few blue lines in the spectrum. With a radio-frequency discharge, the glow is bright blue, the red lines in the spectrum become faint or disappear, and many green and blue lines appear. (The radio-frequency discharge may be produced by putting a spark gap and condenser in the secondary circuit.) At low pressures the radio-frequency discharge usually gives a mixture of the two spectra. The strongest lines observed by Travers in the argon spectrum, along with Harrison's exact wavelengths and relative intensities, are given in Table X. Small quantities of nitrogen tend to suppress the argon spectrum.

TABLE X
Strongest Lines in the Argon Spectrum

	MIT Wavelength Tables (47)	
Travers (118)	Wavelength, A.	Relative intensity
Red spectrum		
7056.6	7055.01	4
6964.8	6965.430	400
6415.2	6416.315	100
6033.7	6032.124	60
5651.0	5650.703	1500
5607.4	5606.732	500
5559.0	5558.702	500
5496.2	5495.872	1000
5451.9	5451.530	500
Blue spectrum		
6033.7	6032.124	60
5739.9	5739.517	500

Krypton. The yellow line 5871 and the green line 5570.5 are the most brilliant; they are distinctly visible when the gas is present in very low concentration in a mixture.

Xenon. With an induction coil, the glow is blue, and the red and green lines are few and faint. With a radio-frequency discharge, the glow becomes green and brilliant, and the spectrum, which is very complex, contains many green lines.

Mercury. The spectrum of mercury is visible when there are only traces of it present. Fortunately, in a short time the mercury vapor is usually absorbed by the electrodes, and the lines of its spectrum disappear.

3. Spectroscopic Detection of Traces of Inert Gases

a. NEON IN HELIUM

Riesz and Dieke (102) reported the detection of 1 part of neon in 200 million parts of helium, using the phenomenon of cataphoresis. The ratio of the intensity of any two inert gas emission lines was recorded automatically. The equipment was calibrated for the particular gases involved; for neon, the 6402 A. wavelength line, and for helium, the 5047 A. wavelength line, were used.

This cataphoresis method is similar to a method described by Skaupy and Bobek (65k).

In a discharge tube containing helium alone, the light is yellow when viewed without filters, but when viewed through "didymium" (a mixture of praseodymium and neodymium used in glass blower's glasses), which absorbs the yellow helium lines, the helium discharge looks deep blue. In the presence of a trace of neon, the color is red.

b. INERT GASES IN HELIUM

Karlik (66) reported the spectroscopic detection of the following quantities of inert gases in helium: neon, 5×10^{-7} mm.^{3}; argon, 6×10^{-6} mm.^{3}; krypton, 4×10^{-7} mm.^{3}; and xenon, 6×10^{-7} mm.^{3} She found it easier to work in the ultraviolet than in the visible portion of the spectrum. She used an all-quartz discharge tube with no interior electrodes; the gas was excited externally by high-frequency power. The tube was cleaned, and its interior surfaces were degassed by pumping while it was being heated, sometimes as long as 2 days, almost to white heat. Absence of interior electrodes obviated the difficulties experienced by many workers with occlusion of gases by the electrodes. A helium pressure of 0.4 to 5 mm. was used. She found that traces of nitrogen, carbon dioxide, hydrocarbons from the stopcock grease, and mercury vapor all tend to suppress the spectra of inert gases present only in traces.

A similar limit of sensitivity was found for the spectroscopic detection of neon in helium by Günther and Paneth (44), and in helium and neon when isolated by the micro techniques of Paneth and Peters (98).

Among the advantages of the use of an emission spectrograph or spectrometer for detection of inert gases are these: (1) in many cases the emission spectrometer will detect very low concentrations of the element; and (2) once two or more lines have been identified, the presence of the element to which they belong is established with considerable certainty.

Possible disadvantages of the spectroscopic method of identification are as follows: (1) although not difficult, it is not as simple to fill a Geissler tube with a gas as merely to feed a gas sample into a gas chromatograph or mass spectrometer; (2) some gases tend to suppress, and others to enhance, the emission of radiation from others.   For example, in a 2:1 mixture of hydrogen and helium, the helium spectrum is suppressed at a total pressure of 2.6 mm. Hg, strong at 0.43 mm., and even stronger than the hydrogen spectrum at 0.012 mm. (85e).   Traces of hydrocarbons greatly modify the spectral intensities of the inert gases (118a).

D. GAS CHROMATOGRAPHY

The principles of gas chromatography are given in Part I of this Treatise.
In using the gas chromatograph for the detection of inert gases, the first problem is to select a suitable packing material for the column.   Gas chromatography is so new that the best packing material for each application has not necessarily yet been found; however, there are several adsorbents that have been tried with some success for gas-solid chromatography of the inert gases.   They are synthetic crystalline zeolites (such as Linde molecular sieves Types 4A, 5A, and 13X), mordenite (11), activated charcoal (61,62), and silica gel (61).   These column-packing materials are used dry.   No work has yet come to the attention of the author in which gas-liquid partition chromatography has been employed for the inert gases.
The selection of a carrier gas depends upon several factors.   Helium is usually employed in the United States, where it is plentiful; it has the advantage that its thermal conductivity differs greatly from the thermal conductivities of most of the gases and vapors being analyzed, thus making it easy to detect traces of components.   If helium itself is to be identified, it cannot be used as the carrier gas; gases which might be used are hydrogen, nitrogen, argon, and carbon dioxide.
Argon is better than nitrogen for the gas chromatography of light gases (for example, helium and neon) when a thermal conductivity cell is used as detector, because the thermal conductivity of argon is smaller than that of nitrogen, thus making a greater contrast with the helium.   Argon is better than carbon dioxide when synthetic crystalline zeolites are to be used as the column-packing material, because the zeolites usually adsorb carbon dioxide.
Janak (61) uses carbon dioxide because it can be absorbed by potassium hydroxide solution after elution.   He separates the inert gas mixtures on activated carbon in a stream of carbon dioxide and then absorbs the carbon dioxide from each fraction, thus obtaining small samples of the separate gases that can be identified by mass spectrometry or emission spectrometry.
Hydrogen as a carrier gas has many of the advantages of helium, but it is flammable and, when mixed with air or oxygen, explosive.
Temperature has a considerable effect on the separations achieved in gas

chromatography. In general, the lower the temperature, the better the resolution. At lower temperatures gases are sometimes adsorbed too strongly for easy elution. At −119°C., for example, it is not practicable to use mordenite as column packing for the analysis of krypton and argon, because the krypton is adsorbed too strongly (11).

Since the choice of conditions for separating a given mixture depends upon the identities and concentrations of the gases present in the sample, the analyst may have to do some experimenting to select the best conditions: packing material, length of adsorbing column, temperature, carrier gas, size of sample, and rate of carrier gas flow. The following examples (31) may be of help.

1. Separation of a Mixture of Neon, Argon, Nitrogen, Krypton, and Xenon

Fig. 9 shows a chromatogram in which helium was used as a carrier gas to separate the other inert gases on a synthetic zeolite. Conditions and re-

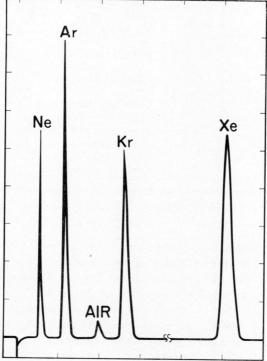

Fig. 9. Chromatogram for mixture of neon, argon, air impurity, krypton, and xenon.

sults are given in Table XI. The small peak labeled "air" in the figure really represents only the nitrogen from a small amount of air in the sample; the oxygen appears with the argon. All the inert gases present in the sample were fully resolved. After all the krypton was eluted, the column temperature was raised to hasten elution of the xenon, which is adsorbed quite strongly on the zeolite at room temperature.

TABLE XI

Separation of Inert Gases in a Stream of Helium

Gas	Concn. in sample, mole %	Retention time	Column temp., °C.
Neon	21	0 min. 32 sec.	30
Argon[a]	28	1 min. 6 sec.	30
Air (nitrogen only)	2	1 min. 58 sec.	30
Krypton	25	2 min. 33 sec.	30
		[3 min. 30 sec.][b]	Column heater turned on
Xenon	24	8 min. 44 sec.	85

Other conditions:

Column length	2.5 m.
Column internal diameter	3.0 mm.
Column packing	Type 13X Linde molecular sieve, 40–60 mesh
Helium flow	84 ml./min. (0°C., 760 mm.)
Helium pressure	20 p.s.i. gage
Size of sample	2.8 cc. (0°C., 760 mm.)
Detector	Thermal conductivity

[a] Includes a little oxygen from a small amount of air impurity in the sample.
[b] Time elapsed, not retention time.

Some other conditions (not shown in Table XI) were tried with the same gas mixture. The effect of reducing the helium flow was merely to spread out the peaks. The effect of substituting Type 5A molecular sieve for Type 13X was to require a higher column temperature, 70°C., until the krypton was eluted, and then a gradual increase in temperature until xenon was desorbed at 140°C. In every case, the gas peaks were all resolved except oxygen plus argon, which always appeared as a single peak. As pointed out in the following paragraphs, however, oxygen and argon can be resolved by use of Type 4A molecular sieve.

2. Separation of a Mixture of Helium, Neon, and Hydrogen

Fig. 10 shows a chromatogram in which pure argon was used as carrier gas to make a complete separation of helium, neon, and hydrogen on activated carbon at a column temperature of about −78°C. (Table XII).

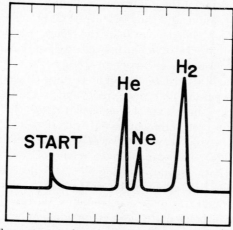

Fig. 10. Chromatogram for mixture of helium, neon, and hydrogen.

Some conditions not shown in Table XII were tried with the same gas mixture, but none of them gave complete resolution of the helium and neon peaks. Conditions like those in the table except that the column tempera-

TABLE XII
Separation of Helium, Neon, and Hydrogen in a Stream of Argon

Gas	Concn. in sample, mole %	Retention time
Helium	33.4	1 min. 5 sec.
Neon	34.1	1 min. 19 sec.
Hydrogen	32.5	1 min. 57 sec.
Other conditions:		
Column length	1.5 m.	
Column internal diameter	3.0 mm.	
Column packing	Burrell high-activity charcoal	
Column temperature	Dry ice–acetone bath	
Argon flow	25 ml./min. (0°C., 760 mm.)	
Argon pressure	6 p.s.i. gage	
Size of sample	0.07 cc. (0°C., 760 mm.)	
Detector	Thermal conductivity	

ture was 26°C. gave almost no resolution of the helium-neon peaks.   Partial resolution was obtained at 26°C. when a synthetic zeolite (Linde Type 5A) was substituted for the carbon packing, but resolution was only slightly better at −78°C.   With Type 13X molecular sieve, only partial resolution was obtained at any temperature tried.

When the composition of the mixture was changed so that most of the gas was air, nitrogen, or argon, and the concentrations of helium and neon were less than 50 p.p.m., complete resolution of the helium and neon was achieved at 40°C. with a column 15 ft. long, packed with activated charcoal, and with either nitrogen or argon as carrier gas (32).

One flaw in the qualitative detection of inert gases by gas chromatography is that with most packing materials argon and oxygen are not resolved. There is one packing (Linde Type 4A molecular sieve) that resolves oxygen and argon, but in this case argon comes out with the nitrogen.

The commercial availability has recently been announced of a mass spectrometer (122,123) that scans a given region of the mass spectrum at rates up to 10,000 times/second, showing on an oscilloscope the mass spectrum of a flowing gas.   By allowing the stream of gas leaving a gas chromatograph to flow through this mass spectrometer, the analyst can see which inert gas or inpurity is being eluted at a given moment.

E. NEUTRON ACTIVATION

The inert gases can be made radioactive by bombardment with neutrons and can then be identified by the radiation emitted; see Section VII-G.

F. OTHER METHODS

Other methods of identification depend upon the actual isolation of the gases; these have been described in Section V.

VII. QUANTITATIVE DETERMINATION

A. INTRODUCTION

The most generally useful methods for the quantitative determination of the individual inert gases are mass spectrometry and gas-solid chromatography, that is, gas chromatography using a dry solid as adsorbent in the chromatographic column.

Mass spectrometry suffers from the disadvantage that most mass spectrometers are rather expensive.   In some work there is also the disadvantage of overlapping mass peaks, but this drawback usually does not apply to analysis of the inert gases if they have previously been freed of all other gases except nitrogen.

Gas chromatographs are usually cheaper than mass spectrometers, and, if money for a commercial model is lacking, a satisfactory unit can be built more readily than can a satisfactory mass spectrometer.

With the exception of hydrogen and deuterium (40), a gas chromatograph cannot distinguish between the isotopes of a given element; therefore, if isotopic composition is to be studied, a mass spectrometer is generally used. Both mass spectrometry and gas chromatography can be used for determining almost any concentration of the inert gases, ranging from traces to large concentrations, depending on available equipment.

If neither a mass spectrometer nor a gas chromatograph is available, concentrations of the inert gases can be determined by emission spectrography or by other methods. For binary mixtures, some physical property (such as thermal conductivity) can be used to determine the composition.

An important part of any physical method of analysis is calibration by gas mixtures of known composition. A procedure for preparing such standard gas mixtures is given in Section IX-A (see also reference 93).

Table XIII gives a brief summary of the generally applicable methods for the analytical determination of the inert gases. Methods limited to binary mixtures are not included in the table but are discussed in Section VII-J.

TABLE XIII

Generally Applicable Quantitative Analytical
Methods for Gas Mixtures Containing Inert Gases

Method	Usual concn. range that can be handled	Smallest actual quantity that can be handled
Mass spectrometry	5 p.p.m.[a] to 100%	
Gas chromatography	10 p.p.m.[a] to 100%	
Emission spectrography	1 p.p.m. to 1%	
Isolation by desorption from activated carbon		10^{-6} mm.^{3}
Neutron activation		10^{-7} g.

[a] These low concentrations require special equipment. In a few special cases, even lower concentrations can be determined.

B. ISOLATION METHODS

The total inert gas content of a gas sample can be determined by removing all other gases and measuring the residue. Methods for removing other gases have been given in Section V-B. Examples of analytical determinations involving isolation methods appear in the following paragraphs.

1. Laboratory Determination of Total Impurities (Argon and Other Gases) in Oxygen

This method is slow but reliable. It is useful only when the total of all the impurities present is less than about 1000 p.p.m. and in the absence of impurities that react with copper at 300°C.

A sample of the oxygen is admitted at a known pressure to a glass vessel filled with freshly reduced copper, prepared by reduction of copper oxide powder or copper oxide–coated wire. The vessel is then heated to a temperature of 300°C. or more and kept there for about 20 minutes while all the oxygen reacts with the copper. The vessel is allowed to cool to room temperature, and pressure readings are made with a McLeod gage until the pressure is constant. The calculation is simple.

$$\frac{\text{Final pressure}}{\text{Initial pressure}} \times 10^6 = \text{p.p.m. total impurities in original sample}$$

If desired, the residual gas may be analyzed in a mass spectrometer or gas chromatograph.

2. Continuous Determination of Argon and Other Inert Impurities in Oxygen

An example of an isolation method is the continuous analysis of 98.5 to 99.8% pure oxygen (67). The gas sample is passed through an oxygen absorber such as an alkaline solution of sodium hydrosulfite, and the small amount of unabsorbed gas, essentially argon plus nitrogen, is dried, picked up in a stream of hydrogen, and passed through a thermal conductivity cell in parallel with a reference stream of pure hydrogen. The chief drawback of this method lies in the absorption step, which entails renewal of the absorbent.

A somewhat better scheme has been proposed (76) in which a metered excess of pure hydrogen is added to a metered flow of sample gas, the gas mixture is passed through a combustion chamber containing a catalyst to burn out the oxygen, the water thus produced is removed, and the thermal conductivity of the residual gas is compared with that of a reference stream of pure hydrogen.

3. Determination of Helium in Iron Meteorites

The sample is dissolved in acid in a closed and previously evacuated vessel. The hydrogen thus produced is burned out over a catalyst with excess oxygen, the oxygen and all heavier gases are adsorbed on activated charcoal cooled by boiling liquid oxygen (59), and the pressure of the residual gas is measured. The residual gas is usually just helium, but its purity may be checked by means of a gas chromatograph, a mass spectrometer, or an emission spectrometer. If the separation process was carried out carefully, the only impurity in the helium should be neon. Neon, if present, may be determined in a gas chromatograph or a mass spectrometer.

4. Determination of Helium in Minerals

Gases liberated from minerals by fusion at 1500 to 2000°C. in a previously evacuated vessel are collected and purified. Hydrogen is removed by passage over hot copper oxide. Other impurities are removed by adsorption on charcoal cooled by liquid nitrogen. The residue, which is usually fairly pure helium, is measured with a sensitive McLeod gage (42). Purity of the helium may be determined with a sensitive gas chromatograph or mass spectrometer or by the spectroscopic method of Riesz and Dieke (102).

C. MASS SPECTROMETRY

The general principles of mass spectrometery are given in Part I of this Treatise.

1. Ordinary Laboratory Samples

. a. GENERAL PROCEDURE

The details of the procedure for the quantitative determination of inert gases will vary with the type of mass spectrometer available, but the main steps for a complete quantitative analysis are usually the same for all instruments.

1. Make a qualitative analysis of the sample, either by use of an Orsat (Section V-B-1) or by a preliminary run in the mass spectrometer.

2. If necessary, subject the sample to chemical or physical treatment, either to eliminate serious interference of mass peaks or to concentrate the desired component. See, for example, reference 93.

3. Run the sample in the mass spectrometer, and also run a pure sample of each component. Calculate the tentative composition of the unknown. "Normalize" the results; that is, recalculate them so that the total is 100.0%.

4. Using individual gases of high purity, make up a standard gas sample having the same composition as the tentative composition calculated in step *3.* Directions for making up the standard gas sample are given in Section IX-A.

5. Run the standard sample, then the unknown, and then the standard sample again. If everything is in order, the two runs with the standard sample should give identical results. Calculate the exact composition of the unknown by comparison with the standard sample. If the sum of the concentrations of the components is not 100.0%, normalize the results. The correction necessary to normalize the analysis after direct comparison with a standard mixture of similar composition should be very small; if it is not, something is wrong, and the source of the error should be located.

6. If the presence of air in the original sample is suspected, nitrogen and oxygen present in the air ratio (78.084:20.946) may be subtracted out, and the analysis again normalized; the result is called the analysis on the "air-free" basis. Because of the uncertainty as to whether the nitrogen and oxygen thus subtracted out are really due to air or might have been present in the original gas being analyzed, the air-free analysis should usually not be reported alone but should be given as a supplement to the composition obtained in step *5* above.

b. Discussion

Preliminary chemical treatment of the sample is usually necessary only if the concentration of the inert gas sought is so low that it must be increased before a reliable determination can be made. The inert gases themselves do not usually interfere seriously with each other's determination except in the case of low concentrations of neon in the presence of large concentrations of argon; here the Ar^{+2} ($m/e = 20$) peak obscures the Ne^+ ($m/e = 20$) peak. Occasionally, however, there may be present some gas or gases (other than the inert gases) that give mass peaks overlapping those of the inert gases and thus cause serious interference. Minor peak interference can usually be taken care of by calculation from the peak heights given by the various isotopes.

The general procedure just outlined may be modified to suit particular circumstances. For example, experience may show that in some cases the tentative composition obtained in step *3* is sufficiently accurate that steps *4* and *5* may be omitted. Whenever a new class of mixtures is to be analyzed, it is best to run through all five steps first to establish whether or not it is safe to omit steps *4* and *5*.

2. Isotopes

a. General Discussion

The mass spectrometer is, in principle, particularly well suited to the determination of the ratios of isotopes present in gas samples. However, in most commercial mass spectrometers the ratio of peak heights produced on the chart by any two isotopes in a gas sample is not necessarily the ratio in which the two isotopes are present in the gas sample. If the correct absolute value of the isotope ratio must be determined, a standard sample containing the same isotopes in a known ratio should be run just before and after the unknown sample. The isotope ratio error is usually greatest at low values of m/e, that is, for the hydrogen or helium isotopes. There are special instruments called "isotope ratio" mass spectrometers, in some of which the absolute value of an isotope ratio can be determined directly from the peak heights on the chart, but not even all isotope ratio mass spectrometers give correct ratios directly.

If it is desired to determine the absolute concentration of some isotope of an element in a gas sample, a suitable method must be devised. If other gases are present, their concentrations may be determined by steps *1*, *2*, and *3* of the procedure given in Section VII-C-1-a, and the concentration of the element sought then calculated by difference. The concentration of the element sought having thus been determined, the concentration of its individual isotopes may be calculated from the ratio of their peak heights, corrected, if possible, by the use of a standard sample containing the isotopes in known ratio.

b. Determination of Argon in Rocks

In recent years there has been considerable interest in the potassium-argon method for determining the ages of rocks (1). This method and the analytical techniques involved are reviewed by Carr and Kulp (20). It is best to liberate the argon by vacuum fusion of the sample without a flux at a temperature somewhat above 1400°C. (45); the high temperature is maintained for half an hour. Radioactive argon-37 has been used as a tracer to check the yield of argon in the vacuum fusion technique; over 98% of the argon present in the rock sample has thus been recovered.

Noninert impurities may be removed by metallic calcium at 750 to 800°C., and the argon-40 content determined in a mass spectrometer after dilution of the argon with a known amount of argon-38 to monitor the extent of contamination by argon of the atmosphere. With care, this contamination can be held to less than 3% of the total argon in the sample.

3. Micro Techniques

Sometimes the concentration of the element sought is so low, or the available sample so small, that commercial laboratory mass spectrometers cannot be used. Occasionally a commercial model may be adapted by an analyst for his special purposes.   Methods of increasing the sensitivity include (26) increasing the sample pressure, increasing the current to the ion source, and installing a more powerful amplifier in the ion pickup system than was originally supplied by the manufacturer of the mass spectrometer. With these methods, the sensitivity of one commercial model was increased by a factor of 1000, so that it became possible to determine helium to about ±1 p.p.m.

Occasionally it is necessary to build a special mass spectrometer to handle unusually small samples.   A number of such instruments have recently been described.   With one of them (101), it is reported that as low as half a million atoms of a xenon isotope or 14 million argon-36 atoms can be detected.   In another (119), gases (for example, argon) with molecular weights below 44 can be analyzed at pressures as low as 10^{-10} mm. Hg. Another (94) was used by Nier to determine the ratio of helium-3 to helium-4 in gas samples.   Inghram (56) determined the ratio of helium-3 to helium-4 in a sensitive mass spectrometer capable of completely resolving the helium-3 peak from the HD peak at the same m/e number.   Other authors (35a) have described a similar instrument.

4. Plant Process Monitoring

Commercial mass spectrometers with sensitivities as low as 25 p.p.m. for some gases are now available for monitoring plant streams.   A unit of this type could, for example, be set on $m/e = 20$ and would then continuously determine the concentration of neon in a stream of helium.   Equipment is made in which several components are monitored, the machine automatically switching from mass to mass every few seconds and recording the peak height at each.   Machines of this type can be used both for recording the analyses and for helping in plant control by operating signals or other devices when a given peak height exceeds a desirable limit.

D. GAS CHROMATOGRAPHY

1. Direct Quantitative Analysis

The gas chromatograph is probably the single most useful instrument for the quantitative determination of the inert gases.   It is relatively inexpensive, fast, easy to standardize, and easy to use.   Convenient commercial models are available for laboratory use and for the monitoring of plant process streams (for example, reference 23).   The construction of gas chromatographs is sufficiently simple that a satisfactory laboratory instrument can be built at fairly low cost.   With suitable detecting devices, traces, as well as high concentrations of gases, can be determined.

Up to the year 1960, gas chromatographs that can distinguish between isotopes of any of the inert gases have not come to the author's attention.

To carry out a quantitative analysis using the gas chromatograph, the analyst should first experiment with various packing materials and conditions of operation until all the components to be determined are fully resolved and identified (see Section VI). When suitable conditions have been found, he should follow the procedure given in Section IX-C. Some examples are presented in the following paragraphs.

a. Helium, Hydrogen, Neon, and Nitrogen

With a charcoal column at the temperature of liquid nitrogen and with hydrogen as carrier gas, helium and neon are clearly separated. Nitrogen is eluted by allowing the column to warm to room temperature. Hydrogen is determined by difference (43).

b. Oxygen, Argon, and Nitrogen with Argon as Carrier Gas

Oxygen and nitrogen are determined with a molecular sieve packing and argon as carrier gas. Argon is determined by difference (43).

c. Oxygen, Argon, and Nitrogen with Helium as Carrier Gas

With a 2.5 m. column of Linde Type 4A molecular sieve at room temperature and helium as carrier gas, oxygen is separated from the other gases, but argon and nitrogen come out together. At −78°C., all three gases are separated, but the oxygen peak is too broad for quantitative analysis; this procedure is quantitative for argon and nitrogen, and oxygen may be determined by difference or directly by some other method on a separate sample (31).

E. EMISSION SPECTROSCOPY

1. General Discussion

The value of the emission spectroscopic method for quantitative analysis lies chiefly in the determination of low concentrations of gases. The method is recommended only when no other convenient method is available for the particular determination, when many determinations on similar samples are to be made, or when a determination is to be made continuously on a stream of gas. In the two latter cases, both the concentration of the gaseous element to be determined and the composition of the rest of the gas mixture must be roughly constant. The chief quantitative application of emission spectroscopy is therefore as a control method in a manufacturing, purification, or blending process.

2. Excitation of the Gas

The excitation of the gas to produce the emission spectrum has been discussed in Section VI-C.

The use of the spectrograph for quantitative analysis depends upon suitable calibration for the particular determination to be made. A good general procedure for calibration is to select a low- to medium-intensity reference line from the spectrum of the main component of the mixture. The intensity of a convenient line from the element to be determined is then compared with the intensity of the reference line. If the main component is present in 99% or higher concentration, the intensity of the reference line will usually not fluctuate appreciably as the concentration of the minor component varies. An effort is made to choose a reference line such that changes in discharge voltage, gas pressure, temperature, and photographic emulsion on the film or plate affect the intensity of the reference line and the monitored line in the same proportion, so that changes in the ratio of the line intensities are caused only by changes in the concentration of the gaseous component being monitored. The monitored line and the reference line should, if possible, be fairly close together in the spectrum to minimize errors due to variation in photographic emulsion sensitivity, should be of roughly the same intensity, and should arise from transitions between atomic levels of about the same energy values (106c). The success of the choice of lines is measured by the reproducibility of the results obtained day after day, with standard gas mixtures, over the concentration range of interest.

For continuous monitoring of a given inert gas or impurity, the intensity of the appropriate spectral lines is measured by photocells or phototubes, the output of which is handled automatically by a suitable electronic network and shown on an indicator or recorder.

3. Determination of Argon

A spectrochemical procedure for determining the ratio of the concentration of argon in a sample only slightly different in composition from air to the concentration of argon in air has been described (82). The sample is passed through an electrodeless type of electric discharge tube at a pressure of 70 μ. The discharge is produced by a 150 mc. generator coupled to the discharge tube with two external electrodes. A direct-reading spectrometer is used to measure the intensity ratio of the 4158.6 A. argon line to the 3998.4 A. nitrogen band head. It takes 1 minute to make a determination.

F. DESORPTION FROM ACTIVATED CARBON OR SILICA GEL

1. General Discussion

The method of Kahle (65h) given in Section V-C-1 is quantitative for all the inert gases except helium and neon, which are measured together.

In Paneth's laboratory (97a), helium and neon are separated on a micro scale by fractional desorption from activated charcoal cooled by liquid nitrogen. When the available sample is large enough, the purity of the separated helium and the purity of the neon are checked spectroscopically. When the size of the sample is too small, experience is depended upon to tell in which fractions the helium and the neon appear, and these fractions are then passed directly into a Pirani gage for pressure measurement. The apparatus and method are described in detail by Glückauf (37a).

2. Determination of Helium in Natural Gas

The U. S. Bureau of Mines has analyzed thousands of samples of natural gas over the years. During this time a convenient, portable apparatus and procedure for the rapid quantitative determination of helium were developed by Frost (3c,34,34a). By this method a determination can be made in less than 10 minutes after the apparatus is in working order. The method is good in the range 0.002% to over 1.0%. Duplicate samples containing a few thousandths of 1% of helium have been analyzed by the Bureau of Mines, results checking to 0.0001%. (The ability to determine very small quantities of helium has become important in connection with the use of helium as a tracer gas for following the movement of gaseous hydrocarbon streams.)

The design of the Bureau of Mines apparatus is based upon the fact that all the components of natural gas except helium are adsorbed quantitatively on coconut charcoal at the temperature of boiling liquid air or nitrogen. The apparatus is made of glass and is equipped with vacuum-type stopcocks lubricated with high-vacuum grease. Both a Pirani vacuum gage and a McLeod gage are provided. The tube containing the charcoal is first heated to about 150°C., and the desorbed gases and vapors are pumped out with a mercury vapor diffusion pump backed by a mechanical vacuum pump. When practically all the gas has been pumped out, the tube of charcoal is cooled by liquid nitrogen. The difference in mercury levels on the McLeod gage should fall to 1 mm. Hg or less. A measured quantity of the gas sample is then introduced into the charcoal tube. All constituents other than helium, neon, and hydrogen are completely adsorbed within 2 minutes. The identity and purity of the helium is checked in a high-voltage discharge tube; pure helium is evidenced by a gold or orange-yellow color in the tube and by the visible helium emission line spectrum as seen in a spectroscope.   The pressure is then measured with the McLeod gage, and the helium concentration in the original sample is calculated.

If there were an appreciable concentration of neon in a gas sample, most of the neon would probably stay unadsorbed.   However, no natural gas is known in which there are more than traces of neon.   If the presence of hydrogen is suspected, the sample should be run on a mass spectrometer or gas chromatograph.

Schröer (107) has described a similar method using silica gel instead of charcoal.

G. NEUTRON ACTIVATION ANALYSIS

1. General Discussion

A general discussion of neutron activation analysis appears in Part I of this Treatise.   In the neutron activation method, the sample is bombarded with neutrons.   Some or all of the atoms in the sample are converted to radioactive isotopes of the elements present.   Since each radioisotope decays with its own characteristic radiation and half life, most of the elements present can be identified, and their concentrations in the sample determined.   When the radiation emitted from the activated sample is too complex, physical or chemical separations of the sample can be undertaken either before or after neutron irradiation.

The best source of neutrons is usually an atomic reactor, because (1) a high neutron flux shortens the length of time necessary for irradiating the sample, (2) elements which are not readily activated, that is, which have small neutron absorption "cross sections," will become radioactive in a reasonable length of time, and (3) elements which give radioisotopes with short lifetimes can be detected, whereas in low neutron fluxes measurable concentrations of the short-lived isotopes may never be formed.   For some purposes a small laboratory source of neutrons, such as a mixture of radium and beryllium salts, is satisfactory.   Such small neutron sources are used in laboratories that do not have access to atomic reactors.   When a small neutron flux is not sufficient to perform the desired analysis, samples may be sent to one of the government or private laboratories that offer activation analysis service.

The most useful neutron activation process is the "n, γ" reaction.   In this, a neutron is captured by a stable atomic nucleus, yielding a highly unstable compound nucleus which immediately stabilizes itself by the emission of its surplus energy in the form of a gamma photon.   The resulting nucleus is isotopic with the original nucleus; its weight is greater by 1 atomic weight unit than the original. The new nucleus may be either stable or radioactive. If stable, it is of no use in neutron activation analysis. If radioactive, it can usually be identified, and its concentration measured, from its characteristic radiation.

To make the activation method quantitative, samples of known composition are usually irradiated simultaneously with the test sample. After irradiation, the known and the unknown samples are processed together. A comparison of the counting rates, corrected to the same time, if rate of decay is important, and corrected for such factors as volume and weight, then makes it possible to estimate the weight of the element in the test sample (81).

2. Xenon and Krypton

Tobin (116) gives a method for the determination of small amounts (10^{-10} to 10^{-8} g.-atom) of krypton or xenon in helium with less than 5% error.

The gas sample containing the krypton or xenon is transferred to a quartz ampule equipped with a thin blister, and sealed off. The ampule is placed in an aluminum capsule and irradiated in an atomic reactor by as uniform a neutron flux as possible.

After a short period of irradiation, the ampule is delivered to a "semihot" laboratory, where the gas in it is transferred to a glass gas-sampling tube in a gas transfer apparatus, the quartz ampule being opened by rupturing the blister with a piece of iron inside the evacuated gas transfer apparatus. The glass gas-sampling tube is equipped with a glass stopcock and a ground-glass joint, so that the gas can readily be transferred to a counting chamber. The radioactivity of the gas sample is then measured with a gamma pulse height spectrometer.

The method is made quantitative by measuring the area under the main energy peak for each gas and comparing with the areas under peaks produced by samples of known composition.

When both xenon and krypton are present in the original gas sample, they may be separated by passing the sample over activated carbon at $-20°C$. Xenon is quantitatively adsorbed, and krypton is not adsorbed (46a). Quantitative determinations may then be made on each gas separately by neutron activation.

3. Limits of Sensitivity

With neutron irradiation in nuclear reactors, the following sensitivities for detection have been found (81); krypton and xenon, 10^{-6} g.; argon, 10^{-7} g.

4. Neutron Activation Cross Sections

The activation cross section values for the naturally occurring isotopes when bombarded by thermal neutrons and the half lives of the daughter radioisotopes produced (66) are given in Table XIV.

TABLE XIV
Data for Neutron Activation Analysis

Naturally occurring isotopes	Atomic cross section, barns	Half life of daughter
Neon-22	0.036 ± 0.015	40 sec.
Argon-38	0.8 ± 0.2	265 yr.
Argon-40	0.53 ± 0.02	109 min.
Krypton-78	2.0 ± 0.5	34.5 hrs.
Krypton-84	0.10 ± 0.03	4.4 hrs.
Krypton-84	0.06 ± 0.02	9.4 yr.
Krypton-86	0.06 ± 0.02	77 min.
Xenon-132	0.2 ± 0.1	5.3 days
Xenon-134	0.2 ± 0.1	9.13 hrs.
Xenon-136	0.15 ± 0.08	3.9 min.

The higher the cross section, the more readily a given element can be activated. Both long and short lifetimes of the daughter elements are useful, provided they are not too long or too short; for example, if the radioisotope of a trace impurity to be determined has a relatively long lifetime and the main component of the sample has a short lifetime, quantitative determination of the impurity may be quite easy. The daughter isotope must have a half life long enough to make it practical to handle and count before the decay has proceeded too far, and short enough so that the rate of decay is convenient for counting in a reasonable length of time.

The type of material given in Table XIV has been recalculated and produced in graphical form for use by analytical chemists by Meinke and Maddock (89).

H. DETERMINATION OF RADIOACTIVE ISOTOPES

When the concentration of radioisotopes in a gas sample is appreciable, the gas is usually analyzed in a mass spectrometer, suitable precautions being taken to protect personnel.

At very low concentrations, and when only one isotope is present in a gas mixture, an electrometer or a Geiger-Müller counter is usually used to assay the radioactivity; from the radioactivity the concentration of the isotope can be calculated. When more than one radioisotope is present in the sample, gamma pulse height spectrometers or beta spectrometers are usually employed. These instruments are capable of distinguishing between gamma photons or beta particles of different energies and can therefore often be applied to gas mixtures without the necessity of preliminary separations.

Winteringham (127a) recommends a Geiger-Müller tube equipped with a thin end window for the counting of argon-41 and krypton-85. This apparatus is similar to that used for assaying carbon dioxide labeled with carbon-14.

I. METHODS FOR BINARY GAS MIXTURES

1. General Discussion

These methods are all based on the measurement of some single physical property of a mixture of gases. In using one of these methods for quantitative analysis, the general requirement is that not more than two gases be present in the sample to be analyzed. This requirement may be met in practice even when there are three or more gases present, provided that the ratio to each other of all the gases present except the gas to be determined is constant. For example, in one stage of the "production" of neon from air, the concentration of nitrogen in a mixture of nitrogen, helium, and neon may be determined by thermal conductivity because the helium/neon ratio is constant, no separation of helium and neon having yet taken place (4).

When the component to be determined differs considerably in molecular weight from all the other components, and when only approximate analyses are needed, the requirement that the ratio of the other components be constant may be somewhat relaxed, for example, in the determination of helium in expired air (49) by thermal conductivity.

Three-component mixtures may also be analyzed if the concentration of any one of the three components is known or can be independently determined. The calibration chart in such a case will consist not simply of a single curve, but of a family of curves, one for each of a number of concentrations of the known component. Since an infinite number of curves cannot be drawn on the chart, the concentration of the unknown is, when necessary, read from the chart by interpolation.

If the gas to be analyzed does not initially meet the requirements outlined for binary composition or the equivalent, a preliminary chemical or physical separation usually has to be carried out before the analytical determination is made.

One advantage of a number of the physical methods used with binary gas mixtures is that they lend themselves well to continuous determination of gas composition in a plant stream.

2. Thermal Conductivity

Gas analysis by thermal conductivity is described in Part I in this Treatise. An example of a specific application of thermal conductivity follows.

a. DETERMINATION OF ARGON/NITROGEN RATIO IN GAS USED FOR THE SYNTHESIS OF AMMONIA

In the synthesis of ammonia, it is important to keep the argon concentration from building up too much in the recycled mixture of hydrogen and nitrogen. Apparatus for the continuous determination of the argon/nitrogen ratio in this recycled gas has been described (17). The gas is scrubbed free of ammonia, hydrogen and traces of methane are oxidized at 700°C. over a copper oxide catalyst containing 1 to 10% ferric oxide, the products of combustion are removed, and the argon/nitrogen ratio is determined by passing the gas through a thermal conductivity cell.

3. Beta-Ray Absorption

Molecules differ in their ability to stop and scatter electrons; this property may be utilized in an analytical method for binary gas mixtures. Convenient equipment is on the market for either intermittent laboratory use or plant process control. Accuracy of the method depends largely on how closely the gas pressure and temperature are controlled and how carefully the calibration with a gas mixture of known composition is carried out; the method is capable of determining helium in nitrogen or oxygen with an accuracy of 1% (95). If the nitrogen/oxygen ratio is constant, the method may be used to determine helium in a three-component mixture.

4. Velocity of Sound

The velocity of sound in a gas can be calculated from the formula

$$V = (\gamma P/d)^{1/2}$$

where V is velocity, in centimeters per second; $\gamma = C_p/C_v$, the ratio of specific heat at constant pressure to specific heat at constant volume; P is pressure, in dynes per square centimeter; and d is density, in grams per cubic centimeter.

If two gases in a mixture differ sufficiently either in the ratio of the specific heats or in their density, the composition of the mixture can be determined by measuring the velocity of sound under controlled conditions. Simple apparatus for making this measurement in the laboratory has been described (125). A vertical glass tube equipped at the top with a stopcock is filled with water and connected at the bottom by a flexible tube to a leveling bulb containing water. The gas sample is admitted to the upper part of the tube. A tuning fork, mounted above the tube, is struck, and while it is humming at frequency f, the water level is slowly lowered until a point of resonance is found. The water is then lowered again to the next point of resonance. The points of resonance are marked on the tube, and the distance, D, between them is measured. This distance is half a wavelength. The velocity of sound is $2Df$. The desired concentration is read from a calibration chart prepared in advance in which the velocity of sound is plotted against the composition of the binary gas mixture. Calibration must, of course, be carried out under the same conditions as the final analysis. The chief source of error is the water vapor; this error can be kept at a minimum by raising and lowering the leveling bulb a few times at the beginning to help saturate the gas sample with water vapor. The velocity of sound in gas is almost independent of small pressure changes in the neighborhood of 1 atm. The change of velocity with temperature is about 0.2% per degree centigrade; whether or not the glass tube is to be water-jacketed and the temperature controlled depends upon the accuracy desired.

Apparatus for automatically determining the velocity of sound, either intermittently or continuously, in a flowing gas has been described (25,74, 80,87).

5. Effusion from an Orifice or Capillary Tube

The effusion time through an actual orifice is approximately proportional to the square root of the molecular weight of a gas; the effusion method can therefore be used to analyze binary mixtures in which one of the gases differs appreciably in molecular weight from the other.

a. Determination of Helium in Mixtures of Helium, Nitrogen, and Oxygen

To determine the concentration of helium in a mixture of helium, nitrogen, and oxygen in the laboratory, three steps are carried out: (1) the effusion time for the sample is measured, (2) the effusion time for laboratory air is measured, and (3) the concentration of oxygen in the sample is separately determined. The per cent helium in the sample is then read off a calibration chart with interpolation, as required, between curves for the different oxygen concentrations.

Simple and inexpensive laboratory apparatus for this analysis has been described (108). A gas buret, or a vertical glass tube with a bulb or wide part in the middle having about 50 cc. volume, equipped at the top with a three-way stopcock, is filled with a confining liquid. The vertical glass tube is connected at the bottom by means of flexible tubing to a leveling bulb. One arm of the three-way stopcock is connected to a gasketed aluminum disk with a 0.005 inch diameter hole in the center; another arm is used as the sample intake. To operate the apparatus, a gas sample is admitted to the vertical tube through the stopcock and allowed to flow through the 0.005 inch hole under pressure from the liquid in the leveling bulb. The time required for the confining liquid to rise from a low mark on the vertical tube to a mark near the top is measured. (This technique is similar to that used for the measurement of viscosities of liquids.) The leveling bulb must, of course, always be at exactly the same height while the time of effusion is being measured. If the confining liquid has appreciable vapor pressure, the gas sample should first be saturated with the vapor by raising and lowering the leveling bulb a few times, but no liquid should be allowed to reach the orifice. Every time a new sample is to be analyzed, the space between the effusion disk and the three-way stopcock should be flushed out with the new gas.

To avoid the necessity of making corrections for temperature and barometric pressure, the effusion time for a sample of laboratory air is measured each time a sample of unknown composition is run. The ratio of the effusion time for the unknown to that for air is calculated. The calibration chart is prepared by plotting this ratio versus composition for a number of samples of known composition.

If the ratio of nitrogen to oxygen is not constant in all samples to be run, the calibration chart will consist of a family of curves, each for a different oxygen concentration, and the concentration of oxygen will have to be determined for each sample, for example, by absorption in a solution of potassium pyrogallate in a gas absorption pipet.

Similar but slightly more elaborate apparatus has been described (125a) in which mercury is the confining liquid and the absolute gas pressure upstream of the orifice is kept more than twice the absolute downstream pressure.

A similar method has been described (71) for small samples of mixtures of xenon with any lighter gas, starting with extremely small samples.

6. Optical Interferometry

The standard methods of optical interferometry may be applied to binary mixtures containing one or two of the inert gases. For example, with the sodium D line as a source of illumination, good results are reported in the analysis of nitrogen-argon mixtures (58).

7. Gas Density

Equipment is available on the market for either the continuous or the intermittent determination of gas density. Best results are obtained, of course, when the two components in the binary gas mixture differ greatly in molecular weight, and therefore in density. Apparatus for the determination of argon in nitrogen with an accuracy of $\pm 0.3\%$ has been described by Zimmer (129). A quick method involving the use of a differential manometer has been described by Kahle (64).

8. Absorption of X-Rays

Zimmer (129) describes a rapid method for the determination of 0.1% or more argon in oxygen, in which x-rays ionize the sample in one chamber and a reference gas in another chamber, and the ionization currents in the two chambers are compared.

9. Absorption of Ultraviolet Light

Visible and infrared radiation is not absorbed by the inert gases, but radiation in the far (short wavelength) ultraviolet region is absorbed and could be used in a manner similar to that employed in ordinary infrared absorption spectroscopy. Little or no work has been done to date on this possibility.

10. Emission of Light

The method of emission spectroscopy described above in Section VII-E can be used for a binary gas mixture.

11. Dielectric Constant

Value of this constant differ sufficiently among the inert gases for which data are available (Table V) that an analytical method could be based on its measurement.

12. Ratio of McLeod Gage Reading to Thermocouple Gage Reading at Room Temperature

This method can be used to analyze very small samples. When one gas in a binary mixture is partly or wholly condensable, a thermocouple gage will show a higher apparent pressure reading than the McLeod gage.   Kenty and Reuter (71) calibrate their apparatus for several different pressures and ratios of gases, thus producing a family of curves from which the composition can be conveniently read over a range of pressures.   Examples of mixtures for which this micro method is suitable are argon-nitrogen, and xenon with almost any other gas.

13. Vapor Pressure of a Liquid Mixture

Measurement of the vapor pressure of a liquid binary mixture has been used to analyze the following mixtures: argon and krypton (33), and argon and nitrogen (52,129).

VIII. DETERMINATION OF IMPURITIES

One of the older uses for argon, and still a very important one, is in filling electric light bulbs having tungsten filaments.   Several of the possible impurities in argon, such as hydrogen, oxygen, and hydrocarbons, would, if present, react with the hot tungsten and shorten the life of the lamp; hence the argon must be substantially free of these harmful impurities.   Argon that meets this requirement is referred to as "lamp grade."   In recent years, krypton and xenon have also been used to fill lamp bulbs, giving lamps of longer life for the same light output, or of higher light output per watt for the same lifetime.   Another large use for the inert gases, especially helium and argon, is in blanketing hot reactive metals, such as titanium, which react with oxygen, nitrogen, hydrogen, moisture, etc.   For these and similar uses the purest possible gases are required, since the hot metal will act as a getter and will take impurities out of the inert gas, thus becoming contaminated.   Other uses also require very pure gases.   To control the purity of inert gases, sensitive analytical methods are required.

For most purposes a mass spectrometer or gas chromatograph adapted to the required use is recommended.   However, in some cases it is cheaper or more practical to employ specific methods for individual impurities. Methods recommended by the author and his associates on the basis of actual experience are given in Table XV, Section VIII-A, and Table XVI, Section VIII-B.   Some other methods are given in Table XVII, Section VIII-C.   All possible methods for determining impurities in the inert gases have not been given; a complete list would be very long.

The methods in Table XVII may in some cases be just as satisfactory as those in Tables XV and XVI, and in special circumstances, a method from Table XVII might even be the best one for a given determination.   In general, however, it would probably be better to consider the recommended methods first.

A. RECOMMENDED LABORATORY METHODS

The methods given below are summarized in Table XV. They are among those actually used in industry. A method must, of course, be selected to fit the particular circumstances, especially if many similar samples are to be analyzed. Most of these methods are designed for determining impurity concentrations of a few parts per million.

1. General Methods

The general methods recommended for determining impurities in the inert gases are based on the use of the mass spectrometer, the gas chromatograph, and the emission spectrograph and have been discussed elsewhere in this chapter.

2. Total Impurities Except Other Inert Gases

a. TOTAL IMPURITIES GREATER THAN ABOUT 0.5%

When there is an appreciable quantity (0.5% or more) of impurities, the total may often be determined rapidly by removing all impurities from a measured sample of gas and then measuring the residue of unadsorbed gas.

The procedure in brief follows: First make a qualitative analysis. Select appropriate methods (Section V above) for removing the impurities, carry out the removal from a measured sample, and then measure the residue. It is usually quickest and most convenient to measure the pressure of a sample before and after removing the impurities, keeping the volume and temperature constant, but it is also possible to measure the volume before and after, keeping the pressure and temperature constant.

b. TOTAL IMPURITIES LESS THAN ABOUT 0.5%

As the concentration of total impurities falls, it becomes more difficult to use the difference method outlined above, although accurate work can be done with sensitive pressure gages or with capillaries for measuring small changes in volume. Sometimes it is best to determine each impurity separately and add the individual determinations to obtain the total.

TABLE XV

Recommended Laboratory Methods for Determination of Purity and of Impurities in Inert Gases

Determination	Approx. possible sensitivity	Method
General methods	5–10 p.p.m.[a] 1–50 p.p.m.[a] 1–10 p.p.m.	Mass spectrometry. Gas chromatography. Emission spectrography.
Total impurities	0.5%	Measuring gas pressure at constant volume and temperature before and after removing impurities, or measuring gas volume at constant pressure and temperature before and after removing impurities. Determining each impurity separately and adding the values for the separate impurities.
Purity of lamp grade argon	3 p.p.m. water and water-forming impurities	Filling a clear glass tungsten filament type electric light bulb with sample, heating the filament under controlled conditions, and examining the glass for streaks.
Acetylene	1 p.p.m.	Colorimetric Ilosvay: formation of red copper acetylide with ammoniacal cuprous chloride solution. (Sensitivity can be increased by prior concentration of acetylene on refrigerated silica gel.)

Carbon dioxide	1 p.p.m.	Absorption in barium hydroxide solution; back-titration with standard hydrochloric acid, with phenolphthalein as indicator.
Carbon monoxide	1 p.p.m.	Combustion over hot copper oxide at 300°C. and determination of carbon dioxide formed.
Hydrocarbons	1 p.p.m.	Combustion over hot copper oxide at 900°C. and determination of carbon dioxide formed.
Hydrogen	1 p.p.m.	Combustion over copper oxide at 300°C. and determination of moisture formed, or mixing with oxygen and burning over hot platinum.
Nitrogen	10 p.p.m.	Measuring volume (at constant pressure) of sample before and after treating with molten lithium.
Nitrous oxide		Mass spectrometry.
Oxygen	1 p.p.m.	Mixing with hydrogen, burning over platinum, and determining moisture formed.
	7 p.p.m.	Reacting with a hot tungsten filament of an electric light bulb and examining the filament for oxide formation.
	10 p.p.m.	Gas chromatography.
Water vapor	0.03 p.p.m.	Freezing out moisture from a measured volume of gas in a trap at −183°C., and then warming the trap and measuring pressure of water vapor.
	5 p.p.m.	Dew point.
	< 0.01%	Absorbing on phosphorus pentoxide or other drying agent and weighing.

[a] Depending upon the nature of the impurity and the sensitivity of the detector.

3. Lamp Grade Argon

This is a quality check for impurities that might interfere with the use of argon in filling electric light bulbs. The technique is similar to that described in Section VIII-A-10-b. This test has, to some extent, been outmoded by the availability of sensitive means for determining the actual concentrations of the separate water-forming impurities in argon, but the quality test is still occasionally used. The procedure is as follows: Seal two glass tubes to opposite sides of a clear glass 500 w. tungsten filament lamp bulb as illustrated in Fig. 11. Evacuate the bulb, and bake it for 15 minutes at 300°C. Admit the argon sample to a pressure of about 5 mm. Hg, and pump out again to flush out desorbed impurities. Cool

Fig. 11. Bulb test apparatus for determining traces of oxygen in argon.

to room temperature, and fill the bulb with the argon sample to a pressure of about ³/₄ atm. Burn the bulb base down for 15 minutes at 110 v., and then examine it by turning it with the hand and looking at the glass against a white background. If there are no streaks on the glass, the argon passes the test. Some lamp manufacturers have suggested similar tests on lower-wattage bulbs, but the 500 w. bulb test is the most critical.

4. Acetylene

There is often some acetylene in the air of cities and in the neighborhood of factories. Since acetylene is nonvolatile at the temperature of liquid oxygen, traces of it may occasionally find their way into krypton and xenon, the least volatile of the inert gases. For the determination of acetylene, the colorimetric Ilosvay method, due originally to Weaver (120) and described in Lunge and Ambler (85f), is recommended. The Ilosvay reagent is an ammoniacal solution of cuprous chloride made by reducing cupric chloride in aqueous solution with hydroxylamine hydrochloride. Acetylene reacts to form a red precipitate of cuprous acetylide, traces of which may be held in suspension for comparison with color standards by the presence of a little gelatin.

5. Carbon Dioxide

For traces of carbon dioxide, absorption in barium hydroxide solution is recommended.

Make up the barium hydroxide solution by saturating water with barium hydroxide, letting stand until the supernatant liquid is clear, decanting off the clear liquid, and diluting the clear liquid with five times its volume of distilled water. This dilute liquid is the reagent. Protect from air.

Pass a metered sample of the gas to be analyzed through a series of bubblers containing measured quantities of the barium hydroxide reagent. The quantity of sample used should be adjusted to the concentration of carbon dioxide expected; for example, for 1 p.p.m. carbon dioxide, a total volume of about 40 ft.^{3} of the gas should be passed through the bubblers at a rate of about 1 ft.^{3}/hour. After all the gas sample has passed through the bubblers, pour the barium hydroxide solution into a flask, rinse out the bubblers, add the rinsings to the flask, and titrate the unreacted barium hydroxide in the solution with 0.1N hydrochloric acid using phenolphthalein indicator.

Titrate with continual swirling to prevent hydrochloric acid from dissolving any of the barium carbonate. Make a blank titration on an equal volume of barium hydroxide reagent handled the same as the absorbing solution except that the step of actually bubbling the sample through the solution is omitted.

6. Carbon Monoxide and Saturated Hydrocarbons

Pass a measured quantity of the gas sample through a tube packed with copper oxide pieces and kept at 300°C., and pass another measured sample through copper oxide at 900°C. Determine the carbon dioxide produced in each case by the barium hydroxide method just described. Also make a carbon dioxide determination on a sample of the gas that has not been passed over copper oxide.

At 900°C., both carbon monoxide and hydrocarbons burn to carbon dioxide on copper oxide. All hydrocarbons with the possible exception of methane burn quantitatively; addition of oxygen and a trace of moisture to the gas sample helps to make the combustion of methane complete. At 300°C. only carbon monoxide burns to carbon dioxide if there are no unsaturated hydrocarbons present.

7. Hydrogen

Pass a metered sample over copper oxide heated to 300°C., and determine the moisture thus produced by one of the methods given in Section VIII-A-11.   (Saturated hydrocarbons are not oxidized by copper oxide at 300°C.; unsaturated hydrocarbons may be partially oxidized.)   Make a blank determination of moisture on a sample of the gas that has not been passed over copper oxide.

An alternative procedure for carrying out the combustion, which may be used if hydrocarbons are absent from the sample, is to mix the sample with oxygen and pass it over a hot platinum filament or hot platinized silica gel.

8. Nitrogen

If there is 0.5% or more nitrogen in the sample, first remove all other impurities by methods mentioned elsewhere in this chapter, and then allow the nitrogen to be absorbed to constant pressure by molten lithium at 325°C.   The difference in pressure of the gas sample before and after the lithium treatment when the gas is confined in a glass vessel of constant volume and temperature determines the nitrogen content of the sample.

Concentrations of nitrogen of less than 0.5% may be determined with a mass spectrometer or by a modification of the molten lithium method in which the volume of the gas is measured very accurately at constant pressure and temperature before and after nitrogen absorption.   In this latter method, heptadecyl alcohol may be used as the confining fluid; the rise of this fluid in a capillary tube attached to the gas-measuring vessel indicates the change in volume due to nitrogen absorption.

9. Nitrous Oxide

This impurity occasionally occurs in crude xenon. Use of the mass spectrometer is recommended for its determination.

10. Oxygen

a. Combustion Method

Mix measured quantities of the sample gas and of dry, oxygen-free hydrogen, pass the mixture over a hot platinum filament or over platinized silica gel, and determine moisture on the resultant gas by one of the methods given in Section VIII-A-11.

b. Lamp Test for Oxygen in Argon

Principle. This test is based on the reaction between traces of oxygen and the tungsten filament in a clear-glass 110 v. 100 w. electric light bulb. Conditions for the test are standardized, and the operator learns to estimate the oxygen concentration from the appearance of the filament (71a,128).

Apparatus

The apparatus is shown in Fig. 11. The clear-glass test bulb is provided with glass inlet and outlet tubes fused to opposite sides of the bulb. Beside it is the standard bulb used for comparison. In the center is a bronze safety valve set at 5 p.s.i. gage. Handles of a needle valve to regulate the gas flow, of a variable transformer to regulate power to the lamp filament, and of a toggle switch are also visible in the picture. The bulbs lying in the foreground are standard reference bulbs. The copper tubing at the right is connected to the compressed gas cylinder by means of the brass pressure fitting. The gas enters the test bulb through the copper tubing and leaves through a copper coil not shown in the picture.

Procedure

Wear safety glasses to protect the eyes from flying glass that might result from rupture of the glass bulb in case too much gas is accidentally admitted. Open the needle valve until the gas leaving the orifice can just be felt with the fingers. (The gas flow should be about 1 ft.^{3}/hr. S.T.P.) Let the gas flow through the bulb for about 5 minutes. Set the dial of the variable transformer to give 85 v. across the filament, and flick the toggle switch on for about 1 second. This procedure will vaporize any oxide left on the test lamp filament from a previous test. (No current passes through the reference lamp filament.) Purge another minute. Set the transformer to 15 v., stop the gas flow by turning off the needle valve, and turn the toggle switch to "on" for exactly 60 seconds. The 15 v. setting should give a filament temperature of about 500°C.

Observe the filament. If it is no different from the filament of a new bulb, the oxygen content is below 20 p.p.m. If the filament shows an over-all dullness with traces of color at the ends, an amount equal to or slightly above 20 p.p.m. is indicated. As the over-all color of the filament approximates a tan color, 40 p.p.m. is approached, and when the tan deepens to a brown and finally a black, 40 to 100 p.p.m. or more are indicated. Compare with previously prepared standard bulbs.

If no discoloration appears, make a final test by setting the transformer to 85 v. and turning the switch on for 1 second. If a wisp of smoke is observed to rise from the filament as the current is turned on, oxygen is present in an amount exceeding 7 p.p.m. If no smoke can be observed, the concentration of oxygen is less than 7 p.p.m. Purge the lamp for the next test, as has been described. A test lamp need not be replaced until the interior of the bulb is so clouded that there is no longer a good view of the filament, or until the filament is burned out.

Interferences. Too much hydrogen or moisture in the argon interferes with this test; if there is more than 100 p.p.m. hydrogen or 20 p.p.m. moisture in the argon being tested, these impurities should be removed first.

Other Applications. The bulb method for determining oxygen in argon can also be used for determining oxygen in other inert gases, but the voltage required to heat the filament to 500°C. is different for each gas: 15 v. for argon, lower for krypton, higher (25 to 30 v.) for helium or neon.

c. Gas Chromatography

Oxygen can be separated from argon and other gases by the use of Linde Type 4A molecular sieve as column packing. If argon is absent from the gas to be analyzed, other types of packing material may be used.

11. Water Vapor

a. Freeze-Out Method

Pass a measured volume of the gas sample slowly through a glass trap containing a little clean glass wool and immersed in liquid air, liquid oxygen, liquid nitrogen, or dry ice. The moisture is frozen and remains in the trap. When all the sample has been passed through, evacuate the apparatus, so that only the frozen moisture is left in the trap. Then close off the apparatus by means of a stopcock, and allow the trap to warm up. Replace the refrigerating bath by a water bath. When the trap has reached the temperature of the bath, read the pressure of the water vapor inside the trap on a closed-end mercury manometer, and calculate the concentration of water in the original sample from the temperature, pressure, and volume of the water vapor. If the trap was cooled by dry ice rather than by one of the low-temperature liquids, a correction must be made for the uncondensed moisture left in the gas sample when it passed through the cold trap; this correction is calculated from the vapor pressure of water at the temperature of the dry ice trap.

If the moisture determination is to be made on argon, krypton, or xenon in a location where there is plenty of liquid air but no vacuum pump, a pair of glass traps filled with silica gel and refrigerated with liquid air, liquid oxygen, or liquid nitrogen may be used instead of a vacuum pump. At this low temperature, silica gel adsorbs argon, krypton, and xenon quantitatively.

The operator must wear goggles because of the possibility of breakage of the Dewar flasks and the evacuated trap. The apparatus should be evacuated before the analysis starts to remove any moisture that may already be present. Accurate results cannot be obtained if the gas sample contains so much moisture that the final pressure of water vapor in the trap would, if the water were entirely vaporized, be greater than the vapor pressure of water at room temperature; if this condition is suspected, the whole determination should be repeated with only half the gas sample used the first time. The cold trap must have enough surface so that the moisture is condensed out quantitatively in a reasonable length of time. When the apparatus is not under vacuum, there should be no gas bubble in the closed end of the mercury manometer.

b. Dew Point Method

Several instruments are on the market for determining dew points to low temperatures. One of these (55) is useful as a quick "go–no go" test to see whether the gas in a cylinder is at least as dry as a given specification requires. A sample of the gas is compressed to a predetermined pressure into a small chamber and then allowed to expand as adiabatically as possible. The expansion produces a fog if the moisture content is above the allowable limit. To make sure that there is plenty of nucleation available for fog formation, a little radium is kept in the gas chamber of the apparatus.

c. Drying Agent Method

For occasional laboratory determinations of moisture, pass a measured sample of the gas through a tube containing a drying agent. Weigh the tube before and after absorption of the moisture. Recommended drying agents are Type 4A molecular sieve, phosphorus pentoxide dispersed in glass wool, and magnesium perchlorate.

B. RECOMMENDED CONTINUOUS FLOW METHODS

Methods used in the inert gas industry and recommended for the monitoring of impurities in plant streams of the inert gases are summarized in Table XVI and discussed here.

TABLE XVI

Recommended Continuous Flow Methods for Determination of Purity and of Impurities in Streams of Inert Gases

Determination	Approx. maximum sensitivity	Method
Over-all purity of an inert gas	10–50 p.p.m.	Thermal conductivity.
Individual impurities	25 p.p.m.[a]	Plant-type mass spectrometry.
	2 p.p.m.[b]	Gas chromatography.
Acetylene	1 p.p.m.	Nondispersive infrared absorption.
Carbon dioxide	1 p.p.m.	Nondispersive infrared absorption.
	5 p.p.m.	Measurement of pH of sodium bicarbonate solution.
Total hydrocarbons	1 p.p.m.	Combustion, followed by carbon dioxide determination.
Hydrogen	1–2 p.p.m.	Combustion with added oxygen over a catalyst, followed by determination of moisture.
	10 p.p.m.	Combustion with added oxygen over a catalyst and measurement of temperature of the catalyst.
Nitrogen in argon	3 p.p.m.	Continuous liquefaction and distillation of the sample and measurement of thermal conductivity of the nitrogen concentrate.
Oxygen	0.01%	Magnetic analyzer, 0–1% full scale.
	0.1 p.p.m.	Hersch electrolytic cell (104,86).
	5 p.p.m.	Combustion with added hydrogen over a catalyst and measurement of temperature of the catalyst.
Water vapor	1 p.p.m.	Electrolysis of phosphorus pentoxide and absorbed water in a special cell, with measurement of electrolysis current.

[a] The sensitivity can sometimes be increased by modification of available instruments.
[b] This sensitivity is reached only in special cases by use of a very sensitive detector.

1. Over-all Purity of an Inert Gas

Sensitive thermal conductivity cells are on the market and can be used to give a good idea of the total impurities in a gas. For this application, thermal conductivity methods have the drawback that the various impurities have quite different thermal conductivities; in practice this draw-back is less important than it sounds because the impurities do not usually vary much when a plant is in steady operation. Any appreciable change in thermal conductivity of the pure inert gas is cause for more extensive analytical work to determine which particular impurity is causing the change.

2. Individual Impurities

Sensitive mass spectrometers and gas chromatographs built for continuous use in a plant are on the market and can be employed for the determination of impurities in the inert gases.

3. Acetylene and Carbon Dioxide

Either of these impurities can be determined in concentrations at least as low as 1 p.p.m. by "nondispersive" infrared plant stream analyzers now on the market.

In the range 0 to 30 p.p.m. and higher, the carbon dioxide concentration may be determined by measurement of the pH of a dilute aqueous solution of sodium bicarbonate kept at a constant temperature and used to scrub out the carbon dioxide. (The chemical reaction between carbon dioxide and the sodium bicarbonate is reversible.) The apparatus and solution must be calibrated by the user so that the carbon dioxide concentration can be determined from a chart on which p.p.m. carbon dioxide are plotted versus pH, or the recorder can be calibrated directly in p.p.m. carbon dioxide.

The following concentrations of sodium bicarbonate are used for various ranges of carbon dioxide concentration in the inert gas:

Concn. of NaHCO$_3$, M	Approx. range, p.p.m. CO$_2$
0.0001	0–30
0.0002	8–100
0.0005	20–300
0.002	50–1000

The determination of carbon dioxide by measuring the pH of a sodium bicarbonate solution in equilibrium with the gas sample is described by Wilson, Orcutt, and Peterson (126).

4. Total Hydrocarbons

A metered flow of the sample gas is mixed with a metered flow of pure oxygen, and the mixture is passed over copper oxide at a temperature of about 900°C. The resulting carbon dioxide is determined by either of the continuous methods given in Section VIII-B-3. Carbon monoxide, if present, must be separately determined (for example, by oxidation over copper oxide at 300°C.), and the amount of carbon dioxide thus formed subtracted, along with the carbon dioxide originally present in the gas, from the amount of carbon dioxide produced by oxidation of the hydrocarbons.

Experience has shown that even at 900°C. methane may not burn quite completely. A trace of moisture seems to catalyze the combustion of methane. If the concentration of hydrocarbons is very low, it may be unnecessary to add oxygen to the inert gas before passing it over the copper oxide, although the presence of oxygen helps to burn methane quantitatively.

5. Hydrogen

Traces of hydrogen may be determined by mixing the inert gas stream with pure oxygen, burning the hydrogen to water over a catalyst, and determining the moisture formed. In a slightly less sensitive method (9), the temperature of the catalyst is recorded as a measure of the hydrogen concentration.

6. Nitrogen in Argon

One of the chief analytical problems in argon production has been the development of a satisfactory method for the continuous determination of traces of nitrogen. A plant stream type of mass spectrometer may be modified to make it more sensitive to nitrogen (26). An entirely different method that has been used to some extent commercially is outlined here (53). The method is accurate to about 3 p.p.m. nitrogen in the original sample argon and can be used over a full-scale range of 0 to 100 p.p.m.

Apparatus

This method employs a low-temperature rectification column for the continuous distillation of liquid argon (79). The packed column, about 14 inches high and 1 inch in diameter, rises above the kettle in which the sample boils. Above the column is the condenser, refrigerated by liquid oxygen. The column is so designed that the gas leaving the top will have a nitrogen concentration 100 times as great as that in the argon fed to the column. A standard thermal conductivity cell sensitive to 100 p.p.m. or less nitrogen in argon is used to measure the nitrogen concentration in the argon leaving the top of the column.

Procedure

The argon sample at a pressure of 10 p.s.i. gage and a flow of about 6 liters/minute (S.T.P.) is precooled by liquid oxygen in a small heat exchanger and enters the kettle as a cold gas, mixing there with the vapor of the boiling argon.   Most of the argon is condensed and then refluxes, but a small portion of it (about 50 cc./minute) is continuously withdrawn as a gas and passed through the thermal conductivity cell.   The level of liquid argon in the kettle is controlled by a float valve assembly; excess liquid is automatically drained away.   Operation of the column is entirely automatic except for the periodic addition of liquid oxygen to the oxygen reservoirs around the condenser and precooler.

Any impurities that are more volatile than argon, such as hydrogen, helium, and neon, will be concentrated along with the nitrogen and thus will prevent the nitrogen determination from being accurate.   However, if the apparatus is working right, the error is on the conservative side; that is, the true nitrogen concentration will never be greater than the figure obtained.

Safety Measure

Make an acetylene test at least every 8 hours on the liquid oxygen.   If there is more than 1.5 p.p.m. acetylene in the liquid oxygen, drain off all the liquid, refill the reservoir, and make another acetylene test.   In any case, drain the liquid oxygen reservoir completely every 24 hours as a precaution against the build-up of acetylene, which might lead to an explosion.

7. Oxygen

Higher oxygen concentrations (0.01% or more) may be determined with commercially available magnetic analyzers (99,109).   In the parts per million range the best method is that of the Hersch (10,48b) electrolytic cell, which has silver-cadmium or silver-lead electrodes and potassium hydroxide as electrolyte.   Several commercial models of the Hersch cell, some of which are sensitive to as low as 0.1 p.p.m. oxygen, have recently appeared on the market (10).   For a sensitivity of about 5 p.p.m., a commercial instrument (9) may be used in which hydrogen is mixed with the flowing gas, the mixture is passed over a combustion catalyst, and the temperature of the catalyst is measured.

8. Water Vapor

The most sensitive, reliable method for continuous moisture determination depends upon the absorption of the moisture by phosphorus pentoxide

TABLE XVII

Other Methods for Determination of Impurities in Inert Gases

Determination	Approx. possible sensitivity	Type[a]	Method in brief	Ref.
Combustible impurities	1 p.p.m.	C	Combustion over platinized silica gel or other suitable catalyst to give carbon dioxide and/or water vapor.	(75)
Impurities, general		C	Electrical: gases flow through an electrolytic rectifier; the leakage current determines the extent of impurities.	(30)
	0.05%	C	Electrical: voltage across a discharge tube is a function of the concentration of total impurities; total pressure of 3.5 mm. is used.	(70)
		C	Electrical: voltage across a uniform current are in a stream of argon is a function of impurities.	(110)
Noncondensable impurities (for example, O_2 or N_2) in xenon		L	Xenon is condensed by liquid nitrogen, and the pressure of the residual gas is measured.	(69)
Carbon dioxide	1 p.p.m.	L–C	Gas is bubbled through a calcium carbonate slurry, and the pH is measured.	(117)
Hydrogen in argon		C	Spectroscopic: high-frequency electrodeless discharge at 0.1–10 mm. pressure gives $H\alpha$ and $H\beta$ lines.	(57)
Hydrogen (in absence of oxygen)	0.1 p.p.m.	C	Colorimetric: reduction of methylene blue–palladous chloride solution at pH 3.9.	(113)
Hydrogen	6 p.p.m.	C	Sonic: the concentration of hydrogen is automatically determined by measuring the phase shift of sound waves at 150 kc.	(5)
	1 p.p.m.	L	Spectroscopic: high-frequency electrodeless discharge excites gas at 2–20 mm. pressure; the $H\beta$ line is isolated by an interference filter.	(111)
Hydrogen fluoride	10 μg.	L	Conductometric. Aqueous boric acid solution is used to scrub gas sample.	(86)
Nitrogen in argon		C	Spectroscopic: high-frequency electrodeless discharge at 0.1–10 mm. pressure gives nitrogen band spectra.	(57)
		C	Electrical: voltage across a uniform current arc in a stream of argon is measured.	(110)

Nitrogen in helium	1 p.p.m.	L	Spectroscopic: high-frequency electrodeless discharge with gas at about atmospheric pressure.	(13)
Nitrogen	0.2%	L	Absorption in molten lithium. Each determination takes 10 minutes.	(84)
	0.1%	L	Absorption by molten lithium at 180–200°C. Reaction is complete in 15 minutes.	(18)
	0.01%	L	Absorption in molten lithium at 500°C. for 1 hour.	(14)
	10 p.p.m.	L	Absorption by titanium at 1050°C. in a silica tube; determination of nitrogen in the titanium by a modified Kjeldahl method. (Found by the author's associates not to be reproducible in the 0–10 p.p.m. nitrogen range.)	(29)
	1 p.p.m.	L	Spectroscopic: high-frequency electrodeless discharge excites gas at 2–20 mm. pressure; nitrogen bands are isolated by an interference filter.	(111)
Oxygen	0.1%	L	Absorption by molten lithium at 180–200°C. Reaction is complete in 15 minutes.	(18)
	0.002%	L	Colorimetric: absorption in cuprous ammonium salt solution.	(50)
	0.02%			(65d)
	0.01%	L	Absorption in mo ten lithium at 500°C. for 1 hour.	(14)
	0.003%	L	Quenching of fluorescence of trypaflavin.	(65e)
	0.001%	L	Colorimetric: oxygen reacts with the reduced form of sodium anthraquinone-β-sulfonate in alkaline solution.	(16)
	20 μg.	L	Colorimetric: absorption in alkaline aqueous pyrogallol.	(124)
	<1 p.p.m.	L	Optical: oxygen is adsorbed on sodium metal, and the thickness of the oxide film is determined optically.	(91)
	1 ± 0.1 p.p.m.	L	Colorimetric: improved Winkler method; oxygen reacts with manganous-potassium iodide solution to give iodine; color is measured in o-xylene.	(112)
Water vapor	0.1%	L	Absorption by molten lithium at 180–200°C. Reaction is complete in 15 minutes.	(18)
	0.5 p.p.m.	C	Optical: absorption of 1216 A. radiation (vacuum ultraviolet) by water vapor.	(35)

in a special cell (68).   The moisture thus absorbed is electrolyzed by application of a d.c. voltage to the cell electrodes; the resulting current is a measure of the rate at which electrolysis takes place and therefore of the moisture concentration in the gas sample.   The phosphorus pentoxide film is of such size and position that over 99% of the gas sample molecules will have a chance to diffuse to the phosphorus pentoxide surface.

Since phosphorus pentoxide reacts with very few compounds other than water, this method is quite specific.   Commercial instruments making use of this principle of moisture determination and sensitive to as little as 1 p.p.m. moisture are on the market.

C. OTHER METHODS

These methods are listed in Table XVII.

IX. RECOMMENDED LABORATORY PROCEDURES

The procedures given in this section are recommended on the basis of actual experience by the author and his associates.

Principle.   Known volumes of each gas at accurately measured pressures and at a fixed temperature are pushed one at a time by a confining liquid into a previously evacuated sample bulb.

A. PREPARATION OF STANDARD SAMPLES OF KNOWN COMPOSITION

Apparatus

Glass laboratory apparatus that may be used for preparing standard samples is shown in Fig. 12.   In this apparatus a mercury leveling bulb is connected by means of flexible rubber tubing via an air bubble trap through stopcock C to a series of three accurately calibrated volumes, for example, 100 cc., 50 cc., and 15 cc.   These together constitute a gas buret.   The bulbs at F and G contain the pure gases that are to be measured and mixed, and the bulb at A is the one in which the mixture is to be made.   K is a thermocouple gage for measuring the pressure when the manifold is evacuated.   J leads to an oil diffusion pump and a forepump.   The cold trap below E helps in obtaining a good vacuum.

Procedure

1.   Attach the bulbs of pure gases to be used in preparing the mixture at the standard-taper joints H and L, and the empty sample bulb at joint M (Notes 1 and 2).

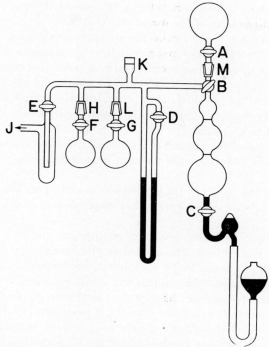

Fig. 12. Apparatus for preparing standard gas mixtures: *A, C, D, E, F, G,* two-way glass stopcocks; *B,* three-way glass stopcock; *H, L,* standard-taper ground-glass joints; *J,* connection leading to vacuum pump; *K,* thermocouple gage for measuring low pressures.

2.   Put a Dewar flask full of liquid nitrogen around the trap below *E,* and start the forepump and the oil diffusion pump.

3.   Open stopcocks *A, D,* and *E,* and turn three-way stopcock *B* so that it is open in all three directions.

4.   When the thermocouple gage *K* indicates a pressure lower than 10 μ, close stopcock *D*.

5.   Open stopcock *C* carefully, and raise the leveling bulb to allow the mercury to rise to the desired calibration mark.

6.   Turn stopcock *B* so that the manifold and the gas buret are connected but the sample bulb is closed off.

7.   Close stopcock *E,* and slowly open stopcock *F* until the desired pressure is obtained on the mercury manometer.   Then close *F*.

8.   Tap the manometer, and read the mercury levels by means of a cathetometer accurate to ± 0.05 mm.

9.   Turn stopcock *B* counterclockwise to connect the gas buret and the sample bulb and to close off the manifold.

10.   Open stopcock *C*, and raise the mercury leveling bulb so that the mercury will force all the measured gas up into the sample bulb.

11.   When the mercury has been raised to a point just beyond stopcock *A*, close stopcock *A*.   An accurately known volume of gas at a carefully measured pressure has now been transferred into the sample bulb.

12.   Lower the mercury level to the desired calibration mark for the next gas, and close stopcock *C*.

13.   Turn stopcock *B* so that it is open in all three directions.   Continue pumping until the thermocouple vacuum gage indicates a pressure under 10 μ.

14.   Measure the gas into the gas buret according to the directions in steps *6* through *9*, with the exception that stopcock *G* is used instead of *F* in step *7*.

15.   Open stopcock *A*, and then carry out steps *10* and *11*.

16.   If more components are desired in the standard mixture, replace the bulbs at *F* and *G* with bulbs containing other gases, and repeat steps *1* through *9* and *15*, except that stopcock *A* is not opened in step *3*.

17.   When all of the gases have been transferred to the sample bulb, remove it from joint *M*, and allow it to stand overnight before using it as a standard sample.   If the standard sample is needed immediately, admit a small amount of mercury to the bulb along with the last gas admitted. Shake the bulb to splash the mercury around to mix the gases.

Notes.   1. To prepare a mixture of accurately known composition, the temperature must be maintained constant during the whole procedure.   If the temperature of the room is not constant, the calibrated gas buret should be kept in a constant temperature water bath.

2. Before preparing the gas mixture, it is necessary to calculate the volume of each gas to be taken.   In general, a volume is chosen such that the measuring pressure for each component will be less than half an atmosphere.   (Keeping the pressure low minimizes deviations from the ideal gas laws.)   Also, it is advisable to add the components in the order of desired concentration, starting with the gas that is to have the lowest concentration in the final mixture and ending with the major component.

Calculation

Let
$$M = P_1V_1 + P_2V_2 + \ldots + P_nV_n$$

where P_1 is the pressure and V_1 the volume of the first pure component, P_2 and V_2 are the pressure and volume of the second pure component, etc.   Then

$$C_1 = (P_1V_1/M) \times 100$$

where C_1 is the concentration, in mole per cent, of the first component in the final gas mixture. The concentrations of the other components are calculated similarly.

B. TYPICAL MASS SPECTROMETER PROCEDURE

Principle. The principles of mass spectrometry are given in Part I of this Treatise. A typical procedure for running a sample follows.

Preparation and Calibration of Instrument

Read the instructions provided with the mass spectrometer for necessary preparations.

There are two alternative methods of calibration: (1) run in succession pure samples of each component of the mixture to be analyzed by the procedure presented here, immediately preceding or following the running of the sample being analyzed; or (2) run a gas mixture of known composition similar to that of the unknown sample immediately before or after (or both, if time is available) the unknown. The second method (2) usually gives more accurate results.

Procedure

Fig. 13 shows the sampling system of one type of mass spectrometer. Connect gas cylinder A to needle valve D. With all traps cooled and the vacuum pumps operating, adjust the stopcocks so that vessels F and G, the manifold, and the copper line are evacuated all the way to cylinder valve B. While the line from the mass spectrometer to the cylinder is being evacuated, turn on the chart drive and scanning mechanism, and make a background run to obtain the peak heights of any residual components present. Peaks at m/e values of 28 and 44 (carbon monoxide and carbon dioxide) are usually found.

When the pressure shown on the thermocouple gage is less than 10 μ, close needle valve D, open cylinder valve B, and adjust 3-way stopcock 6 to close off vessel G from both the pumping system and the manifold. Close stopcock 5 and turn three-way stopcock 4 so as to connect F to the manifold and to close off vessel G. Open valve D cautiously, and let the gas sample flow in until a pressure close to 100 mm. is read on mercury manometer M. Record the exact pressure. Then close B and D.

Turn stopcock 4 to close off the manifold and connect vessels F and G. Immediately start a timer. The measured gas sample expands from F to G and flows through the leak into the mass spectrometer tube, where the molecules are ionized. The ions are dispersed according to the ratio of

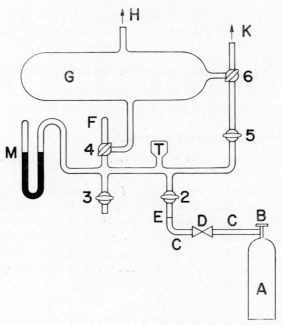

Fig. 13. Mass spectrometer sampling system: *A*, container for gas sample to be analyzed, for example, steel cylinder; *B*, cylinder valve; *C*, flexible copper tubing; *D*, metal
needle valve; *E*, Kovar metal-to-glass seal; *F*, calibrated volume for gas sample; *G*,
expansion vessel for gas sample; *H*, exit to leak; *K*, connection leading to vacuum pumps;
M, closed-end mercury manometer; *T*, thermocouple gage for measuring low pressures.

mass to electric charge (m/e), and the ion flow at each m/e value is measured
by the electronic scanning, amplifying, and recording system.

Experience will show what length of time should be allowed to pass
after the gas sample is admitted to expansion vessel *G* before starting the
chart drive and scanning mechanism. For one type of mass spectrometer,
this time is 3 minutes. As soon as the right time has elapsed, start the
chart drive and scanning mechanism to obtain the mass spectrum over the
desired range.

If it is desired to run a different gas sample next, replace cylinder *A*
with a cylinder containing the next sample. As soon as the scanning of the
first sample has been completed, follow the procedure for the second sample. In some cases, the background run may be omitted; experience will
tell.

If there is no interference at the m/e peak to be used to calculate the
concentration of a certain component, the calculation is straightforward:

$$C' = \frac{P_k \text{ (unknown)}}{P_k \text{ (standard)}} \times \frac{P_{mm} \text{ (standard)}}{P_{mm} \text{ (unknown)}} \times 100$$

where C' is the tentative concentration, in mole per cent, of the component; P_k is the peak height; and P_{mm} is the pressure recorded in the procedure.

The exact concentration, C, of the component in mole per cent is then found from the formula

$$C = 100C'/M$$

where M is the total of all the C' values found for all gases in the sample being analyzed. If M is not between 90 and 110, something is seriously wrong. Possible sources of error include these: (1) one or more components have not been identified and included in the summation—as a check on the components present, a portion of the gas sample should be run through a gas chromatograph; (2) something is wrong with the mass spectrometer; (3) a manipulative error has been made; (4) an error has been made in the calculations.

If there is interference at all of the m/e peaks for a given component, the simple method of calculation just presented cannot be used. An indication of how to proceed in the case of interference follows.

Example. A sample containing a mixture of neon, argon, and krypton is run in the mass spectrometer, followed by pure samples of each of the separate gases. The pressure (P_{mm}) to which the sample intake vessel of the mass spectrometer is filled is read on the manometer and recorded in each case. The peak heights (P_k) are measured for the following peaks: 22, 40, and 84. There is no interference at the 22 and 84 peaks, but Kr^{+2} contributes to the 40 peak, and its effect must be subtracted before the argon concentration can be calculated.

The peak heights obtained with pure krypton were 22,190 at 84 and 216 at 40, and for the unknown sample, 7,720 at 84 and 35,000 at 40. Correction may be made for the Kr^{+2} contribution to the argon peak.

$$(216/22,190) \times 7,720 = 75$$

The argon contribution to the 40 peak is therefore $35,000 - 75 = 34,925 =$ corrected P_k for argon.

The tentative concentration is then calculated for each element by means of the formula

$$C' = \frac{P_k \text{ (unknown)}}{P_k \text{ (pure gas)}} \times \frac{P_{mm} \text{ (pure gas)}}{P_{mm} \text{ (unknown)}} \times 100$$

The results are normalized by multiplying each mole per cent thus obtained by $100/M$, where M is the total of the values of C' for all the gases in the mixture.

The first two rows of Table XVIII show the data obtained and the results of the calculations made for this example. All starting pressures were the same; hence, no pressure corrections were made.

TABLE XVIII

Quantitative Analysis of an Inert Gas Mixture with a
Mass Spectrometer

| Gas | m/e | Peak height (P_k) | | | Concn., mole % | |
| | | Pure gas | Unknown | | Tenta-tive | Normalized and rounded off |
			Uncor.	Cor.		
Neon	22	1,220	238	238	19.51	19.4
Argon	40	75,900	35,000	34,925	46.01	45.9
Krypton	40	216	35,000	75		
Krypton	84	22,190	7,720	7,720	34.79	34.7
					100.31	100.0
Neon	20	11,020	5,220	2,137	19.39	19.4
Argon	20	6,700	5,220	3,083		
Argon	40				46.01	45.9
Krypton	84				34.79	34.7
					100.19	100.0

All gases in this example were started in the mass spectrometer at the same pressure.

A cross check on the neon concentration may be obtained as follows (see first two of lower four rows in the table).

In the mass spectrum of the unknown, the peak height at $m/e = 20$ is 5220. Part of this is from Ne^+ and part from Ar^{+2}. The contribution from argon can be calculated from the peak heights at 40 and 20 in the spectrum for pure argon and from the argon contribution to the peak at 40 for the unknown.

$$(6,700/75,900) \times 34,925 = 3,083$$

Subtracting this result from 5,220 leaves $P_k = 2,137$ for Ne^+.

The tentative concentration of neon is $(2,137/11,020) \times 100 = 19.39$ mole %, which gives a rounded, normalized figure of 19.4%, the same as the figure obtained by using the peak height at $m/e = 22$ for calculation of the neon concentration.

C. TYPICAL GAS CHROMATOGRAPH PROCEDURE

The principles of gas chromatography are explained in Part I of this Treatise. Although the procedure given here is specifically for one model of the Burrell Corporation Kromo-Tog line of chromatographs, the same general outline would apply to any gas chromatograph.

Apparatus

Fig. 14 is a self-explanatory schematic diagram of one model of a gas chromatograph.

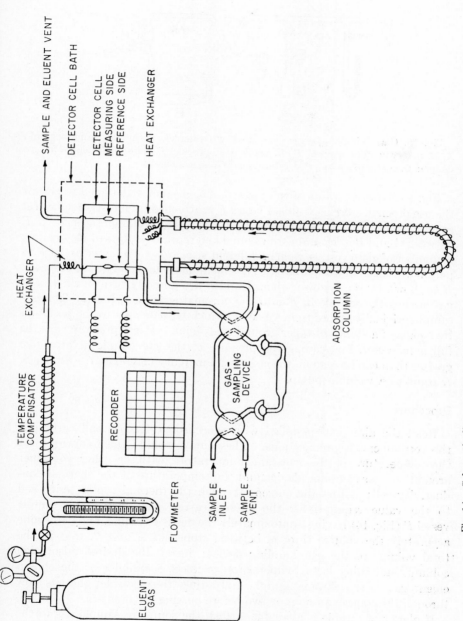

Fig. 14. Schematic diagram of gas chromatograph. (Courtesy of Burrell Corporation.)

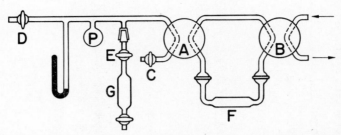

Fig. 15. Glass sampling system for small gas samples, gas phase chromatograph: A, B, four-way stopcocks; C, D, E, two-way stopcocks; F, calibrated volume for gas sample; G, gas sample tube; P, pressure gage or long manometer.

Fig. 15 shows a portion of the gas-sampling system, redesigned to permit the use of small samples.   Glass vessel F is attached by means of spherical ground-glass joints to stopcocks A and B.   The volume trapped in F between A and B is accurately measured and represents the sample volume. A number of glass vessels, each of different size, are available for use at F to permit variation of sample size.   The eluent gas enters and leaves stopcock B as shown by the arrows; when A and B are properly turned, the eluent gas sweeps the sample in F into the chromatographic column.   The gas sample originally comes from vessel G, which is connected to the manifold by means of a standard-taper ground-glass joint.   P is a pressure gage, or full manometer, for reading the pressure of the gas sample at pressures greater than can be read on the closed-end mercury manometer.   Stopcock D leads to a vacuum pump.

Procedure

Read the directions supplied with the chromatograph, and carry out the recommended preparations.   These may include the following: set the temperature of the constant temperature bath or other container around the gas-sampling device and the temperature of the thermal conductivity cell; adjust the current through the thermal conductivity cell to the value required for the chosen carrier gas; install the sample vessel F (Fig. 14) having approximately the desired volume, and determine accurately the volume trapped between stopcocks A and B, that is, the total volume of the gas-sampling device; install the desired adsorption column, and bring it to temperature; connect a cylinder of the chosen eluent gas to the chromatograph, and adjust the flow; let the gas flow through the column an hour or two before making the first run.

If plenty of sample is available, attach the source of sample gas to the sample inlet (Fig. 14), and turn stopcock A so as to flush out the gas-sampling device, venting the sample to the air. Turn off the flow of sample gas at the source, and then turn stopcock A (Fig. 15) to trap a known volume of sample in the gas-sampling device. Read the barometer to determine the pressure. The temperature is held constant by thermostatic control around the sampling device.

If only a small quantity of sample is available, proceed as follows: Turn stopcock A (Fig. 15) to evacuate the manifold and the gas-sampling device. The closed-end manometer tells the progress of the evacuation. When a good vacuum has been attained, close stopcock D, and open stopcock E to admit the sample from the sample tube to vessel F. Read the pressure on the pressure gage, P, and turn stopcock A to isolate the gas sample in the gas-sampling device.

Turn stopcock B to admit the measured gas sample to the stream of carrier gas. Wait a few minutes for all of the sample to be swept out of vessel F, and then return stopcock B to its previous position.

Normally the operator has nothing more to do until elution of the sample is complete. However, occasionally it may be desirable to raise the temperature of the column while a run is in progress. This is done after all the components that are eluted in a reasonable length of time have left the column, in order to hasten elution of the remaining components. An example of this procedure was given in Table XI, which gives data for a run in which the temperature of the column was raised from 30 to 85°C. to elute the xenon. At 30°C. the elution of xenon would have required several hours.

Identification of Components. Each component of a gas mixture has, under a given set of conditions, a characteristic "retention time," that is, time elapsed between introduction of the sample and the appearance of the peak in the pen trace on the recorder chart. (Typical recorder chart traces are shown in Figs. 9 and 10.) The retention time does not usually vary with the concentration of the component in the gas mixture. Thus, for qualitative identification of the components, it is necessary only to know to what specific gas each retention time corresponds. This can be determined by running samples of pure gases through the column and measuring the retention times until all the gases in the unknown have been identified. A more direct approach is to take samples of the carrier gas as it leaves the column, timing the sampling in such a way that each sample contains one of the unknown components. The component is then identified in a mass spectrometer or in an emission spectrograph. This process is simplified by using a high-velocity, scanning type of mass spectrometer in conjunction with the gas chromatograph.

Identification of the component may be made easier if it can readily be separated from the eluent gas.   For example, if the eluent gas is helium, the component may sometimes be frozen out, and the helium pumped off.   The sample is then allowed to warm up and is fed to a mass spectrometer.

Quantitative Determination of Components.   Under favorable conditions each component in the gas mixture gives a separate peak.   To determine the concentration of each component, proceed as follows: (*1*) measure the area under each peak on the chart with a polar planimeter or by other means;   (*2*) run a mixture of known composition similar to that of the unknown, or (less desirably) run samples of the separate pure components one at a time, following the same procedure as for the unknown;   and (*3*) calculate the concentration of each component in the unknown by the formula

$$C = P'V'AC'/PVA'$$

where C is the concentration of a given component in the sample; C' is the concentration of the same component in the pure gas or standard gas mixture; P and V are pressure and volume, respectively, of the sample; P' and V' are pressure and volume, respectively, of the pure gas or standard gas mixture;   and A and A' are areas under the peaks for the sample and the standard, respectively.

The accuracy of the analysis is better, the closer the composition, pressure, and volume are for the unknown and for the standard gas sample.   If pure components are run instead of a standard mixture, the areas under the peaks should be close to those obtained from the sample.

If complete resolution is not achieved, or needs to be improved, the following factors, taken singly or collectively, may help: a smaller sample, a lower flow of carrier gas, a lower column temperature, a different packing material for the column, and a longer column.

If only very small samples of the unknown gas are available, there may be an appreciable error in measuring the sample.   In that case, the formula for calculating the results may give somewhat erroneous absolute results, although the ratios of the concentrations of the components to each other should be accurate.   This source of error may be obviated by making a complete quantitative analysis of the unknown, adding the percentages to get the total (M), and then normalizing the results if the total is not 100.0%.   This normalization is performed simply by multiplying each tentative gas concentration by the factor $100/M$.

Example.   A gas sample is put through a gas chromatograph under various conditions until complete resolution of all components is obtained.   They are identified, and their concentrations are roughly estimated (in mole per cent) to be as follows: argon, 50%; krypton, 10%; and neon, 40%.

TABLE XIX
Quantitative Analysis of an Inert Gas Mixture by Gas Chromatography

| Gas | Area under peak | | Compn., mole % | | |
	Standard	Unknown	Standard	Unknown, first calculation	Unknown, normalized
Argon	653	684	50.0	52.4	53.0
Krypton	127	115	10.0	9.05	9.2
Neon	365	342	40.0	37.4	37.8
			100.0	98.85	100.0

Areas are in arbitrary units.

A standard gas sample with this composition is now prepared and run through the gas chromatograph under conditions identical with those used for the unknown. The areas under the peaks in both the chromatograms are then measured, and the results calculated by means of the formula given in Section IX-C-8. The analysis of the unknown may then be normalized. The areas measured and the calculated compositions for this example are given in Table XIX.

Acknowledgment

The author wishes to extend thanks to the members of the staff of the Research and Engineering Laboratories of Linde Company who have been of assistance in preparing this chapter, and in particular to the following persons:

Arthur C. Jenkins for compiling the tables of isotopes and the properties of the inert gases.

Norbert R. Mumbach and Daniel R. Acker for helping to write the section on preparation of standard gas samples and on mass spectrometry.

Robert F. Dwyer for helping to write the recommended procedure for gas chromatography.

Herbert G. Guillaume and Carroll P. Smith for help in selecting, and for correcting the first draft of, recommended procedures for determining impurities in the inert gases.

Ezra Erb for information on new developments in the gas chromatography of the inert gases.

All those listed above and also Clair M. Birdsall, Howard B. Bradley, Salem Thomas Clark, Leslie G. Dowell, Thaddeus J. Lewanski, Adam H. Malik, Paul H. Mohr, Jean M. Mutchler, Walter R. Neuhaus, Robert G. Pankhurst, Paul E. Peters, and Ernest R. Shull, for critically reading part or all of the chapter, pointing out errors, and suggesting improvements.

REFERENCES

1. Aldrich, L. T., and A. O. Nier, *Phys. Rev.*, **74**, 876 (1948).
2. Alterthum, H., A. Lompe, and R. Seeliger, *Physik. Z.*, **37**, 833 (1936).
3. Anderson, C. C., and H. H. Hinson, *U. S. Bur. Mines Bull.* No. 486 (1951), (a) p. 7; (b) pp. 7–8; (c) p. 17; (d) pp. 29–44; (e) p. 81.
4. Angehofer, A. W., and B. M. Dewey, *Instruments*, **26**, 580 (1953); through *Chem. Abstr.*, **47**, 7263f (1953).

5. Anonymous, *Chem. Eng. News*, **35**, 112 (Jan. 7, 1957).
6. Anonymous, *Chem. Eng. News*, **35**, 30 (Aug. 19, 1957).
7. Anonymous, *Chem. Week*, **75**, 93 (Oct. 16, 1954).
8. Aston, F. W., "Mass Spectra," in M. A. Whiteley, *Thorpe's Dictionary of Applied Chemistry*, 4th ed., Vol. VII, Longmans Green, New York, 1946, p. 519.
9. Baker, J. T., and Co., Newark, N. J., Deoxo unit.
10. Baker, J. T., and Co., Newark, N. J., Minoxo unit. Similar units are now being offered by Beckman Instruments, Fullerton, Calif., and by Analytic Systems Co., Pasadena, Calif. See P. A. Hersch.
11. Barrer, R. M., and A. B. Robins, *Trans. Faraday Soc.*, **49**, 807–15 (1953).
12. Baxter, G. P., *J. Am. Chem. Soc.*, **61**, 1597 (1939).
13. Bochkova, O. P., and E. Ya. Shreider, *Vestnik Leningrad. Univ.*, **11**, No. 16, *Ser. Fiz. i Khim.* No. 3, 57 (1956); *Chem. Abstr.*, **51**, 2472f (1957).
14. Bowman, R. E., and C. B. Hartly, *Welding J.* (*N. Y.*), **29**, 258-s (1950).
15. Boyce, J. C., *Revs. Modern Phys.*, **13**, 1 (1941); (a) p. 4.
16. Brady, L. J., *Anal. Chem.*, **20**, 1033 (1948).
17. Brown, E. H., and J. E. Cline, *Ind. Eng. Chem., Anal. Ed.*, **17**, 286 (1945).
18. Burbo, P. Z., *Zavodskaya Lab.*, **16**, 1498 (1950); through *Chem. Abstr.*, **45**, 9925g (1951).
19. Cady, G. H., and H. P. Cady, *Ind. Eng. Chem., Anal. Ed.*, **17**, 760 (1945).
20. Carr, D. R., and J. L. Kulp, *Bull. Geol. Soc. Am.*, **68**, 763 (1957).
21. Cattell, R. A., and H. P. Wheeler, Jr., "Helium," in R. E. Kirk and D. F. Othmer, *Encyclopedia of Chemical Technology*, Vol. 7, Interscience, New York–London, 1951, pp. 398–408.
22. Clusius, K., and G. Dickel, *Z. physik. Chem.* (*Leipzig*), **B44**, 397, 451 (1939); **B48**, 50 (1940); *Naturwissenschaften*, **28**, 461, 711 (1940); through ref. 65, p. 64, and ref. 120.
23. Consolidated Electrodynamics Corp., *Anal. Chem.*, **30**, 10A (1958).
24. Crane, E. J., Private communication, July 17, 1958.
25. Crouthamel, C. E., and H. Diehl, *Anal. Chem.*, **20**, 515 (1948)
26. Davis, C. E., R. H. Hunt, and M. J. O'Neal, Jr., *Anal. Chem.*, **29**, 1720 (1957).
27. Dieke, G. H., "Atomic and Molecular Physics," in D. E. Gray, *American Institute of Physics Handbook*, Sec. 7, McGraw-Hill, New York, 1957, pp. 14–15.
28. Dieke, G. H., and H. M. Crosswhite, *J. Opt. Soc. Am.*, **42**, 433 (1952).
29. Dombroski, H. S., *Anal. Chem.*, **26**, 526 (1954).
30. Drager, O. H., Brit. Pat. 716,015; through *Anal. Abstr.*, **2**, 252 (1955).
31. Dwyer, R. F., and R. P. Hueber, Tonawanda Research and Development Laboratory, Linde Co., Division of Union Carbide Corp., Unpublished work, 1958.
32. Erb, E., Tonawanda Engineering Laboratory, Linde Co., Division of Union Carbide Corp., Unpublished work, 1958.
33. Fastovskii, V. G., *Zavodskaya Lab.*, **15**, 1417 (1949); through *Chem. Abstr.*, **44**, 4370f (1950).
34. Frost, E. M., Jr., *U. S. Bur. Mines Rept. Invest.* No. 3899 (1946).
34a. Frost, E. M., Jr., (to U. S. A.), U. S. Pat. 2,601,272 (June 24, 1952); through *Chem. Abstr.*, **46**, 10590a (1952).
35. Garton, W. R. S., M. S. W. Webb, and P. C. Wildy, *J. Sci. Instr.*, **34**, 496 (1957).
35a. Gentner, V. W., and J. Zähringer, *Z. Naturforsch.*, *Pt. a*, **10a**, 498 (1955).
36. Gill, A. H., "Gas Analysis," in N. H. Furman, *Scott's Standard Methods of Chemical Analysis*, 5th ed., Vol. II, Van Nostrand, New York, 1939, (a) pp. 2336–9; (b) p 2349; (c) pp. 2421–4.

37. Glückauf, E., *Proc. Roy. Soc. (London)*, **185A**, 98 (1946); (a) **185A**, 108 (1946).
38. Glueckauf, E., "The Composition of Atmospheric Air," in Thomas F. Malone, *Compendium of Meteorology*, American Meteorological Society, Boston, 1951, (a) pp. 3–10.
39. Glueckauf, E., K. H. Barker, and G. P. Kitt, *Discussions Faraday Soc.*, No. 7, 199 (1949); (a) p. 209.
40. Glueckauf, E., and G. P. Kitt, *Atomic Energy Research Establ. (Gt. Brit.) Rept.* C/R 1847 (1956).
41. Glueckauf, E., and G. P. Kitt, *Proc. Roy. Soc. (London)*, **A234**, 557 (1956).
42. Goodman, C., and R. D. Evans, *Rev. Sci. Instr.*, **15**, 123 (1944).
43. Greene, S. A., Paper given before the Division of Analytical Chemistry, 112th Meeting, ACS, New York, Sept. 8, 1957, *Abstract No. 87*, p. 35B.
44. Guenther, P. L., and F. A. Paneth, *Z. phys. Chem.*, **A173**, 401 (1935).
45. Guldner, W. G., and A. L. Beach, *Anal. Chem.*, **22**, 366 (1950).
46. Hahn, O., F. Strassmann, and W. Seelmann-Eggebert, *Z. Naturforsch.*, **1**, 545 (1946); (a) p. 550.
47. Harrison, G. R., *Massachusetts Institute of Technology Wavelength Tables*, Wiley, New York (No date given. Introduction written in 1939), (a) p. xii.
48. Harrison, G. R., R. C. Lord, and J. R. Loofbourow, *Practical Spectroscopy*, Prentice-Hall, New York, 1948, (a) pp. 429–31.
48b. Hersch, P. A., *Anal. Chem.*, **32**, 1030 (1960).
49. Hickom, J. B., E. Blair, and R. Frayser, *J. Clin. Invest.*, **33**, 1277 (1954); through *Anal. Abstr.*, **2**, 1603 (1955).
50. Hoffman, E., *Mikrochemie*, **25**, 82 (1938); through *Chem. Abstr.*, **33**, 1625⁹ (1939).
51. Hollander, J. M., I. Perlman, and G. T. Seaborg, *Revs. Modern Phys.*, **25**, 469 (1953).
52. Holleman, H. C. A., *Philips' tech. Rundschau*, **5**, 89 (1940); through *Chem. Abstr.*, **36**, 4382⁴ (1942).
53. Houston, R., and Latimer, R. E., *IS. Journal*, **3**, 490 (1956).
54. Hughes, D. J., and J. A. Harvey, *U. S. Atomic Energy Comm. Rept.* BNL-325 (1955); D. J. Hughes and R. B. Schwartz, *U. S. Atomic Energy Comm. Rept.* BNL-325 Suppl. No. 1 (1957).
55. Illinois Testing Laboratories, Alnor dew point tester.
56. Inghram, M. G., E. Long, and L. Meyer, *Phys. Rev.*, **97**, 1454 (1955).
57. Ishida, R., *Repts. Govt. Chem. Ind. Research Inst., Tokyo*, **51**, 342 (1956); through *Chem. Abstr.*, **51**, 948*i* (1957).
58. Izvekov, I. V., *Zavodskaya Lab.*, **15**, 1383 (1949); through *Chem. Abstr.*, **44**, 3840*i* (1950).
59. Jacobi, R. B., *Sci. J. Roy. Coll. Sci.*, **9**, 16 (1939); *Chem. Abstr.*, **33**, 5772² (1939).
60. Jacobs, M. B., *The Analytical Chemistry of Industrial Poisons, Hazards, and Solvents*, 2nd ed., Interscience, New York–London, 1949, (a) p. 21.
61. Janak, J., *Chem. listy*, **47**, 464 (1953); through *Chem. Abstr.*, **48**, 3196*i* (1954).
62. Janak, J., *Chem. listy*, **47**, 1348 (1953); through *Chem. Abstr.*, **48**, 3854*b* (1954).
63. Jones, R. A., and M. A. Dubs, "Neon, Argon, Krypton, and Xenon," in R. E. Kirk and D. F. Othmer, *Encyclopedia of Chemical Technology*, Vol. 7, Interscience, New York–London, 1951, pp. 408–19.
64. Kahle, H., *Chem. Fabrik*, **16**, 144 (1943).
65. Kahle, H., "Edelgase: Helium, Neon, Argon, Krypton, Xenon, Emanation," in R. Fresenius and G. Jander, *Handbuch der Analytischen Chemie*, Springer, Berlin,

1949, Part III, Vol. VIIIa, pp. 1–97; (a) pp. 6–9; (b) p. 16; (c) p. 19; (d) p. 25; (e) p. 26; (f) p. 53; (g) pp. 54–7; (h) pp. 60–2; (i) p. 63; (j) p. 64; (k) pp. 64–5.

66. Karlik, B., *Sitzber. Akad. Wiss. Wien, Math.-naturw. Kl., Abt. IIa*, **145**, 145 (1936).
67. Karwat, E., and A. Hölzl (to Gesellschaft für Linde's Eismaschinen A-G.), Ger. Pat. 810,323 (Aug. 9, 1951); *Chem. Abstr.*, **47**, 9866h (1953).
68. Keidel, F. A., "A Novel, Inexpensive Instrument for Accurate Analysis for Traces of Water," Paper given at the Pittsburgh Conference on Analytical Chemistry and Applied Spectroscopy, Pittsburgh, Pa., Feb., 1956.
69. Kenty, C., *Rev. Sci. Instr.*, **17**, 158 (1946).
70. Kenty, C. (to General Electric Co.), U. S. Pat. 2,654,051 (Sept. 29, 1953).
71. Kenty, C., and F. W. Reuter, Jr., *Rev. Sci. Instr.*, **18**, 918 (1947); (a) p. 921.
72. Khlopin, V. G., and E. K. Gerling, *Natural Gases (USSR)*, No. 4/5, 62 (1932); through *Chem. Abstr.*, **31**, 3339³ (1937).
73. Shirley, E. L., C. F. Pachucki, and L. K. Lolas, *U. S. Atomic Energy Comm. Rept.* KAPL-1890 (Nov. 14, 1957).
74. Kniazuk, M., and F. R. Prediger, *Instr. and Automation*, **28**, 1916 (1955); through *Anal. Abstr.*, **3**, 1547 (1956).
75. Kobe, K. A., and R. A. MacDonald, *Ind. Eng. Chem., Anal. Ed.*, **13**, 457 (1941).
76. Kressley, L. J., and L. K. Frevel, U. S. Pat. 2,829,953 (April 8, 1958).
77. Kurie, F. N. D., "Nuclear Physics," in D. E. Gray, *American Institute of Physics Handbook*, Sec. 8, McGraw-Hill, New York, 1957, pp. 98–128.
78. Lahr, P. H., Tonawanda Research Laboratory, Linde Co., Division of Union Carbide Corp., Unpublished work, 1957.
79. Latimer, R. E.; *A.I.Ch.E. Journal*, **3**, 75 (1957).
80. Lawley, L. E., *Chem. & Ind. (London)*, **78**, 200 (1954).
81. Leddicotte, G. W., and S. A. Reynolds, *U. S. Atomic Energy Comm. ORNL Rept.* CF 56-7-106 (1957).
82. Lee, T., *Appl. Spectroscopy*, **9**, 5 (1955).
83. Liempt, J. A. M. van, and W. van Wijk, *Rec. trav. chim.*, **56**, 755–759 (1937).
84. Liempt, J. A. M. van, and W. van Wijk, *Rec. trav. chim.*, **58**, 964 (1939); through *Chem. Abstr.*, **34**, 961⁴ (1940).
85. Lunge, G., and H. R. Ambler, *Technical Gas Analysis*, Gurney and Jackson, London, 1934, (a) pp. 10–20; (b) pp. 51–7; (c) pp. 89–115; (d) pp. 123–49; (e) p. 201; (f) p. 261.
86. Manning, D. L., and J. C. White, *U. S. Atomic Energy Comm. Rept.* ORNL-1538 (1953); also in *Anal. Chem.*, **25**, 1648 (1953).
87. Martin, A. E., *Ind. Chemist*, **31**, 60 (1955); through *Chem. Abstr.*, **49**, 8637i (1955).
88. Martin, A. J. P., and R. L. M. Synge, *Biochem. J.*, **35**, 1358 (1941).
89. Meinke, W. W., and R. S. Maddock, *Anal. Chem.*, **29**, 1171 (1957).
90. Moeller, T., *Inorganic Chemistry, an Advanced Textbook*, Wiley, New York, 1952, (a) p. 381; (b) p. 382.
91. Moyer, J. W., and W. A. Ruggles, *J. Opt. Soc. Am.*, **44**, 86 (1954).
92. Mullen, P. W., *Modern Gas Analysis*, Interscience, New York–London, 1955.
93. Newton, A. S., *Anal. Chem.*, **25**, 1746 (1953).
94. Nier, A. O., *Natl. Acad. Sci.–Natl. Research Council Publ.* No. 400, 7 (1956).
95. Norhagen, A., and E. Obeblad, *Acta Radiol.*, **43**, 487 (1955).
96. Paneth, F. A., *Quart. J. Roy. Meteorol. Soc.*, **65**, 304 (1939).
97. Paneth, F. A., *Endeavour*, **12**, 5 (1953); (a) p. 10.
98. Paneth, F., and K. Peters, *Z. physik. Chem.*, **134**, 353 (1928); (a) p. 356.
99. Pauling, L., R. E. Wood, and J. H. Sturdivant, *J. Am. Chem. Soc.*, **68**, 795 (1946).
100. Phillips, C., *Gas Chromatography*, Academic Press, New York, 1956, (a) p. 83.

101. Reynolds, J. H., *Rev. Sci. Instr.*, **27**, 928 (1956); (a) p. 934.
102. Riesz, R., and G. H. Dieke, *J. Appl. Phys.*, **25**, 196 (1954).
103. Rogers, W. A., R. S. Buritz, and D. Alpert, *J. Appl. Phys.*, **25**, 874 (1954).
104. Ruark, A. E., and H. C. Urey, *Atoms, Molecules, and Quanta*, McGraw-Hill, New York, 1930, (a) p. 182.
105. Santangelo, M., *Ann. geofis. (Rome)*, **5**, 27 (1952); through *Chem. Abstr.*, **46**, 9467e (1952).
106. Sawyer, R. A., *Experimental Spectroscopy*, Prentice-Hall, New York, 1952, (a) p. 27; (b) p. 28; (c) p. 328.
107. Schröer, E., *Z. anal. Chem.*, **111**, 161 (1937).
108. Schwenther, F. F., and H. K. Fallin, *Bull. Johns Hopkins Hosp.*, **61**, 210 (1937).
109. Seffern, O. K., *Instruments*, **26**, 1211 (1953).
110. Seitz, R. O. (to Air Reduction Co.), U. S. Pat. 2,640,870 (June 2, 1953); through *Chem. Abstr.*, **47**, 7838h (1953).
111. Servigne, M., P. G. de Montgarevil, and D. Dominé, *Compt. rend.*, **242**, 2827 (1956).
112. Silverman, L., and W. Bradshaw, *Anal. Chim. Acta*, **12**, 526 (1955).
113. Silverman, L., and W. Bradshaw, *Anal. Chim. Acta*, **15**, 31 (1956).
114. Struwe, F., R. Johow, and E. Pietsch, "Edelgase," in R. J. Meyer, *Gmelins Handbuch der anorganischen Chemie*, Verlag Chemie, Berlin, 1926, System-Nummer 1, pp. 232–41.
115. Templeton, D. H., "Isotopes," in R. E. Kirk and D. F. Othmer, *Encyclopedia of Chemical Technology*, Vol. 8, Interscience, New York–London, 1952, (a) pp. 90–1.
116. Tobin, J. M., *Acta Met.*, **5**, 398 (1957); also in *U. S. Atomic Energy Comm. Rept.* TID-7526 (Pt. 1), 129 (1957).
117. Toren, Paul E., and B. J. Heinrich, *Anal. Chem.*, **29**, 1854 (1957).
118. Travers, M. W., *The Experimental Study of Gases*, Macmillan, London, 1901, (a) p. 297; (b) p. 302; (c) pp. 302 and 313; (d) pp. 311–13.
119. Wagener, J. S., and P. T. Marth, *J. Appl. Phys.*, **28**, 1027 (1957).
120. Weaver, E. R., *J. Am. Chem. Soc.*, **38**, 352 (1916).
121. Wichers, E., *J. Am. Chem. Soc.*, **80**, 4121 (1958).
122. Wiley, W. C., and I. H. McLaren, *Rev. Sci. Instr.*, **26**, 1150 (1955).
123. Wiley, W. C., *Science*, **124**, 817 (1956).
124. Williams, D. D., C. H. Blackly, and R. R. Miller, *Anal. Chem.*, **24**, 1819 (1952).
125. Williams, M. M. D., H. O. Brown, W. B. Dublin, and W. M. Boothby, *Proc. Minn. Acad. Sci.*, **13**, 46 (1945); (a) p. 49.
126. Wilson, P. W., F. S. Orcutt, and W. H. Peterson, *Ind. Eng. Chem., Anal. Ed.*, **4**, 357 (1932).
127. Winteringham, F. P. W., *Lab. Practice*, **4**, 288 (1955); (a) p. 289.
128. Zambito, A. T., *Food Inds.*, **21**, 1554 (1949).
129. Zimmer, Karl G., *Angew. Chem.*, **54**, 33 (1941).

GENERAL REFERENCES

Large Compendia

Analysis of the Inert Gases

Kahle, H., "Elemente der Achten Hauptgruppe; Edelgase," in R. Fresenius and G. Jander, *Handbuch der Analytischen Chemie*, Springer, Berlin, 1949, Part III, Vol. VIIIa, pp. 1–97.

Struwe, F., R. Johow, and E. Pietsch, "Nachweis und Bestimmung der Edelgase," in R. J. Meyer, *Gmelins Handbuch der anorganischen Chemie*, 8th ed., Verlag Chemie, Berlin, 1926, System-Nummer 1, pp. 232–41.

General Information on the Inert Gases

Briscoe, H. V., "The Inert Gases," in J. Newton Friend, *A Text-book of Inorganic Chemistry*, Griffin, London, 1919, Vol. I, Part II, pp. 293–360.

Kirk, R. E., and D. F. Othmer, *Encyclopedia of Chemical Technology*, Vol. 7, Interscience, New York–London, 1951, articles on "Helium," pp. 398–408, and "Helium-Group Gases," pp. 408–19.

Mellor, J. W., *A Comprehensive Treatise on Inorganic and Theoretical Chemistry*, Longmans, Green, London, 1930, Vol. VII, Chap. XLVIII, pp. 889–951.

Pascal, Paul, *Nouveau Traité de Chimie Minérale*, Masson, Paris, 1956, Vol. I, pp. 941–1083.

Struwe, F., R. Johow, and E. Pietsch, "Edelgase," in R. J. Meyer, *Gmelins Handbuch der anorganischen Chemie*, Verlag Chemie, Berlin, 1926, System-Nummer 1, pp. 1–251.

Thorpe, J. F., and M. A. Whiteley, *Thorpe's Dictionary of Applied Chemistry*, 4th ed., Longmans, Green, London. See articles under the individual names of each of the inert gases. Dates range from "Argon," 1937, to "Xenon," 1954.

Monographs, Shorter Compendia, and Review Articles

Gas Analysis and Instrumental Methods

Berl, W. G., *Physical Methods in Chemical Analysis*, Academic Press, New York, 1951, Vol. II, chapter on "Gas Analysis by Methods Depending on Thermal Conductivity," pp. 387–437.

Berl, W. G., *Physical Methods in Chemical Analysis*, Academic Press, New York, 1956, Vol. III, chapters on "Gas Chromatography" and "Neutron Spectroscopy and Neutron Interactions in Chemical Analysis."

Ewing, G. W., *Instrumental Methods of Chemical Analysis*, McGraw-Hill, New York, 1954, chapters on "Emission Spectroscopy," "Mass Spectrometry," and "The Analysis of Gases."

Furman, N. H., *Scott's Standard Methods of Chemical Analysis*, 5th ed., Van Nostrand, New York, 1939, Vol. II, pp. 2336–433.

Lunge, G., and H. R. Ambler, *Technical Gas Analysis*, Gurney and Jackson, London, 1934.

Mullen, P. W., *Modern Gas Analysis*, Interscience, New York–London, 1955, 1959.

Paneth, F. A., *Endeavour*, **12**, 5 (1953).

Travers, M. W., *The Experimental Study of Gases*, Macmillan, London, 1901.

Willard, H. H., L. L. Merritt, and J. A. Dean, *Instrumental Methods of Analysis*, 2nd ed., Van Nostrand, New York, 1951, chapters on "Thermal Conductivity and Other Methods for the Analysis of Gases" and "Mass Spectrometry."

Emission Spectrography

Brode, W. R., *Chemical Spectroscopy*, 2nd ed., Wiley, New York, 1943.

Candler, C., *Practical Spectroscopy*, Hilger and Watts, London, 1949.

Harrison, G. R., R. C. Lord, and J. R. Loofbourow, *Practical Spectroscopy*, Prentice-Hall, New York, 1948.

Herzberg, G., and J. W. T. Spinks, *Atomic Spectra and Atomic Structure*, Dover, New York, 1944.

Sawyer, R. A., *Experimental Spectroscopy*, Prentice-Hall, New York, 1951.

Gas Chromatography

Keulemans, A. I. M., and C. G. Verver, *Gas Chromatography*, Reinhold, New York, 1957.

Phillips, C., *Gas Chromatography*, Academic Press, New York, 1956.

Mass Spectrometry

Barnard, G. P., and E. C. Bullard, *Modern Mass Spectrometry*, Institute of Physics, London, 1953.

Field, F. H., and J. L. Franklin, *Electron Impact Phenomena and the Properties of Gaseous Ions*, Academic Press, New York, 1957.

Inghram, M. G., and R. J. Hayden, *Mass Spectroscopy*, Nuclear Science Series, Report No. 14, National Academy of Sciences–National Research Council, Washington, D. C., 1954.

Robertson, A. J. B., *Mass Spectrometry*, Methuen, London, 1954.

General Information on the Inert Gases

Cook, G. A., *Argon, Helium, and the Rare Gases*, Interscience, New York–London, in press.

Keesom, W. H., *Helium*, Elsevier, New York, 1942.

Laffitte, P., and H. Brusset, *Les Gaz Inertes, l'Hydrogènes, les Halogens*, Masson, Paris, 1955, pp. 7–32.

Part II
Section A

THE ALKALI METALS

By Silve Kallmann, *Ledoux & Company, Teaneck, New Jersey*

Contents

301

Contents (*continued*)

Contents (*continued*)

Contents (*continued*)

Contents (*continued*)

Contents (*continued*)

I. INTRODUCTION

Alkali is a name that was first applied to the water-soluble portion of plant ashes, with land plants furnishing mainly potassium carbonate and sea plants mostly sodium carbonate. The metals produced from alkali salts comprise the alkali metal group consisting of lithium, sodium, potassium, rubidium, cesium, and francium.

A. OCCURRENCE

1. In Nature

a. LITHIUM

Lithium, the lightest of the alkali metals, discovered in 1817 by Arfvedson, is one of the most universally distributed elements (178). Although it occurs in silicate rock in only spectroscopic traces, there are several minerals containing several per cent lithium. The following should be mentioned (99,142,367): spodumene, $LiAlSi_2O_6$; polylithionite, KLi_2-$AlSi_4O_{10}F_2$; lepidolite, with the approximate composition $Si_3O_9Al(Li,K)_2$-$(OH,F)_2$; petalite, $(Li,Na)AlSi_4O_{10}$; zinnwaldite, $(K,Li)_3FeAl_3Si_5O_{16}$-$(OH,F)_2$; triphilite and lithiophylite, $Li(Fe,Mn)PO_4$; and amblygonite, $(Li,Na)Al(PO_4)(F,OH)$. Small amounts of lithium are also found in alkali feldspar, in muscovite and beryl, and, through the disintegration of lithium minerals, in spring and mineral waters. Sea water also contains small amounts of lithium, and some plants, particularly certain tobacco plants, accumulate the small amounts of lithium normally found in the soil.

b. Sodium

Sodium, isolated electrolytically by Davy in 1807 although previously recognized, is widely distributed in nature in the form of various minerals and salts. It comprises 2.75% of the lithosphere and is therefore the sixth most abundant element in the earth's crust. Sodium occurs in some minerals as a major constituent and in others in small or trace quantities. In igneous rock, sodium is a constituent of the soda feldspar albite, $NaAlSi_3O_8$, of sodium calcium feldspar plagioclase, an isomorphous mixture of $NaAlSi_3O_8$ and $CaAl_2Si_2O_8$, and of the soda-potash feldspar anorthoclase, $NaAlSi_3O_8,KAlSi_3O_8$. It also occurs in large deposits of water-soluble salts resulting from evaporation of inland seas, in the form of rock salt, $NaCl$, soda, Na_2CO_3, trona, $Na_2CO_3 \cdot NaHCO_3$, saltpeter, $NaNO_3$, borax, $Na_2B_4O_7 \cdot 10H_2O$, glauberite, $Na_2Ca(SO_4)_2$, mirabilite, $Na_2SO_4 \cdot 10H_2O$, and thenardite, Na_2SO_4. Nearly all terrestrial waters contain sodium, principally in the form of $NaCl$. The sodium chloride content of ocean water amounts to about 2.5%.

c. Potassium

Potassium, isolated electrolytically in 1807 by Davy, is also an abundant element, comprising 2.58% of the lithosphere. In igneous rock it is a constituent of feldspars, such as orthoclase and microcline, both $KAlSi_3O_8$, of the potassium mica muscovite, $H_2KAl_3(SiO_4)_3$, and of leucite, $KAl(SiO_3)_2$. Through the disintegration of minerals, potassium is found in soils and the ocean. Since soils absorb potassium salts more strongly than sodium salts, the potassium content of the ocean water is substantially lower than the sodium content. Potassium occurs also in large secondary deposits of water-soluble salts formed by evaporation from inland seas. Because of their origin, these deposits are always found on top of rock salt. They contain the potassium in the form of sylvite, KCl, carnallite, $KCl \cdot MgCl_2 \cdot 6H_2O$, kainite, $MgSO_4 \cdot KCl \cdot 3H_2O$, picromerite, $MgSO_4 \cdot K_2SO_4 \cdot 6H_2O$, syngenite, $CaSO_4 \cdot K_2SO_4 \cdot H_2O$, and polyhalite, $2CaSO_4 \cdot MgSO_4 \cdot 2H_2O$. There are also deposits of KNO_3. Plant ashes contain considerable K_2CO_3.

d. Rubidium and Cesium

Rubidium and cesium, discovered in 1860 and 1861, respectively, by Bunsen and Kirchhoff with the help of the spectroscope, occur in minute quantities in a number of minerals, such as feldspar, beryl, micas, leucite, and spodumene. The lithosphere contains about $4 \times 10^{-3}\%$ rubidium and about $7 \times 10^{-5}\%$ cesium. Although there is no specific rubidium mineral, pollucite, a rare cesium aluminum silicate, $2Cs_2O \cdot 2Al_2O_3 \cdot 9SiO_2 \cdot H_2O$, contains about 35% cesium oxide and certain beryls contain from 0.1 to 4.5% Cs_2O. However, most rubidium and cesium is recovered from lepidolite, which contains, besides lithium, from 0.2 to 1% and more rubidium and from 0.1 to 0.8% cesium. Small amounts of rubidium and cesium are also found in carnallite. In the disintegration of silicates, rubidium and cesium are leached out and are therefore found in trace amounts in mineral spring, river, and sea water.

e. Francium

It was shown (320) that francium results from the loss of an alpha particle by actinium-227, which decays by a branched-chain mechanism, only 1.2% going to francium, element 87. The rest goes to thorium-227 by beta decay (cf. Section II-A-2). This fact and the short half life of francium (21 minutes) prevented its earlier discovery.

2. In Industrial Products and Processes

Since the alkali metals form compounds with almost all anions, only the most important industrial products and uses can be mentioned.

a. Lithium

Because of its great heat capacity and high boiling point, lithium metal excels as a heat exchanger in nuclear reactors (260). Lithium metal and salts are also mentioned in connection with thermonuclear reactions. The metal is applied in metallurgy as a scavenger of unwanted gases. Lithium fluoride and chloride are used in both welding and brazing operations and also as prisms in spectroscopy. Lithium chloride and bromide are used in air conditioning and refrigeration, and lithium carbonate in ceramic and glass formulations, in lithium soaps, and in lubricating oil. Lithium greases are heat-resistant and are extensively used in aircrafts.

b. Sodium

The largest single demand for sodium metal is for the production of the sodium-lead alloy used in the manufacture of the antiknock agent tetra-ethyl lead. Like lithium, sodium metal is an important heat transfer agent. It is used in the manufacture of dyes, perfumes, drugs, and various chemicals and in the production of titanium and zirconium by the Kroll process. Small amounts of sodium are added to various metals to lower the surface tension. Sodium chloride is an important raw material in the manufacture of hydrochloric acid, chlorine, and metallic sodium. Large quantities are consumed as food preservatives and cattle food and in the production of dyes, ceramic glazes, glass and leather. Sodium nitrate is used in the manufacture of nitric acid and potassium nitrate and as a fertilizer and oxidizing agent. Sodium carbonate finds use in producing drugs, dyes, glass, soap, paper, caustic soda, paints, leather, and textiles. Sodium hydroxide is used in petroleum and vegetable oil refining and in the soap, paper, textile, and rubber industries. Among other industrially important sodium salts, the following should be mentioned: the bicarbonate, sulfate, phosphate, borate, dichromate, cyanide, citrate, fluoride, permanganate, peroxide, and hypochlorite.

c. Potassium

Potassium metal, particularly when alloyed with sodium in NaK, is being extensively investigated as a heat transfer agent. Potassium chloride is an important fertilizer. Potassium carbonate serves as a raw material in manufacturing various chemicals. It is used in pharmaceutical preparations and in tanning, electroplating, process engraving and lithography, the dyeing and bleaching of textiles, and the manufacture of special glasses. Potassium nitrate finds use in explosives and matches, in pickling meat, and as fertilizer. Potassium hydroxide is consumed in the manufacture of soap and oxalic acid and in lithography. Other industrially important potassium salts are the chlorate, ferrocyanide, permanganate, phosphate, and iodide.

d. Rubidium and Cesium

Cesium metal has found some applications in photoelectric cells and radio tubes. Rubidium and cesium salts have found limited usage in medicinal preparations. The direct conversion of atomic energy into electric power using cesium metal vapor as one element of a thermocouple technique was recently announced. Biggest potential uses for both cesium and rubidium lie in the space arena (87a). Cesium, for example, is easily ionized and thus makes a plasma at a reasonably low temperature. It is therefore a leading contender for the role of fuel in ion propulsion motors for space travel. Rubidium, on the other hand, is a serious contender for the role of a heat transfer fluid in nuclear rockets.

3. In Organic Substances

a. In Living Organisms

Sodium and potassium are two of the indispensable constituents of animate matter. In living organisms, sodium and potassium as the chief basic elements assume the vital functions of maintaining a fixed pH and water balance (40). In combination with the HCO_3^- radical, sodium is mainly extracellular, or outside the cell membrane. Potassium is mainly within living cells in combination with the chloride ion. Sodium exerts control over the acid-base and water balance of the cell environments while potassium maintains vital cell functions by its higher concentration within the cell membrane. Plasma contains 330 mg. of sodium and 20 mg. of potassium per 100 ml., and muscle tissue contains 80 mg. of sodium and 320 mg. of potassium per 100 ml. Lithium, rubidium, and cesium are essential in some species (221), but in others they may actually be toxic.

b. In Plant Material

Plant material usually is high in potassium and low in sodium. The amount of alkali metals found in plants depends both on climatic factors and on the concentrations of the alkalies and other constituents of the soil. It has been shown (173) that the analysis of leaves, rather than the analysis of the total plant, reflects the composition of the soil and the capacity of plants to assimilate various essential substances.

c. In Vegetable and Animal Foods

Although the sodium content of vegetable foods, such as fruits, cereals, and nuts, is low, canned foods or preserves may contain considerable sodium chloride (63). The presence of sodium benzoate as a preservative also appreciably increases the sodium content of preserved food. The potassium content of vegetable food is much greater and amounts to 1200 to 3000 p.p.m.   On the other hand, foods of animal origin, such as meats and fish, contain considerably more sodium than potassium.

d. In Organo-alkali Compounds

In the synthesis of organic substances, organo-alkali compounds are finding increasing use.   They are prepared by the reaction of alkali metals with alkyl or aryl halides and are the most reactive organometallic compounds that can be formed.   Lithium dispersions have found applications in catalytic polymerizations and have been investigated as possible replacements in the Ziegler, Grignard, Wurtz, Friedel-Crafts, and other organic reactions (87).

e. In Medicinals

Organic compounds containing the alkali metals play an important role in pharmaceutical preparations.   Particularly well known are such sodium salts as the acetrizoate, p-aminobenzoate, p-aminosalicylate, amobarbital, ascorbate, benzosulfimide, caprylate, gluconate, glutamate, iodomethamate, lactate, thyroxine, penicillin, salicylate, and sulfanilate.

B. INDUSTRIAL PRODUCTION OF ALKALI METALS AND IMPORTANT ALKALI COMPOUNDS

1. Alkali Metals

The alkali metals are prepared from alkali salts by various techniques. Best known are the electrolytic processes, which are divided into the fused melt and the nonaqueous solution types.   In the Downs cell, a mixture of $NaCl$ and $CaCl_2$ is the electrolyte.   These two compounds form a eutectic, containing 66.8% $CaCl_2$, which melts at 505°C.   A typical feed to the Downs cell contains 58 to 59% $CaCl_2$ and 41 to 42% $NaCl$.   The anode is a graphite block projecting upward from the bottom of the cell and surrounded by a cylindrical steel or copper anode.   The sodium metal produced is 99.9% pure (388).   The Castner cell uses fused sodium hydroxide as the electrolyte.   Lithium metal is produced by the electrolysis of fused $LiCl$ and KCl in a cell consisting of a graphite anode and a steel cathode.   During the electrolysis at 400°C., the lithium metal produced floats on the electrolyte surface and is ladled off and poured into ingots. A grained dispersion can be prepared by pouring the molten metal into oil maintained at 150°C. (87).   Potassium and sodium-potassium alloys are prepared thermochemically by the reduction of molten KCl with sodium (86).   Rubidium and cesium are produced similarly by the reduction of their chlorides with calcium. Other processes involve the electrolysis of solutions of fused alkali chlorides and aluminum chloride in organic solvents, such as nitrobenzene (418), the thermal reduction of alkali hydroxides with carbon or carbides in a vacuum, and the displacement of the alkali metals from their molten salts with metallic iron (418).

2. Alkali Hydroxides

The hydroxides are prepared by two important processes. One is the double decomposition reaction between calcium hydroxide and alkali carbonates; the calcium carbonate is removed by filtration, and alkali hydroxides remain. The second process involves the electrolysis of aqueous alkali chloride solutions.

3. Alkali Carbonates

In excess of 4,000,000 tons of sodium carbonate are produced annually by the Solvay process which utilizes $NaCl$, CO_2, $CaCO_3$, and NH_3 as raw materials in an ingenious sequence of reactions resulting in a full recovery and the reuse of the ammonia and carbon dioxide (388,399). For the preparation of potassium carbonate by the Solvay process, ethyl alcohol must be added because of the marked solubility of potassium bicarbonate in ammonium chloride solution. Potassium carbonate is also obtained by heating under pressure solutions of magnesium and potassium chloride (carnallite) saturated with CO_2. It is also extracted from wood and plant ashes. Lithium carbonate is prepared from sintered spodumene by extraction with sulfuric acid and precipitation of Li_2CO_3 with sodium carbonate (418). The carbonates of rubidium and cesium are obtained by passing CO_2 into the solution of the respective hydroxide.

4. Alkali Chlorides

The main source of sodium chloride consists of large natural deposits. Potassium chloride is derived from carnallite. Lithium, rubidium, and cesium chlorides are prepared by treatment of their carbonates or hydroxides with hydrochloric acid.

5. Other Important Alkali Salts

The alkali carbonates are frequently used in the preparation of various alkali metal salts by neutralization with the desired acid. The alkali bromides can be obtained by the reaction of alkali chlorides with ferric bromide. Sodium nitrate is prepared from Chile saltpeter, and potassium nitrate by the reaction of sodium nitrate and potassium chloride. Sodium sulfate is obtained as a by-product of the production of hydrochloric acid and NaCl and sulfuric acid and also by passing hot SO_2 gas and air over salt. Potassium sulfate is produced by the treatment of potassium chloride with sulfuric acid and also by fractional crystallization of kainite. Phosphates result when phosphoric acid is neutralized with alkali carbonates. The cyanides are obtained by the interaction of alkali carbonates, carbon, and ammonia. Arsenates and arsenites are prepared by the reaction of alkali bicarbonates and the appropriate oxides of arsenic. Chromates are formed by roasting chromite with alkali carbonates and limestone and leaching with alkali sulfates. Alkali citrates result when calcium citrate is treated with alkali sulfates and the calcium sulfate is filtered off. The acetates and oxalates are obtained by neutralization of the acids with alkali carbonates.

C. TOXICOLOGY AND INDUSTRIAL HYGIENE

All the alkali metals oxidize rapidly in air and must therefore be stored immersed in naphtha, kerosene, toluene, or some similar liquid which does not contain oxygen. They react energetically with water and alcohols, liberating hydrogen. The heat evolved is sufficient to cause fire and explosions. The alkali metals can be handled with safety in dry atmospheres of inert gases, such as argon or nitrogen. Carbon tetrachloride should never be brought into contact with alkali metals.

Alkali hydroxides destroy tissues, thus causing severe burns, owing to their solvent action on protein. Inhalation of the dusts or mists of these materials is capable of causing serious injury to the entire respiratory system. When containers of caustic soda are being opened, utmost care should be taken to protect the eyes. The best antidote against caustic burns is copious amounts of water, followed by weak acids.

The toxicology of other alkali compounds should be considered from the standpoint of the anions involved.

1. Cesium-137 Hazard

The problems of widespread, low-level radioactive contamination from nuclear weapons testing have been increasingly discussed during the last few years. Besides strontium-90, the principal concern is the fall-out and entry into the biosphere of cesium-137. The presence of cesium-137 in human beings and in food has recently been demonstrated (282). The similarity of the decay chains of the fission products of mass 90 and mass 137 indicates that distribution of cesium-137 and strontium-90 in bomb debris is similar (10,11).

$$^{90}Kr \xrightarrow{\text{33 sec.}} {}^{90}Rb \xrightarrow{\text{2.7 min.}} {}^{90}Sr \xrightarrow{\text{28 yr.}} {}^{90}Y \xrightarrow{\text{64 hrs.}} {}^{90}Zr \text{ (stable)}$$

$$^{137}I \xrightarrow{\text{19 sec.}} {}^{137}Xe \xrightarrow{\text{3.4 min.}} {}^{137}Cs \xrightarrow{\text{27 yr.}} {}^{137m}Ba \xrightarrow{\text{2.6 min.}} {}^{137}Ba \text{ (stable)}$$

Both nuclides have two gaseous or volatile predecessors. Cesium-137, like strontium-90, is formed at relatively late times after bomb detonation and is not proportionally included in the larger and more refractory particles that fall out locally. Stratospheric storage and distant deposition will therefore be high for both nuclides. However, there are differences in the characteristics of the two nuclides. Whereas the behavior of strontium becomes very complex, once it enters the biosphere, and reflects a summation of all past fall-outs, cesium-137 is apparently poorly taken up from the soil by plants (301), and its biological half times (the times necessary for organisms to eliminate one-half of the nuclide) are comparatively short, viz., 140 days in man (463) and 20 days in the cow (182). These factors suggest that the concentrations of cesium-137 in people and in milk and other foods may constitute a direct and relatively simple measure of fall-out rate. Cesium-137 measurements on soils might provide a more convenient method than strontium-90 measurements for estimating integrated fall-out. Cesium-137 and strontium-90 are similar in that they are soluble and closely related to potassium and calcium, respectively, which are normal base exchange cations in soil and essential constituents of living matter. In this respect, cesium-137 and strontium-90 differ from other high-yield fission products which are not ecologically concentrated. Because of the metabolic similarity of cesium and potassium, the procedure has been adopted of reporting cesium-137 results as cesium-137/potassium-40 ratios (11), akin to reporting strontium-90 as strontium-90/calcium ratios (254). The average potassium content of the adult male is estimated to be about 133 g., which is equivalent to about 400 potassium-40 gamma disintegrations/second. The average radiation dose received from cesium-137 is $^1/_{20}$ of that received from natural radiopotassium and 1% of the average total dose from all natural sources. The amount of cesium-137 now present in the population of the United States averages 0.006 μc., shows no marked dependence on geographic location, and is not believed to be a decisive factor in the long-term hazards from weapons testing and reactor waste material (11).

The maximum permissible amounts of alkali radioisotopes in total body and the maximum amounts in air and water for continuous exposure are indicated here (294).

Element	Organ	μcuries in total body	μcuries per ml. of water	μcuries per ml. of air
^{24}Na	Total body, 7×10^4 g.	15	8×10^{-3}	2×10^{-6}
^{42}K	Muscle, 3×10^4 g.	20	1×10^{-2}	2×10^{-6}
^{86}Rb	Muscle, 3×10^4 g.	60	3×10^{-3}	4×10^{-7}
^{137}Cs	Muscle, 3×10^4 g.	90	1.5×10^{-3}	2×10^{-7}

II. PROPERTIES

A. PHYSICAL PROPERTIES

1. Alkali Metals

Some physical properties of the alkali metals are summarized in Table I. All alkali metals are silvery white in appearance, very soft, and ductile. They are easily fusible because there are not enough outer electrons to bind an atom firmly to its neighbor in the solid state (418). It should also

TABLE I
Physical Properties of the Alkali Metals (262,313,418)

	Lithium	Sodium	Potassium	Rubidium	Cesium
Atomic number	3	11	19	37	55
Atomic weight	6.940	22.991	39.096	85.48	132.91
Melting point, °C.	179	97.8	63.7	39.0	28.5
Boiling point, °C.	1336	880	760	700	670
Hardness	0.6	0.4	0.5	0.3	0.2
Density, g./cc.	0.530	0.963	0.857	1.594	1.992
Heat capacity, cal./g.	0.941	0.293	0.18	0.08	0.0482
Atomic radius, A.	1.55	1.90	2.35	2.48	2.67
Radius of cation, A.	0.60	0.95	1.33	1.48	1.69
Oxidation potential, v.	3.06	2.72	2.93	2.99	3.04
Ionization potential of gaseous atom, v.	5.37	5.12	4.32	4.16	3.87
Volume of ion, 10^{-23} ml.	0.14	0.37	0.99	1.36	1.95
Thermal conductivity of liquid metal, cal./cm./sec.	0.5919 (183°C.)	0.2055 (100°C.)	0.1073 (200°C.)	0.07 (m.p.)	0.044 (m.p.)
Electrical resistivity of liquid metals, μohms	45.25 (230°C.)	9.65 (100°C.)	13.16 (64°C.)	23.15 (50°C.)	36.6 (30°C.)
Electrical conductivity (Cu = 100)	18	37	24	14	8
Latent heat of fusion, cal./g.	158	27.05	14.6	6.1	3.77
Latent heat of vap., cal./g.	4680	1005	496	212	146
Volume change on fusion, vol. %	1.5	2.5	2.41	2.5	2.6

TABLE II

Isotopes of the Alkali Metals (179,220)

Isotope	Abundance, %	Type of decay[a]	Half life[b]	Energy of radiation, m.e.v.[c]	Method of production and genetic relationships
$^{6}_{3}\text{Li}$	7.52				
^{7m}Li		I.T.	5.2×10^{-14} sec.	-0.48 spect.	B-n-α
^{7}Li	92.48				
^{8}Li		β^-	0.825 sec.	13 ($\sim$90%) $\sim$6 ($\sim$5%) 3 ($\sim$5%) spect.	Li-n-γ; Li-d-p; ^{7}Li-n-γ; spall. C, N, Ne, A, Kr, Xe; Be-γ-p; B-n-α; B-γ-$2p$; B-γ-$2pm$
^{9}Li		β^-	0.168 sec.		Be-d-$2p$; B-p-$3p$; B-d-$3pn$; B-γ-$2p$; C-d-$4pn$; C-p-$4p$
$^{20}_{19}\text{Na}$		β^+	0.385 sec.	$3.5 < \beta^+ < 7.3$ est.	Ne-p-n; Na-γ-$3n$
^{21}Na		β^+	22.8 sec.	2.50 spect.	^{20}Ne-p-γ; Ne-d-n; Ne-p-n; Mg-p-α; ^{24}Mg-p-α
^{22}Na		β^+	2.60 yr.	0.542 spect.	F-α-n; Ne-d-n; ^{21}Ne-p-γ; Na-n-$2n$; Mg-d-α; spall. Mg, ^{25}Mg, ^{26}Mg, Fe, Cu
^{23}Na	100				
^{24}Na		β^-	15.06 hrs.	1.390 spect. coinc.	Na-d-p; Na-n-γ; Mg-d-α; Mg-n-p; Mg-γ-p; Al-n-α; Al-d-pa; Al-γ-$n2p$; Al-p-$3pn$; Si-γ-$n3p$; spall. Al, Fe, Cu, Sn; spall. fission Cu, U
^{25}Na		β^-	58 sec.	3.7 ($\sim$55%) 2.7 ($\sim$45%) abs.	Mg-γ-p; Mg-n-p; Al-γ-$2p$
$^{37}_{19}\text{K}$		β^+	1.3 sec.	4.6 scint. spect.	K-γ-$2n$
^{38}K		β^+	7.7 min.	2.8 spect.	Cl-α-n; K-n-$2n$; K-p-pn; K-γ-n; Ca-d-α
^{39}K	93.08				
^{40}K	0.0119	β^-	1.32×10^{9} yr.	1.33 spect.	Natural source
^{41m}K		I.T.	6.7×10^{-9} sec.		Daughter ^{41}A
^{41}K	6.91				
^{42}K		β^-	12.44 hrs.	3.58 (75%) 2.04 (25%) spect.	A-α-pm; K-d-p; K-n-γ; Ca-n-p; Sc-n-α; spall. Co, Cu; daughter ^{42}A

Isotope	Abundance	Decay	Half-life	Energy	Notes
43K		β⁻	22.4 hrs.	0.81, 0.24 spect., abs.	A-α-p
44K		β⁻	18 min.	0.990 spect.	Ca-n-p
Rb		E.C. 87% β⁺ 13%	4.7 hrs.		Br-α-2n; parent 81Kr
82mRb		β⁺	1.25 min.	~3 abs.	Daughter 82Sr
82Rb		E.C. 94% β⁺ 6%	6.3 hrs.	0.775 (76%) 0.175 (24%) spect.	Br-α-n; Kr-d-2n; not daughter 82Sr
83Rb		E.C.	83 days		Br-α-2n; daughter 83Sr; parent 83mKr
84mRb		I.T., E.C. (weak)	23 min.		Br-α-n; Rb-n-2n
84Rb		E.C., β⁺, β⁻	34 days	1.629 (39%) 0.822 (58%)	Br-α-n; Kr-α-pn; Rb-n-2n; Sr-d-α
86mRb		I.T.	0.9 × 10⁻⁶ sec.		Daughter 86Sr
85Rb	72.15				Fission U
86mRb		I.T., no E.C.	0.99 min.		Rb-n-γ
86Rb		β⁻, no β⁺ (limit 0.002%)	19.5 days	1.82 (80%) 0.72 (20%) spect.	Rb-n-γ; Rb-γ-n; Sr-d-α; spall. fission Bi; U; fission U
87Rb	27.85	β⁻	6 × 10¹⁰ yr.	0.275 spect., scint. spect.	Natural source; fission U; parent 87Sr
88Rb		β⁻	17.8 min.	5.30 (78%) 3.6 (13%) 2.5 (9%)	Rb-n-γ; fission Th; fission U; daughter 88Kr
89Rb		β⁻	15.4 min.	4.5 abs.	Fission U; daughter 89Kr; parent 89Sr
90Rb		β⁻	2.74 min.	5.7 abs.	Fission U; daughter 90Kr; parent 90Sr
91mRb		β⁻	1.67 min.	4.6 abs.	Fission U; daughter 91Kr; parent 91Sr; ancestor 91Y
91Rb		β⁻	14 min.	3.0 abs.	Fission U; daughter 92Kr; parent 91Sr
92Rb		β⁻	80 sec.		Fission U; daughter 92Kr; ancestor 92Y
93Rb		[β⁻]	[Short]		Fission U; daughter 93Kr; ancestor 93Y
94Rb		[β⁻]	[Short]		Fission U; daughter 94Kr; ancestor 94Y
95Rb		[β⁻]	[Short]		Fission U; daughter 95Kr; ancestor 95Zr
97Rb		[β⁻]	[Short]		Fission U; daughter 97Kr; ancestor 97Zr; fission 235U, Pu

(continued)

TABLE II (continued)

Isotope	Abundance, %	Type of decay[a]	Half life[b]	Energy of radiation, m.e.v.[c]	Method of production and genetic relationships
$_{55}^{125}$Cs		β^+	45 min.	2.03 spect.	I-α-6n
^{127}Cs		β^+	5.5 hrs.	1.2 spect., abs.	I-α-4n; parent ^{127}Xe; daughter ^{127}Ba
^{128}Cs		β^+, E.C.	3.8 min.	3.0 abs.	Daughter ^{128}Ba
^{129}Cs		E.C., no β^+	31 hrs.	Conv. ~ 0.3 abs.	I-α-2n; daughter ^{129}Ba
^{130}Cs		β^+, E.C., β^-	30 min.	β^+ 1.97 spect. β^- 0.442 spect.	I-α-n
^{131}Cs		E.C., no β^+	9.6 days		I-α-γ; daughter ^{131}Ba
^{132}Cs		E.C.	7.1 days		Cs-n-2n
^{133m}Cs		I.T.	6.0×10^{-9} sec.		Daughter ^{133}Xe
^{133}Cs	100				
^{134m}Cs		I.T.	3.2 hrs.	0.648 (75%)	Cs-n-γ; Cs-d-p
^{134}Cs		β^-, no E.C.	2.3 yr.	0.09 (24%) spect.	Cs-n-γ; Cs-d-p; Ba-d-α
^{135m}Cs		I.T.	2.8×10^{-10} sec.		Daughter ^{135}Xe
^{135}Cs		β^-	3.0×10^6 yr.	0.21 abs.	Daughter ^{135}Xe; fission U
^{136}Cs		β^-	13.7 days	0.35 abs.	La-n-α; spall. fission Th, U; fission Th, ^{233}U, ^{235}U, Pu
^{137}Cs		β^-	33 yr.	0.523 spect.	Spall. fission Th; fission Th, U, ^{233}U, Pu; parent ^{137m}Ba; daughter Xe^{137}
^{138}Cs		β^-	32.9 min.	3.40 (coinc. with 1.4 γ) ~ 2.9, ~ 2.0 spect., β - γ coinc. abs.	Ba-n-p; fission Th, Pa, U; daughter ^{138}Xe; descendent ^{138}I
^{139}Cs		β^-	9.5 min.		Fission Th, U; daughter ^{139}Xe; descendent ^{139}I; parent ^{139}Ba
^{140}Cs		β^-	66 sec.		Fission U; parent ^{140}Ba
^{141}Cs		[β^-]	Short		Daughter ^{141}Xe; Ancestor ^{141}La

^{142}Cs	β^-	~1 min.		Fission U; parent ^{142}Ba
^{143}Cs	$[\beta^-]$	Short		Daughter ^{143}Xe; Ancestor ^{143}Ce
^{144}Cs	$[\beta^-]$	Short		Daughter ^{144}Xe; Ancestor ^{144}Ce
$^{212}_{87}$Fr	E.C. 56%	19.3 min.	6.409 (37%), 6.387 (39%), 6.339 (24%) spect.	Spall. Th; parent ^{212}Em
^{217}Fr	α	5×10^{-3} sec.	8.3 range emuls.	Descendent ^{225}Pa
^{218}Fr	α	0.02 sec.; delay coinc.	7.85 ion ch.	Daughter ^{222}Ac; parent ^{214}At
^{219}Fr	β stable		7.30 ion ch.	Daughter ^{223}Ac; parent ^{215}At
^{220}Fr	α	27.5 sec.	6.69 ion ch.	Daughter ^{224}Ac; parent ^{216}At
^{221}Fr	α	4.8 min.	6.30 ion ch.	Daughter ^{225}Ac; parent ^{217}At; daughter ^{221}Em
^{222}Fr	β^- 99+%, α 0.01%	14.8 min.		Spall. Th; parent ^{222}Ra; ancestor ^{214}Bi
^{223}Fr	β^-	21 min.	β^- 1.2 cl. ch.	Natural source; daughter ^{227}Ac; parent ^{223}Ra; parent ^{219}At

[a] E.C., electron capture; I.T., isomeric transition.

[b] Delay coinc., half life determination by measurement of the time interval between two successive nuclear events to establish the lifetime of the state responsible for the second event.

[c] Experimental methods: spect., magnetic deflection (magnetic spectrograph or spectrometer or counter with magnetic field); est., estimated; spect. coinc., spectrometer or spectrometers arranged with coincidence counters; abs., absorption; scint. spect., measurement of pulses produced by a scintillating crystal or solution; conv., internal conversion electrons; coinc., coincidence counters; coinc. abs., beta and gamma coincidence counters with absorbers; range emuls., measurement of energy of alpha particle by its range in a nuclear track plate emulsion; ion ch., measurement of pulse sizes in ionization chamber or proportional counter; cl. ch., cloud chamber (with magnetic field in case of beta particles).

be noted that both the melting and boiling points of the alkali metals decrease with increasing atomic weight. Although, generally speaking, the density increases with increasing atomic weight, sodium is heavier than potassium. All the alkali metals crystallize with the body-centered cubic structure. The metals form various alloys with each other. The melting point of the sodium-potassium eutectic, NaK, with the formula K_2Na, containing 78% potassium, is 12.6°C., whereas that of another binary sodium-potassium alloy containing 56% sodium is 19°C. Other alloy combinations of the five alkali metals also form eutectics with low melting points. For instance, the sodium-rubidium system forms a eutectic at approximately 80% rubidium, and the rubidium-cesium system forms a eutectic at 31% rubidium.

a. LITHIUM (262)

Lithium is the least dense of all normally solid elements, and it is the least reactive and least typical of the alkali metals. It can be melted and poured in dry air without losing its bright surface. It does not combine with dry oxygen below 100°C. and reacts only slowly with cold water, perhaps because of the low solubility of lithium hydroxide. Lithium is harder than the other alkali metals but softer than lead.

b. SODIUM

An outstanding characteristic of sodium, particularly in the molten state, is its reactivity with most gases other than the noble gases. Solid sodium tarnishes almost immediately when exposed to air, owing to the formation of a film of oxide.

c. POTASSIUM

Potassium is even more reactive than sodium. Unlike sodium, which forms a monoxide, potassium, when exposed to the action of oxygen, oxidizes finally to the superoxide KO_2, which is the stable oxide of potassium at room temperature.

d. RUBIDIUM AND CESIUM

Both rubidium and cesium are soft, ductile, and very reactive, igniting spontaneously in air.

2. Isotopes of the Alkali Metals

Some of the isotopes of the alkali metals are of considerable interest to science and industry (see Table II). The separation of the stable isotopes is possible by several procedures. Thus, the electrolysis of KCl has produced an enrichment factor ($^{39}K/^{41}K$) of 1.0054 (440), whereas the electrolysis of lithium chloride indicates a separation factor ($^{6}Li/^{7}Li$) of 1.055 (418). The $^{39}K/^{41}K$ enrichment factor will obviously be less than the $^{6}Li/^{7}Li$ factor because of smaller differences in mass relations.

Lithium-6 deuteride is mentioned as a fuel in connection with thermonuclear reactions. The ^{7}Li (p, n) ^{10}Be reaction can be used to produce neutrons (20).

Sodium-24, with a half life of 14.9 hours, is produced by neutron activation and is extensively used in medicine to locate the sites of obstructions in blocked arteries, to study the function of sodium chloride in blood circulation, and to determine the rate of flow of blood in cerebrospinal fluids (197,345).

Ordinary potassium is the lightest naturally occurring radioactive element. It contains 0.0119% of beta- and gamma-emitting ^{40}K with a half life of 1.3×10^9 years.

$$^{40}_{19}K \longrightarrow {}^{40}_{20}Ca + e$$

$$^{40}_{19}K + e \longrightarrow {}^{40}_{18}Ar + \gamma$$

The argon in the atmosphere may have been formed in this manner (262). The decay of ^{40}K to form ^{40}Ar is an isotopic chronometer of particular interest and is applied to the determination of the ages of rocks (83). The ^{40}K gamma activity has been used as an index of the amount of lean meat in meat products (239). Similarly, the potassium content of human beings as measured by the activity of ^{40}K in a "human counter" was shown to be related to body water content (12,464). Potassium-42, produced by neutron activation, is also being used in medicine to study the water exchange and potassium metabolism of the body (47,197,345).

About 28% of natural rubidium is beta-emitting ^{87}Rb with a half life of 6.3×10^{10} years. A determination of the $^{87}Sr/^{87}Rb$ ratio has been used to establish the ages of certain rocks (259). Because of its relatively long half life of 27 years, ^{137}Cs, a product of the fission of uranium, is frequently mentioned in connection with nuclear fall-out problems (cf. Section I-C). No stable isotope of francium exists. The short half lives of its various radioactive isotopes and the continual growth of impurities have hampered the detailed study of its chemical properties. It has been established, however, that in most of its chemical reactions the element closely resembles cesium.

B. ELECTROCHEMICAL PROPERTIES

Latimer reports the oxidation potentials included in Table I for the alkali metals against normal aqueous solutions of the ions.

TABLE III
Emission Spectra

Wavelength, A.	Arc relative intensity	Spark relative intensity	Wavelength, A.	Arc relative intensity	Spark relative intensity
Lithium					
2562.5	150	15	4972.0	500	
2741.3	200		6103.6	2000	300
3232.6	1000	500	6240.1	300	
4602.9	800		6707.9	3000	200
Sodium					
2852.8	100		5670.2	600	
3092.7	50	200	5675.7	150	
3302.3	600	300	5688.2	300	
3303.0	300	150	5890.0	9000	1000
4668.6	200	100	5895.9	5000	500
4982.8	200	100	6154.2	500	100
5149.1	400		6180.8	500	100
5153.6	600				
Potassium					
3217.0	100	20	6911.3	300	
3446.5	150	100	6939.0	500	
3447.4	100	75	7664.9	9000	400
4044.1	800	400	7699.0	5000	200
4047.2	400	200			
Rubidium					
3848.7	100		6159.6	400	
3350.9	150		6206.3	800	100
3461.6		200	6298.3	1000	150
3492.8		300	6299.2	300	50
3531.6		100	7280.0	400	
3587.1	200	40	7408.2	500	
4201.9	2000	500	7618.9	1000	
4215.6	1000	300	7757.7	1000	
5648.1	400		7759.4	400	
5653.7	200		7800.3	9000	
5724.5	600		7925.3	100	
6070.8	600	50	7947.6	5000	
Cesium					
3476.9	100		7990.7	100	
3611.5	200		8015.7	200	
3876.4	300		8078.9	100	
3888.7	150	10	8079.0	1000	
4555.3	2000	100	8521.1	5000	
4593.2	1000	50	8761.4	500	
7609.0	500		8943.6	2000	
7944.1	800				

C. OPTICAL PROPERTIES

1. Emission Spectra

Some of the alkali metal lines observed in the arc and spark spectra are listed in Table III (54).

2. X-Ray Spectra

Of the three light alkali metals, only the following lines have analytical importance: lithium, K_α, $\lambda = 240.00$; sodium, K_α, $\lambda = 11.909$; potassium, K_α, $\lambda = 3.742$, and K_β, $\lambda = 3.454$.

Both K and L lines of rubidium and cesium are analytically important and are listed here.

Rubidium		Cesium	
K_{α_1}	0.926	K_{α_1}	0.401
K_{β_1}	0.829	K_{β_1}	0.355
L_{α_1}	7.318	L_{α_1}	2.892
L_{β_1}	7.075	L_{β_1}	2.683
L_{β_3}	6.788	L_{β_2}	2.511
LL	8.363	LY_1	2.348

D. CHEMICAL PROPERTIES

The electronic configurations of the alkali metals are presented in Table IV. It should be noted that the single electron in the outer shell is voluminous and that it can be readily transferred to anions. In the case of sodium, for instance, the radius of the atom (one-half the distance between neighboring sodium nuclides in sodium metal) is 60% greater than that of the ion (one-half the distance between the sodium and fluorine or chlorine nuclei in NaF or NaCl); this means that the 10 inner electrons occupy one-fifth the volume of the atom and the valence electron occupies the other four-fifths (162). The atomic radii of the alkali metals are greater and the ionization potentials smaller (cf. Table I) than those of any other group. Every alkali ion contains the same number of electrons as one of the noble gases. The readiness of the alkali metals to form ions, the stability of these ions, and the lack of chemical reactivity of the noble gases can therefore be attributed to the same cause, the extraordinary stability of configurations of 2, 10, 18, 36, 54, and 86 electrons about an atomic nucleus. Removal of additional electrons is not possible by chemical means because of the high potentials involved (313). Thus, the second ionization potential of sodium is 47.3 e.v. greater than the ionization potential for the inert gas neon (162).

TABLE IV

Electronic Configuration of the Alkali Metals

Element	Atomic number	K	L		M			N				O			P			Q
		$1s$	$2s$	$2p$	$3s$	$3p$	$3d$	$4s$	$4p$	$4d$	$4f$	$5s$	$5p$	$5d$	$6s$	$6p$	$6d$	$7s$
Lithium	3	2	1															
Sodium	11	2	2	6	1													
Potassium	19	2	2	6	2	6		1										
Rubidium	37	2	2	6	2	6	10	2	6	10		1						
Cesium	55	2	2	6	2	6	10	2	6	10		2	6		1			
Francium	87	2	2	6	2	6	10	2	6	10	14	2	6	10	2	6		1

Shells: K, L, M, N, O, P, Q.
Subshells: s, p, d, f, etc.

Differences in the chemical properties of the alkali metals depend largely upon the ease with which they part with the voluminous outer electrons. The electron affinities or ionization potentials decrease with increasing atomic weight, lithium being the least reactive and cesium the most reactive of the five alkali metals. This behavior is caused by the screening effect of the increasing number of electrons separating the positive charge of the nucleus from the valence electron (418).

The ease with which the alkali metals give up the outer electrons is illustrated by their reactions with water. They readily give off their valence electrons to form hydrogen and hydroxide ion. The vigor of this reaction increases with the increase in the atomic weight to the extent that potassium, rubidium, and cesium ignite when placed in water (418). Although the alkali metals ions are hydrated in aqueous solution, only lithium and sodium retain their water of hydration in their solid salts. Hydrated potassium salts are also known, but the water in such hydrates is generally anion water (162).

Almost all of the compounds formed by the alkali metals are ionic, as is clearly indicated by the high melting points, low volatilities, high solubilities in water, and low solubilities in nonpolar liquids. Because of the inertness of the alkali ions, the chemistry of their compounds is largely determined by the associated anions, with the cations exerting only a comparatively minor influence through variations in ionic dimensions, heats of hydration, and other physical properties which show a gradation as the atomic weight increases.

1. Lithium

Lithium is the least typical and least reactive of the alkali metals. It is much harder and higher melting than the other alkali metals, does not react with dry oxygen below 100°C., and therefore forms a peroxide only with great difficulty. Its reaction with water is rather slow, partly owing to the low solubility and adherence of lithium hydroxide. In addition, its melting point is above 100°C., and the metal remains solid during the reaction. The other alkali metals, on the other hand, melt as a result of the initial reaction; consequently, fresh metal is continuously exposed to the attack of the water, and the reaction proceeds at a faster rate than is possible in the case of the solid lithium (162). However, lithium dispersions that ignite almost at once in the presence of moisture have been prepared (87). Lithium reacts with hydrogen between 500 to 800°C. to form the hydride, LiH. Since potassium does not form a hydride at this temperature, lithium can be freed from traces of potassium by heating in hydrogen at 700 to 800°C. to distil off the potassium (262). Lithium reacts at high temperatures with carbon to form acetylides, which hydrolyze with the formation of acetylene. With nitrogen, it reacts exothermically in the presence of moisture. With alkyl halides, it forms lithium alkyls, which are far more covalent than the corresponding sodium and potassium compounds (87b).

In a comparison of the cited properties of lithium and its compounds to those of the other alkali metals, it becomes apparent that lithium differs from its congeners much more than do the latter among themselves. The properties of lithium bear a strong resemblance to those of magnesium. This similarity is clearly shown by the solubilities of lithium salts. Like the corresponding magnesium salts, the hydroxide, phosphate, arsenate, fluoride, stearate, and carbonate are sufficiently insoluble in water and certain organic reagents to be of analytical interest. This "diagonal relationship" of lithium and magnesium is not unique, since other elements in the periodic system resemble the elements at their lower right or their upper left more than their own congeners (for example Be and Al, or B and Si). Effects of atomic size and charge contribute to this relationship (162); it suffices to mention here that the ionic radius of lithium is very close to that of magnesium (0.60 to 0.65 A.).

It should be noted that the ionization potential of lithium is higher than that of any other alkali metal (cf. Table I); its standard reduction potential is about as negative as that of cesium and more negative than those of sodium and potassium. This indicates that ionization of lithium atoms is energetically more difficult than the conversion of sodium or potassium atoms to their respective ions, but that the difficulty of conversion of the solid metals to the respective hydrated ions is in the opposite direction (162). Thus it has been shown that the very high energy of hydration of the lithium ions makes lithium the best reducing agent of all the alkali metals, although cesium is the best electron donor.

2. Sodium

The reaction of sodium with water is energetic, and possibly explosively rapid, if the contact interfaces are large. The action of sodium in contact with moisture in the atmosphere is interesting in that the end product after heating is Na_2O, which causes a considerably increased attack on metal containers holding sodium (262). Sodium reacts vigorously with methanol, forming sodium methoxide, CH_3ONa, also called sodium methylate. However, the reaction with alcohol is less energetic than that with water and decreases in order from primary to secondary to tertiary and higher alcohols.

Sodium and other alkali metals are appreciably soluble in liquid ammonia without the release of hydrogen gas. The solutions are blue if dilute and bronze-colored if concentrated. The concentrated solutions are excellent electrical conductors. A saturated solution of sodium, for instance, shows a conductance value of 0.5047×10^3 mhos (235), which represents as good a conductor as many a metal. For some purposes, such a solution may be thought of as containing metal ions and ammoniated electrons (162). This dissociation into cations and electrons is accompanied by a sudden change in the conductivity of the solution (418). Careful evaporation of the solution produces the respective alkali metal, whereas, in the presence of impurities which act as catalysts, hydrogen gas is liberated and an alkali metal amide is formed.

Unlike lithium, sodium is unreactive with nitrogen at all known temperatures. However, it reacts with most hydrogen-containing gases with the displacement of the hydrogen and the formation of the sodium salt. With hydrogen fluoride and hydrogen chloride, the attack is slight. In the molten state, it reacts with hydrogen itself to form the hydride, NaH, which can be decomposed by heating at high temperatures. Sodium has also reduced the halides of many metals ($TiCl_4$, $ZrCl_4$, $AlCl_3$).

Nearly all simple sodium salts are easily soluble in water. Difficultly soluble are sodium antimonate, sodium fluosilicate, sodium aluminum fluoride (cryolite), and various triple acetates. Sodium hydroxide, which is used extensively as a reagent and in various industrial processes, is a very strong base and precipitates ions of all the other metals (except As, Tl, K, Cs, Li, and Rb) from solutions as oxides or hydroxides. These are all insoluble in water except for $Ba(OH)_2$, $Sr(OH)_2$, and $Ca(OH)_2$. Some of the hydroxides are amphoteric and dissolve in an excess of sodium hydroxide (273).

3. Potassium

Potassium is similar to sodium in most of its chemical reactions, but it reacts even more vigorously than sodium with water, alcohol, ammonia, and other polar solvents. When exposed to the action of oxygen, potassium forms the superoxide, KO_2, a strong oxidizing agent that probably has been responsible for some explosions involving potassium metal. KO_2 oxidizes S, P, As, Sn, Sb, Zn, Cu, Fe, Ag, and Pt to the oxides. The superoxide contains the O_2^- ion, has one unpaired electron per negative ion, and is consequently paramagnetic. Thus it occupies a position between the oxygen molecule, which has two unpaired electrons, and the peroxide molecule, which has the same configuration as the fluoride molecule.

Potassium differs further from sodium in that an explosive carbonyl is formed when it reacts directly with carbon monoxide (262). Whereas lithium and sodium react only superficially with liquid bromine, potassium detonates on contact. Of all the alkali metals, potassium forms the least stable hydride. Nearly all simple potassium salts are soluble in water. Difficultly soluble and of analytical importance are the perchlorate, acid tartrate, chloroplatinate, cobaltinitrite, picrate, dipicrylaminate, periodate, and tetraphenylboron.

4. Rubidium and Cesium

Rubidium and cesium are even more reactive than potassium. Their salts with various anions resemble so much the corresponding potassium compounds as to cause serious difficulties in the analysis of mixtures of the three heavy alkali metals. It has been noted (162) that with anions of weak acids the heavy alkali metals form the most soluble salts whereas for anions of strong acids the reverse holds true. Thus Cs_2CO_3 is 200 times as soluble in water at room temperature as is Li_2CO_3, but $LiClO_3$ is about 65 times as soluble as $CsClO_3$. This behavior is explained by the resemblance of the lithium ion to the hydrogen ion (162).

5. Francium

The identity of francium was established, after separation from all nonalkali cations, by coprecipitation with cesium perchlorate. The radioactivity follows the cesium perchlorate and decays by beta emission with a half life of 21 minutes. Francium has the chemical properties expected from its position in the periodic system (418). Besides the perchlorate, the following francium salts have been isolated: the chloroplatinate, chlorobismuthate, chloroantimonate, chlorostannate, and cobaltinitrite.

III. SAMPLING

In any given case, the object is to obtain a representative sample. The methods of obtaining such a sample vary with the nature of the material and are of all degrees of complexity.

A. METALLIC SAMPLES

Sampling of the metallic alkalies presents many difficulties owing to the extreme reactivity of these substances with oxygen, nitrogen, and moisture, even at room temperature, and to their reactivity with glass and quartz at elevated temperatures. One difficulty in obtaining a representative sample results from the fact that the solubilities of most impurities in the alkali metal are temperature-dependent. If, in taking a sample of molten alkali metal for analysis, the temperature is lowered, loss of impurities may occur owing to precipitation. Many sampling techniques have been developed (263). In one method (315), some of the liquid metal is drawn into a $1/4$ inch Pyrex tube about 12 inches long. When the metal has solidified, the ends of the tube are sealed. Then the tube may be broken in an inert atmosphere. In another technique (432), a liquid metal is placed in a glass flask, and weighed samples are obtained by drawing portions of the metal through a special sampling device into ampules in an inert atmosphere. At temperatures above 350°C., sampling devices must be constructed of metal.

B. MINERALS, GLASSES, CEMENTS, SOIL

The sampling of these and similar substances follows usual patterns; that is, a representative sample of sufficient size is reduced by crushing, pulverizing, screening, quartering, mixing, and riffling to a suitable sample for analysis.

C. ALKALI SALTS

1. Caustic Soda and Potash

These substances are sold in solid, flake, ground and powdered forms. In the sampling of dry forms, great care must be exercised since the caustic will absorb water and carbon dioxide from the air. Sampling time should therefore be held to a minimum. Solid caustic soda is not homogeneous, owing to segregation of the impurities, particularly in the lower portions of the cake, the "cone" (400). Representative portions from the cone and body of the cake must be obtained and placed into dry canning jars. For the sampling of caustic soda or potash, the top layer is usually removed and the sample obtained from the center. Caustic soda liquor is sampled by obtaining a continuous "drip sample" during the unloading operations; or a "dip sample" is procured by lowering a stoppered bottle to the desired depth and removing the stopper by means of a chain attached to it.

2. Soda Ash, Potassium Carbonate, Alkaline Detergents

These and many other inorganic alkali salts are at times difficult to sample because of their tendency to absorb moisture and/or carbon dioxide. Details of good sampling procedures depend on the nature of the material, the type of shipment, and the container. The sample for analysis should be stored in tightly sealed glass containers.

D. BIOLOGICAL SAMPLES

Because of the great variation in composition and the often limited quantity of sample available, no clear-cut sampling procedure can be described for biological materials. However, improper sampling of clinical specimens may lead to erroneous results, as is illustrated by normal blood (173). Although erythrocytes (4000 p.p.m. potassium) contain about 20 times as much potassium as does serum (200 p.p.m., potassium), an exchange of the potassium in the two substances continuously takes place. Normally, the processes of life strictly maintain the difference in the potassium concentration of blood cells and serum. Freshly drawn blood, however, shows an immediate transfer or diffusion of potassium from the erythrocytes to the serum. This diffusion is largely dependent on the temperature prevailing when the blood sample is taken and processed and also on the emotional condition of the patient. If not properly controlled or standardized, the diffusion may lead to incorrect interpretation of the potassium content of serum. Similar changes have been noted in the case of plasma, with the additional observation that anesthesia causes a decrease and burn injuries a marked increase in the potassium content.

IV. SEPARATION AND ISOLATION

A. DECOMPOSITION, DISSOLUTION, AND OTHER PRELIMINARY TREATMENT OF INORGANIC MATERIALS

Classical procedures dealing with the analysis of the alkali metals are based on the prior removal of all other cations and all anions other than chloride. Because it is rare that one of the alkali metals occurs unaccompanied by one or more other members of the group, the first step in older procedures usually consisted of collecting and weighing the combined alkali chlorides, and the final step, of determining the potassium (plus rubidium plus cesium) and calculating the sodium "by difference." (Since alkali sulfates are insoluble in most organic solvents proposed for the separation of the individual alkali metals, weighing as the sulfate is permissible only when only one of the alkali metals is present.) Several errors are possible if the old approach is followed. The purity of the alkali chlorides, even after many tedious separations, is often in doubt. Further, if the sodium is subsequently determined by difference, any error in the combined chlorides or the potassium value is reflected in the sodium figure. This is particularly serious if potassium preponderates or if the sample unexpectedly contains rubidium and cesium. In addition, the analyst is seldom sure, particularly in rock analysis, of the absence of lithium.   N.B.S. flint clay No. 97, for instance, contains 0.22% Li_2O, which is about twice its Na_2O content.

During recent years, the introduction of specific reagents or techniques for the determination of the individual alkali metals in the presence of each other and various cations and anions has enabled the analyst to avoid time-consuming separations.   The most revolutionary simplification in sample preparation has been made possible by flame photometric procedures.   Because of the many new approaches recently introduced into the analytical chemistry of the alkali metals, the analyst is advised to review carefully the nature and composition of his sample and to select a technique that leads to the final measurement of the desired element with the least number of preliminary steps.

1. Alkali Metals

All of the analytical procedures, except those for oxygen, hydrogen, and carbon, used to determine the impurity content as well as the major elements of alkali metals require that the sample be dissolved in water or alcohol.   Sodium can be dissolved in any of the alcohols.   It can also be dissolved in a controlled manner in water if the dissolution is carried out under an atmosphere of nitrogen and the sodium is added in small portions. Considerable care is necessary when liquid sodium-potassium alloys are dissolved.   Methods in which the NaK is dissolved in dry ice–methanol slush or in a methanol-hexane mixture have been described (314,446). In addition, NaK can be dissolved in methanol in an inert atmosphere. Potassium and alloys containing substantial amounts of rubidium and/or cesium are even more reactive than sodium and should be dissolved under a blanket of nitrogen or argon in butyl or isopropyl alcohol.

After the solution of the metal in water or alcohol, the strongly alkaline solution is acidified with hydrochloric acid, and the alcohol is expelled by evaporation.   The presence of large quantities of alkali chloride salts generally does not interfere with the determination of trace impurities (cf. Section VII-A-6).   For the determination of the individual alkali metals, separations may or may not be required, depending on the equipment available and the technique chosen.

2. Silicate Minerals, Glass, Ceramics, Refractories

a. J. L. Smith Method (178,396)

Until recently, the J. L. Smith method was preferred by most analysts engaged in mineral analysis.   In brief, it consists in heating the finely ground substance with ammonium chloride and calcium carbonate.   After the sintered mass has been leached with water and filtered, the alkalies are obtained in solution as the chlorides, together with some calcium hydroxide. In classical gravimetric analysis, the calcium is removed by precipitation with ammonium carbonate. The resulting calcium carbonate is reprecipitated, and traces of soluble calcium are removed, after expulsion of most of the ammonium salts by evaporation and gentle ignition, by precipitation with a little ammonium oxalate. SO_4^{-2}, if present, is precipitated with barium chloride, the excess of which is removed with ammonium carbonate.

Two reasons for the popularity of the Smith procedure have been that nonalkali constituents of the sample, particularly magnesium, are left behind, either as insoluble oxides or calcium salts, and that removal of large quantities of sulfate ion with barium chloride, as in the Berzelius method, with the inherent danger of losing alkali salts by occlusion, is avoided. In recent years, the Smith method has lost some of its earlier popularity, since few chemists attempt any more to collect the combined chlorides. However, the original sintering step still finds wide application in the analysis of those refractory silicates which would only incompletely or difficultly yield to an acid attack.

Of various modifications of the J. L. Smith method, the following changes deserve mention: The use of ammonium chloride can be avoided by the substitution of calcium chloride as a chloride source (368). If barium chloride is used, the sulfate ion can be removed simultaneously with the insoluble oxides (409). It has been shown that the aqueous extract of the J. L. Smith method, after the expulsion of residual ammonium salts by boiling, is well suited for the direct determination of potassium as the tetraphenylboron salt without the removal of the calcium (91). Similarly, sodium can be directly determined in the aqueous extract by one of the triple acetate procedures (142,374).

b. Hydrofluoric Acid Method (38)

In the hydrofluoric acid method, often referred to as the Berzelius method, the powdered sample is decomposed by heating with a mixture of sulfuric and hydrofluoric acids. Because of the ease of the initial decomposition, the method has been thoroughly investigated, and many modifications have been proposed to simplify the subsequent steps of isolating the alkali metals. The hydrofluoric acid attack has found wide application in preparing silicate samples for the flame photometric determination of the alkali metals. Among the comparatively few silicates that are not, or are only incompletely, attacked are the andalusite group, topaz, beryl, zircon, and certain tourmalines. These must be decomposed by the J. L. Smith method. Some refractory silicates yield to a fusion with ammonium fluoride and a subsequent conversion to sulfates (378). A number of procedures have been suggested to expedite the treatment of the sulfuric acid solution of the alkalies. The older chemists eliminate the sulfate ion by precipitation with an excess of barium chloride, evaporate the solution to dryness, dissolve the salts in a little water, and precipitate the R_2O_3 group, phosphates, and magnesium by the addition of barium hydroxide. (Calcium hydroxide in the form of milk of lime is used by some instead of barium hydroxide.) After filtration, the excess barium is removed by precipitation with ammonium carbonate. The filtrate is evaporated to dryness, and ammonium salts are removed by ignition. The residue is dissolved in a little water, and the ammonium carbonate separation is repeated. If calcium hydroxide has been used instead of barium hydroxide, the last traces of calcium are removed with ammonium oxalate instead of ammonium carbonate. After evaporation and ignition, the pure alkali chlorides are obtained.

The precipitation of various cations with barium or calcium hydroxide, although cumbersome and involved, was dictated in older procedures by the necessity of quantitatively removing magnesium before weighing the alkali metal chlorides. It has been shown that these tedious steps can be avoided by precipitating the magnesium as magnesium oxalate in an 85% acetic acid solution (117). The R_2O_3 group elements are removed with ammonia, and the filtrate is evaporated to 15 ml. before hydrolysis of the magnesium with ethyl oxalate. The alkali metals are weighed as the sulfates, with potassium being finally determined as the chloroplatinate. Sodium is calculated by difference or is determined in the potassium filtrate (307). In another procedure, the precipitation of large quantities of the sulfate ion with barium chloride and the use of barium or calcium hydroxide are avoided by decomposing glass samples containing less than 5% alumina with hydrofluoric and oxalic acids and removing all nonalkali elements as oxalates or 8-hydroxyquinolates (401).

For the determination of potassium in silicates, the sample can be decomposed with hydrofluoric and perchloric acids. After evaporation, residual fluorine is removed by steam distillation. Aluminum, iron, calcium, magnesium, manganese, sodium, and lithium perchlorates are dissolved in anhydrous ethyl acetate, and the potassium is weighed as the perchlorate (452). Similarly, sodium can be directly determined as the triple acetate after decomposition of the sample with hydrofluoric and perchloric acids and evaporation of the solution to fumes of perchloric acid twice, with the intermittent addition of a little water (374). Of interest, too, is a method that relies on thermal decomposition of perchlorates into nonalkali oxides and alkali chlorides, extraction of the alkali chlorides with hot water, removal of calcium and residual magnesium as oxalates and 8-hydroxyquinolates, and weighing of the combined alkali chlorides (271).   The perchloric acid medium has also been used to collect sodium and potassium as a mixture of chlorides and perchlorates by precipitation with butyl alcohol, containing hydrogen chloride (211).   Aluminum, lithium, magnesium, calcium, iron, etc., do not interfere, and barium, lead, and strontium, which form insoluble chlorides, can be removed as carbonates after the butyl alcohol–hydrogen chloride separation.

c. Other Separation Procedures

Certain silicate minerals can be decomposed with hydrofluoric acid alone. The solution is then evaporated to dryness, the residue is dissolved in water, and aluminum, iron, magnesium, and fluorine are precipitated with calcium oxide.   After filtration, the excess calcium is removed as carbonate and oxalate, as in the J. L. Smith method (222).   It has been noted that the calcium oxide precipitate retains significant amounts of lithium, which can be recovered only by adding ammonium chloride to the ignited residue and subjecting the mixture to a J. L. Smith–type fusion (210). Similarly, it has been stated that calcium carbonate and oxalate tend to occlude lithium (172).   The alkalies of silicates, particularly meteorites, can be quantitatively recovered, after volatilization in a stream of air, by sintering the sample with a mixture of calcium carbonate and calcium chloride at 1200°C. in a platinum ignition tube (113,130).   A critical investigation carried out with radioactive tracers (^{42}K, ^{86}Rb, ^{134}Cs) indicates that losses of the alkali metals occur in all the procedures discussed above. The acid procedures show losses due to spattering; the J. L. Smith method, due to volatilization.   Additional losses occur by absorption and occlusion in precipitates, especially in barium sulfate, which cannot be reprecipitated. Losses are also observed when ammonium salts are volatilized (153).

d. Preparation for Flame Photometry

For acid-insoluble samples, a J. L. Smith attack is recommended.   It has been pointed out that by a careful control of the leaching process a constant calcium oxide content of 1530 to 1720 p.p.m. can be maintained in the extract (41,169).   If an equal amount of calcium oxide is added to standard solutions of sodium and potassium, flame photometric measurements can be carried out without the prior removal of calcium.   In the determination of traces of the alkali metals, the calcium is liable to inter-

fere seriously and should be removed as carbonate or oxalate. Interference from the radiation of calcium and other alkaline earths can be
avoided or minimized by the addition of aluminum salts (369,401) (cf.
Section VI-B-1). In another modification, the J. L. Smith fusion is acidified with dilute hydrochloric acid, silica is removed by filtration, and
sodium and potassium are determined flame photometrically after com-
plexation of the calcium with ammonium phosphate (306).

If samples are acid-soluble, treatment with hydrofluoric and sulfuric
or perchloric acids is generally recommended. If the residue after filtration
indicates an incomplete decomposition of the sample, the acid treatment
is repeated. The solution is transferred to an appropriate-size volumetric
flask and is then ready for flame photometric measurements (350). Separation of the matrix elements is advantageous, particularly when small
quantities of the alkali metal are concerned. One of the methods involves
solution of the sample in hydrofluoric and sulfuric acids, evaporation to
fumes, solution of the salts in water, and precipitation of the R_2O_3 group
elements and calcium with ammonia and ammonium carbonate. The
alkalies are then determined in an aliquot of the filtrate (51,431b). Since
ammonium salts exert a quenching effect on the radiation of the alkali
metals (cf. Section VI-B-1), for the determination of trace quantities the
R_2O_3 group can be removed by precipitation with calcium carbonate, and
the soluble calcium by precipitation as the sulfate (183). For the determination of trace amounts of lithium, basic lead carbonate has been suggested to remove the R_2O_3 group (115).

3. Cements

The official ASTM method, which is intended for umpire-type analysis,
still recommends the conventional J. L. Smith attack and the determination
of the combined alkalies as sulfates and the potassium as the chloroplatinate (9). An optional, more rapid method is based on the decomposition
with nitric, hydrofluoric, and perchloric acids. After evaporation, the
perchlorates are thermally decomposed to chlorides. An aqueous extract
is prepared, and sodium is determined in one aliquot as sodium zinc uranyl
acetate, and the potassium in another aliquot as potassium chloroplatinate (9). Flame photometry is particularly well suited to the determination
of alkalies in cement. Silica must be removed because of its depressing
effect on the calcium radiation, which is superimposed on the emission of
the sodium (104). Sample preparation consists merely in dissolution of
the sample (usually 0.5 to 1 g.) in dilute hydrochloric acid and filtration
into a volumetric flask. The principal interference due to calcium can be

compensated for with standards containing an amount of calcium comparable to that found in the solution of the sample. Lithium can be determined in portland cement by fundamentally the same procedure (132a,275).

4. Soils

a. TOTAL ALKALIES

This determination is not often required. The J. L. Smith method or an HF attack can be used.

b. EXCHANGEABLE POTASSIUM

The determination of available or exchangeable potassium and, to a lesser degree, of sodium is frequently required to establish the fertility of soils, the improvements they may require, and the choice of fertilizers and also to detect deficiency diseases in plants. The following determinations are frequently carried out. Potassium and sodium soluble in ammonium acetate are determined by treating a 10 g. sample in an Erlenmeyer flask for 2 hours with a cold, neutral, $1N$ solution of ammonium acetate (13). The solution is filtered and calcium is removed by precipitation with ammonium oxalate. Alternatively, the calcium can be eliminated upon the addition of a small amount of ammonium oxalate to the extracting solution (375). Nitric acid is added to the filtrate, and the solution is evaporated to dryness. The residue is then ignited to eliminate organic matter and ammonium salts. After solution in dilute acetic acid, potassium is determined as the cobaltinitrite. If proper precautions are taken to insure the complete absence of ammonium salts, the potassium can be more advantageously determined as potassium tetraphenylboron, since removal of calcium is unnecessary and the introduction of ammonium salts is thus avoided.

Other extractants used to determine the fertility of soils are water (58), $0.05N$ acetic acid (63), dilute hydrochloric acid (173), 10% sodium acetate in $0.5N$ acetic acid (80), $0.1N$ barium acetate (63), and 0.7% calcium lactate (aqueous solution) neutralized with hydrochloric acid to pH 3.6 (173). These extractants are usually used in connection with flame photometric determinations of the alkalies. The removal of cations and anions other than potassium depends on the composition of the soil. Unless present in negligible amounts, calcium should be removed by precipitation as the oxalate, and organic matter and ammonium salts should be destroyed by evaporation with nitric acid, ignition, and dissolution of the residue in dilute hydrochloric acid (276). If a calcium determination is also required, the oxalate precipitation is, of course, omitted. An ammonia separation in the presence of Fe^{+3} is then necessary to remove PO_4^{-3}, which would interfere with the calcium determination. If the removal of calcium is omitted, the standard solutions must contain an amount of this element comparable to that found in the solution of the soil. If calcium lactate is used as an extractant, the calcium is precipitated with a measured amount of oxalic acid, and the potassium is determined flame photometrically after mixing of the solution, without the necessity of filtration. Naturally, standards must contain identical amounts of all reagents (173).

5. Fertilizers

Sodium is not commonly determined as a macro constituent of fertilizers. However, the determination of potassium, a major plant nutrient, is frequently required. The official AOAC (Association of Official Agricultural Chemists) Lindo-Gladding chloroplatinate method still is widely used in industry (13).

a. Mixed Fertilizers

A representative sample (usually 2.5 g.) is dissolved by boiling with dilute ammonium oxalate, with a little diglycol stearate added to prevent foaming. The solution is then rendered ammoniacal and filtered. A few milliliters of sodium hydroxide solution is added to an aliquot (to combine with phosphoric acid during the subsequent ignition), and the solution is evaporated to dryness in a quartz dish. A little sulfuric acid is then added, and the solution is again evaporated to dryness. The residue is gently ignited and then dissolved in dilute hydrochloric acid, prior to the chloroplatinate precipitation of the potassium. It has been shown that losses of potassium may occur during the ignition, owing to spattering or volatilization (323). The following treatment has therefore been suggested: the aliquot is boiled after the addition of a little nitric acid; then hydrochloric acid is added, and the solution is evaporated to near dryness (13).

b. Potash Salts (Sylvite, Carnallite, Kainite)

The sample is dissolved in hot water without the addition of ammonium oxalate and ammonia. An aliquot representing 0.5 g. of sample is then treated as in the procedure for mixed fertilizers.

c. Nitrate Fertilizers

The sample is dissolved as in the procedure for potash salts. However, the aliquot is treated once with hydrochloric acid before the addition of chloroplatinic acid.

d. Organic Fertilizers

A representative sample (usually 10 g.) is ignited at a low heat in a muffle to destroy organic matter. The salts are dissolved in a little hydrochloric acid, ammonia and ammonium oxalate are added, and an aliquot is treated as in the procedure for mixed fertilizers.

e. New Approaches in Sample Preparation

Anion exchange resin in the chloride form has been suggested for the removal of phosphates and sulfates prior to the determination of potassium as the perchlorate (17). Similarly, cation exchange resins have been used for the removal of sulfate and phosphate ions in mixed fertilizers. The aqueous solution of the sample is passed through the cation exchange resin. After the removal of SO_4^{-2} and PO_4^{-3}, potassium and ammonium are eluted with $4N$ hydrochloric acid. Ammonium is expelled from the eluate with sodium bicarbonate, and the potassium is finally precipitated as the perchlorate. (For a discussion of ion exchange methods, see Section IV-C-2.)

Sodium tetraphenylboron has replaced chloroplatinic acid and perchloric acid to a large extent as precipitating agent for potassium in fertilizer. The sample preparation is identical with that described for the chloroplatinic acid method. It should be noted, however, that NH_4^+ is also precipitated quantitatively with tetraphenylboron. Ammonium salts can be expelled by boiling, after the solution has been rendered alkaline with sodium hydroxide (203). For the simultaneous determination of potassium and ammonium, and for methods designed to obviate the effect of NH_4^+, consult the discussion on tetraphenylboron, Section VI-A-3-d.

f. Preparation for Flame Photometry

It has been shown that equal precision and accuracy with a saving of more than half the time can be obtained by determining potassium in fertilizers by flame photometric methods (133,329). The solution can be prepared by the official AOAC method (13). The addition of mono- or diammonium phosphate has been recommended to prevent interference from calcium by inhibiting the calcium radiation or by precipitating calcium phosphate. As in the case of cements, calcium can also be eliminated by precipitation with ammonium oxalate. If phosphate or oxalate is used, its effect on the potassium radiation must be counteracted by adding ammonium phosphate or oxalate to the standards (63). Barium hydroxide can be used to remove simultaneously sulfate, phosphate, and calcium

(44). For the determination of potassium in sodium nitrate, the interfering effect of the large excess of sodium must be compensated for by the addition of sodium nitrate to the standards.

6. Mineral and Industrial Waters, Water-Formed Deposits

The official AOAC method for mineral waters, although long and tedious, is still used in umpire-type analysis (13). One to 5 liters of water is acidified with hydrochloric acid and evaporated to dryness. After removal of the silica, SO_4^{-2} is precipitated with barium chloride. The filtrate is evaporated to dryness, and the residue is ignited and treated with barium hydroxide, mainly to remove magnesium. After filtration, calcium and excess barium in the filtrate are precipitated as the carbonates. The alkalies are finally weighed as the chlorides. Lithium is separated from sodium and potassium by the ether-alcohol method (311). The insoluble sodium and potassium chlorides are dissolved in water, potassium being subsequently determined as chloroplatinate. Sodium is calculated by difference. Frequently the water is of sufficient purity to afford the direct determination of sodium as the triple acetate and of potassium as the tetraphenylboron compound. For a discussion of interfering substances consult Sections VI-A-2 and VI-A-3.

Flame photometry is ideally suited for the determination of the alkali metals in water since they are usually found in concentrations that fall well within the optimum ranges for flame photometric methods. As a matter of fact, both rubidium and cesium were discovered by a flame technique. Frequently it is unnecessary to carry out any evaporations, ignitions, or dilutions. Indeed, no other treatment than filtration may be required. The preparation of standard solutions is equally simple, since the effect of potentially interfering elements is largely eliminated by the natural dilution of the alkali metals. Water with a very low alkali content is concentrated by evaporation. On the other hand, water with a high sodium content may require dilution. Large amounts of calcium should be precipitated as oxalate. Oxalic acid must then also be added to the standards. See Section VI-B-1 for details on the preparation of radiation buffers and other techniques designed to eliminate various forms of radiation interferences.

Water-formed deposits are first ignited in a platinum crucible at 700°C. to eliminate organic matter. The residue is dissolved in hydrochloric acid, and silica is removed by filtration. The ignited sample may also be treated with sulfuric and hydrofluoric acids to decompose silicates. The solution is then evaporated to dryness, and the residue is dissolved in hydrochloric acid for the flame photometric determination of the alkali metals (373).

7. Pure Metals and Alloys

Flame photometric methods are appropriate for the determination of small amounts of alkalies in pure metals. Frequently no separations are required. However, possible interference from the major constituent must be kept in mind (63). Thus aluminum as the matrix element significantly depresses sodium radiation and must be compensated for by the addition of aluminum to the standards. Analyses of aluminum alloys containing copper require the addition of both aluminum and copper to the standards (184,185). The depressing effect of the aluminum is sometimes so pronounced as to require its removal as $AlCl_3$, by saturation of the cold solution of the sample with hydrogen chloride gas (212). To compensate for the depressing effect of large amounts of lithium on sodium and potassium radiation, an empirical working curve can be prepared (191), or, as some prefer, the bulk of the matrix alkali metal may be removed by ion exchange (12a). On the other hand, to determine lithium in magnesium-lithium-aluminum alloys, interference from aluminum and magnesium on the lithium radiation is counteracted by the addition of these two elements to the standard solution (344, 415). Similar techniques of sample preparation and standardization have been used in the determination of sodium and potassium in zinc-cadmium phosphors (101) and beryllium (63). Lead does not interfere with the determination of traces of alkali metals as long as the same amount is added to the standard solutions; to avoid health hazards, however, it is best removed as the sulfate (145). For the determination of lithium, a frequent impurity, in beryllium oxide, health regulations require that the flame excitation be carried out in a well-ventilated hood containing a specially constructed absorbing filter (251). Among other applications of the flame photometric approach, the determination of traces of cesium in bismuth and bismuth-uranium alloys should be mentioned (449).

8. Various Inorganic Cations and Anions

If a particular procedure so requires, interfering cations and anions can be removed by one or a combination of several techniques. Electrolysis with a mercury cathode is useful for removing large amounts of certain heavy metals. Extraction or filtration of metals as cupferrates, 8-hydroxy-quinolates, etc., may be of value at times. Very helpful are separations based on ion exchange and paper chromatography.

B. DECOMPOSITION, DISSOLUTION, AND OTHER PRELIMINARY TREATMENT OF ORGANIC SUBSTANCES

1. Plant Material

In the official AOAC method (13) for the determination of the alkali metals in plants, the sample is moistened with dilute sulfuric acid and is then ignited in a muffle. The ash is dissolved in dilute hydrochloric acid, the R_2O_3 group is removed by an ammonia separation, the filtrate is evaporated to dryness, and the residue is ignited to expel ammonium salts. The magnesium is removed by a barium hydroxide separation, and the calcium and barium are removed by an ammonium carbonate precipitation. The alkalies are finally weighed as combined chlorides, and the potassium is determined as the chloroplatinate or perchlorate. If only a potassium determination is required, the preliminary removal of the R_2O_3 group and the barium hydroxide separation are omitted, and calcium is removed, together with the R_2O_3 group, with ammonium carbonate. The filtrate is evaporated to dryness, NH_4 salts are removed by ignition, and the potassium is determined as the chloroplatinate.

Much more rapid than the AOAC procedure is the method based on wet ashing of the sample with nitric and perchloric acids, evaporation to dryness, solution of the salts in hot water, filtration, and precipitation of the potassium as the chloroplatinate (354). It has been shown that potassium can be directly determined in the hydrochloric acid solution of plant ashes by precipitation with sodium tetraphenylboron (7). For the rapid determination of sodium in plants, 10 g. of dried plant is ignited, the residue is dissolved in dilute hydrochloric acid, and phosphorus is precipitated by the addition of calcium chloride and ammonia. The filtrate is evaporated to a small volume, and the sodium is precipitated with either zinc or magnesium uranyl acetate reagent (13).

The hydrochloric acid solution obtained after the AOAC wet ashing procedure is well suited for the flame photometric measurement of either sodium or potassium or both. Dry ashing, followed by solution of the residue in dilute hydrochloric acid, can also be used. If calcium is present in the ash in very high concentrations, it should be removed with ammonium oxalate. Only if calcium is also to be determined will it be necessary to remove the phosphate ion.

2. Vegetable and Animal Foods

For the determination of potassium or sodium in fruits, fruit products, and cheese, a sufficiently large sample, usually 10 to 30 g. is dried in a platinum dish and is then ignited at a temperature not exceeding 550°C.

until all organic matter is destroyed (13).   The ash is dissolved in a few drops of hydrochloric acid, and the potassium is directly determined as the chloroplatinate or tetraphenylboron.   For the determination of sodium as the triple acetate, phosphorus should first be removed by precipitation as calcium phosphate, as described for plant material.

For the flame photometric determination of potassium and sodium, it is necessary to ash butter, milk, and similar foods.   Liquid samples containing little solid substance can be directly analyzed after suitable dilution.   However, fruit juices and alcoholic beverages should be ashed first, because alcohols greatly enhance and sugar markedly decreases the radiation of sodium and potassium (173).   If calcium is determined simultaneously with the alkali metals, phosphorus must be removed.   This separation is most conveniently accomplished by ion exchange (292) (cf. Section IV-C-2).   To avoid separations or evaporations, it is often possible to add matching organic substances to the standards in proper proportions. For instance, for the direct determination of sodium and potassium and calcium in water extracts of dried beets, standards can be prepared with sugar solutions as a base (82).   In the analysis of beer for sodium and potassium, the "background" consists of dextrin, alcohol, and the inorganic constituents of beer (411).

3. Biological Samples

The following groups of clinical samples are frequently analyzed for sodium and potassium (63): liquids—serum, plasma, whole blood, lymph, milk, saliva, urine, peritoneal fluids, cerebrospinal fluid, gastrointestinal fluid; soft tissue—brain, muscle, liver, etc.; hard tissue—bones.

Because of the great variation in composition and the limited amount of sample frequently available, no clear-cut sample preparation can be described.   Sometimes, particularly with flame photometric methods, liquid samples can be analyzed after suitable dilution, without deproteinization or destruction of organic matter (63,173).   Although such samples as serum, plasma, and urine can thus be analyzed without ashing, results are usually more certain if sugars, proteins, and similar substances are eliminated first.   Samples of tissue, bone, and feces must always be ashed.

Dry ashing is best carried out in a platinum crucible at 550°C. after preliminary drying of the sample at 100°C.   Higher temperatures should not be used, since alkali metals may be lost by volatilization.   A little concentrated hydrochloric acid or nitric acid is added to the residue, and, after evaporation to dryness, the ignition is repeated.   Final dissolution of the ash depends upon its composition and on whether a chemical or flame photometric method will be used. The chloride medium is preferred for flame photometry. Destruction of organic substances by hot oxidizing acids (wet ashing) is often employed. Nitric acid (173) or a mixture of nitric and perchloric acids (63) is commonly used. Some analysts have developed methods based on the extraction of the alkali metals with dilute nitric acid, water, or other solvents (270). These methods are empirical and cannot necessarily be applied to any other substance than the one originally investigated. A common method of protein removal is with the aid of dilute trichloracetic acid (393a). For the determination of sodium and potassium, various ion exchange procedures may be used to remove interfering substances (cf. Section IV-C-2). Thus, for the determination of sodium in bones, calcium, magnesium, potassium, and phosphates are retained on cation exchange resin while sodium is found in the 100 to 300 ml. zone of the $0.7N$ hydrochloric acid eluate (132).

C. SEPARATIONS OF THE ALKALI METALS

Older procedures for the determination of the individual alkali metals require prior removal of all nonalkali constituents of the sample, followed by weighing of the combined alkali metals as chlorides. Subsequent chemical separations of the individual alkali metals by conventional methods are complicated. Many analysts therefore avoid these chemical separations by using methods that permit the determination of individual alkali metals in the presence of each other, or specific reagents that separate the desired element from all the other alkali metals. However, recently introduced ion exchange procedures greatly simplify the separation of the individual alkali metals from each other and often from many cations and anions.

1. Precipitation Methods

a. SEPARATION OF LITHIUM FROM THE OTHER ALKALI METALS

A number of methods are based on the comparatively large solubility of lithium chloride and the small solubilities of sodium, potassium, rubidium, and cesium chlorides in various organic reagents. The methods are of two types, characterized by extraction of lithium chloride or precipitation of the other chlorides. The first group comprises the larger number of methods, with alcohol-ether mixture (336), pyridine (207), isobutyl alcohol (457), acetone (59), dioxane (387), and n-propyl alcohol saturated with HCl gas (327) being suggested as extractants. In the other general type of procedure, the mixed chlorides are dissolved in a small amount of water, from which the alkali chlorides, other than lithium chloride are precipitated—either by addition of an organic solvent, such as alcohol-ether mixture (311) or n-butyl alcohol containing hydrogen chloride (210), or by dehydration of aqueous solution of the mixed chlorides with organic solvents of high boiling points, such as isoamyl alcohol (158) or 2-ethylhexanol (73).

The main objection to methods in the extraction category is based on their pronounced tendency toward occlusion of lithium chloride and/or hydroxide by the other alkali chlorides, which makes repeated treatments of the insoluble residue necessary. The precipitation methods are therefore superior. Because of the very slight solubilities of potassium chloride and sodium chloride in 2-ethylhexanol (0.01 and 0.08 mg., respectively, per 100 ml.) this solvent has largely replaced other reagents. Lithium is determined in the 2-ethylhexanol solution either gravimetrically (73) or volumetrically (434a,444) (cf. Section VIII-A-1).

b. Separation of Potassium (Rubidium and Cesium) from Sodium and Lithium

Potassium, rubidium, and cesium can be separated from sodium and lithium by precipitation as the chloroplatinate, tetraphenylboron, cobaltinitrite, dipicrylaminate, periodate, and perchlorate. The first five procedures are intended mainly for the determination of only potassium and are discussed in Section V-B-3. The n-butyl alcohol–ethyl acetate method can be used for the determination of lithium and sodium in addition to potassium. The alkali chlorides are converted to perchlorates, and the lithium and sodium are extracted with the butyl alcohol–ethyl acetate mixture. After filtration, the perchlorates of potassium, rubidium, and cesium remain in the residue, ready to be dried and weighed. Ethyl acetate is removed from the filtrate by evaporation, and the sodium is precipitated with a solution of hydrogen chloride in n-butyl alcohol and finally weighed as NaCl. Lithium is finally converted to Li_2SO_4 and weighed (453).

For the determination of a small amount of sodium in the presence of a large amount of potassium, it may be desirable to remove the bulk of the potassium. This separation can be performed by adding perchloric acid to the saturated aqueous solution of the chlorides (141). For the determination of a small amount of potassium in the presence of a large amount of sodium, most of the sodium can be removed by passing hydrogen chloride gas into the ice cold concentrated aqueous solution of the chlorides and filtering (374).

c. Separation of Potassium, Rubidium, and Cesium from Each Other

No entirely satisfactory chemical methods are available for the separation of the three heavy alkali metals. The analyst should, therefore, whenever possible, avoid chemical procedures and either use ion exchange separations (cf. Section IV-C-2) or determine the rubidium and/or cesium by methods requiring no prior separations, such as flame photometric (cf. Section VI-B-1), emission spectrographic (cf. Section VI-B-2), or x-ray fluorescence (cf. Section VI-B-3) procedures. Of the two most reliable chemical procedures, one is based on differences in the solubilities of the chlorides of the three alkali metals (62a,437), and the other on the successive use of 9-phosphomolybdic acid to precipitate both rubidium and cesium, of silicotungstic acid to precipitate only cesium, and of chloroplatinic acid to finally precipitate all three elements (304). Among the many other methods suggested, the following two deserve mention. One, based on the insolubility of cesium chloroplatinate and the solubility of rubidium and potassium chloroplatinates, allows a separation by fractional crystallization (438). In the other method, mixtures of potassium, rubidium, and cesium chlorides are treated with an iodide to form of KI, RbI$_3$, and CsI$_3$. The RbI$_3$ decomposes to RbI and I$_2$. The iodine is extracted with carbon tetrachloride and then is added to a potassium iodide solution and titrated with sodium thiosulfate. The mixture of KI plus RbI plus CsI$_4$ remaining is titrated with sodium thiosulfate, and thus the cesium is found (465).

2. Ion Exchange Methods

a. Introduction

Since the alkali metals form the most pronounced cations, under normal conditions they are not retained by anion exchange resins. Therefore, the discussion here can be limited largely to cation exchangers. A cation exchanger is basically an insoluble compound with a readily exchangeable positive ion, such as the hydrogen ion, held in place by an electronegative charge. As the solution enters the column, certain cations, in our case the alkali metals, compete with exchangeable H$^+$ ion for a position on the resin and partly or fully replace it. Thus rendered insoluble by the resin, the alkali metals are adsorbed on the column while the hydrogen enters the solution. In an ideal case, as the solution passes through the resin bed, the alkalies are quantitatively replaced by H$^+$, and the solution flowing from the resin is free from alkali metals. If the solution contains two or more of the alkali metals, they will compete for the position previously occupied by the H$^+$. The alkali metal with the greatest affinity for the resin will either be retained by or remain longer on the resin and thus will elute after the alkali metal with less affinity. This degree of affinity is merely an expression of the effects due to the concentration of H^+ and alkali ions, change of ions in competition, ionic size, degree of hydration, ionic diffusion rate, complexing degree of eluent, etc. (56).

For the separation of sodium from potassium, the chloride solution containing the two alkali metals is introduced into a column containing a great excess of cation exchange resin of the sulfonic acid type. A large excess of resin is required so that the "breakthrough point" is not reached during the sorption step. Sodium and potassium are adsorbed in a band at the top of the column while H^+ enters the solution, the free acid being removed by water (357).

After the sorption step, sodium and potassium are eluted by passing dilute hydrochloric acid (for example, $0.1N$ HCl) through the column. When the acid first comes in contact with the adsorbed sodium and potassium, the two alkali metals are partially replaced and move down the column. Fresh acid causes this replacement to proceed while the first part of the solution comes into contact with a second portion of the resin, causing a new shift in the composition of the solution and resin phase. Since the potassium ions have a higher replacing ability than the sodium ions, the composition of the solution will be shifted successively, so that the ratio Na^+/K^+ in solution will increase as the solution moves down the column. Thus a complete separation of sodium and potassium ions proceeds in different bands which move down at different rates, sodium appearing in the effluent first and potassium in a subsequent interval after the elution of the sodium is completed.

Since the affinity of cations for cation exchange resin increases with increasing valence, the alkali metal ions are less readily adsorbed than bivalent cations and still less readily adsorbed than trivalent cations. Therefore, the separation of sodium and potassium from magnesium, the polyvalent cation most difficult to separate from the alkalies, is possible. The affinity of the individual alkali metal ion for cation exchange resin increases with decreasing hydrated ionic radius or, with what amounts to the same thing, with increasing basicity. From activity coefficient data (50), the sequence of adsorption among the alkali metals is $Cs^+ > Rb^+ > K^+ > NH_4^+ > Na^+ > Li^+$. For sulfonic acid-type cation exchangers, the exchange equilibrium constants of the alkali ions with the H^+ ion are (209) 0.69, 1.24, 1.58, 2.30, and 2.62, respectively ($H_3O^+ = 1.00$).

b. PRINCIPAL APPLICATIONS

A number of practical ion exchange procedures, of which only the most important can be mentioned here, have been developed.

Colloidal Dowex 50 is used in one method to fill a column with a cross-sectional area of 3.80 cm.^{2} to a height of 59 cm., thus providing a bed volume of 224 ml. (37). Sodium, potassium, and magnesium chlorides, dissolved in 0.7M hydrochloric acid, are introduced into the column, which previously has been conditioned with the same acid. Elution with 0.7M hydrochloric acid results in a first fraction of 370 ml., which is discarded, a second fraction of 160 ml. containing the sodium, and a third fraction of 190 ml. containing the potassium. Under these conditions, magnesium does not appear in the eluate until at least 1100 ml. have been eluted. The sulfate ion, if present, is removed in the first fraction and therefore does not interfere with the separation. Sodium and potassium can be determined in their respective fractions by conventional methods.

In an application of the same general procedure to the determination of lithium, sodium, and potassium in silicates (420), the sample is decomposed by a Berzelius-type attack with hydrofluoric, hydrochloric, and sulfuric acids. The dry residue is dissolved in 0.7M hydrochloric acid, and ferric and aluminum hydroxides are precipitated by the addition of an excess of cadmium oxide. (Although cadmium is bivalent, it does not interfere with the subsequent chromatographic separation; it forms a stable chloride complex of the type $CdCl_4^{-2}$, which is not retained by the cation exchange resin.) When the filtrate is transferred to a 37 cm. $\times$ 2.4 cm.^{2} column containing colloidal Dowex 50, sieved through 120 mesh and treated with 0.7M hydrochloric acid, the first 130 ml. of eluate contains the cadmium, the following 50 ml. the lithium, the next 60 ml. the sodium, and the next 100 ml. the potassium.

Another investigator (341) avoids the removal of the R_2O_3 group elements by adsorbing all cations, after a Berzelius-type attack, on Amberlite IR-120 in a 0.1N hydrochloric acid medium and eluting the sodium and potassium with 0.12N hydrochloric acid.

Instead of hydrochloric acid, a 0.1N perchloric acid medium can be used to separate sodium from potassium on a column of Amberlite IR-100 20 cm. long and 11 mm. in diameter and having a flow rate of 0.12 ml./minute. The first 190 ml. of eluate contains all the sodium; the potassium is completely retained by the resin (215).

In another chromatographic scheme (116), sodium and potassium, as well as iron, aluminum, magnesium, and calcium, are separated in successive steps by (1) adsorbing all cations on Amberlite IR-120 in the hydrogen form, thus removing the sulfate ion; (2) eluting all cations with dilute hydrochloric acid; (3) passing an 8N hydrochloric acid solution of the same cations through an anion exchange column containing Amberlite IRA-400 in the chloride form, thus adsorbing iron, which later can be eluted with $0.1N$ hydrochloric acid; (*4*) passing the chloride solution of the remaining cations, after removal of the excess acid, again through Amberlite IR-120 in the hydrogen form; (*5*) eluting the sodium with $0.4N$ hydrochloric acid in the fraction between 200 and 340 ml. and the potassium between 540 and 820 ml.; (*6*) eluting the aluminum with 5% citric acid between 600 and 900 ml.; (*7*) eluting the magnesium with $1N$ hydrochloric acid between 40 and 100 ml. and the calcium between 360 and 680 ml.

A somewhat different procedure is based on the adsorption of lithium, sodium, and potassium in a $0.1N$ hydrochloric acid–20 to 30% methyl alcohol medium on Amberlite IR-120. Lithium is eluted first with $0.2N$ hydrochloric acid in 30% methyl alcohol, sodium next with $0.2N$ hydrochloric acid, and potassium finally with $0.5N$ hydrochloric acid (303).

Cation exchange procedures have been used to a large extent to separate neutron-activated mixtures of the alkali metals. One investigator (56), using 100 to 120 mesh Amberlite IR-1 resin in the hydrogen form, a column of 1 cm. I.D. and 140 cm. length, a flow rate of 1 ml./minute, and $0.10N$ hydrochloric acid as an eluent has successfully separated neutron-activated mixtures of ^{42}K and ^{86}Rb, containing also tracers of ^{22}Na and ^{137}Cs. Radiometric analysis of the effluent shows that the fraction between 500 and 850 ml. contains the sodium, that between 1050 and 1550 ml. the potassium, and that between 1700 and 2300 ml. the rubidium; the cesium appears after 5500 ml. and is not quantitatively eluted in the next 2000 ml. of eluate. Another investigator (93) working with neutron-activated mixtures, and using Dowex 50 in the hydrogen condition, reports some overlap of the rubidium-cesium fractions, whereas a third one (216) first separates sodium and potassium by elution with $0.1N$ hydrochloric acid and subsequently rubidium and cesium with $1N$ hydrochloric acid. The same eluents have also been recommended for the determination of rubidium and cesium in sodium-potassium alloys and related materials (69).

Although radiometric analysis is ideally suited for the determination of neutron-activated mixtures, the elution of the alkali metals can also be followed by conductivity measurements (448).

c. OTHER CATION PROCEDURES

The determination of lithium in lithium-magnesium alloys is greatly simplified by adsorbing the magnesium and eluting the lithium in a $0.5N$ HCl medium (449a). Lithium, beryllium, and aluminum have been separated (181) by eluting the lithium with $0.1N$ hydrochloric acid, the beryllium with $0.05N$ calcium chloride, and the aluminum with $4N$ hydrochloric acid. Sodium and potassium can be determined after cation exchange separations in samples of milk ash (419), human blood (15)), urine

(429), and bone (132). Several investigators (283,343) have emphasized the exceptional ability of sulfonated phenolic–type cation exchangers to adsorb cesium out of concentrated sodium solutions at pH 13. The special selectivity of these resins for cesium has been ascribed to the phenolic structure of the exchanger, since nuclear sulfonic resins under the same conditions do not show this property (283). Thus, a few milligrams of cesium can be separated from large quantities of sodium chloride by passing the saturated sodium chloride solution, 0.5N in sodium hydroxide, through Duolite C-3, a phenolic methylenesulfonic resin (343).

Phosphates interfere with the determination of sodium as the triple acetate, and sulfates with the determination of potassium as the perchlorate and chloroplatinate. These and other interfering anions can be removed by means of cation exchangers in the hydrogen form (34,357). Cation exchange allows rapid determinations of potassium in kainite and mixed fertilizers consisting of superphosphate, ammonium sulfate, and potassium salts. The removal of phosphate by ion exchange is not only more rapid but also more accurate than precipitation by ferric, zinc, barium, or calcium salts. The separation is performed by passing a 0.1N hydrochloric acid solution of the sample through the cation exchanger, which is then washed with water. The alkali metals, which have been adsorbed, are then eluted with 1N hydrochloric acid and are subsequently determined by conventional methods.

Since many cyanide complexes are sufficiently stable that they can be passed through cation exchange resin without adsorption (357), certain metallic cations can be converted to complex cyanides and thus separated from the alkali metals. Similarly, chromate, molybdate, vanadate, tungstate, phosphomolybdate, phosphotungstate, and silicotungstate can be separated from the alkali metals by cation exchange techniques. The separations are achieved by passing the solution through a cation exchanger in the ammonium form. Upon rinsing with water, the anions are obtained in the effluent while the alkali metals are quantitatively retained by the resin. Treatment with hydrochloric acid then yields the alkali metals.

d. ANION PROCEDURES

Since the alkali metals mainly form stable cations, anion exchange resins are used primarily for the removal of interfering anions. However, it is possible in EDTA media to separate some of the alkali metals from each other. Although this technique is only marginal for the elements heavier than sodium, it affords an excellent separation of lithium from sodium. When cesium, sodium, and lithium in a $2.5 \times 10^{-3} M$ EDTA solution (pH

0.9) are passed through a Dowex 1 resin bed, cesium appears in the effluent first, followed by sodium. Lithium is finally eluted with $0.25M$ EDTA solution (pH 4.2) (236,296).

It has been reported that uramildiacetic acid has the ability to form stable complexes with lithium and sodium but not with potassium (67). Although the procedure involves the formation of anions, cation exchangers, both Amberlite IR-120 and Amberlite IRC-50, are employed to achieve the separation, with the uncomplexed potassium appearing first in the eluate. Because of pH requirements, the resins are used in the OH cycle by pretreating the exchanger with either dimethylamine or tetramethylammonium hydroxide. In the system used, the relative affinities of cations for the exchanger are $K^+ < NH_4^+ < Na^+ < (CH_3)_2NH_2^+ < Li^+ < (CH_3)_4^+$.

Sodium and potassium can be separated from cyanide, ferrocyanide, ferricyanide, zinc, nickel, and copper by passing the solution through a column containing strongly basic anion exchange resin in the hydroxyl form. The effluent will contain only alkali hydroxide, which can be titrated with standard acid (147). Similarly, sodium and potassium can be separated from sulfate and phosphate by passing the solution through a column containing resin in the chloride form (17,148). Sulfate and phosphate ions are quantitatively exchanged for chloride ions, while the alkali metals pass into the eluate.

Cobalt, zinc, iron, and cadmium, which form stable chloro anions, are taken up by strongly basic anion exchange resin in various hydrochloric acid media and thus separated from the alkali metals (213,236). Also, cobalt, nickel, copper, iron, and vanadium are quantitatively adsorbed by anion exchange resin in the citrate form, while the alkali metals pass through the column (357).

Fluoride and sulfate ions can be removed by passing the perchloric acid solution of a silicate sample, resulting from the decomposition with hydrofluoric and perchloric acids, through an acid alumina exchanger. The column removes F^- and SO_4^{-2} ions. Potassium, in the effluent, can be determined as the perchlorate (102).

The ability of calcium and magnesium to form stable chelates with EDTA in water–ethyl alcohol solutions can be applied to the separation of the alkalies from the alkaline earths (358). The bivalent metals are taken up in a column filled with a mixture of an anion exchange resin in the EDTA and acetate form. The alkali metals appear in the effluent, which is passed directly through a second column containing an anion exchanger in the OH^- form. The alkali hydroxides obtained in the effluent of the second column are titrated with standard acid.

3. Paper Chromatographic Methods

a. INTRODUCTION

Paper chromatography permits the rapid separation and subsequent estimation of microgram quantities of the alkali metals in various substances, such as minerals, soil, water, and living organisms. Published methods describe the separation of the alkali metals from each other and other cations by partitioning of the ions between an aqueous medium and an organic solvent. The migration of the individual constituents of the mixture relative to the migration of the solvent, the R value, serves as a guide to the differences in the mobilities of ions, complexes, and organic solvent. The principal value of paper chromatographic methods lies in the resolution of complex mixtures. Like ion exchange methods, those based on paper chromatography do not serve directly for the detection or determination of the alkali metals. After partitioning, the position of the ions must be revealed by spraying the paper with certain solutions which indicate the presence and amounts of the alkali metals and other cations or anions by color (26,66,119,159,355,406) or fluorescence under ultraviolet light (159,280,377). Among other detection or measuring devices, flame photometric, isotopic dilution, planimetric (28,119), polarographic (431), electrolytic (238), and even gravimetric (28) techniques have been recommended. Radiochemical methods serve not only for the detection of the alkali metals, but the half lives provide for their identification, and the intensities of the radiation can be used for their estimation (136,144,249,250). Because the paper chromatographic methods are very specific, the detection techniques employed with them frequently need not be specific at all. Thus silver nitrate has been used for the simultaneous detection of all the alkali metals (26,66,355,431), cobaltinitrite reagents serve for the identification of potassium, rubidium, and cesium (28,280,406), zinc uranyl acetate reagent identifies both sodium and lithium (264,280), and beta or gamma counters establish the presence of one or more radionuclides in the presence of others (144).

Chromatographic methods are variable in approach, in equipment used, in details, in size, in sorbent, and in solvent. Excellent books (46,248, 331,412) and review articles (250,413,414) are available for a full discussion of principles and equipment.

b. APPLICATIONS

Some of the solvents used in early paper chromatographic work have been investigated, and the R_f values recorded (85). In one application, the alkali chlorides (lithium, sodium, and potassium) are applied to the paper in a neutral solution, and methyl alcohol is used as a solvent. The spots are revealed by spraying the paper with a mixed solution of silver nitrate and fluorescein and then drying to detect the accompanying chloride ions (66). Propanol–10% methanol is suitable for the separation of potassium, sodium, lithium, ammonium, and magnesium (355). Again the paper strip is sprayed with silver nitrate; it is then exposed to diffused light and washed with water for the detection of the chloride ion. Pentanol-methanol (3:7) and ethanol-methanol (1:1) are also effective solvent mixtures (26). Lithium, ammonium, sodium, and potassium have been found to migrate in that order. The metals are revealed by a spray consisting of indophenol dye and silver nitrate. The chlorides appear pink against a blue background and after exposure to light become dark brown against a light brown background. A maximum of 500 γ of combined sodium and lithium, in the form of chlorides, can be separated by a 4:1 mixture of methyl alcohol and butyl alcohol; the detection and estimation with ultraviolet light of 2.5 to 500 γ of sodium or lithium as fluorescent zinc uranyl acetate is possible in the presence of 500 γ each of potassium, rubidium, cesium, calcium, barium, strontium, and magnesium (280). It is suggested (431) that a sample of molasses be prepared for the chromatographic separation by being first wet-ashed and then ignited at 600°C. SO_4^{-2} is exchanged for Cl^- upon passage of the solution through an anion exchange column. After chromatography, the spots are detected with silver nitrate and exposure to sunlight. The paper is cut into pieces, each zone is extracted with $0.1N$ sulfuric acid, and the Cl^- is determined by polarography (431).

In another method, a 8:2 ethanol–$0.1N$ hydrochloric acid medium is recommended for the determination of potassium. The chromatogram on the dried paper is developed with sodium lead cobaltinitrite, NaPbCo-$(NO_2)_6$. After drying, the area of the spot is compared with those of standard spots obtained on the same paper (planimetry) or quantitated by excision and weighing on an analytical balance (28). In another system, up to 1 mg. of combined potassium, rubidium, and cesium chlorides is partitioned by a mixture of 55% hydrochloric acid, 35% butyl alcohol, and 5% isobutyl methyl ketone. Lead cobaltinitrite is also used in this method for the estimation of 5 to 1000 γ of potassium, rubidium, or cesium (280). It has been shown that a solvent mixture of acetic acid, ether, and nitric acid (4:5:1) separates lithium, sodium, potassium, and ammonium from magnesium, calcium, strontium, and barium. The individual ions are then separated with a mixture of methanol, nitric acid, and hydrochloric acid (8:1:1) (293). The alkalies can also be separated from the alkaline earths (all cations in the form of acetates) with ethanol–

20% $1N$ acetic acid as a solvent.   The separated ions are converted into
colored violurates (119).   Thiovioluric acid has a certain advantage over
violuric acid in that it forms colored spots which fluoresce strongly (377).
To prepare a sample of serum for chromatographic separation and subsequent color development with violuric acid, the protein is removed with
trichloroacetic acid, and all cations are converted to acetates by passing
the solution through Amberlite IRA-410 resin in the acetate form.   After
application of the resulting $2N$ acetic acid solution to the paper, the chromatogram is developed with 4:1 96% ethanol–$2N$ acetic acid.   After drying
at 50°C., the paper is sprayed with $0.1N$ violuric acid and dried.   The
alkali and alkaline earth metals show colored spots, the areas of which are
measured by planimetry.   Isopropyl alcohol–pyridine–water–acetic acid
(8:8:4:1) has been suggested for the separation of 0.1 to 10 γ of potassium,
sodium, calcium, magnesium, barium, strontium, and beryllium in a
method that uses a very simple apparatus and that is particularly suited
for the analysis of blood and other biological fluids.   A great number of
cation detector solutions that develop colors or fluorescence were investigated, and the usual spraying technique was replaced by addition of the
ion detector solution to the solvent front line with a pipet (159).

A promising solvent recently introduced is a mixture of phenol and hydrochloric acid (406); it has been successfully applied to the separation of
potassium, ammonium, rubidium, and cesium in ascending paper chromatography.   A 10% aqueous solution of sodium cobaltinitrite in 5%
acetic acid is used as a spray to make the positions of the ions observable
by the formation of yellow precipitates.   Cold water washing removes
the excess reagent.   Thirty-two other ions were tested and did not produce yellow spots.   If the strips are heat-dried and sprayed with alcoholic
α-nitroso-β-naphthol solution made alkaline with sodium hydroxide, the
spots appear brown against a green background, and the sensitivity is
increased.   The same reagent (phenol saturated with $2N$ hydrochloric
acid) was used in both columnar (cellulose powder) and paper chromatography (136) to separate cesium-134 from rubidium-86 (250), cesium-131
from irradiated barium carbonate (249), and cesium-137 from a nitric
acid solution of irradiated uranium.   A mixture of phenol-methanol–hydrochloric acid (57:22.5:20, w/v/v) is used as a reagent to separate the
chlorides of lithium and sodium and of potassium, rubidium, cesium, and
ammonium by descending paper chromatography.   After removal from
the tank, the papers are dried and then sprayed with zinc uranyl acetate
to reveal sodium and lithium by their fluorescence in ultraviolet light.
For the detection of potassium, rubidium, cesium, and ammonium, the
papers are sprayed with ethanol and a solution of lead cobaltinitrite and

then dried, and the spots are compared with standard spots. The spots of ammonium and potassium are gray, rubidium is brown, and cesium is yellow-brown. The minimum amounts of the elements detectable in the presence of 10 μmoles of any other or total of all others are 0.1 μmole of sodium, potassium, rubidium, and cesium and 0.25 μmole of lithium and ammonium. The method is well suited for the determination of small quantities of rubidium and cesium in rocks (264).

In a recent procedure (285a) potassium, rubidium, and cesium are separated as yellow picrates. The mixed nitrates or chlorides are placed on Whatman No. 4 filter paper. The spots are dried at 60°C., and 1 or 2 drops of a 1 solution of sodium picrate in acetone is placed on the spots. The paper strip is dipped into nitrobenzene saturated with water. After the solvent has ascended 15 cm., the chromatogram is removed and dried at 60°C. The picrates of potassium, rubidium, and cesium are dissolved in acetone and determined colorimetrically.

All paper chromatographic methods discussed previously use neutral or acid media. Another method involves the separation of the hydroxides of lithium, sodium, and potassium with ethanol–20% H_2O as a solvent in both column and paper chromatography (65). Phenol red, bromophenol blue, phenolphthalein, and bromothymol blue are suitable alkali indicators.

c. Electrochromatography (Paper Electrophoresis)

Electrochromatographic methods depend on the differential electrical migration of the ionized or electrically charged components of mixtures of the alkali metals through a background electrolytic solution that is fixed or stabilized in a porous medium (412). The separation of the migrating ions depends primarily upon their differential migration and upon their selective sorption by the medium. Various kinds of filter paper, differing in thickness, density, and isoelectric point, are employed in paper electrochromatography and may be used as strips, pads, or sheets.

Several methods that cover the alkali metals have been published recently (120,363,376). It has been shown (120) that in most acid media both the alkali metal and the alkaline earth cations migrate rapidly with much cross contamination. However, in weakly acid and alkaline solutions of complex-forming acids (for example EDTA), the alkaline earths form complexes which migrate as anions and separate completely from the uncomplexed alkali metal cations. Under various conditions tested, cesium, rubidium, and potassium form a single rapidly migrating zone, followed by sodium and lithium. Lithium, sodium, potassium, magnesium, and cesium plus rubidium are separated from mixtures of their ions by paper electrophoresis with ammonium carbonate solution. At the end of the run, the ammonium carbonate is removed by volatilization, and the paper is sprayed with an indicator to develop the chromatogram (363).

V. QUALITATIVE DETECTION AND IDENTIFICATION

In pure solutions, the alkali ions impart specific intense colors to the flame of a Bunsen burner, lithium producing crimson red, sodium yellow, potassium bluish violet, and rubidium and cesium red-violet colorations.

A. SPECTROSCOPIC EXAMINATION

The most sensitive and simple ways to detect and identify the alkali metals are by spectroscopy and flame photometry. Solid samples are best excited by an arc or spark technique. Liquid samples and material easily soluble in water or acids are more conveniently examined in a flame photometer.

1. Lithium

The usable spectral lines for lithium are these (142): λ 6707.9 A., λ 6103.6 A., λ 4603.2 A., and λ 3232.7 A. The most sensitive line for flame photometric purposes is 6707.9 A. For spectrographic analysis, the sensitivity of the plate for the visible spectrum must be kept in mind. Limits of detection: in flame work, 10^{-2} to 10^{-3} p.p.m. (63,155,173); in spectroscopy, 0.1 to 1 γ (142).

2. Sodium

Sodium is easily excited by flame arc and spark sources. In the visible spectrum, the doublet 5895.9–5890.0 A. is most useful, particularly in flame photometry. In the ultraviolet region, the doublet 3302.3–3302.9 A. is most commonly used. Limits of detection: by flame, 10^{-4} p.p.m. (63, 155,173); by arc excitation, 10^{-3} to 10^{-4} γ (142); by spark excitation, 10^{-1} to 1 γ.

3. Potassium

Potassium is also easily excited by flame, arc, and spark sources. The most sensitive lines lie in the visible spectrum at λ 7664.9–7699.0 A. (red doublet) and at λ 4047.2–4044.2 A. (blue doublet). In the ultraviolet region, the 3447.4–3446.5 A. doublet is less sensitive. The red doublet is most useful for flame photometry: the blue doublet is preferred for spectroscopic work, unless red-sensitive photographic plates are used. Limits of detection: by flame, 10^{-3} to 10^{-4} p.p.m. (red doublet); by arc excitation, 10^{-3} to 10^{-2} γ; by spark, 1 to 10 γ.

4. Rubidium

Rubidium is easily detected by spectral analysis. The most sensitive lines, located in the visible spectrum at λ 7947.6 A. and λ 7800.3 A., are well suited for flame photometry and also for spectroscopy if red-sensitive plates are used. The very sensitive λ 4215.6–4201.8 A. lines are more suited for photographic purposes, however. Limits of detection: in flame work, λ 7800.3 A., 10^{-2} p.p.m., and λ 7947.6 A., 3×10^{-2} p.p.m.; in spectroscopy, by arc excitation, 10^{-2} to 10^{-1} γ, and by spark excitation, 1 to 10 γ.

5. Cesium

The most sensitive cesium lines are in the infrared spectrum at λ 8943.6 A. and λ 8521.2 A. They are well suited for flame photometry and also for spectroscopy if infrared-sensitive plates are used. The lines 4593.2 A. and 4555.3 A. are useful for spectroscopic purposes. In the ultraviolet, the less sensitive doublet 2525.6–2630.6 A. can also be used. Limits of detection: in flame work, λ 8521.2 A., 10^{-1} p.p.m., and λ 8943.6 A., 2×10^{-1} p.p.m.; in arc spectroscopy, λ 4555.3 A., 10^{-1} to 1 γ.

B. CHEMICAL METHODS

In the course of chemical separations, the alkalies are found in solution after removal of the H_2S, $(NH_4)_2S$, and alkaline earth groups. This solution still contains magnesium and ammonium salts. If necessary, magnesium can be removed as the 8-hydroxyquinolate. Ammonium salts can be removed by ignition. The residue is dissolved in water and tested for the individual alkali metals. Paper chromatographic methods are ideally suited for this purpose. Although paper chromatography only provides a separation of the individual alkali metals from each other and from other ions, the solutions applied to the paper after partitioning serve to detect and identify the desired alkali metal (cf. Section IV-B-3).

1. Lithium

a. PRECIPITATION AS LITHIUM STEARATE (142)

Lithium stearate, $C_{16}H_{35}COOLi$, unlike the stearates of the other alkali metals, is only slightly soluble in isoamyl alcohol. Reagent: 2 g. of ammonium stearate is dissolved in 100 ml. of isoamyl alcohol, or 0.55 g. is dissolved in 100 ml. of 2-ethylhexanol (73). Test: The mixed alkali chlorides are extracted with hot amyl alcohol or 2-ethylhexanol, and two and one-half times the volume of reagent is added at room temperature.   A precipitate denotes lithium.   Limit of detection: 25 γ of lithium in 1 ml. of solution.

b. Precipitation as Lithium Potassium Ferric Periodate (335)

Lithium salts form a yellowish white precipitate, $LiKFeIO_6$, with an alkaline solution of ferric periodate.   Other alkali metals do not interfere, although ammonium salts do.   Reagent: 2 g. of potassium periodate is dissolved in 10 ml. of $2N$ potassium hydroxide.   The solution is diluted to 50 ml., 3 ml. of 10% ferric chloride is added, and the solution is diluted to 100 ml. with $2N$ KOH.   Micro test: One drop of reagent is added to 1 drop of neutral solution.   The resulting solution is heated to 45 to 50°C. If the lithium concentration exceeds 5 γ, a precipitate will form immediately.   Limit of detection: 0.25 γ.

c. Precipitation as the Complex Periodate (347)

Lithium forms an insoluble complex periodate with a strongly alkaline potassium periodate solution.   As much as 50 mg. of sodium or ammonium or 100 mg. of potassium does not form precipitates.   Ammonium salts, however, retard or even prevent the precipitation of lithium and should therefore be expelled.   Reagent: 24 g. of KOH is dissolved in water, and 10 g. of potassium metaperiodate is added.   When clear, the solution is diluted to 1 liter.   Test: To 1 ml. or less of test solution, an equal volume of reagent is added.   Limit of detection: 0.5 mg. of lithium in the cold or 0.1 mg. of lithium if the solution is first heated to 70°C.

d. Other Qualitative Tests

Lithium salts can be precipitated by a mixture of potassium ferricyanide and hexamethylenetetramine.   Characteristic octahedral crystals, which are visible under a microscope, are produced.   Sodium, potassium, rubidium, cesium, and ammonium do not interfere.   As little as 0.6 mg. of lithium is detectable at a concentration of 1:50,000 (228). Lithium gives a green fluorescence with 8-hydroxyquinoline in slightly alkaline 95% ethyl alcohol solution; as little as 5 γ of lithium in 25 ml. can be detected (441).   Lithium reacts with dipivaloylmethane in basic solution to form a chelate that can be extracted with ether (166).   Precipitations of lithium as the fluoride in the absence of magnesium (81), as the carbonate (152) or the phosphate (31), in the absence of alkaline earths, and as zinc uranyl acetate in the absence of sodium (2) serve in special cases to detect or identify lithium.

2. Sodium

a. PRECIPITATION WITH ZINC URANYL ACETATE

Sodium reacts with zinc uranyl acetate in neutral or weak acetic acid solution to form a yellow crystalline triple acetate precipitate, $NaZn(UO_2)_3(C_2H_3O_2)_9 \cdot 6H_2O$ (24,25). The solubility of the precipitate is less in 50% alcohol than in water. Interferences are phosphates, arsenates, molybdates, sulfates in the presence of potassium, lithium in concentrations greater than 1 mg./ml., and potassium in concentrations greater than 50 mg./ml. Lithium can be removed as the fluoride (25), and phosphates and arsenates with zinc carbonate or calcium hydroxide (29) or by ion exchange (17,34). Molybdenum can be complexed with citric acid (168). Reagent: 100 g. of uranyl acetate, 30 g. of zinc acetate, and 30 ml. of glacial acetic acid are dissolved in 1000 ml. of water. A few milligrams of sodium chloride is added, and the solution is allowed to settle for 24 hours and is then filtered. Test: To the solution of the sample, preferably less than 5 ml., eight times its volume of reagent is added. Limit of detection after 30 minutes of standing: 1:20,000. If a 50% alcohol medium is chosen, the limit is increased to 1:50,000; more than 5 mg. of potassium per millimeter, however, will then interfere (142).

b. PRECIPITATION WITH MAGNESIUM URANYL ACETATE

Instead of zinc uranyl acetate, magnesium uranyl acetate reagent is frequently used (75,206). The most sensitive reagent contains 32 g. of uranyl acetate, 100 g. of magnesium acetate, 20 ml. of glacial acetic acid, and 500 ml. of ethyl alcohol per liter (206). More than 0.5 g. of potassium, 1 g. of lithium, and 7 g. of zinc per liter interfere. Test: To the solution of the sample, two and one-half times its volume of reagent is added. Limit of detection: $1:2 \times 10^8$ (142). A less sensitive, but more specific, reagent consists of 25 g. of uranyl acetate, 150 g. of magnesium acetate, 780 ml. of glacial acetic acid, and 100 ml. of water (206). Up to 100 g. of potassium and 10 g. of lithium per liter do not interfere. Test: To the solution of the sample, an equal volume of reagent is added. Limit of detection: 1:1500.

c. PRECIPITATION WITH DL-METHOXYPHENYLACETIC ACID

DL-Methoxyphenylacetic acid forms a sodium salt, $C_6H_5CH(OCH_3)COOH \cdot C_6H_5CH(OCH_3)COONa$, that is difficultly soluble in water (339). This reagent is more selective than the zinc or magnesium uranyl acetates, inasmuch as 30 mg. of lithium as the chloride or the nitrate does not interfere. Reagent: 133.3 g. of reagent and 278 ml. of $1.08N$ aqueous solution of tetramethylammonium hydroxide are dissolved in 1 liter of absolute ethanol. The solution is allowed to stand for 12 hours at 0°C. and then is filtered before use. Test: To 1 ml. of test solution, 3 ml. of reagent is added. The solution is placed in a water bath at 15°C. A voluminous white precipitate of the sodium acid salt forms within 15 minutes when as little as 0.6 mg. of sodium is present. Larger amounts of sodium precipitate within a minute.

d. Other Reagents

Sodium may be precipitated with potassium antimonate, with fluosilicic acid, and with other double uranium acetates (nickel, cobalt, copper, and cadmium) (142), but these reagents do not offer advantages over the reagents described in the preceding paragraphs.

3. Potassium

a. Precipitation with Sodium Tetraphenylboron

Potassium forms a white precipitate, $K(C_6H_5)_4B$, with sodium tetraphenylboron in alkaline, neutral, and weakly acid solutions (459). Interfering elements are ammonium and silver, which can be removed easily, and rubidium, cesium, and univalent thallium. EDTA may be used to mask completely the effect of a great number of ions. Reagent: 3% aqueous solution. Test: To the solution of the sample, preferably less than 5 ml., 1 drop or more of reagent is added. The test is best performed at about pH 5.4, which can be maintained by a sodium acetate–acetic acid buffer (8). At this pH, the limit of detection is $1:3.5 \times 10^5$. The sensitivity decreases with increasing acidity.

b. Precipitation with Chloroplatinic Acid

Chloroplatinic acid precipitates yellow K_2PtCl_6 in weak hydrochloric acid solution. Ammonium salts, rubidium, and cesium interfere. Reagent: 10 g. of platinum is dissolved in aqua regia. The solution is evaporated several times to dryness with intermittent additions of HCl and then is diluted with 10% HCl. Test: To the hydrochloric acid solution of the alkali metals, 1 ml. or less of reagent is added. The solution is evaporated on a water bath to syrupy consistency, and the residue is treated with 80% alcohol at 20°C. Yellow crystals of K_2PtCl_6 remain insoluble. Limits of detection: in water, 1:590 (142); in 80% ethanol, 1:50,000 (178); in ethyl alcohol containing excess reagent, considerably more than 1:50,000 (178).

c. Precipitation with Sodium Cobaltinitrite

Sodium cobaltinitrite precipitates yellow crystalline $Na_2KCo(NO_2)_6$ or $NaK_2Co(NO_2)_6$ in neutral or weakly acid solution. Interfering elements are rubidium, cesium, ammonium, thallium, barium, zirconium, lead, and mercury. Test: One-half g. of sodium cobaltinitrite is dissolved in 3 ml. of cold water and added to the concentrated solution of the sample. The potassium can be present as the chloride, nitrate, or sulfate. Free mineral acid must be neutralized with sodium hydroxide before the solution is acidified with acetic acid. Alkaline solutions must first be acidified. Limit of detection: 1:27,000 (142). If an equal volume of 95% ethanol is added, the limit of detection is 1:50,000.

d. Precipitation with Sodium Silver Cobaltinitrite (62)

The sensitivity of the potassium test with sodium cobaltinitrite can be increased by adding silver nitrate to the reagent, thus leading to the formation of $Ag_2KCo(NO_2)_6$ and $AgK_2Co(NO_2)_6$, which are both much more insoluble than the corresponding sodium-potassium salt. The interfering elements are the same as in the sodium cobaltinitrite method, with the addition of the halogens. Test: To the concentrated neutral or slightly acid solution, 1 drop or more of 25% sodium cobaltinitrite is added, followed by sufficient silver nitrate until the solution becomes about $0.01N$ in $AgNO_3$. Limit of detection: $1:10^5$.

e. Precipitation with Dipicrylamine

Dipicrylamine, $C_6H_2(NO_2)_3NHC_6H_2(NO_2)_3$, forms an orange-red crystalline precipitate with potassium salts (299). Up to 180 times as much sodium or lithium as potassium does not interfere with the test. The alkaline earths must be removed, since the reagent contains sodium carbonate. Cesium, rubidium, thallium, lead, and mercury also form crystalline precipitates with dipicrylamine. Reagent: 0.2 g. of dipicrylamine is dissolved in 20 ml. of water and 2 ml. of $1N$ sodium carbonate. The reagent is cooled and filtered. Test: To 1 ml. or less of the ice cold solution of the sample, slightly alkaline to thymol blue, 1 ml. or less of reagent is added. Limit of detection: about 0.1 γ.

f. Precipitation with Perchloric Acid

Perchloric acid precipitates from concentrated solutions white, crystalline $KClO_4$, difficultly soluble in cold water and much more insoluble in ethanol and ethyl acetate. Moderate amounts of lithium, sodium, and ammonium do not interfere, but rubidium and cesium also form insoluble perchlorates. Limits of detection: in water, 1:1400; in ethanol, 1:30,000; in ethyl acetate, 1:200,000.

g. OTHER REAGENTS

Among the many other reagents that are occasionally used for the detection of potassium, dilituric acid should be mentioned (140). Interfering elements are ammonium, rubidium, cesium, magnesium, and barium. Reagent: 0.1N solution of dilituric acid in 40% alcohol. Limit of detection: 1:50,000.

4. Rubidium and Cesium

Like potassium, rubidium and cesium form insoluble compounds with sodium tetraphenylboron, chloroplatinic acid, sodium cobaltinitrite, dipicrylamine, perchloric acid, and dilituric acid. Consequently, the reagents recommended for potassium can, in its absence, be used for the detection and identification of rubidium and cesium. Unfortunately, however, rubidium and cesium rarely occur without potassium, and so the analyst is advised to use techniques that permit differentiation among potassium, rubidium, and cesium. Of great value are methods based on paper chromatography, ion exchange, emission spectroscopy, flame photometry, x-ray fluorescence, and neutron activation. A few reagents that are specific for rubidium plus cesium, or for cesium only, in the presence of potassium have been recommended.

a. PRECIPITATION WITH SODIUM BISMUTH NITRITE

Sodium bismuth nitrite precipitates rubidium and cesium as $Rb_2(Cs_2)$-$NaBi(NO_2)_6$ from a weakly nitric acid solution (22). Lithium, sodium, potassium, ammonium, alkaline earths, NO_3^-, SO_4^{-2}, and CH_3COO^- do not interfere; however, halogens must be absent. Reagent: 10 g. of bismuth nitrate is dissolved in 100 ml. of water containing 50 g. of sodium nitrite. The solution is filtered before use. Limits of detection: rubidium, 1:690; cesium, 1:2000.

b. PRECIPITATION WITH SILICOMOLYBDIC ACID

Rubidium and cesium react with silicomolybdic acid, $H_4[Si(Mo_3O_{10})_4$-$(H_2O)_x]$, to form yellow precipitates. The other alkali metals and ammonium do not interfere, but thallium does (290). Reagent: 172 g. of molybdenum trioxide is dissolved in 400 ml. of hot 15% (w/v) sodium hydroxide; 500 ml. of water is added, followed by 350 ml. of $11N$ nitric acid; 28 g. of sodium silicate ($9H_2O$) is dissolved in 125 ml. of hot $2N$ sodium hydroxide and added to the molybdenum solution. The resulting yellow solution is evaporated to 800 ml. and filtered. Test: To 5 ml. of sample solution, 2 ml. of reagent is added. Limits of detection: rubidium, 1:200; cesium, 1:6300.

c. PRECIPITATION WITH STANNIC CHLORIDE

Rubidium and cesium react with a solution of stannic chloride in ethanol, in a 1:3 medium of hydrochloric acid and ethanol, to form white precipitates of rubidium and cesium stannic chlorides. Sodium and potassium interfere but can be removed as chlorides prior to the addition of the stannic chloride reagent. Ammonium salts also interfere. Limit of detection: rubidium, 1:363; cesium, 1:2740 (416).

d. PRECIPITATION OF CESIUM WITH SILICOTUNGSTIC ACID

Cesium reacts with silicotungstic acid, $H_8SiW_{12}O_{42} \cdot H_2O$, in $6N$ hydrochloric acid to give a white precipitate (304). Potassium, sodium, lithium, and the alkaline earths do not interfere. Up to 4 mg. of rubidium per 1 ml. of solution is without effect.

VI. DETERMINATION

A. CHEMICAL PROCEDURES

1. Lithium

The determination of lithium is frequently combined with the separation from the other alkali metals by taking advantage of the solubility of lithium chloride in various organic reagents (cf. Section IV-C-1). After evaporation of the organic solvent, the residue is treated with nitric and sulfuric acids, and the lithium is finally weighed as the sulfate.

a. PRECIPITATION AS THE COMPLEX PERIODATE

Lithium can be quantitatively precipitated as a complex periodate by a strongly alkaline potassium periodate solution (347). Although the method is less rapid and somewhat less accurate than those based on the use of organic solvents, it does not require the prior removal of other alkali metals present in amounts normally found in minerals. As much as 150 mg. of sodium is without effect if the precipitation is carried out in the cold. The method may be attractive to those chemists who prefer volumetric procedures since the precipitate after filtration can be dissolved in dilute sulfuric acid, potassium iodide added, and the liberated iodine titrated with sodium thiosulfate solution. There exists no integral stoichiometric relationship between the proportions of lithium and iodine because the precipitate contains somewhat less lithium than would be expected by the formula Li_5IO_6. The thiosulfate solution must therefore be standardized under the conditions of the actual test.

b. Precipitation as Lithium Potassium Ferric Periodate (334)

In an alkaline medium, lithium can also be precipitated as lithium potassium ferric periodate, $LiKFeIO_6$, by the addition of a reagent prepared by dissolving potassium periodate and ferric chloride in dilute potassium hydroxide. An analysis of the precipitate obtained in a 0.8 to $1.0N$ potassium hydroxide medium indicates the composition $LiKFeIO_6$, whereas in weaker solutions of potassium hydroxide the composition corresponds to $LiK_3Fe_2(IO_6)_2$. Sodium interferes and must be removed prior to the precipitation of the periodate; this is a distinct drawback of the method. As in the lithium periodate method, the precipitate, in this case $LiKFeIO_6$, is treated with dilute acid and potassium iodide, and the liberated iodine is titrated with a standard solution of thiosulfate or arsenate (334). Alternatively, the precipitate can be dissolved in acid, and the iron determined photometrically as the thiocyanate (295,359).

c. Precipitation as the Complex Ferricyanide

After the separation of lithium from the other alkali metals by extraction with dry n-propanol and the removal of the solvent by evaporation, lithium can be recovered in the residue by solution in a solvent mixture consisting of hexamine, water, and acetone and precipitated as a complex ferricyanide by the addition of a mixture of ferricyanide and hexamine solutions. The precipitate, which has the probable formula $2Li_3Fe(CN)_6 \cdot K_3Fe(CN) \cdot 5[(CH_2)_6N_4 \cdot 6H_2O]$, can be collected and weighed. Alternatively, the precipitate can be dissolved in water, and the yellow color measured. In a micro modification of the procedure for amounts of lithium below 50 γ, the precipitate, collected on a filter stick, is dissolved in water and ethanol, and a leucomalachite green solution is added for the color development. In this procedure, heavy metals interfere and must be removed by the usual means. The amounts of alkali metals in the form of chloride that can be tolerated in 1 ml. of solvent solution at 20°C. are as follows: K, 30 mg.; NH_4, 5 mg.; Na, 5 mg.; Rb, 50 mg.; and Cs, 30 mg. (135).

d. Thoron Photometric Procedure (240,300,422)

Lithium forms an orange complex with o-(2-hydroxy-3,6-disulfo-1-naphthylazo)benzenearsonic acid ("Thoron") in a strongly alkaline medium. The color is appreciably intensified by acetone. Amounts of lithium from 10 to 80 γ per 10 ml. final volume in the aqueous medium and from 1 to 10 γ per 10 ml. final volume in the 70% acetone medium can be determined with an accuracy of ±3%. Full color development is achieved in about 30 minutes and does not change for at least 4 hours. In an acetone-water medium, calcium and magnesium in amounts less than 10 times the amount of lithium present cause little interference. Larger amounts of calcium and magnesium can be precipitated with potassium hydroxide and potassium carbonate prior to the color development. Sodium up to 50 times the amount of lithium can be tolerated. Sodium at 100:1 ratio causes a 5% positive error. Any ion that precipitates with potassium hydroxide or carbonate must be absent. Ammonium in amounts of 5 mg. or more causes a positive error, but the interference can be overcome by heating the sample with 0.2 ml. of 20% potassium hydroxide solution to drive off ammonia before adding the other reagents. The precision of the procedure is about 3%. The sensitivity is high, in the order of about 0.1 γ/ml.

e. Other Useful Reagents

After the separation of lithium chloride from sodium and potassium chlorides (Section IV-C-1) with acetone, lithium can be titrated with a 0.01 or 0.001M solution of cuprous perchlorate in acetone (400a). The end point is determined either conductometrically or photometrically by means of the red color formed by the addition of a cuprous salt in acetone to lithium chloride in acetone. A method suggested more than 100 years ago (39,413a) and based on lithium phosphate, Li_3PO_4, as a weighing form was recently improved by using choline phosphate as a precipitating agent in a 50% 2-propanol medium (77). Neither sodium nor potassium interferes. The phosphorus in the precipitate can be determined photometrically by the molybdenum blue method (302). As little as 0.01 mg. of lithium can thus be determined. Determinations of lithium as the aluminate (160), as a triple acetate analogous to the sodium salt (281), and as the fluoride (81) have been suggested from time to time, but do not indicate advantages over the methods discussed in the preceding paragraphs.

2. Sodium

a. PRECIPITATION AS ZINC URANYL ACETATE AND AS MAGNESIUM URANYL ACETATE

Sodium forms fewer insoluble salts than does potassium, and hence its determination has been one of the more troublesome tasks in analytical chemistry. However, thanks to the extensive work that has been carried out on the uranyl acetate reagents, satisfactory methods have been developed. The literature devoted to the precipitation of sodium as one of the triple acetates is extensive, and it is doubtful whether there has ever been so much controversy about the compounds formed by a particular reagent, especially in regard to the exact amount of water of hydration (29,30). The zinc uranyl acetate method (24,25,225), and the magnesium uranyl acetate method (75), in which the respective uranyl acetate reagents serve as precipitants, are the two procedures most widely used at the present time. Special precautions must be taken to insure the quantitative precipitation of the sodium. The reagent, as well as the solution of the sample, must be concentrated, and alcohol saturated with triple acetate must be used to wash the precipitate. The composition of the precipitate is either $NaZn(UO_2)_3(C_2H_3O_2)_9 \cdot 6H_2O$ or $NaMg(UO_2)_3(C_2H_3O_2)_9 \cdot 6H_2O$. The authors of the magnesium method believe that the number of molecules of water in the resulting precipitate is 6.5. Because of the small conversion factor, the difference between the percentage value for sodium calculated for 6 molecules of water and that calculated for 6.5 molecules is so small that it is well within the limits of experimental error.

Most analysts feel that there is little to choose between the two reagents, although each has its adherents, who claim certain advantages for their favorite procedure. This writer feels that the zinc uranyl acetate method is more precise and sensitive for amounts of sodium less than 8 mg. but that the magnesium uranyl acetate method is better for amounts up to 50 mg.

The reagent containing magnesium has an advantage over the zinc-containing reagent in regard to potassium interference. The maximum amount of potassium tolerable with the zinc reagent is 25 mg./ml. of solution (24,25). If the sample contains more potassium, it must be removed, preferably by precipitation as the perchlorate, prior to the precipitation of the sodium (141). The magnesium reagent, on the other hand, allows considerably more potassium. Thus, in precipitating 10 mg. of sodium with 100 ml. of reagent, 0.25 g. of potassium has no significant effect. The sulfate ion interferes in the presence of potassium, owing to the formation of insoluble potassium sulfate. The sulfate ion can be removed with barium chloride. More than about 1 mg. of lithium interferes with either reagent by forming triple salts analogous in composition to the sodium triple acetate (74). Lithium should therefore be removed prior to the sodium precipitation, preferably by the addition of an ammoniacal ammonium fluoride solution (24,25), the excess of which is eliminated by repeated evaporations with hydrochloric acid. Since cesium and rubidium in amounts up to 0.1 g. and ammonium salts in amounts up to 1 g. do not interfere with either method (141), the direct determination of sodium in rubidium and cesium compounds is possible. Calcium and barium do not interfere if the solution or the reagent does not contain the sulfate ion. Strontium is without effect with the magnesium reagent but should be removed prior to application of the zinc reagent. Moderate amounts of hydrolyzable elements, such as iron, chromium, aluminum, and beryllium, do not interfere if the solution is kept acid. Possible interference from molybdate can be avoided by adding just enough citric or tartaric acid to form a complex (168). Proteins or biological substances should be removed, preferably with trichloroacetic acid.

In the gravimetric determination of sodium with the uranyl acetate reagents, phosphate is probably the most common interfering ion. Arsenates interfere similarly. In most volumetric and photometric sodium methods, however, the presence of phosphate or arsenate can be disregarded, since uranyl phosphate and uranyl arsenate are insoluble in the water used to dissolve the triple acetate. In the gravimetric procedures, the removal of the phosphate and arsenate ions is imperative and can be achieved by precipitation with uranyl acetate in a weakly acid medium (45), with magnesium in an ammoniacal solution (45), with ferric ion (163), with calcium hydroxide (68), or, as some analysts prefer, with zinc carbonate in a feebly hydrochloric acid medium (29,30,178,308). It has been shown that both cation and anion separations are very effective in removing the phosphate ion (34,148,357). The interference of phosphates, lithium, and excessive amounts of potassium can be obviated by treating the triple acetate, after it has been washed with alcohol, with a solution of hydrogen chloride in n-butanol. This treatment leads to the formation of insoluble sodium chloride, residual potassium chloride, and soluble lithium and phosphate salts. The sodium chloride is dissolved in water and again precipitated as the triple acetate (379).

(1) Volumetric Procedures

Titration procedures are useful for determining small quantities of sodium after precipitation as the triple acetate. Most volumetric techniques are based on the reduction of the uranyl ion prior to titration with an oxidimetric reagent. The reduction can be achieved with metallic aluminum (90), zinc (52), cadmium, copper (205,206), titanous chloride (291), the Jones reductor (146,225), and the lead reductor (278). Oxidation of U^{+4} to U^{+6} can be obtained with standard solutions of potassium permanganate (90), ceric sulfate (146), and potassium dichromate (226). Among other volumetric procedures that have found application are the titration of the zinc in sodium zinc uranyl acetate with EDTA (124,178a) and of the uranium with disodium hydrogen phosphate (71). A potentiometric titration procedure, based on the reaction of sodium in milligram quantities with a solution of zinc uranyl acetate in an 85 to 95% ethanol medium, has also been described (426), as has an indirect method based on the polarographic measurement of the uranyl diffusion current when the triple acetate is dissolved in $0.5M$ hydrochloric acid (84) (cf. Section VI-C-6). The uranium content of the triple acetate can also be determined radiometrically (105a).

(2) Colorimetric Procedures

A great number of colorimetric procedures have been suggested for determining one or the other component of the triple acetate precipitate. These methods are particularly useful for the determination of very small quantities of sodium in biological material and are often based on the color of the uranyl ion in aqueous solution (75,274) or after reaction with potassium ferrocyanide (241,425), sodium citrate (198), ammonium thiocyanate (231), ammonium carbonate and hydrogen peroxide (14), or sulfosalicylic acid (100). Alternatively, the determination of sodium can be based on the colorimetric determination of the bivalent element used in conjunction with uranyl acetate.

(3) Other Uranyl Acetate Reagents

Advantages are claimed for cobalt uranyl acetate as being immune against potassium interference (70). Uranyl acetate reagents containing nickel (122), copper (76,322), manganese (85b), and other divalent elements have also been investigated. The introduction of these divalent elements into the uranium reagents may be attractive to those chemists who wish to determine sodium in the presence of much potassium. Potassium is to some extent precipitated as a double acetate when present in high concentrations. This behavior leads to high sodium results if the determination is based on the uranium content, but not if the divalent element is determined instead (360). In addition, the photometric determination of cobalt, nickel, copper, or manganese is considerably easier than that of zinc or magnesium.

b. Determination as the Chloride or the Sulfate

The most accurate method for determining large amounts of sodium is by weighing the chloride. Sodium can be precipitated by adding a solution of hydrogen chloride in n-butanol to the butanol solution remaining after the determination of potassium as the perchlorate (453) (cf. Section VI-A-3). Sodium can also be recovered from the platiniferous filtrate of a potassium determination after expulsion of the alcohol and precipitation of the platinum with hydrogen (178). Sodium, in the filtrate from the metallic platinum, is collected and finally weighed as the chloride. To determine sodium as the sulfate, which can be heated to much higher temperatures than the chloride, a small excess of sulfuric acid is added to the solution of the sodium salt of a volatile acid. The solution is evaporated to complete dryness, and the residue is carefully ignited and then reignited after the addition of a little powdered ammonium carbonate.

c. Other Methods

The precipitation of sodium with DL-methoxyphenylacetic acid, previously used only in qualitative analysis (339), has been extended to quantitative analysis (338a). The sample solution is treated at 25 to 30°C. with a 50% excess of a partly neutralized 70% aqueous ethanolic solution of DL-methoxyphenylacetic acid. The precipitated acid sodium salt is collected, washed with acetone, dissolved in hot water, and titrated with 0.05 or 0.1N NaOH. None of the common elements interfere. Potassium and lithium need not be removed. The accuracy of the procedure is claimed to be as high as that of the zinc uranyl acetate method.

Sodium can be precipitated from a concentrated solution of the chloride by the addition of a threefold excess of a 10% aqueous solution of magnesium-1-naphthylamine-8-sulfonate octahydrate and an equal volume of 96% ethanol (107). The precipitate is filtered off and washed with a saturated solution of sodium 1-naphthylamine-8-sulfonate and then with pure ethanol. It is finally dried to constant weight at 105°C. In a volumetric modification of the method, the precipitate is dissolved in hot water and potassium bromide. Upon the addition of concentrated hydrochloric acid and an excess of an 0.1N solution of potassium bromate, the tribromo derivative of 1-naphthylamine-8-sulfonic acid is formed. The excess of potassium bromate is then determined iodometrically.

Sodium ions react in a weak nitric acid medium with cesium, bismuth, and nitrite ions to form a yellow triple nitrite resembling the sodium potassium cobaltinitrite and having the approximate composition $6NaNO_2 \cdot 9CsNO_2 \cdot 5Bi(NO_2)_3$ (22,23). Even large amounts of potassium do not interfere. The triple nitrite can be weighed, or its nitrite content can be determined either volumetrically or colorimetrically in exactly the same way as with the potassium cobaltinitrite (106,141,427) (cf. Section VI-A-3). If preferred, its bismuth content can be made the basis of a photometric determination. Sodium can also be precipitated as the antimonate by the addition of a solution of potassium antimonate in an alcohol medium. The precipitate, $Na_2O \cdot Sb_2O_5 \cdot nH_2O$, can be weighed (234), or its antimony content determined volumetrically (232) or colorimetrically (466). Lithium tetra-p-tolylboron was recently introduced as a reagent for the precipitation of sodium (361b). Potassium, rubidium, and cesium, which are also precipitated, can be removed by a prior precipitation with lithium tetraphenylboron.

3. Potassium

Four reagents have been extensively used for the determination of potassium: namely, chloroplatinic acid, perchloric acid, sodium cobaltinitrite, and sodium tetraphenylboron. The literature covering these reagents is extensive, and only a brief description of the various approaches can be given here.

a. CHLOROPLATINATE METHOD

The chloroplatinic acid procedure is one of the oldest gravimetric methods, having been introduced more than 120 years ago (324). Despite the cost of the reagent, the method has been widely used and is still the official AOAC procedure for analyzing fertilizers (13), although in recent years it has encountered serious competition from the perchlorate, tetraphenylboron, and flame photometric techniques. The method is based on the insolubility of potassium chloroplatinate in ethanol; the corresponding sodium and lithium salts are soluble. Rubidium, cesium, and ammonium, however, also form insoluble chloroplatinates. To prevent the contamination of potassium chloroplatinate with sodium chloride, which is insoluble in ethanol, excess reagent is added to the mixed chlorides before evaporation. (Instead of chloroplatinic acid, lithium chloroplatinate can be used (395). The potassium chloroplatinate thus obtained is supposed to be of theoretical composition.) To prevent the occlusion of mother liquor in crystals of potassium chloroplatinate, sufficient water is added to the sample solution to avoid the formation of crystals upon the addition of the reagent; during the subsequent evaporation, the potassium chloroplatinate precipitates without significant occlusion of mother liquor.

Ammonium salts interfere by forming insoluble ammonium chloroplatinate and must be removed by repeated evaporations with aqua regia, followed by hydrochloric acid, prior to the addition of the reagent. Organic substances that can reduce chloroplatinic acid to metallic platinum must, of course, be absent. Nitrates, bromides, and iodides should be converted to chlorides by repeated evaporations with hydrochloric acid. Sulfates interfere in the presence of sodium by causing the formation of sodium sulfate, which is insoluble in alcohol. The alkaline earths, with the exception of barium, form alcohol-soluble chloroplatinates. Barium chloroplatinate tends to decompose into insoluble barium chloride.

In the Lindo-Gladding method (257), sulfates, nitrates, and phosphates do not interfere. The potassium chloroplatinate is first washed with 80% alcohol, then, for the removal of sulfates, etc., with a saturated solution of ammonium chloride, and then again with 80% alcohol. The presence of sulfates, phosphates, nitrates, carbonates, borates, silicates, alkaline earths, iron, and aluminum can be disregarded by dissolving the potassium chloroplatinate, previously washed with alcohol, in hot water, adding hydrochloric acid, and precipitating the platinum with magnesium. The platinum is filtered off, washed, and ignited (177,436). In another modification, the potassium chloroplatinate is converted, by gentle ignition in a stream of hydrogen, into platinum and water-soluble potassium chloride (141). Either the residual platinum is weighed, or the potassium chloride is determined gravimetrically or volumetrically after extraction with water.

For the photometric determination of small amounts of potassium, the potassium chloroplatinate is finally washed with absolute ethanol. After the alcohol has completely evaporated, the precipitate is dissolved in hot water containing 1 drop of hydrochloric acid, and the red color of K_2PtI_6 is produced by the addition of a potassium iodide solution (79,96,236a). In the stannous chloride photometric procedure (297), the potassium chloroplatinate is dissolved in hot water and reduced to colloidal platinum, which is stabilized by stannous chloride. The intensity of the yellow-red solution is proportional to the amount of potassium present. Extremely small quantities of potassium (2 to 12 γ) can be determined by adding a known amount of chloroplatinic acid to the solution of the sample, extracting the excess reagent with a mixture of ethyl acetate and butanol, and measuring the absorbance of the solution in the ultraviolet region at 264 mμ (111).

b. Perchlorate Method

The determination of potassium as the perchlorate is frequently combined with the separation from sodium and/or lithium by using a mixture

of n-butanol and ethyl acetate as extractant (453). This extraction procedure has been modified into a more rapid precipitation method consisting
in dissolving the dry mixed perchlorates in 2 or 3 ml. of hot water and precipitating the potassium by the addition of 100 ml. of boiling n-butanol
containing 1% of perchloric acid (394). In other methods, various concentrations of ethanol containing 0.2% and more of perchloric acid, have
been used to extract soluble perchlorates (141). For all perchlorate
methods, sulfates and ammonium salts must be absent. The sulfates can
be removed with barium chloride, an excess of which does not interfere
because of the solubility of barium perchlorate in alcohols. The perchlorates of the alkaline earths, aluminum, and iron are also soluble in
ethyl alcohol. In their presence, to avoid the thermal decomposition
of perchlorates into insoluble oxides the perchloric acid solution of the
sample must not be evaporated to complete dryness.

c. COBALTINITRITE METHOD

Prior to the development of flame photometric methods and the introduction of the tetraphenylboron reagent, the potassium cobaltinitrite
method was widely used for determining small amounts of potassium in
various materials, particularly in biological substances. Extensive literature covers the method (29,30,141), and only the more salient features will
be discussed here.

Potassium is quantitatively precipitated in acetic or weakly nitric acid
solution with sodium cobaltinitrite reagent. Depending on various conditions prevailing during the precipitation, such as temperature, concentration of reagent, and amount of sodium present, the composition of the
precipitate varies between $K_2NaCo(NO_2)_6 \cdot nH_2O$ and $K_3Na_3[Co(NO_2)_6]_2 \cdot nH_2O$. Much conflicting evidence has been presented as to the most
suitable conditions for precipitation (141). All reports emphasize the
necessity for maintaining consistent working conditions and for establishing empirical factors or calibrations in all gravimetric, volumetric, and
photometric procedures.

Precipitation is usually carried out in a small volume (10 ml. or less)
by adding to the neutral or slightly acid solution a fivefold excess of reagent.
The precipitate should stand cold for at least several hours and then be
collected on a Gooch crucible and washed with cold water containing a
little reagent. Micro methods usually employ centrifugation and decantation (or drawing off with a bent capillary pipet) of the supernatant
liquid. Because of the uncertain composition of the precipitate, larger
quantities of potassium (more than 0.1 g.) should be determined as the

perchlorate or the chloroplatinate, after dissolution of the precipitate in dilute hydrochloric or perchloric acid (141). Only small quantities of potassium can be determined by weighing the precipitate, which has been collected on a Gooch crucible and washed free from reagent with 80% alcohol.

(1) Volumetric Procedures

Most volumetric procedures are based on the oxidation of nitrite to nitrate. In these methods the actual composition of the cobaltinitrite remains uncertain; variations in the water content of the precipitate naturally can be disregarded. In older procedures, oxidation is carried out with a standard solution of potassium permanganate, the excess of which is back-titrated with a standard sodium oxalate solution (233,328) or determined iodometrically (103,199). Because of its greater stability, ceric sulfate is now preferred as the oxidant. The excess of ceric sulfate can be determined iodometrically (217) or by back-titration with ferrous ammonium sulfate with o-phenanthroline as indicator (57). Potassium dichromate has also been used for the oxidation of the nitrite precipitate (192). In a compleximetric titration procedure, the potassium cobaltinitrite precipitate is dissolved in hot dilute hydrochloric acid, and a few crystals of urea are added. After the addition of ammonia, sodium chloride, and murexide, the solution is titrated to a permanent violet color with EDTA (126).

(2) Colorimetric Procedures

For the determination of small amounts of potassium precipitated with cobaltinitrite reagent, a number of photometric procedures have been suggested (424). Nitroso-R salt (338,380), choline hydrochloride plus potassium ferrocyanide (112,196), or ammonium thiocyanate (252) is used to determine the cobalt in the precipitate. This determination can also be made by dissolving the precipitate in a solution containing EDTA and hydrogen peroxide and measuring the pink coloration (61).

For the photometric determination of the nitrite in the precipitate, the precipitate is reacted with a definite volume of standard potassium dichromate, and the amount of reduction is measured (433). The precipitate can also be dissolved in dilute sodium hydroxide and treated with 1-naphthylaminesulfanilic acid to form a red azo dye (6,53). If the nitrite is made to diazotize sulfanilic acid, the resulting compound can be complexed with dimethylaniline to form methyl orange (447). Upon diazotization with indole, a red to violet color results owing to the formation of nitrosoindole (364). Nitrite can also be reacted with p-nitroaniline hydrochloride and coupled with naphthylamine in strongly acid solution to give a red azo dye (468).

The potassium in the nitrite precipitate can be determined by using radioactive cobalt-60 in the precipitant and determining the activity of the solution of the precipitate (229). The potassium determination can also be based on a polarographic measurement of the cobalt content of the cobaltinitrite precipitate (313a).

(3) Other Cobaltinitrite Reagents

Some workers have recommended the introduction of other cations into the nitrite reagent. The best-known variation is silver cobaltinitrite (60a,62,194), which is probably the most sensitive of all potassium reagents and which produces a precipitate of a remarkably consistent composition. Lithium cobaltinitrite (109), zinc cobaltinitrite (3), and sodium lead cobaltinitrite (141) have also been suggested. In one reagent, nickel has been substituted for cobalt, and calcium for sodium. Potassium is precipitated and weighed as $K_2Ca[Ni(NO_2)_6]$ (4).

d. SODIUM TETRAPHENYLBORON REAGENT

The tetraphenylboron complex, $[(C_6H_5)_4B]^-$, is unusual in that its sodium and lithium salts are very soluble in water and dilute acids whereas the corresponding potassium, rubidium, and cesium salts are very insoluble (458–460). Ammonium, thallium, silver, and certain organic nitrogen substances also form insoluble compounds with the tetraphenylboron complex, but their interference with the determination of potassium can easily be overcome.

Some of the outstanding advantages of methods employing sodium tetraphenylboron $((Ph)_4BNa)$ are as follows (157): The potassium salt corresponds exactly to the formula $(Ph)_4BK$. Its solubility is extremely small compared with solubilities of other potassium salts. It has excellent thermal stability and can be dried at 110 to 120°C. The precipitation characteristics and filterability are good, particularly if the precipitation is carried out in weak mineral acid solution. The high equivalent weight of the precipitate and the resulting high conversion factor are extremely favorable. If the precipitation is carried out in dilute mineral acid solution, no interference is encountered from any common cations or anions. One of the remarkable features of the reagent is its adaptability to the determination of both trace amounts and macro quantities of potassium. Consequently, the range of suggested methods extends from trace amounts of potassium in physiological samples (402), milk (366), wine (340), and sea water (404), through the medium concentration range of potassium, as in plant ash (7) and silicates and glasses (91,243), to potassium in fertilizers (134,371).

A number of gravimetric and volumetric methods utilizing the sodium tetraphenyl boron reagent have been developed, of which the most important are discussed here.

(1) Gravimetric Procedures

The first detailed gravimetric procedure recommended precipitation of potassium in a hot neutral solution (460). The precipitate was filtered, washed with water, and dried at 120°C. This simple gravimetric technique has subsequently undergone a number of changes, most of which have been introduced to improve the filterability of the precipitate. This improvement is partly achieved by carrying out the precipitation in a weak acetic acid (337) or, better, in a weak mineral acid medium (223). However, discussion of the most suitable acid medium has produced conflicting statements. Although, according to one source, a $0.1N$ mineral acid medium produces a coarse and readily filterable precipitate (223), one investigator finds that the final solution should be not more than $0.001N$ in respect to acid (154), another feels that the acidity should be at least $0.2N$ (403), and still another, reporting simultaneously, prefers 0.000001 and $0.01N$ acid media (91). In the hands of this writer, mineral acid concentrations ranging between 0.05 and $0.1N$ have produced the most satisfactory results.

If ammonium is present in the sample, it is also quantitatively precipitated. For the determination of either potassium or ammonium, the tared precipitate is dissolved in a few milliliters of acetone, a little sodium hydroxide is added, and the solution is evaporated on a steam bath sufficiently to expel ammonia. The cool solution is filtered through a dry tared glass crucible, which is dried at 105°C., cooled, and weighed. The ammonium content is calculated by difference. The interference of ammonium with the determination of potassium can also be avoided by rendering the solution slightly alkaline with sodium hydroxide, heating to boiling, adding formaldehyde, and then precipitating the potassium with $(Ph)_4BNa$ (33,118). EDTA may be used to prevent interference from substances that precipitate in an alkaline medium (33). The interference of large quantities of alkaline earths can be avoided by adding sodium carbonate, and then the reagent, to the acid solution. Subsequently, the insoluble carbonates are dissolved in dilute acetic acid (337).

Sodium fluoride has been used to complex iron in weakly acid solution prior to the addition of (Ph)$_4$BNa (351).

(2) Volumetric Procedures

Most volumetric methods are based on the precipitation of (Ph)$_4$BK, filtration, removal of excess reagent, and solution of the precipitate in a suitable solvent, usually acetone. Finally, the (Ph)$_4$B$^-$ ion is titrated with one of the following reagents: silver nitrate (35,351), mercuric chloride and sodium hydroxide (128), perchloric acid (125), or standard acid after conversion of the precipitate to potassium metaborate by ignition (127). The titration with silver nitrate is carried out very conveniently amperometrically at a potential of -0.1 v. vs. the mercury pool reference electrode (123).

In a somewhat different approach, a lithium tetraphenylboron solution is used to precipitate and titrate the potassium, the end point being detected conductometrically (337). As the potassium ions are replaced by the less mobile lithium ions, the conductivity of the solution decreases until the equivalence point is reached. Then the conductivity increases with the lithium ion concentration. In another method, an excess of (Ph)$_4$BNa reagent is added. After filtration, an excess of standard ammonia solution is added. The resulting precipitate is filtered, and the excess ammonium ion in the filtrate is titrated, after addition of formaldehyde, with standard sodium hydroxide solution (186). In still another titration method, the (Ph)$_4$BK is dissolved in acetone and titrated with a solution of ceric sulfate or ceric ammonium nitrate in $2N$ perchloric acid (402). Potassium tetraphenylboron can be converted to free tetraphenylboron acid by passing the acetone solution of the salt through a strongly acid cation exchange resin. The free acid in the eluate is titrated with a standard sodium hydroxide solution (129). In a nonaqueous titration method, the acetone solution of the (Ph)$_4$BK, containing some acetic anhydride for dehydration, is titrated with a standard solution of perchloric acid in glacial acetic acid containing some acetic anhydride (125). An EDTA volumetric procedure has been described which is based on the reaction of (Ph)$_4$B$^-$ with a mercuric EDTA complex. EDTA is released and titrated in an acetate-buffered medium with a standard zinc solution using 1-(2-pyridylazo)-2-naphthol as indicator (129a) or in an ammoniacal medium with a standard magnesium solution using Eriochrome Black T as indicator (354a). Potassium in concentrations from 2.2×10^{-3} to $2 \times 10^{-2}M$ in acetate buffer can be directly titrated amperometrically with 0.05 to 0.15M (Ph)$_4$BNa by making 17 to 25 measurements of the anodic depolarization current of the titrant at the dropping mercury electrode (8a,393b).

Recently (362) a procedure was introduced that eliminates the necessity of transferring or recovering the (Ph)$_4$BK precipitate. In this method, the potassium is precipitated with a standard (Ph)$_4$BNa solution. A slight excess of reagent is added to ensure complete precipitation of the potassium, and the excess is determined by titration with a standard quaternary ammonium salt solution in the presence of bromophenol blue. Whereas the original method involves the use of cetyltrimethylammonium bromide (CTAB) as a titrant, any quaternary ammonium compound capable of forming colored salts with bromophenol blue may be substituted. For instance, Zephiran Chloride (ZCl), available in local pharmacies as a 12.8% aqueous solution, is satisfactory. The procedure was originally intended for the determination of potassium in fertilizers. Therefore, to prevent the interference of the ammonium ion, present in many fertilizers formaldehyde is added to the slightly alkaline solution of the sample (33). With minor modifications, the method can be applied to the determination of potassium in various types of material previously analyzed by other gravimetric methods. For instance, the method has been used to determine potassium in manganese ore (386). In the absence of the ammonium ion, the complexing step with formaldehyde can be omitted.

(3) Spectrophotometric Procedure

The precipitate is dissolved in a 3:1 methyl cyanide–water solution. The solution is diluted to 25 ml. in a volumetric flask, and the concentration of the potassium is determined from the extinction at 266 mμ. The absorption spectra of (Ph)$_4$B$^-$ occur at 266 and 274 mμ. The method is valid over the range 5×10^{-4} to $7.5 \times 10^{-5}M$. As in all (Ph)$_4$BK methods, NH$_4$, Cs, Rb, Tl, Ag, Hg, and amines interfere (325).

e. POTASSIUM PERIODATE METHOD (201,451)

Potassium can be precipitated quantitatively as the periodate, KIO$_4$, by the addition of aqueous periodic acid to the concentrated solution of the sample. The precipitation is completed by the addition of a mixture of equal parts of aldehyde-free ethanol and anhydrous ether. The precipitate is collected on a Gooch crucible and washed with cold ethyl acetate. After drying at 105°C., it is weighed as KIO$_4$. A titrimetric finish is also possible, the precipitate being dissolved in a boric acid–borax buffer, potassium iodide being added, and the liberated iodine being titrated with sodium arsenite. The periodate is reduced to iodate in the reaction IO$_4^-$ + 2I$^-$ → IO$_3$ + I$_2$. Iodate, if present in the reagent, does not interfere. With the periodate reagent, potassium can be separated from Al, Ca, Co,

Li, Mg, Ni, Na, and Zn. As little as 0.4 mg. of potassium can be separated from 70 times as much sodium. NH_4, Cs, Cr, Fe, Mn, and Rb interfere. Calcium and sulfate together interfere, owing to the formation of double potassium calcium sulfate. Small amounts of sulfuric acid, nitric acid, phosphoric acid, and boric acid may be present, but large amounts of these acids cause gelatinous precipitates, which are difficult to filter. The gravimetric finish is not possible in the presence of sulfate, owing to precipitation of Na_2SO_4. However, sulfate does not interfere with the volumetric finish. Chlorides must be absent because they cause reduction of the periodate ion.

f. Dipicrylamine Method

Potassium forms a difficultly soluble orange-red salt, $[(NO_2)_3C_6H_2)]2NK$, upon the addition of lithium, sodium, or magnesium dipicrylaminate. After filtration, the precipitate is washed with ice cold water and then dissolved in hot water, and the red complex is determined photometrically (253,360). The potassium salt is soluble in acetone, also, giving a yellow to orange-red solution that can be measured photometrically (94,150,224). The determination of potassium can be carried out polarographically by measuring the wave height due to dipicrylamine reagent before and after the addition of the solution containing the potassium (286,287). A titrimetric finish in which the end point is determined amperometrically is also possible (470). In all methods involving dipicrylamine, rubidium, cesium, thallium(I), and ammonium ion interfere. Lead, mercury, and all cations that can be precipitated by the alkaline reagent also interfere. Small amounts of elements that can be precipitated in an alkaline medium may be removed by boiling the solution of the sample with a slight excess of magnesium oxide (360).

g. Other Reagents

The potassium salt of hexyl(2,2',4,4',6,6'-hexanitrodiphenylamine), precipitated by the addition of the sodium or calcium salt, is only slightly soluble in an excess of the reagent. Rubidium and cesium are also precipitated. The precipitate is filtered through a Gooch crucible and washed with ice water. Sodium, magnesium, and calcium do not interfere. Tartaric acid permits the precipitation of potassium in the presence of iron and aluminum. Most cations can be removed by treatment with magnesium oxide (361). Potassium can also be precipitated as the picrate upon the addition of an alcoholic solution of picric acid. Although the filtered precipitate can be weighed or dissolved in hot water and titrated, a photometric determination, based on the yellow color of the aqueous solution of potassium picrate, appears most suitable (72). Other potassium reagents worthy of mention are dilituric acid (311a,333), fluoboric acid (265a,267,353a), and aniline tartrate (187).

4. Rubidium and Cesium

All reagents described in the preceding pages for the determination of potassium also precipitate rubidium and cesium. Unless based on ion exchange procedures (cf. Section IV-B-2), the separation of the three heavy alkali metals is difficult and involved (cf. Section VIII-A-3). Small amounts of cesium can be precipitated with molybdosilicic acid (64). After filtration, the precipitate of cesium molybdosilicate is dissolved, and the molybdosilicate is reduced to a heteropoly blue. Potassium and a limited amount of rubidium can be present. More recently, another photometric procedure, which is also based on a heteropoly blue color and which utilizes the selective and quantitative precipitation of small amounts of cesium with tungstosilicic acid, was suggested. The blue color here, however, is not developed by treating the precipitate but rather by treating the supernatant liquid. The intensity of the color developed from the unreacted known excess of tungstosilicic acid in the supernatant liquid is inversely proportional to the amount of cesium present (237). Up to 7.5 mg. of potassium, 0.56 mg. of rubidium, 25 mg. of sodium, and 25 mg. of lithium are said to cause no interference. Many other substances can be present in moderate amounts. However, aluminum, iron(III), chromate, and permanganate must be absent, and not more than 1 mg. each of copper, molybdenum, ammonium, nitrate, and nitrite can be tolerated. Traces of rubidium and cesium can be determined photometrically with hexanitrohydrazobenzene as reagent (88). The precipitate is dissolved in acetone and alcohol. An aliquot of the solution is diluted with water, and the absorption is measured. Lithium, calcium, strontium, barium, and magnesium and sodium in moderate amounts have little effect. It is claimed that $Na_2AgBi(NO_2)_6$ for the separation of rubidium and cesium from potassium and either $NaBiI_4$ or $KBiI_4$ for the separation of cesium from rubidium have advantages over previously used reagents (170b).

B. OPTICAL PROCEDURES

1. Flame Photometry

a. INTRODUCTION

When we consider the remarkable recent developments in flame photometry and spectrophotometry, we think mainly in terms of the alkali metals and recall that the beginning of flame photometry dates back to 1860 and the discovery of Kirchhoff and Bunsen that certain spectral lines they observed were attributable to individual alkali metals. Even now, when we realize that a great number of other elements can be determined with flame photometers and spectrophotometers, we consider the advantages of these instruments mainly in the light of alkali metals analysis. Thus, in the clinical field, flame photometric methods have largely replaced conventional chemical alkali metal procedures, and very accurate determinations of sodium and potassium in plasma, urine, and other biological fluids can be obtained in minutes, aiding the clinician in rapidly establishing critical differences between normal and pathological compositions. In other fields, improvements in alkali metal analysis brought about by flame photometric methods have been equally impressive.

Undoubtedly, many analysts who determine the alkali metals routinely by flame photometric methods seriously question the value of chemical procedures. They compare the simplicity and speed of flame photometric techniques with the complexity of chemical techniques. The question, therefore, naturally arises as to whether there remains any justification whatever for determining the alkali metals by wet chemical methods. The answer to this question is "yes" and "no." Flame photometry in many respects is clearly superior to chemical procedures. There are, however, certain limitations.

The principal advantages of flame photometric methods for the determination of the alkali metals are summarized as follows (173). It is frequently possible to determine a number of alkali and nonalkali elements in the same solution of the sample without the necessity of any chemical separations. For instance, the determination of the combined or individual alkali metals by chemical methods usually requires the removal of all nonalkali cations and limits the number of permissible anions; the flame photometric determination of the alkali metals, on the other hand, can be carried out in the presence of a great number of cations and anions as long as the solution of the standard is of similar composition. The amount of sample required for flame photometric determinations of the alkali metals is frequently smaller than that used in micro- or even ultramicroanalysis. This advantage may be decisive in biochemistry, medicine, and criminology, where frequently only a limited amount of sample is available. Flame photometry offers considerable time saving when a great number of alkali determinations are required on the same or similar types of materials, thus justifying the somewhat time-consuming preparation of standard solutions. The accuracy obtainable in flame photometry equals and sometimes exceeds that of the best chemical procedures, particularly when minor concentrations of the alkali metals are involved. Flame photometric methods are therefore well suited for the determination of traces of the alkali metals, even in the presence of major concentrations of nonalkali cations.   The determination of the alkali metals by flame photometric methods does not require the attention of an experienced chemist.   Once a method has been established, all routine operations can be carried out by technicians.   A remarkable feature of flame photometric methods is their ability to differentiate between the three heavy alkali metals.   As was pointed out in the discussion of chemical methods, the presence of rubidium and/or cesium in potassium determinations is frequently disregarded because the separation of these three elements involves a forbidding number of steps.   On the other hand, with proper instrumentation, less than 1 p.p.m. rubidium or cesium can be determined in the presence of major quantities of potassium by flame photometric methods.

One limitation of flame photometric methods is that, as in all spectrochemical procedures, measurements are only relative and require comparison with standard solutions.   The apparatus required is expensive, compared to the equipment used in chemical analysis of the alkali metals.   It is clear that, if only an occasional alkali determination is required, the preparation of standard solutions and calibration curves may be more time-consuming than the performance of a chemical procedure.   Generally speaking, therefore, flame photometric methods are superior when a great number of identical determinations are required.   It must also be remembered that the preparation of the solution of an unknown sample may not reveal the presence of interfering substances.   It is therefore often necessary to carry out preliminary tests to determine the composition of unknown material in order to ensure the absence of interfering ions or to prepare correcting standard solutions.   In view of the pro and con opinions of flame photometric procedures, it is felt that chemical methods will be largely but not completely replaced by flame photometry.

b. Principles and Characteristics

The general principles involved in flame photometry and the necessary instrumentation have been ably treated in several recent books and discussions (63,173,270,279).   The literature covering this area is extensive, comprising nearly 1000 publications up to March, 1956 (272).   Only the most important factors affecting the determination of the alkali metals can be discussed here.

The development of flame photometric methods for the alkali metals is closely connected with that of other forms of emission spectroscopy.   The absence of adequate standards led to techniques in which samples could be handled in solution, as in the porous hollow electrode (121), the porous flat electrode (389), the copper electrode (139), and the disk electrode (310): Flame photometry is also a solution technique, but, unlike the spark techniques just mentioned and the d.c. arc method often employed in emission spectrography, no ionization of the atoms takes place with most elements. Thermal excitation is followed by an emission of light due to the return of the excited neutral atoms to the ground state. The alkali metals, however, are partially ionized by very hot flames, and this behavior causes certain complications. The spectra of the alkali metals are very simple, with most valuable lines in the visible region. Early flame work employed large prisms as dispersing elements and photographic plates as radiation detectors (261). This system is still used in special cases where a high degree of dispersion is required. Since the alkali metals have low excitation potentials, they emit strongly in cooler flames. Some investigators (5,173,349) prefer these to avoid ionization of the alkali metals with the resulting mutual radiation interference. On the other hand, the higher the heat, the greater the sensitivity that can sometimes be obtained. Although sodium is three to four times as sensitive in an acetylene flame as in an illuminating gas flame, the sensitivity of potassium, because of its greater tendency to ionize, is about the same in both flames.

The choice of the optical system for the determination of the alkali metals depends on the composition of the sample to be analyzed and the sensitivity required. Filter photometers are limited in application to those samples and those elements that, like sodium and potassium, produce simple spectra. They are, therefore, extensively used in the clinical field. However, filter photometers are incapable of separating the radiations from two elements whose spectral lines are close together. Thus, the most sensitive rubidium line at 780.00 mμ can be seriously affected by the strong potassium line at 766.5 mμ. Since separation of these lines cannot be achieved by a filter photometer, monochromators and detectors must be used that provide sufficient resolution and sensitivity for work with narrow slits. Monochromators are essential when samples and elements other than the alkali metals must also be analyzed. As to suitable detectors, phototubes or barrier layer cells are satisfactory for most work involving the alkali metals. For more exacting requirements, as in the determination of a trace of one alkali metal in the presence of interfering radiation from other alkali or nonalkali metals, photomultipliers are much to be preferred. These sensitive detectors also allow the use of more dilute solutions of the alkali metals, which often leads to greater accuracy (356).

c. DETERMINATION

The preparation of the sample for flame photometric measurements is treated in Sections IV-A-2 and IV-A-5. A typical detailed procedure is given in Section VIII-B-6. The following remarks cover factors that must be considered before setting up a specific procedure.

(1) Internal Standard Method

It will be recalled that in emission spectrography some element frequently is added in known concentration. The ratio of the intensity of a certain line of the desired element to one of the internal standard is used as a measure of the concentration of the element investigated. Flame photometers containing spray chambers to control the dispersion of the aerosol usually employ correcting internal standards to avoid drop-size interference. The use of the internal standard is made possible in some instruments by two exit slits or two filters and two detectors. For determinations of sodium and potassium, lithium is usually used, with the lithium line at 670.8 mμ serving as internal standard or monitor for the sodium line at 589.3 mμ and the potassium line at 766.5 mμ (137). Lithium is selected because it matches fairly closely the physical and chemical characteristics of sodium and potassium, and the excitation potentials of the resonance lines of the three alkali metals are similar. Potassium serves as an internal standard for lithium determinations.

Much controversy exists concerning the value of the internal standard method. The following advantages are cited by its proponents (137,173): (1) Better reproducibility is obtainable than with single straight intensity measurements. (2) Systematic errors due to variations in the viscosity and surface tension are greatly reduced. (3) Mutual radiation interference of various elements is largely eliminated. (4) Demands on the performance of atomizers and burners are less exacting.

Opponents of the method (155,173,270) maintain that (1) internal standards cannot be depended upon to cure mutual radiation interference, as, for instance, the enhancement (or depression in some flames) of sodium and potassium radiations; (2) the addition of another radiating element increases both the background and the chances that additional emission lines may not be resolved by the filter or monochromator; and (3) significant errors may result if the solution of the sample unexpectedly contains the internal standard as an impurity. The opponents of the internal standard also feel that the radiation produced by a well-designed burner-atomizer combination should remain constant as long as the flame conditions are kept stable and a steady flow of solution is maintained. They assert that the stability of most photoelectric detectors is excellent and that calibration is simple and rapid. When the stability of the detector is poor, they declare, the internal standard does not improve matters, since the responses of the detectors used for the desired element and internal standard lines may vary significantly. They also state that, although various factors affecting emission cannot readily be controlled in photographic arc and spark spectrography, so that an internal standard is necessary, in flame photometry these variables can be controlled.

(2) Interferences

Because of their low excitation potentials, the alkali metals are comparatively free from radiation interferences. The determination of these elements, however, is subject to possible interferences due to variations in combustion processes and, to some extent, to the usual interferences encountered in emission spectroscopy, including mutual line interference, interference by mutual excitation or suppression, and interferences due to band spectra. In addition, anion interference, which is not encountered in other spectrochemical procedures, must be mentioned (114). It is difficult to compare data reported in the literature. Some work has been done with filter photometers, and some with spectrophotometers containing monochromators with different atomizers and various types of burners. Much of the information is therefore conflicting and valid only for a particular instrument or a specific procedure.

The interferences most frequently encountered in alkali metal analysis are as follows:

1. Anion interference. Free acids generally depress the radiation of the alkali metals by reducing the number of free ions through the formation of stable combinations with various acid radicals (312). See Fig. 1. Thus the depressing effect of a large excess of chloride on the emission of rubidium and cesium has been explained as being due to the formation of molecules such as $RbCl$ and $CsCl$ (270). Free sulfuric acid has a greater depressing effect than hydrochloric acid or nitric acid. Nevertheless, a sulfuric acid medium can be chosen to control the more serious depression of the lithium radiation by aluminum (60) and to depress the interference of calcium in the determination of sodium (47a). Phosphates have a pronounced inhibiting effect on the flame intensity of potassium, and less on sodium (105). Carbonate and bicarbonate ions (193) and borate and oxalate ions (312) also decrease the intensity of the sodium radiation. The addition of certain "buffers" to prevent the depression of the alkali radiation has been suggested (114). It is claimed that the internal standard method corrects the inhibiting effect of acids (36). The tendency of the

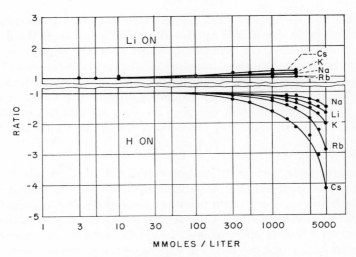

Fig. 1. Radiation interference of lithium and hydrogen.

alkali metals to form in cool flames hydroxides that cannot be excited is a form of anion interference and decreases in the following order: Li > Cs > Rb > K > Na. Thus, flames containing hydrogen cause the formation of considerable lithium hydroxide, but only little sodium hydroxide (173).

2. Cation interference. Although the alkali metals are comparatively free from cation interference, their radiation can be depressed or enhanced to some degree by certain elements. Again, much conflicting data, which can only be explained by the use of different apparatus and procedures, has been published in the literature. It is generally agreed that high concentrations of magnesium and/or aluminum have a depressing effect on the intensity of the alkali radiation. Whereas a 10:1 ratio of magnesium or aluminum depresses the intensity of the lithium line only slightly, a ratio of 100:1 causes considerable suppression (415). Although this effect is serious when traces of the alkali metals are being determined, it can, provided the sensitivity of the alkali radiation is not too greatly impaired, be compensated for by the addition of approximately the same concentration of magnesium and/or aluminum to the standard solutions (184,188). Frequently preferred, however, is the outright removal of these interfering elements, as is described under sample preparation (115) (see Section IV-A). As aluminum has an even greater depressing effect on the radiation of calcium and strontium than on that of the alkali metals, it can be used to eliminate the effect of these elements on the radiation of the alkali metals (195,427a). Ammonium salts inhibit the radiation of the alkali

metals, and so excess acid should be eliminated by evaporation and not by neutralization. When introduced in the course of sample preparation, ammonium salts should be destroyed by ignition or treatment with aqua regia. Certain organic solvents enhance the emission spectra of the alkali metals. The greatest increase is caused by acetone, followed by methanol, ethanol, and propanol, in that order (219). Other organic compounds that increase the intensity of the alkali emission are glycerol, ethers, acetaldehyde, and carboxylic acids. It is thought that the enhancement of the alkali radiation is due to the formation of radicals with the added compounds that act by direct excitation or by preventing interference of radicals normally present in the flame (382).

3. Flame spectrum and background. The measurement of the radiation produced by the alkali metals always includes more or less of the flame background produced by molecular bands, such as CH, OH, and C_2 and of a continuous spectrum, resulting from the emission of CO molecules. The alkali metals markedly increase the continuous spectrum. Of all the flames available, the oxygen-hydrogen flame gives the best metal/background ratio. The flame background can be disregarded when the intensity of the alkali metal line is strong; it cannot be disregarded when the intensity of the line is weak. Corrections for flame background can be made by preparing a solution that contains all reagents but no alkali metal and deducting the reading from those of samples and standard solutions.

4. Radiation interference. Sodium enhances the potassium radiation (349). Since even the finest monochromators are unable to eliminate this interference, it cannot be dismissed as being due simply to the appearance of sodium radiation at the potassium wavelength in inferior optical systems. Potassium affects the sodium radiation also, but to a lesser degree. Many reasons have been advanced in the past for this enhancement. The following explanation is now generally accepted (173,349): Ionized alkali atoms cannot easily be excited in the flame. Because of their noble metal configuration, they are unable to emit the resonance lines of the alkali metals. In the case of significant ionization, few alkali atoms are present in the ground state ready for excitation. Potassium, rubidium, and cesium (171) are largely ionized by the acetylene flame. When sodium is simultaneously introduced into the flame, an excess of electrons is formed, which suppresses the ionization of the potassium according to the mass action equation. As a consequence, more potassium atoms remain in the ground state to be excited by the flame. The following equation has been suggested (173):

$$K_P = P_{M^+}P_e/P_M$$

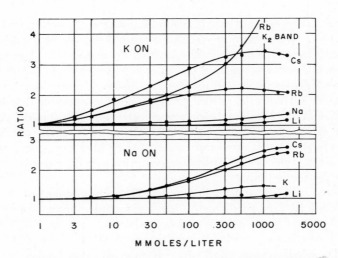

Fig. 2. Radiation interference of potassium and sodium.

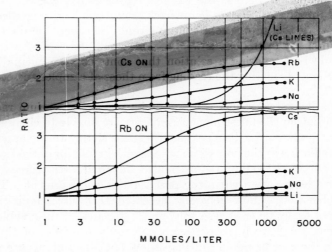

Fig. 3. Radiation interference of cesium and rubidium.

The constant K_P depends to a large degree on the flame temperature. P_{M^+} is the partial pressure of the ionized metal, P_e, the partial pressure of electrons, and P_M, the partial pressure of the unionized metal. Since with higher potassium concentrations ionization decreases, owing to re-absorption and related phenomena, the enhancing effect of the sodium becomes less pronounced. The effect of the alkali metals on the cesium

radiation has recently been described (120a). The mutual radiation interference of the alkali metals is demonstrated in Figs. 1, 2, and 3 (161).

Some investigators have reported that no radiation interference is encountered when an instrument of adequate resolving power is used (218),
and others that the alkali metals decrease their respective emissions (36).
If such a decrease occurs, it must be due to the fact that the energy required to excite a certain alkali metal is consumed by other alkali atoms
(173). This behavior could be expected when the excitation potentials of
two alkali metals are nearly the same, as in the case of rubidium with 1.59
e.v. and potassium with 1.61 e.v. It can be assumed that the depression of
alkali lines by certain cations is due to similar absorption of the alkali
emission.

It is worthwhile to remember that all mutual radiation interferences
vary to a great degree with the flame temperature and with the size and
operation of burners, atomizers, spray chambers, and optical systems.
Therefore, data derived from one instrument are not necessarily valid for
others.

Correction of Radiation Interferences. The following methods can be
used to compensate for the effect of sodium on the potassium radiation
(similar procedures can be used to correct for radiation interferences of
other alkali metals). A number of standard potassium solutions containing
varying amounts of sodium are prepared. The sodium and potassium lines
are measured, and the calibration curve corresponding to the concentration of sodium in the sample is used. This method is especially useful
if the sodium content of samples varies considerably. In another approach,
the sodium content of the sample is first determined. Standard potassium solutions containing the sodium concentration previously established
are then prepared. This method is most attractive for the determination of potassium in solutions containing approximately the same concentration of sodium. In another technique, an excess of sodium is added
to the solutions of samples and standards, in order to saturate the flame
with sodium. At the saturation level, variations in the sodium content of
various samples and standards do not affect the potassium radiation.
This addition of sodium as a radiation buffer is rejected by some analysts
because so much sodium is required to reach the saturation point that it
may lead to clogging of the burner. In addition, the question of the purity
of the sodium may arise, particularly when traces of potassium are being
determined. Thus prior collection of the potassium as potassium tetraphenylboron after enrichment with ammonium tetraphenylboron has been
recommended (295a). Other analysts, however, feel that the advantages
of radiation buffers far outweigh their disadvantages. Thus, to determine

sodium and potassium in water, buffers have been suggested containing (1) potassium, calcium, and magnesium for sodium determinations and (2) sodium, calcium, and magnesium for potassium determinations (439). It has also been suggested that the solution of the sample be diluted to the point that very weak standard solutions can be used and the mutual interference of the alkali metals thus be minimized or eliminated (42). This method is feasible only when sensitive equipment of good optical resolving power is available. In the determination of alkali metal impurities in cesium salts, lithium and sodium can be determined by the use of standards containing no cesium, but the determination of potassium and rubidium requires standards containing the same concentration of cesium as the samples (332).

2. Spectrochemical Procedures (284)

a. INTRODUCTION

The discussion of emission spectrochemical procedures for the determination of the alkali metals rightly follows the discussion of flame photometric methods; for flame photometry, a branch of emission spectroscopy, is used for the bulk of such analyses. It appears appropriate to emphasize the close relationship of flame photometry with other forms of emission spectroscopy. In all branches of optical emission spectroscopy, including flame photometry, atoms of a sample are energized so that one or more electrons are shifted from their "home" orbit to one farther away from the nucleus. Upon the return of an electron to a lower orbit, a corresponding amount of energy is released in the form of electromagnetic radiation. The principal distinction between flame photometry and emission spectroscopy is the source of energy. In the former, it is, of course, a flame; in the latter, an arc or sparklike discharge.

Although they are not really fundamental, there are other distinctions between the two techniques. In flame photometry, the detector is photoelectric and reads instantaneous values. By contrast, the usual detector in emission spectroscopy integrates the energy with time. The photographic plate is the most common and simplest such integrator; electronic integrators are employed in more elaborate equipment. Flame photometry does not require integration because of the inherent stability of the flame source, as contrasted with arcs and sparks, and also because of the homogeneity of solution samples. Samples in emission spectroscopy are frequently solids in which considerable segregation of the alkali metals is not uncommon. To complete this comparison, some of the advantages of flame photometry for the determination of the alkali metals should be mentioned. In most instances, flame photometry is definitely to be preferred over more conventional emission spectroscopy. Cost of the equipment for the former is a small fraction of that for an emission spectrograph, microphotometer, source unit, plate processor, etc. Furthermore, and now with reference specifically to the alkalies, the prominent spectral lines of lithium, sodium, potassium, rubidium, and cesium fall in the red and near infrared regions. Emission spectroscopy is at its best in the ultraviolet.

This is not to say that there are no advantages to emission spectroscopy for the determination of alkalies. Indeed, when sample size is small, emission spectrochemical means must be use. The photographic emulsion records the spectrum during a time so short that it would be impossible to take readings on a meter. Another advantage of emission methods is that samples need not be dissolved, and thus preparation time is saved. Further, the determination of the alkali metals is often only part of the problem. Whereas flame photometry is most useful for the alkalies, and perhaps the alkaline earths, the emission spectrograph permits the simultaneous determination of around 70 elements. Finally, the emission spectrographic method offers a permanent record of the results that may be studied and verified, if necessary, at a later date.

b. Theoretical Considerations

It has been mentioned already that the prominent lines of the alkalies are readily excited by low-temperature flames and that the lines themselves are in the long-wave regions. Theoretically, this means that the excitation potentials of these elements are low. Practically, this means that the spectrographer will use the d.c. arc or the a.c. arc for such determinations. A related characteristic is volatility. The alkalies are generally more volatile than other elements. Anticipating this, the spectrographer often makes a moving-plate run of his samples first. This procedure involves taking a series of exposures at intervals of about 10 to 30 seconds while the arc is running. From the spectrograms, he prepares a curve of intensity vs. time for each of the elements to be determined. A typical plot will show parallel curves for the alkali metals burning off together during the beginning of the arcing. The contours of curves of other elements will be different. Frequently, for this reason, the spectrographer decides to determine the alkalies in a separate burning from the other elements. Another reason for this step is that, on most spectrographs, a separate wavelength setting in the visible region is required for the alkalies. Other elements are usually determined in the region 2300 to 4000 A.

c. PRACTICAL CONSIDERATIONS

The spectral lines usually chosen for the determination of the alkali metals are presented in Table V. An ultraviolet line, as well as a visible line, is given. Since in all instances the visible line is the stronger, it would appear preferable, particularly when the elements are to be determined at trace levels. This consideration brings up the problem of the

TABLE V
Prominent Spectral Lines of the Alkali Metals

Element	Spectral lines, A.		
Lithium	3232.6	6707.8	
Sodium	3302.3	5895.9	
Potassium	4044.1	7664.9	
Rubidium	4201.9	7800.2	
Cesium	4555.4	8521.1	8943.5

photographic emulsion. The most commonly used emulsion in the red and near-infrared regions is either I-L or I-N, manufactured by Eastman Kodak Co. Because red-sensitive emulsions are rather troublesome, spectrographers frequently prefer to use the lines in the ultraviolet, where, practically speaking, they are able to achieve adequate sensitivity with far superior precision and accuracy. Another reason for using the ultraviolet rather than the longer wavelength region relates to the spectrograph. The dispersion of prism spectrographs becomes progressively poorer toward higher wavelengths. This behavior, in turn, results in poorer sensitivity toward higher wavelengths, as the signal/noise ratio worsens. On grating spectrographs, the grating is usually blazed for high intensity in the ultraviolet. Therefore, despite the fact that the lines in the red are inherently stronger, those in the ultraviolet may appear stronger with such instruments. In emission spectroscopy, there generally is no problem with elements at relatively high concentrations. The material may be diluted to optimum concentration levels for the elements. Determining trace elements, however, is a problem. Some data on the approximate concentrations of alkali metals detectable by ordinary techniques are presented in Table VI.

The figures in Table VI apply to commercial 1.5 to 3 m. grating spectrographs or Littrow prism spectrographs. To improve the threshold of sensitivity, especially when there is sufficient sample on hand, the following techniques may be employed:

1. Replicate burnings to take advantage of the fast burn-off of the alkalies.

TABLE VI
Approximate Minimum Concentration of Alkali Metals Detectable
by Ordinary Spectrographic Techniques

Element	Wavelength, A.	Concn., %
Lithium	6707.8	0.0001
Sodium	3302.3	0.001
	5859.9	0.0001
Potassium	4044.1	0.01
	7664.9	0.0005
Rubidium	7800.2	0.001
Cesium	8943.5	0.01

2. The use of high-speed plates such as 103-F rather than Spectrum Analysis No. 1 or No. 2, ordinarily used. (All these are Eastman Kodak plates.)

3. The use of a narrow entrance slit.

4. Careful choosing of the exposure interval to take advantage of the burn-off characteristics.

5. The use of low heat discharges so that most of the energy is transferred to a very few spectral lines. In this regard, it is often preferable to use oscillating or interrupted discharges, which permit the sample to cool off during a portion of the cycle.

6. The use of center-post electrodes, which serve the same purpose, that of keeping the sample relatively cool.

7. The use of graphite anode caps. Each cap fits closely over a standard electrode and has a small hole on top through which the sample vaporizes. By controlling the rate of vaporization and centering the vapors in the arc column, the sensitivity of alkali determinations is frequently improved.

d. REPRODUCIBILITY

Since most alkali determinations are run with arc sources, the precision to be expected is around 5 to 10% of the amount present. One way to improve the coefficient of variation is to dissolve the sample so that any one of the several solution techniques may be employed. The rotating electrode method, in which the arc is directed to the top edge of a disk that dips down into the solution, is probably the best such technique. Since an arc is required, many of the other solution techniques, such as those using the porous cup and the Lucite cup, are ruled out. The rotating electrode technique has the added advantage of preventing rapid burn-off of the alkalies. Since fresh solution is being fed into the arc at all times, virtually all elements vaporize at the same time. If solution techniques are not practical, one important way to improve reproducibility is to make careful moving-plate studies beforehand. As already indicated, such preliminary tests quickly reveal the proper exposure period. Another suggestion is to add an internal standard resembling the alkali metals, such as calcium or strontium, or, for that matter, another alkali metal itself. Indium has also been used (342a). In addition, mixing the sample with graphite powder often serves to steady the arc. Particle size plays an important part in reproducibility, and so mechanical mixing and grinding is preferable to hand mixing.

e. Typical Procedures

A number of procedures have been published for the determination of the alkali metals in various materials. Most of the techniques have appeared in the new edition of *A.S.T.M. Methods for Emission Spectrochemical Analysis* (18). For instance, one method (461) describes the determination of sodium and potassium as well as five other elements in silica refractories. A separate burning is employed for sodium and potassium, with an overdamped condenser discharge as the source. With the volatility of the alkalies and the necessity for a weak excitation source being taken into consideration, a combination of a pulsating source and a center-post electrode is used for effectively reducing the temperature. The separate burning for a relatively short period keeps the background for these elements down and so enhances their sensitivity. In a method covering the analysis of lithium-bearing ores, iron is determined in addition to the alkalies (305). In this method, the sample is dissolved and evaporated on the end of a graphite electrode. An a.c. arc discharge is used, partly to keep the temperature relatively low. A third method (348) illustrates the advantage of emission spectroscopy over flame photometry when other elements are to be determined along with the alkali metals. In this procedure, lithium, sodium, and potassium are determined in addition to nine other elements. Silica brick and glass sand form the matrix. If more than 4% total alkali metals is present in the sample, it becomes necessary to convert the matrix to another form. Lithium hydroxide may be used for this purpose. This procedure naturally precludes the determination of lithium. Because of the low ionization potentials and high volatility of the alkali metals, there is a suppression of lines of other elements in such matrixes. Erroneous results may be reported if standards and samples are not closely similar. Dilution with certain substances is the generally accepted means for controlling this variable. Lithium hydroxide is chosen by some (348). Other substances often used are graphite powder, lithium carbonate, zinc oxide, and aluminum oxide. Recently a mixture of copper oxide and graphite was suggested (428). The conversion of samples and standards to similar or identical matrixes becomes an absolute necessity when the sample composition is completely unknown. A combination of lithium carbonate and graphite has been proposed for this purpose (397). Zinc oxide and graphite are also used (405). The same principle has been employed in the determination of lithium in various lithium minerals by a fusion of the sample with sodium carbonate (96a). A summary of these procedures has appeared (285).

Comments thus far have been confined to the determination of the alkali metals rather than to the analysis of alkali products. Emission spectroscopy is also being widely used for the latter. For instance, two methods (456) have been described that are useful for the determination of trace elements in caustic soda, soda ash, and other sodium salts. These methods employ an a.c. arc on solutions. Metallic impurities in alkali salts from a fraction of a p.p.m. copper and silver to 10 p.p.m. silicon can thus be determined. For a discussion of spectrographic methods for the determination of certain impurities found in the pure alkali metals see Section VII-A-6.

3. X-Ray Emission Spectrography

a. INTRODUCTION

At the present time, no instrumental method of analysis is growing in popularity as fast as x-ray emission spectrography. The analytical chemist unfamiliar with this method will do well to consider it as analogous to optical spectrography, the difference lying mainly in the mode of excitation and the measuring devices. In x-ray emission spectrography, radiation from an x-ray tube is directed to the sample. This primary beam excites the elements in the sample to give off a secondary or fluorescent radiation, the wavelength of which is characteristic of the element excited. This fluorescent radiation passes through a collimator, so that only a parallel beam impinges on the analytical crystal. The crystal serves as a diffracting grating separating the radiation into various wavelength components. The diffracted beam enters a counter, which scans an arc around the crystal and measures the x-radiation as a function of the wavelength. Because of the small number of lines in the characteristic x-ray spectra and the simple relation of the relative intensity to the fraction of the element present in the specimen, the x-ray region frequently offers certain advantages over the optical region for spectrochemical analysis. Excellent summaries and reviews of x-ray emission spectrography, which record the early history

(174) and recent developments (43,143,255,256), are available. They should be consulted for detailed theories and practical applications.

b. APPLICATION

When the determination of lithium and sodium by x-ray spectrography is considered, some of the inherent limitations of the method become apparent. The region of low atomic number is poorly suited to the practical application of this technique owing to problems arising from the long wavelengths of the characteristic x-ray lines. As the atomic number decreases, these lines merge with the ultraviolet. Even before this happens, the x-ray lines begin to present serious absorption problems. Absorption by air of x-radiation from 2 A. wavelength and higher becomes so pronounced as to limit the detection of lithium to special techniques, involving vacuum, ruled grating and photographic plates (383), and also to preclude, for all practical purposes, the determination of sodium. Some increase in the sodium x-ray intensity can be obtained (Na > 5%) by permitting the x-rays to pass through a medium less dense than air, such as helium. Although x-ray spectroscopy thus has little to offer as a means for detecting or determining lithium and sodium, it has been developed into an excellent tool for the determination of potassium, rubidium, and cesium. In previous pages, the close resemblance of the analytical chemistry of the three "heavy" alkali metals was discussed. It was pointed out that all common precipitants for potassium also bring down rubidium and cesium and that any subsequent separation of these three alkali metals, unless ion exchange procedures are employed, is uncertain and requires a forbidding number of steps. Although the determination of small amounts of individual members of this group, even in the presence of each other, can also be achieved by optical spectroscopy, flame photometry, and radioactivation analysis, for larger amounts, x-ray spectroscopy represents a superior analytical tool.

c. TECHNIQUES

Early work was limited to the determination of potassium in soil (78,175). The finely pulverized sample is intimately mixed with enough manganese oxide to provide four times as much manganese as potassium. The intensity ratios of the potassium K_α line ($\lambda = 3.744$) and the manganese K_{β_1} line, second order ($\lambda = 3.820$), are established with several hours of exposure time and photographic plates. Calcium enhances the potassium radiation to some extent, but not the manganese radiation. In the presence of considerable calcium, cadmium is preferred, as internal stand-

TABLE VII
Wavelengths of the K_α Lines of the Alkali Metals
(Unresolved α_1 and α_2)

Element	Wavelength K_α, A.
Lithium	240.00
Sodium	11.909
Potassium	3.744
Rubidium	0.927
Cesium	0.402

ard, its L_{β_1} line (λ = 3.739) being used. It has been shown that with the powerful x-ray tubes and sensitive measuring devices available today the time of analysis can be reduced to about 3 minutes for potash concentrates and to about 6 minutes for potash tailings, once a working curve has been established (165). Since the long-wavelength K-radiation of potassium is strongly absorbed by air, the x-ray path has to be enclosed in a plastic bag and flooded with helium. The rate of flow of helium through the system has a marked effect on the counting rate for the potassium K-radiation. Higher pressures and more rapid rates of flow of helium in the chamber increase the counting rate appreciably. However, at a rate of 3700 ml./minute, the counting rate varies only slightly with small variations in the helium flow, indicating that all or nearly all of the air is displaced from the chamber. A tungsten target x-ray tube is operated at 50 kv. and 40 ma., the Geiger tube is operated at 1500 v., sodium chloride is used as the analyzing crystal, and the K_α (λ = 3.744) line is found at 83.07 degrees (2θ). For the preparation of working curves, a number of dry, −200 mesh samples of potash concentrates and tailings are used. These are samples that have been previously analyzed by the chloroplatinate method and that contain from 0.8 to 61.5% K_2O. The counting time ranges from 112 counts/second for the 61.5% sample to 17 counts/second for the 0.8% tailing. No background corrections are required since absorption and scattering by the matrix composition are low and essentially constant. The presence of higher–atomic numbered elements would be expected to alter the slope of the working curve. Results based on the x-ray spectrographic method agree well with those obtained by the chloroplatinate procedure.

Potassium in the range 5 to 150 γ has been extracted from aqueous potassium chloride solutions and from mica surfaces, where it is present as an exchangeable ion, and then determined by x-ray emission spectroscopy. To carry out the extraction, rectangles of Nalfilm-1 cation exchange membrane, equilibrated with hydrochloric acid and washed with water, are placed into polyethylene beakers containing either potassium chloride solutions or mica and distilled water. After 24 hours, the films are removed, dried, and suspended in the sample holder of the apparatus. A tungsten target is used for excitation at 50 kv. and 50 ma. The radiation is diffracted by an EDDT (ethylenediamine ditartrate) crystal into a gas flow proportional counter tube with argon-methane (9:1) gas. Helium is used to displace the air in the optical path. The background is determined by counting 2 degrees in θ above the K_α peak of potassium. Blank membranes exhibit counting rates corresponding to about 5 γ of potassium (467).

The determination of cesium (0.05 to 7.9%) and rubidium (0.01 to 3.20%) in lepidolite, microcline, beryl, morganite, and biotite can be carried out with remarkable accuracy by x-ray spectroscopy (21). A lithium fluoride analyzing crystal and krypton-halogen–filled Geiger tubes are used. Strontium as strontium carbonate is used as the internal standard for rubidium, and iodine as silver iodide for cesium. The K_α lines of rubidium and strontium ($\lambda = 0.926$ and 0.875, respectively) are in a favorable wavelength range, whereas the K_α lines of cesium and iodine ($\lambda = 0.401$ and 0.433, respectively) are less favorably located. The use of the internal standard method minimizes the effect of line voltage variations to about 2%. This effect is insignificant if measurements are repeated. Sample briquets contain 0.940 g. of sample, 0.060 g. of internal standard mixture (5 parts of silver iodide to 1 part of strontium carbonate), and 1 g. of aluminum-carborundum mixture. Counting rates are, for 1% cesium, 25 counts/second over a background of 25 counts/second and. for 0.2% rubidium, 125 counts/second over a background of 85 counts/ second. Instead of a background correction, a zero correction, derived from a synthetic blank, is used, because mica, beryl, and feldspar are of similar atomic number, and so the matrixes are almost constant. Further, cesium K_α and iodine K_α are hard radiations, so that matrix effects are small. The working curve for cesium, which is empirical, is prepared with synthetic standards using quartz as a matrix. As the curve for rubidium is a straight line, only one standard and a blank are required. Results based on this x-ray procedure agree with those obtained by flame photometry and radioactivation.

The gravimetric determination of potassium in mica, feldspar, and other silicates often is concluded with the weighing of the perchlorate. Rubidium, if present, will count as potassium. To correct for the presence of rubidium, or to determine the element, the perchlorates are dissolved in hot water and transferred to a 50 ml. or smaller volumetric flask. Rubidium K_α is measured at $\lambda = 0.927$ with a tungsten target tube operated at 50 kv. and 30 ma., a lithium fluoride analyzing crystal, and a scintillation counter. A working curve is prepared by dissolving potassium perchlorate, containing varying amounts of rubidium perchlorate, in water, transferring the solutions to volumetric flasks, and measuring the K_α-radiation of the rubidium (214).

Pollucite, a rare cesium mineral of the composition $(Cs,Na)_2O \cdot Al_2O_3 \cdot 5SiO_2 \cdot H_2O$, contains up to 35% Cs_2O and, in addition, varying amounts of all the other alkali metals. The determination of cesium in the presence of potassium by chemical procedures is most difficult. Good results can be obtained by the following x-ray procedure: 2 g. of the 300 mesh sample is ground for 1 hour with 3 g. of cornstarch before briquetting; working curves are prepared with analyzed samples (21 to 35% Cs_2O). The samples used as standards are analyzed by a combination of chemical and flame photometric methods as follows: cesium plus potassium plus rubidium is collected and weighed as perchlorate; the perchlorate is dissolved in water, and the amounts of potassium and rubidium are determined flame photometrically and deducted from the weight of the combined perchlorates. Alternatively, the potassium and rubidium correction is established by x-ray fluorescence. For the x-ray determination of cesium in unknown samples and standards, a tungsten target tube operated at 50 kv. and 30 ma., a lithium fluoride analyzing crystal, and a scintillation counter are used.

C. POLAROGRAPHIC PROCEDURES

1, Introduction

There is comparatively little recent literature on the polarographic determination of the alkali metals. Most procedures were developed before 1950 and have been ably described elsewhere (141,226,435). This discussion is therefore limited to a brief summary of the polarographic technique as it applies specifically to the determination of the alkali metals. The polarographic approach has certain characteristics that make it attractive for the determination of small amounts of the alkali metals in special material. In the absence of interfering elements, it has the advantage of being direct and rapid. Although it cannot compete with flame photometry with regard to speed and absence of interference from various sources, it is well suited for the determination of small concentrations, with which chemical methods either fail or give inaccurate results.

2. Reduction Potentials

Although the alkali ions possess very negative reduction potentials, well-developed and reproducible waves can be obtained for several reasons (226). The alkali metals form with mercury stable amalgams with reduction potentials about 1 v. lower than those of the pure metals. Fortunately, the reduction of the hydrogen ion on mercury requires a potential about 0.8 v. more negative than on platinum. Furthermore, in neutral or alkaline solutions the reduction potential of hydrogen is 0.5 to 0.8 v. more negative than in acid solution. These three combined effects explain why the alkali metal ions are reduced more easily than the hydrogen ion. In an acid medium, however, the hydrogen discharge is the predominant factor preventing the reduction of the alkali metal ions. The most serious limitation of the polarographic method lies in the mutual interference of the alkali metals, caused by the closeness of their half-wave potentials. This results, in the case of mixtures, in one single cumulative wave. In an alkaline medium containing tetraethylammonium hydroxide as supporting electrolyte, the half-wave potential of the sodium ion is −2.07 v., of the potassium ion −2.10 v., of the rubidium ion −1.99 v., and of the cesium ion −2.05 v. Only the lithium ion, with a half-wave potential of −2.31 v., is sufficiently removed from the rest of the alkali metals to allow its individual determination in the presence of the other alkali metals (469). The sum of the more common sodium and potassium cannot be determined unless the ratio of sodium to potassium is known. Although their polarographic waves are additive, the sum of the wave heights does not give the total alkali content, because equal concentrations of sodium or potassium do not produce equal wave heights. A technique described recently, however, permits the determination of the ratio of two alkali metals without prior chemical separations (108). By increasing the concentration first of one and then of the other metal by a known amount, two new polarographic points are obtained from which the ratio of the two components can be calculated. Initially, graphs are drawn from solutions of identical concentrations of the salts in question, and, from the difference between maxima and minima of the waves, the proportions of the two metals present in an unknown solution are calculated.

3. Supporting Electrolytes

Because of the requirements for a neutral or an alkaline solution, there is only a limited choice of supporting electrolytes among the tetraalkylammonium halides and hydroxides. These substituted ammonium ions have reduction potentials several tenths of a volt more negative than the ammonium ion. The following supporting electrolytes have been suggested: tetramethylammonium hydroxide (227,265), tetramethylammonium chloride (227,265), ethyltrimethylammonium hydroxide (372), alcoholic tetraethylammonium hydroxide (319,469), aqueous tetraethylammonium hydroxide (435), lithium hydroxide (469), and tetrabutylammonium iodide. Tetraethylammonium hydroxide appears now to be the preferred supporting electrolyte. It is superior to tetramethylammonium hydroxide because the reduction potential is several tenths of a volt more negative, thus providing a more definite plateau following the alkali wave (435). High-purity tetraethylammonium hydroxide salts are difficult to obtain, and the purification of solutions containing some reducible substances or alkali metals is involved. On the other hand, tetraethylammonium bromide can be easily purified by recrystallization from water-ethanol solutions. The hydroxide solution is subsequently prepared as follows (435): To the solution of 21 g. of tetraethylammonium bromide in 100 ml. of water 12 g. of moist silver oxide is added with constant stirring to facilitate the conversion of the bromide to the hydroxide. The silver bromide is filtered off, and a polarogram of the solution is obtained, covering the range 1.5 to 2.3 v. applied potential. If a resulting wave indicates the presence of reducible impurities, the bromide salt must be purified by crystallization, or the silver oxide by washing with water.

4. Calibration and Analysis of Samples (435)

To prepare a calibration curve, 5 ml. of tetraethylammonium hydroxide and 1 ml. of water are transferred to a polarographic cell maintained at 25°C. After purging with nitrogen and adjusting the droptime of the capillary to 4 seconds/drop, a polarogram is obtained over the range of 1.5 to 2.3 v. Then 0.10 ml. of a standard sodium or potassium solution (0.2 mg./ml.) is added, and, after purging again with nitrogen, another polarogram is obtained. The addition of standard alkali solution is repeated until sufficient data have been obtained to prepare a calibration curve. From each wave height measurement, the wave height due to tetraethylammonium hydroxide and water is deducted. It is of utmost importance to use the identical procedure for the preparation of the calibration curve and the analysis of samples.

5. Interferences

If the sample contains significant amounts of other ions, they must also be added to the standard solution. Aluminum does not interfere with the determination of sodium and/or potassium because the aluminate ion formed in the strongly alkaline solution of the tetraethylammonium hydroxide is not reduced. Thus, sodium can be determined in hydrous aluminum oxide by dissolving the finely ground sample first in $18N$ sulfuric acid. After removal of any silica by evaporation and filtration, sodium is determined by transferring an aliquot of the solution into a polarographic cell containing 5 ml. of tetraethylammonium hydroxide and recording the polarogram. Similarly, sodium plus potassium can be determined in silicates after decomposition with hydrofluoric and sulfuric acids (435). A drop of phosphoric acid may be added to the dry residues; tetraethyl-ammonium hydroxide will then cause the precipitation of the phosphates of iron and/or aluminum, titanium, calcium, and magnesium (265). The precipitates need not be filtered off when their amount is small. It is reported (265) that the presence per milliliter of as much as 300 γ of aluminum, manganese, copper, cadmium, or magnesium, 50 γ of calcium, 80 γ of mercury(II) or lead, 20 γ of ammonium ion, 9 γ of zinc, and 1 γ of iron interferes only slightly with the sodium determination. Larger quantities of these elements interfere and must be removed. The removal of interfering substances may be effected by conventional methods. Thus iron(III) can be separated by an ether separation, lead by precipitation as the sulfate, and calcium by precipitation as the carbonate. Group separations, such as mercury cathode electrolysis or sulfide precipitation, can also be employed. It is particularly important that organic matter, which the sample may contain or which may be introduced in the course of the analysis, be destroyed either by wet ashing or by ignition. Boron and phosphates do not interfere, even in large amounts (226).

6. Other Methods

Several indirect polarographic methods for the determination of potassium in blood serum have been proposed. In one method (330), a polarogram is obtained of a solution of sodium cobaltinitrite in the presence of gelatin and ammonia; then another polarogram is obtained after blood serum is added. The potassium in the blood serum will remove part of the nitrite reagent by precipitation of potassium cobaltinitrite, which is removed by centrifugation. From the change in the polarogram, it is possible to determine the amount of potassium present. In another potassium method, dipicrylamine is used as precipitating agent (286,287). The concentrations of this reagent prior to and after the addition to ashed blood serum are determined polarographically. From the change in the polarogram, the potassium content can be calculated. Potassium precipitated as the tetraphenylboron salt (cf. Section VI-A-3), $(C_6H_5)_4BK$, is soluble in N,N'-dimethylformamide. Polarograms of this solution in a supporting electrolyte of tetrabutylammonium iodide are proportional to potassium concentrations over the range 0.0002 to 0.0075M, corresponding to 0.08 to 3 mg. of potassium. The half-wave potential is -1.55 v. with a mercury pool (123). The potassium tetraphenylboron precipitate can also be ignited to KBO_2, the latter dissolved in acetone, and the potassium determined polarographically with tetramethylammonium hydroxide as a supporting electrolyte (176). For the determination of sodium, it is of interest that 0.1625 to 0.975mM solutions of sodium zinc uranyl acetate in 0.5N hydrochloric acid give well-defined polarographic diffusion currents (84). The currents are directly proportional to the concentration of the triple acetate salt. This technique is recommended for the determination of extremely small amounts of sodium in biological substances when only a limited amount of sample is available.

D. RADIOCHEMICAL METHODS

1. Neutron Activation Procedures (244,288)

a. INTRODUCTION

Most elements, when irradiated by the neutrons of a chain-reacting pile (or by the charged particles from an accelerator), give rise to artificially radioactive species that have their own characteristic modes of decay and radiations. The rate of decay and the radiation emitted are characteristic of the nuclide produced and will not be exactly duplicated by any other radionuclide. This specificity makes radioactivation analysis an unusual technique in that it is free from interference by other elements. Also, once the irradiation has been completed, there is no danger of contamination such as that experienced by conventional analytical methods. The principles of the method and the applications of radioactivation analysis have been treated in detail by several authors (49,247,289,421).

The neutron activation method in its simplest form, as applied to the determination of the alkali metals, consists in exposing samples containing an unknown amount of one or more of the alkali metals, together with standards containing known amounts of the alkali metals, to a neutron flux and comparing the activities produced. The use of comparison samples eliminates the necessity of monitoring the flux of neutrons (or other nuclear particles), which is usually a difficult quantity to measure or control. By this procedure, it is only necessary to measure the activity produced in the sample and in the standard and to calculate the percentage of the alkali metal in the unknown by a simple ratio. The activity present at a time t after the pile irradiation is $A = Nf\sigma S$, where A is the activity in disintegration per second, N is the number of atoms of the target nuclide, f is the neutron flux per square centimeter per second, σ is the activation cross section (probability) for the reaction in square centimeters per atom, and S is the saturation factor, $1 - e^{-\lambda t}$, or the ratio of the amount of activity produced in time t to that produced in infinite time. The decay constant, λ, is related to the half life of the radionuclide produced by $\lambda =$

0.693/half life.   In terms of weight, W, of the element, and assuming that the rate of production of the radioactivity, given by $Nf\sigma$, is constant during irradiation, the preceding equation may be written as

$$W = AM/(6.02 \times 10^{23}f\sigma S)$$

In this equation, M is the chemical atomic weight of the element sought.

In those samples in which the major constituent is an element which gives practically no activity or only a short-lived activity on irradiation and which, in addition, contains only a single alkali metal or other element that can be activated, it is possible to detect the latter by simply measuring the radiation from the sample and from the standard after irradiation. If a sample contains a second element which can be activated but which has a different half life, this element can be measured after the complete decay of the shorter-lived activity.   Also, direct measurement can be accomplished on the basis of differences in the types and energy of radiation emitted.   Some radioactive nuclides emit only beta particles, whereas others emit both beta and gamma particles.   In general, however, it cannot be assumed that the major portion of the sample does not become activated during irradiation.   Therefore, a chemical separation of the alkali metal sought is frequently required.   This is accomplished as follows: After irradiation, a known amount of the alkali metal investigated is added as an inactive isotopic carrier to the solutions of both the specimen and the comparative sample.   The "carrier element" is chemically processed to separate it from other elements.   Since the reactions usually give less than quantitative yield, corrections for chemical yield must be made. Then a comparison of the activity of the isotope produced in the unknown is made against the activity of the isotope produced in the standard.   The purity of each activity may be checked by measurements of half lives and absorption techniques.

b. Applications

With specific reference to the alkali metals, Table VIII shows the products of slow-neutron bombardment.   It is evident that ^{24}Na and ^{42}K are desirable nuclides. ^{88}Rb is too short-lived for most work. ^{86}Rb and ^{134}Cs are rather long-lived, but the high cesium cross section partially compensates for this disadvantage.   The sensitivity is the amount of the element producing in 10 half lives or in one month, whichever is shorter, a readily measurable amount of radionuclide, in this case, 40 disintegrations/second.   The flux, 5×10^{11} neutrons/cm.^{2}/second, is that normally obtained in the ORNL Graphite Reactor.

TABLE VIII
The Products and Sensitivities of Detection of Slow-Neutron Activation
of the Alkali Metals

Target	Product	Half life	Radiation	Sensitivity, γ
^{6}Li	^{3}H	12.1 yr.	β^-	a
^{7}Li	^{4}He	Stable		a
	^{8}Li	0.9 sec.	β^-, 2α	a
^{23}Na	^{24}Na	15.8 hrs.	β^-, γ	0.007
^{41}K	^{42}K	12.4 hrs.	β^-, γ	0.08
^{85}Rb	^{86}Rb	19 days	β^-, γ	0.03
^{87}Rb	^{88}Rb	17 min.	β^-	0.3
^{133}Cs	^{134m}Cs	3 hrs.	I.T., e	ca. 1.0
	^{134}Cs	2 yr.	β^-, γ	0.03

^{a} Detection requires special equipment.

To elaborate on the data appearing in Table VIII, reference is made to the reaction occurring during the irradiation of sodium and the subsequent decay of activation products. The reaction is as follows:

$$^{23}\text{Na} + n \longrightarrow {}^{24}\text{Na} + \gamma$$

It is more commonly written as ^{23}Na (n, γ) ^{24}Na, which means that the stable isotope of sodium of weight 23 "captures" a neutron to give an isotope of sodium of weight 24 plus a quantum of energy, which is emitted as a gamma ray. ^{24}Na is radioactive and undergoes a second change as follows:

$$^{24}\text{Na} \longrightarrow {}^{24}\text{Mg} + \beta^- + \gamma \qquad \text{(Half life = 15.0 hours)}$$

where β^- is 1.40 m.e.v., and γ is 1.38 m.e.v. and 2.76 m.e.v.

This rate of decay (a half life of 15.0 hours) and the energy with which the beta particles and the gamma photons are emitted are characteristic of this nuclide and will not be duplicated exactly by any other nuclide.

Radioactivation analysis has been applied to the determination of trace quantities of sodium and potassium in a variety of materials (19,48,107a, 245,246,342,390). Rubidium and cesium have been determined less extensively. In the determination of the alkali metals, the simple method of direct, or nondestructive, radioactivity measurement, as well as the determination after separation and isolation by such techniques as precipitation or ion exchange, have been utilized. A discussion of the application of these methods follows.

(1) Lithium

The sensitivity of lithium in the (n, γ) reaction is very poor because of adverse nuclear properties, the half life of the resulting radioisotope, ^{8}Li, being only 0.8 second.   With special equipment, it is possible, however to exploit the following reactions for the determination of lithium: ^6Li $(n, \alpha) \rightarrow {}^3H$ and ^{16}O $({}^3H, n)$ ^{18}F (200).

(2) Sodium

Sodium has been determined in mixed lithium-sodium sulfates by a direct radioactivity measurement technique (245).   Portions of the unknown sample, together with known amounts of standard samples, as Na_2CO_3, are irradiated under the same reactor conditions for 1 hour.   The bulk constituent, lithium, gives no appreciable radioactivity.   However, sufficient ^{24}Na is produced to permit a rapid analysis.   After discharge from the pile, the samples and aliquots of the comparative sample are placed in individual radioactivity-free glass tubes (usually 10 mm. $\times$ 75 mm. Pyrex culture tubes), and the ionization effects of the gamma rays produced by the decay of the ^{24}Na are read directly in a high-pressure gamma ionization chamber (48).   A simple ratio of the readings of the ion current per weight of the unknown to the ion current per weight of comparative sample gives results that compare very favorably with those obtained by spectrographic analysis.   Sodium in sodium oxalate can be determined by the direct measurement technique with equally good results (245).

Precipitation methods have a wider range of application than direct measurement methods.   In one excellent procedure, the radioisotope ^{24}Na and the isotopic carrier are precipitated with zinc uranyl acetate reagent (24).   Since uranium, upon precipitation as sodium zinc uranyl acetate, gives rise to U $\times$ beta radioactivity (from ^{238}U alpha decay), a count taken several hours after the initial separation of the sodium would, because of the growth of the beta activity, lead to erroneous results.   In order to avoid the interference from uranium, it is suggested that sodium be separated from uranium with a solution of hydrogen chloride in n-butanol.   To carry out the analysis (245), the sample (in this case, metal foil), after irradiation, is dissolved in a small amount of hydrochloric acid.   To this solution a known amount of inactive sodium is added as an isotopic carrier.   Small amounts of copper, iron, strontium, cobalt, phosphate, and potassium are also added as "holdback" carriers.   The heavy elements are separated by precipitation with H_2S and ammonia.   After boiling the solution to remove the sulfide ion, excess ammonia and ammonium carbonate are added to separate strontium.   After evaporation and ignition to remove the ammonium salts, the residue is dissolved in a few milliliters of water.   Excess zinc uranyl acetate reagent is then added, and the resulting mixture is allowed to digest 30 to 45 minutes.   After centrifugation, the precipitate is washed several times with dilute zinc uranyl acetate reagent, 95% alcohol, and ether. It is then treated with a 12% solution of hydrogen chloride in n-butanol (453) and digested for 10 minutes at a temperature of 15 to 20°C. The precipitate is washed with a mixture of 10 ml. of ether and 10 ml. of n-butanol reagent and is then transferred to a tared filter paper, washed with ethyl ether, and dried at 110°C. for 10 minutes. After cooling, it is weighed as NaCl, mounted, and counted. The results, all in the parts per million range, agree closely with those obtained by spectrochemical analysis. The method has also been successfully applied to the determination of sodium in aluminum (Na $\approx$ 10 p.p.m.) and in potassium carbonate (Na $\approx$ 100 p.p.m.) (245).

Ion exchange procedures involving cation exchange resin have been used to separate sodium (as well as potassium, rubidium, and cesium) (55,56) (cf. Section IV-B-2). With these techniques, sodium has been accurately determined in irradiated samples of potassium carbonate and rubidium carbonate (245).

(3) Potassium

Potassium has been determined in magnesium and lithium salts (245) by collecting the potassium (^{42}K; half life = 12.4 hours) on an isotopic carrier of potassium and subsequently precipitating the chloroplatinate, K_2PtCl_6. To carry out the analysis, a known amount of inactive potassium is added as isotopic carrier to the solution of the irradiated sample. Also, a small amount of each of the following cations is added as holdback carrier: Cu, Fe, Co, Ba, Sr, and Na. After separation of heavy metals by H_2S and ammonia precipitations, followed by the removal of the alkaline earths with ammonium carbonate, the filtrate is evaporated to dryness, and the ammonium salts are quantitatively removed by ignition. The residue is dissolved in a little water and a few drops of hydrochloric acid (cf. Section IV-A-3), and the potassium is precipitated with an excess of chloroplatinic acid reagent. Absolute ethanol is then added until the solution contains 60 to 70% alcohol by volume. A few milliliters of ethyl ether is added, and the precipitate is allowed to settle during cooling in an ice bath. The K_2PtCl_6 is then transferred to a tared filter paper and washed with small portions of ethanol. It is dried at 110°C., cooled, weighed, mounted, and counted. Results agree well with those obtained by spectrochemical procedures.

Ion exchange methods similar to those mentioned for the determination of sodium have been successfully used in determining microgram amounts of irradiated potassium in rubidium carbonate (55,245).

(4) Rubidium and Cesium

Both precipitation and ion exchange methods have been used to determine traces of rubidium and cesium in various samples after irradiation. With techniques similar to those described for sodium, rubidium has been sought, but not found, in samples of sodium carbonate. A rubidium carbonate sample analyzed for cesium by ion exchange and subsequent count of the activity indicated the same cesium content (0.02%) as that established by spectrochemical analysis (245). Neutron activation analysis has been used to determine 0.01 to 100 γ of rubidium and cesium in sea water after a preliminary concentration on cation exchange resin (391). The method has also been applied to the determination of rubidium and cesium in seaweeds, marine sediments, and coals (391). The chemical separations were based on cobaltinitrite and cesium bismuth iodide precipitations. A similar procedure has been suggested for the determination of rubidium and cesium in sodium-potassium alloys and related substances (92). Again, the individual alkali metals are first separated by a cation exchange procedure.

2. Analysis of Radiochemical Mixtures

a. DETERMINATION OF EXCHANGEABLE SODIUM AND POTASSIUM

Related to the radiometric determination of traces of the alkali metals after neutron activation is the use of ^{24}Na and ^{42}K in the simultaneous determination of total body exchangeable sodium and potassium. The two elements are so closely related physiologically (cf. Section I-A-3) that it often is important to know the body content of each element at the same time.

In the methods that have been suggested for this purpose, measured amounts of ^{24}Na and ^{42}K are administered. After equilibrium has been established (24 to 40 hours), a sample of plasma or urine is collected. The specific activity of each element (radioactive concentration divided by stable concentration) is found by a combination of counting and flame photometry. When the total activity of the isotope in the body is divided by the specific activity, the quotient is the total amount of exchangeable stable element in the body (15,16,47,197,345). To overcome the difficulties involved in differential counting of a mixture of these two radioelements, with such similar radioactive and chemical properties, usually chemical procedures, such as ion exchange (15,16) or precipitation of potassium as cobaltinitrite (197,291a) or tetraphenylboron (291a), are used. Alternatively, a differential counting technique involving two detectors, one sensitive to the gamma rays of both elements and the other more sensitive to the stronger beta rays of ^{42}K, may be applied (345).

Recently, a unique procedure was introduced (47) that requires only a single gamma-sensitive detector. This procedure is based on the fact that at equilibrium the specific activity of each element is the same in all body compartments and that in some body compartments, for example, plasma, red cells, and urine, the relative concentrations of the two elements differ, so that these concentrations can be easily determined flame photometrically. Thus, to determine simultaneously sodium and potassium, aliquots of the injected doses of ^{24}Na and ^{42}K are counted in a gamma-sensitive system. After equilibrium has been established, plasma and urine samples are obtained and counted. These urine and plasma samples are then analyzed flame photometrically for sodium and potassium. The total counts of the two samples and their sodium and potassium concentrations are then applied to a special "mathematical resolution" formula to obtain the specific activities of sodium and potassium. These in turn are applied to the usual formula for total body electrolyte.

b. DETERMINATION OF RADIOCESIUM

The problems of widespread low-level radioactive contamination from nuclear weapons testing (cf. Section I-C) and the monitoring of radioactive wastes before their discharge into the soil or other environments have created increasing demands for accurate determinations of ^{137}Cs. On solid samples, radiometric measurements have been made with the Los Alamos "human counter" (12), a large liquid scintillation detector that is capable of counting gamma rays from human subjects and from samples of foodstuffs up to several hundred pounds in weight with 100% geometrical efficiency (11). The determination of cesium-137 in fission product solutions generally requires at least four principal separation steps (242): (1) an initial precipitation of cesium, (2) a ruthenium volatilization step to remove residual ^{103}Ru and ^{106}Ru, (3) a scavenging precipitation step for further decontamination, and (4) a final precipitation of cesium in a form suitable for mounting and beta or gamma counting. It is believed that a usable radiocesium procedure should have a decontamination factor of about 10^5 for contaminant nuclides. The initial precipitation step is the most important part of the procedure because if adequate separation from other salts is not obtained the succeeding decontamination steps become more difficult (242). In most radiochemical procedures for ^{137}Cs, it is common to accept a low chemical yield in order to obtain high radiochemical purification. In such cases, it is required that a macro amount of normal cesium be added to the sample solution to obtain a final precipitate that is weighable in order to establish for each analysis the chemical yield.

One rapid cesium method for simple fission product mixtures consists merely of fuming the sample with hot perchloric acid to expel ruthenium, dissolving the soluble perchlorates in ethanol, and filtering, weighing, and counting the final $CsClO_4$. The chemical yield is established through the use of a known amount of cesium carrier (89). Up to 500 γ of ^{137}Cs in 5 liters of solution can be quantitatively captured on 160 mg. of precipitated thallium molybdophosphate, the activity of the precipitate then being proportional to the contained [137]Cs (170a). In another rapid procedure, anion exchange resin in the carbonate form has been suggested for the absorption of all ions except the alkali metals (321,462). In one modification of this method the sample is fumed with perchloric acid to volatilize ruthenium (321) before passing the solution through the anion exchange column, whereas in another modification an aliquot of the sample solution is adjusted to pH 1 and cesium carrier and ruthenium, zirconium, and barium holdback carriers are added prior to transferring the solution to the column (462). The ^{137}Cs in the eluate is in equilibrium with a short-lived daughter, [137]Ba, the activity of which is measured on a gamma scintillation spectrometer. In another procedure, anion exchange resin in the hydroxide form is used to separate ^{89}Sr and ^{137}Cs from other fission products (97). Before the solution is passed through the ion exchange column, cerous nitrate is added as holdback carrier for radiocerium. Strontium is separated from cesium by treating the eluate with sodium carbonate.

It has been shown (167) that radiocesium can be collected with cesium and/or potassium dipicrylaminate. Cesium or potassium carrier is added to the solution, which is then neutralized to pH 2 to 4. Small amounts of ferric chloride and strontium nitrate are added, and the solution is rendered alkaline with sodium carbonate. After centrifuging, the supernatant liquid is twice more scavenged as before and then is slightly acidified with hydrochloric acid. A small amount of strontium holdback carrier is added, and the cesium is then precipitated with magnesium dipicrylaminate. After cooling at 0°C., the precipitate is filtered, washed with ice water, finally washed with ether, and then dried, weighed, and counted. The removal of [144]Ce, ^{90}Sr, ^{90}Y, [106]Ru, [95]Zr, and [95]Nb is 99.5% effective.

Sodium tetraphenylboron has been suggested by several authors as precipitant for radiocesium (170,202), although others have reported some difficulties in obtaining quantitative precipitation at high acidities (208). In one procedure, after the addition of cesium carrier and zirconium, lanthanum, and ruthenium holdback carriers, the cesium is precipitated in a $0.4N$ nitric acid medium with tetraphenylboron reagent (202). The precipitate is collected on a filter, and the gamma activity is counted. This procedure is said to give decontamination factors of about 100 for zirconium, niobium, and the rare earths and from 20 to 100 for ruthenium. In another tetraphenylboron procedure (170), other fission products are first removed by the addition of sodium hydroxide and sodium carbonate with iron, barium, lanthanum, and zirconium being used as carriers. After a second scavenging step, the supernatant liquid is acidified with hydrochloric acid, and the cesium is precipitated with tetraphenylboron reagent. The precipitate, consisting of radio- and carrier cesium tetraphenylboron is twice reprecipitated with intermittent solution in acetone. It is finally collected on a filter disk, washed, dried, weighed, and counted. Old mixed fission products contain only ^{137}Cs, whereas young fission products contain ^{136}Cs also. In the former case, the separated cesium may be counted on a well-type scintillation counter, whereas the presence of ^{136}Cs requires counting on a multichannel gamma ray spectrometer. The method provides a decontamination factor of 10^6 for the following radionuclides: ^{90}Sr, ^{103}Ru, ^{95}Zr-^{95}Nb, and ^{144}Ce.

To determine low concentrations of radiocesium in water, three different approaches have been shown to yield satisfactory results. All three methods use $CsClO_4$ as the final weighing form (208).

1. To a 1 liter sample acidified with nitric acid, cesium carrier, ammonium molybdate solution, and phosphoric acid are added. The dense yellow precipitate of cesium ammonium phosphomolybdate is allowed to settle, the bulk of the supernatant liquid is decanted off, and the remaining solution with precipitate is centrifuged. After washing with nitric acid $(1M)$, the precipitate is dissolved in ammonia. The solution is acidified, and the molybdenum precipitated as lead molybdate. In the supernatant liquid, lead is precipitated with ammonium carbonate, centrifuged, and discarded. The supernatant solution is evaporated to dryness to expel ammonium salts, perchloric acid is added, and the cesium is finally collected and weighed as the perchlorate and then mounted and counted.

2. Cesium and potassium carriers are added to 1 liter of the sample and are then precipitated as cobaltinitrites. After decanting of the supernatant liquid, centrifuging, and washing, the precipitate is dissolved in hydrochloric acid, and the cesium is subsequently precipitated as the silicotungstate. After centrifuging, decanting of the supernatant liquid, and further washing, the precipitate is dissolved in dilute sodium hydroxide and scavenged by the precipitation of ferric hydroxide in the alkaline medium. After removal of the ferric hydroxide, perchloric acid is added, and the solution evaporated to fumes for the removal of WO_3 and SiO_2. After centrifuging, the supernatant solution is evaporated to fumes of perchloric acid, and the cesium is finally collected and weighed as the perchlorate.

3. In an ion exchange procedure, 1 liter of sample solution is passed through a cation exchange column in the hydrogen form. The cesium is eluted with $6M$ hydrochloric acid and is then precipitated as the silico-tungstate.

In another procedure, which avoids the use of perchloric acid, radio-cesium of satisfactory radiochemical purity is separated from solutions containing 10^4 to 10^6 times as much activity in other radionuclides (450). The sample is first scavenged by sulfide precipitation of tellurium, ru-thenium, antimony, and silver carriers, then by hydroxide precipitation of lanthanum, cerium, yttrium, zirconium, and niobium carriers, and finally by carbonate precipitations of barium and strontium. These scavengings are repeated, and then $Cs_8SiW_{12}O_{42}$ and Cs_2PtCl_6 are each precipitated twice. This procedure is claimed to give greater than 90% recoveries. A similar procedure, which involves perchloric acid fuming for the removal of radioruthenium, yields radiocesium of very high purity but is only 60% quantitative (131). In an entirely different procedure, radiocesium is carried on a cobaltous cobalticyanide precipitate formed in about $3N$ sulfuric acid medium. This separates it from large amounts of other fission product contaminants except ruthenium. After dissolution of the pre-cipitate in $5N$ sulfuric acid, the ruthenium is volatilized by boiling in the presence of periodic acid. Further decontamination steps involve a ferric hydroxide scavenging and a reprecipitation of the cobaltous-cobalticyanide (242). It is reported that this procedure gives a decontamination factor greater than 10^5 for the gamma-emitting Zr-[95]Nb, [106]Ru, [144]Ce, and [125]Sb and that the recovery of radiocesium is greater than 99%. Other complex cobalticyanides that produce more than 90% radiocesium recoveries are those of zinc and cadmium (365). Nickel ferrocyanide has also been investigated (277).

To determine the extent of horizontal and vertical transport of long-lived fission products deposited on the surface of the Atlantic Ocean from nuclear weapons tests, as much as 200 liters of water has been processed in one operation (417). To remove ^{90}Sr, [144]Ce, and [147]Pm, the sea water, after the addition of strontium, iron, and cesium carriers, is rendered alkaline with sodium carbonate. The clear supernatant liquid is siphoned off and then is treated with sodium cobaltinitrite reagent to precipitate the cesium along with the normal amounts of potassium and rubidium found in ocean water. The filtered and washed cobaltinitrite precipitate is dissolved in hydrochloric acid, and the cesium is precipitated as cesium silicotungstate. After filtration and washing, the precipitate is dissolved in dilute sodium hydroxide, and the solution is passed through a column containing Dowex 1, which removes the anions resulting from the decomposition of the silico-tungstate. Subsequently, the cesium, eluted with $0.001M$ sodium hydroxide, is precipitated as the perchlorate. The cesium perchlorate, still containing some rubidium and lighter alkali metals, is dissolved in $0.30M$ hydrochloric acid, the solution is passed through Duolite C-3, a phenol-sulfonic-type cation exchanger, and the cesium is finally eluted with $3.0M$ hydrochloric acid. In the eluate, the cesium is collected and weighed as the perchlorate and is then mounted and counted.

Although the metabolism of radiocesium in biological systems has been studied in appreciable detail (182), no consideration was previously given to the consequences of the differential behavior of ^{137m}Ba, the radioactive daughter of ^{137}Cs. According to the decay scheme, ^{137}Cs decays by beta emission with a 33 year half life to ^{137m}Ba, which in turn decays by gamma emission with a half life of 2.6 minutes to a stable state. In the organism, ^{137}Cs would be expected to have a metabolic behavior similar to that of potassium, whereas ^{137m}Ba would be expected to behave more like calcium. It was recently reported (434) that 4 to 7 days after ^{137}Cs administration ^{137m}Ba exceeded the ^{137}Cs-^{137m}Ba equilibrium proportion in bone and plasma by factors of 3 and 14, respectively, in the living animal. This demonstrates the in vivo escape of ^{137m}Ba from sites of ^{137}Cs accumulation.

c. Determination of Potassium and Rubidium by Their Natural Radioactivity

The natural radioactivity of potassium and rubidium has been proposed as the basis of analytical methods for the determination of these two elements. That ^{40}K, with a half life of 1.32×10^9 years, is the radioactive isotope of potassium was shown in 1937 (398). The abundance of this lightest naturally occurring radioactive isotope has been established as 0.0119% (298). Its decay involves the production of ^{40}Ar and ^{40}Ca (398, 423). ^{40}K is both a beta and gamma emitter. Natural rubidium contains a radioactive isotope, ^{87}Rb, with an abundance of 27.85% and a half life of 5.0×10^{10} years. ^{87}Rb emits only a rather soft beta ray, only one-third as energetic as that of potassium. The radioactivity is only a measure of the amount of radioactive ^{40}K or ^{87}Rb. Since the analyst is usually interested in the total amount of the two elements, the development of analytical methods had to wait until the isotopic composition of the two elements could be accurately determined. All methods that have been proposed for the determination of potassium and/or rubidium by measurements of the natural activity are based on the assumption that the activity of a given sample is directly proportional to its potassium and/or rubidium content and that no isotopic separation occurred during any of the ordinary processes to which the sample may have been subjected. It has actually been shown (397a) that there exists no variation either in the $^{39}K/^{40}K$ or in the $^{39}K/^{41}K$ ratio in various rocks, in sea water, and in commercial potassium.

Interference in methods based on counting the natural radioactivity of samples must be expected from elements of the uranium-radium, uranium-actinium, and thorium series and also from lutecium and samarium. Whereas lutecium and samarium are very rare, possible interference from uranium in equilibrium with its decay products is roughly 2000 times the activity of potassium (151). Thus, a mineral sample containing 0.0005% U_3O_8 exhibits about the same amount of measurable beta activity as one containing 1% of K_2O. The correction needed in radiometric analysis of an average granite containing 5% potassium and 0.0005% U_3O_8 is therefore 20%. Since potassium does not emit alpha particles, an alpha count of the sample determines the magnitude of any correction that must be applied to the beta ray assay. It is also necessary to apply density corrections if samples of differing density are analyzed by comparison with a standard.

In the first analytical application of the natural radioactivity of potassium (27), 200 ml. of a potassium solution was placed in a jacket surrounding a thin-walled Geiger counter, which counted the radioactivity entering the counter. The measured activity was found to increase with the concentration of the solution, but the increase was not quite proportional to the potassium concentration. This was attributed to the increased self-absorption of the radiation in the more dense solutions. In the determination of potassium in fertilizers containing from 40 to 60% K_2O, results by the counting method show a standard deviation from those by the chemical method of 0.78% and a coefficient of variation of 1.57% (236b,455). Rubidium and potassium in mixtures of their chlorides can be determined to $\pm0.5\%$ by measuring the beta activity of ^{40}K and ^{87}Rb, with and without the use of a 0.05 mm. aluminum absorber, by counting thicknesses of 90 mg./cm.^{2} for 3 hours (164). The counting method has also been applied to the determination of potassium in glass (189) and various salt mixtures (230). A unique application of the method is the determination of the natural ^{40}K activity in man by means of the Los Alamos human counter (12). This natural ^{40}K activity in man amounts to about 0.013 μc. as gamma rays and can be measured to a precision of better than 5% in less than 2 minutes (11).

d. Age Determination of Rocks Based on the ^{40}Ar/^{40}K Ratio

The age determination of rocks is a subject of importance to geology and allied disciplines. Methods based on radioactivity remain the only means of absolute measurements of age. The decay of ^{40}K to form ^{40}Ar is an isotopic chronometer of especial interest (83). The widespread occurrence of potassium minerals and the relatively high concentration of potassium in basalt, which covers a large part of the oceanic globe, makes this particular age determination procedure one of outstanding geological importance. The method can also be applied to minerals of metamorphic rocks, such as schist and gnéiss. The decay scheme for ^{40}K is essentially as follows:

$$^{40}_{19}K \longrightarrow {}^{40}_{20}Ca + e$$

$$^{40}_{19}K + e \longrightarrow {}^{40}_{18}Ar + \gamma$$

The branching ratio $\lambda\gamma/\lambda\beta$, determined by various techniques, ranges from 0.105 to 0.115. The energy of the single gamma that is associated with the decay to ^{40}Ar exceeds the maximum beta energy of the ^{40}Ca branch. The activity is considered to be associated with the electron capture to an excited state of ^{40}Ar. The equation for argon accumulation in a mineral is

$$^{40}Ar = [NR/(1 + R)] \{\exp [(1R)\lambda\beta t] - 1\}$$

where ^{40}Ar is the number of ^{40}Ar atoms formed in time t (in years); $\lambda\beta$ is the fraction of ^{40}K atoms decaying per year to ^{40}Ca; N is the number of ^{40}K atoms left at time t; and R is $\lambda\gamma/\lambda\beta$. For an age determination, ^{40}Ar and ^{40}K are measured; t can then be calculated if the constants R and $\lambda\beta$ are known. However, $\lambda\beta$ and $\lambda\gamma$, and hence R, are not known with high precision. Measurements of the γ activity range from 2.6 to 3.6 disintegrations/second per gram of potassium, whereas those of the β activity range from 23 to 34 disintegrations/second per gram of potassium. Recent work (83) places the γ activity at 3.33 ± 0.09 and the β activity at 82.6 ± 0.09.

Several assumptions are made in age determinations: (1) that no argon is trapped within the mineral at the time of its formation, (2) that potassium and argon are not added or subtracted during the lifetime of the mineral, (3) that values for isotopic abundance of potassium (0.0119 ± 0.0001%) (298) are correct, and (4) that the analysis is correct. Factors 1, 3, and 4 present no significant problems. However, it has been indicated (83) that variable amounts of argon can be lost from some minerals. Feldspar retentivity usually is lower than that of micas. In practice, this method of age determination requires the quantitative determination of both elements.   The potassium determination can be performed by wet chemical or flame photometric methods.   The argon determination involves the quantitative release of argon from the sample, purification, and mass spectrometric measurements using isotope dilution techniques.

E. STABLE ISOTOPE DILUTION TECHNIQUES (98)

The general subject of the application of the stable isotope dilution technique as an analytical tool was recently reviewed (190).   In brief, the method consists in the use of a tracer isotope as an internal standard in mass spectrometric analysis.   The method has the advantage that complete or known chemical recovery of the element to be analyzed is not necessary.   The second great advantage is the sensitivity of the method, which makes it eminently suited for sub–parts per million range.   However, this great sensitivity does not preclude its use in the macro range, as, for instance, in the determination of potassium in silicates.

Contamination is the major problem encountered in the isotope dilution technique.   Resulting errors are all additive, and they are not compensated by small losses.   Consequently, it is necessary to take appropriate steps to guard against contamination.   Contamination can be avoided to a great degree by employing simplified procedures requiring a minimum number of very pure reagents.   These simplified procedures are permissible because low yields can be accepted with the isotope dilution method without error.   A typical procedure encompasses the following steps: (1) a weighed portion of the sample is dissolved in an appropriate solvent; (2) a known weight of an isotopically enriched tracer of the element in question is added to the sample solution (usually in form of an aliquot of a standard stock solution);   (3) tracer and sample are thoroughly equilibrated;   (4) the element in question, consisting of an equilibrated mixture of normal and tracer isotope, is extracted chemically (this step is not always necessary); and (5) the change in isotopic composition of the sample, caused by the dilution with the isotopically enriched spike, is determined mass spectrometrically.

A detailed procedure for the determination of potassium in silicates follows (149).   A sample weighing 0.5 to 2.5 g. is decomposed in a platinum dish with 5 to 10 ml. of hydrofluoric acid and 2 to 5 ml. of perchloric acid. The solution is evaporated to fumes of $HClO_4$, diluted with water, and transferred to a 100 ml. volumetric flask.   A known aliquot of the solution, usually 2 ml. (determined both volumetrically and gravimetrically), to which a known amount of ^{41}K tracer has been added, is transferred to a small beaker and evaporated to dryness after the addition of a small amount of sulfuric acid.   The sulfates are dissolved in about 0.5 ml. of water, and from 10 to 100 γ of the K_2SO_4 is placed on a preheated (in vacuum to volatilize contaminants) tantalum filament. Isotope ratios are then obtained by scanning the mass spectrum and graphically measuring peak heights. The only quantitative steps in the procedure are the addition of the ^{41}K tracer solution, the measurement of the 2% aliquot, and the measurement of the peak heights.

Stable isotopes are available from both the United States Atomic Energy Commission and the British Atomic Energy Commission. Obviously, the preparation of the tracer solution is important because the accuracy of the analysis is directly dependent on the accuracy with which the tracer solution has been prepared. A simple method of preparing the tracer is to add a weighed amount of tracer to a known volume of solvent. However, there are two disadvantages to the method: (1) a large amount (that is, of the order of 50 mg.) of sample is necessary for an accurate gravimetric determination, and (2) the result depends on the purity of the tracer. A preferable method is to calibrate the tracer against a standard solution of a reagent grade potassium salt. A known volume of tracer solution is added to a known amount of a pure salt solution. The difference between the isotopic ratio before mixing and that after mixing allows the tracer concentration to be determined. The best possible tracer is one whose abundance differs from the normal isotope abundance by the greatest possible factor. A good approximation to this ideal is available. For example, the isotope ratio of the tracer obtainable from the United States Atomic Energy Commission is given here.

	^{39}K	^{40}K	^{41}K	Ref.
ORNL (EY626)	0.789	0.002	99.21	(149)
Normal	93.08	0.0119	6.91	(298)

For the purpose of calculation, the following ratios and quantities may be designated:

$R_1 = {}^{41}K/({}^{41}K + {}^{39}K + {}^{40}K)$ = atomic fraction of ^{41}K in normal potassium

$R_2 = {}^{41}K/({}^{41}K + {}^{39}K + {}^{40}K)_{tracer}$ = atomic fraction of ^{41}K in tracer potassium

$R_3 = {}^{41}K/({}^{41}K + {}^{39}K + {}^{40}K)_{mixture}$ = atomic fraction of ^{41}K in mixture

M_1 = μmoles of potassium in sample

M_2 = μmoles of potassium added as tracer

Equating the sum of the amount of ^{41}K in tracer and standard to the amount of ^{41}K in the mixture,

$$M_1R_1 + M_2R_2 = (M_1 + M_2)R_3$$

Solving for M_1,

$$M_1 = M_2(R_2 - R_3)/(R_3 - R_1)$$

Example. One g. of a sample is dissolved in 100 ml. of solution. To a 2 ml. aliquot is added 2 ml. of a solution containing 1 μ mole/ml. of potassium with the composition about 99.21% ^{41}K. The isotope ratio of the mixture is determined by mass spectrometry to be $R_3 = 0.328$. What is the potassium concentration in the unknown sample in per cent?

$M_1 = 2$ μmoles $\times$ $(0.992 - 0.328)/(0.328 - 0.069)$
     $= 5.12$ μmoles
     $= 5.12 \times 10^{-6} \times 39.14$ g. $= 200 \times 10^{-6}$ g. or $50 \times 200 \times 10^{-6} = 10 \times 10^{-3}$ g.
     in the 100 ml. of solution containing 1 g. of unknown. Thus the unknown contains 1% potassium.

The isotope dilution technique has been used to find the age of stony meteorites by determining the $^{87}Rb/^{87}Sr$ ratio (370). Known amounts of rubidium and strontium of different isotopic compositions are added to the dissolved meteorite. Rubidium and strontium are isolated as chlorides by ion exchange prior to evaporation of a drop of solution containing 0.05 γ of strontium and 0.05 γ of rubidium on a tantalum strip. The stable isotope dilution technique has also been applied to the determination of lithium in rocks (393) and of rubidium in rocks and sea water (392).

VII. ANALYSIS OF ALKALI METALS, ALLOYS, AND COMPOUNDS

A. ALKALI METALS AND ALLOYS (407)

Many of the analytical procedures used for the alkali metals involve, as a preliminary step, conversion to the corresponding alkali metal hydroxides or salts. It is therefore not surprising that the analysis of the free alkali metals is, in many ways, quite similar to the analysis of the corresponding salts or hydroxides. Thus, for example, the procedure used to determine trace chloride in lithium hydroxide can be applied almost without modification to the determination of chloride impurity in lithium metal. However, some of the analytical procedures used for the alkali metals do have unique features, and these will be discussed in some detail.

The liquefied alkali metals have recently been studied as possible heat transfer fluids. This work has provided the major impetus for the recent developments in the analytical chemistry of the alkali metals. At an early stage, it was found that the presence of trace impurities, at the parts per million level, can have profound influence upon the corrosiveness of the liquid alkali metals. The development of suitable analytical procedures was necessary before the impurity level in the alkali metals could be measured and controlled. The sampling of the alkali metals and alloys involves many difficulties (cf. Section III-A), caused mainly by the vigorous reactivity of these substances with air, water, and containing vessels and by the temperature dependence of the solubilities of various impurities.

1. Determination of Sodium Monoxide in Sodium or Sodium-Potassium Alloys

The principle of all the methods given here is that the alkali metal is removed from the sample and the base equivalent is then assumed to be a measure of the oxygen content of the sample. Oxide, hydroxide, and hydride can contribute to the total base equivalent of the residue. If these are present in unknown proportions, the base equivalent of the residue is by itself no measure of the oxygen content of the sample. The usefulness of the mercury extraction and butyl bromide methods is derived from the fact that, in the large majority of cases of practical interest, the oxygen content far exceeds the hydrogen content of the sample. Under the conditions of the distillation procedure, sodium hydride and sodium hydroxide are decomposed. Hydrogen, therefore, does not interfere with the distillation method.

a. MERCURY EXTRACTION METHOD

The mercury extraction method depends upon the fact that the alkali metals dissolve in mercury while compounds of the alkali metals remain insoluble. The alkali metal is physically separated from the oxide by repeated extractions with mercury (85a,315,316,454). The procedure briefly is as follows: A portion of mercury is added to the sodium, and a vigorous reaction results, with the formation of a liquid sodium amalgam. The sodium oxide floats on the surface of the amalgam. The bulk of the amalgam is then drawn off through a capillary stopcock at the base of the container. Loss of the oxide through the stopcock is prevented by the small column of amalgam remaining in the container. Further portions of mercury are added and drawn off until tests show that the last traces of metallic sodium have been removed from the container. The sodium oxide remaining in the container is dissolved in a small volume of water and titrated with $0.01M$ acid. In the original method (315,316), purified argon or nitrogen is used as a cover gas. An essential part of the apparatus consists of a thin rubber tube. A modified procedure (454) can be operated either under high vacuum or with purified inert gas, and the use of the rubber tubing is eliminated. The precision values reported for this method are close to 0.0010 wt. % oxygen. Sodium-potassium eutectic alloy, which consists of 77.2 wt. % potassium and 22.8 wt. % sodium, freezes at −12.3°C. This alloy can be analyzed in exactly the same manner as sodium.

b. Butyl Bromide Method

This method, as applied to sodium, was first described in 1954 (445). Subsequently, improvements were introduced in the preparation of the reagent and in sample handling, and a modified procedure for use with sodium-potassium alloys was reported (384). The method is based on the fact that the alkali metals react with organic halides to form neutral salts whereas the oxides do not react.

$$2Na + 2C_4H_9Br \longrightarrow 2NaBr + C_8H_{18}$$

$$Na_2O + C_4H_9Br \longrightarrow no\ reaction$$

For the analysis of sodium, a solution of 40 to 60% n-butyl bromide in hexane is used. Sodium-potassium alloy, which reacts more vigorously, is treated initially with a 10 to 25 vol. % solution of n-butyl bromide, and the temperature is kept at 30 to 35°C. by intermittent cooling on a dry-ice bath. After the bulk of the alkali metal has reacted, heating to 60 to 70°C. is necessary in order to drive the reaction to completion. The oxides are then extracted with water and titrated with standard acid. In using this method, it is necessary that the last traces of alkali metal be reacted and that the reagents used be very thoroughly dried. The method is relatively rapid and has the advantage that the same sample can be used in analyzing for both oxygen and metallic impurities. The method has also been used for the determination of metallic sodium in the presence of sodium hydride (279a). It was observed that, when metallic sodium in liquid ammonia is titrated with n-butyl bromide in hexane, a sharp color change from blue to colorless appears at the end point.

$$2Na + C_4H_9Br + NH_3 \rightarrow NaBr + NaNH_2 + C_4H_{10}$$

c. Distillation Method

Still another method (443) involves the removal of sodium from the sodium oxide by distillation at 425°C. at a pressure of less than 5 μ of mercury. The sodium oxide, which remains behind, is then titrated with standard acid.

d. Infrared Method

Traces of oxygen in sodium metal can also be determined by infrared spectrophotometry by treating the sample with alkyl bromide, dissolving the reaction mixture in water; and converting the resulting NaOH into $NaHCO_3$ by passing in an excess of CO_2; the dried salts ($NaBr$–Na_2CO_3) are compressed into disks, and the absorbance of the Na_2CO_3 is measured at 11.38 μ (102a).

2. Determination of Lithium Oxide in Lithium

Attempts to extend the methods developed for sodium to lithium meet with difficulties. The butyl bromide method fails because it is impossible to quantitatively react the lithium with the butyl bromide. The mercury extraction procedure, as applied to lithium, has serious disadvantages. The amalgamation process requires considerable care if the reaction is to be done inside a glass vessel. Neither of these methods, in which the base equivalent of the unreacted or undissolved residue is measured, distinguishes between oxide, nitride, hydride, carbide, etc. Although the nonspecificity of the two methods is not too serious a disadvantage in the case of sodium, it is serious in the case of lithium. Lithium readily forms nitrides, and the nitride content of metallic lithium is usually comparable to the oxide content. In addition, the hydride of lithium, and most probably the carbide and phosphide, are considerably more stable than the corresponding sodium compounds.

a. Karl Fischer Titration Method

Several different approaches have been used to determine the oxygen content of lithium metal. One method (408) involves the conversion of the oxygen in the lithium to water and subsequent determination of this water with Karl Fischer reagent. The sample of lithium is initially dissolved in absolute methanol. This solution is combined with an excess of salicylic acid. The water that is formed in stoichiometric amount from the oxide is titrated with Karl Fischer reagent. The following chemical reactions occur:

$$2Li + 2CH_3OH \longrightarrow 2LiOCH_3 + H_2$$

$$Li_2O + CH_3OH \longrightarrow LiOH + LiOCH_3$$

$$LiOCH_3 + C_6H_4OHCOOH \longrightarrow LiC_6H_4OHCOO + CH_3OH$$

$$LiOH + C_6H_4OHCOOH \longrightarrow LiC_6H_4OHCOO + H_2O$$

$$SO_2 + I_2 + 3C_5H_5N + CH_3OH + H_2O \longrightarrow$$
$$C_5H_5NHSO_4CH_3 + 2C_5H_5NHI$$

Nitride, carbide, and hydride do not interfere. Special precautions are necessary to prevent the introduction of contaminants, such as air or moisture, into the analytical apparatus. The dead stop direct titration method is used in the Karl Fischer titration. Various refinements in the titration procedure are necessary to obtain the desired accuracy and sensitivity. The reproducibility of this method is 10 to 20 γ of oxygen. One serious disadvantage of this method is that a large blank correction is necessary for the water content of the methanol, even though the methanol is carefully dried to a water content of 5 to 10 p.p.m.

A similar procedure has been applied to the determination of hydroxide in lithium hydride (142a).

b. RADIOACTIVATION PROCEDURE

Another approach is based on neutron activation (442). The sample of lithium is packed in lithium fluoride and irradiated with neutrons. Samples of known oxygen content, such as Li_2CO_3, are irradiated simultaneously. The nuclear reactions that occur are

$$^6Li + {}_0^1N \longrightarrow {}^4He + {}^3H$$

$$H_3 + {}^{16}O \longrightarrow {}^{18}F + {}_0^1N$$

The ^{18}F activity (half life = 1.87 hours, $\beta^+ = 0.65$ m.e.v.) can be determined with standard radiochemical procedures.

3. Determination of Hydrogen in Alkali Metals

a. DIFFUSION GASOMETRIC METHOD

A unique method has been developed for the determination of hydrogen in sodium and in sodium-potassium alloys (318). The metal is sealed inside an iron capsule. The capsule is placed inside the vacuum system, which is then evacuated. The capsule is heated to 700°C. At this temperature, the hydrogen in the sample evolves and diffuses through the walls of the capsule. From a determination of the hydrogen pressure inside a static system, the hydrogen content of the sample can be computed. Hydrogen present as sodium hydroxide is recovered because at temperatures in excess of 450°C. the following reaction takes place:

$$2Na + 2NaOH \longrightarrow 2Na_2O + H_2$$

An average deviation of 0.0010 wt. % hydrogen has been reported. This method is most probably not satisfactory for hydrogen in lithium, because of the exceptional stability of lithium hydride.

b. Isotope Dilution Method

In another method for the determination of hydrogen in sodium and in sodium-potassium alloys (180), deuterium gas is heated with the sample of alkali metal to 460°C.   Under these conditions, there is a rapid exchange of hydrogen isotopes.   The isotopic composition of the gas, in equilibrium with the alkali metal, is analyzed with a mass spectrometer.   From this analysis, the hydrogen content of the alkali metal can be calculated.   The standard deviation is about 3 γ of hydrogen.   This method has the advantage that it does not depend upon the quantitative extraction of hydrogen from the sample.

c. Vacuum Fusion and Similar Methods

Some preliminary work on the determination of hydrogen in lithium using a vacuum fusion apparatus with a tin bath has been reported (266). This approach seems promising.   A similar method has been used for the determination of hydrogen in lithium hydride (32,138).   It is probably applicable also to the determination of hydrogen in lithium and other alkali metals.   In this method, the sample is placed in a tin or mercury bath, which is then heated to boiling.   The mercury or tin combines with the alkali metal that is formed from the dissociation of the hydride.   The activity of the alkali metal is thereby reduced, and the dissociation of the hydride is favored.   The hydrogen evolved is determined by a gasometric method.

4. Determination of Nitrogen in Alkali Metals

Lithium is the only alkali metal that readily forms a stable nitride. The determination of nitride in lithium involves reaction with water to produce lithium hydroxide and ammonia.   The ammonia and part of the water are distilled into a small beaker containing a few milliliters of dilute sulfuric acid.   An aliquot of the distillate is mixed with Nessler reagent, and the absorbance at 420 mμ is measured (361a).

5. Determination of Carbon in Alkali Metals

a. Total Carbon

A combustion procedure for the determination of carbon in sodium-potassium alloys has been described (410).   In this procedure, a sample of about 100 mg. is ignited in a stream of oxygen.   The carbon in the sample is converted to carbon dioxide, which is then absorbed in an Ascarite-Drierite micro absorption bulb. The combustion tube is made of quartz, and the section containing the sample is externally heated to 950°C. Apparently sufficient heat is evolved in the region where combustion occurs to prevent combination of the carbon dioxide with the alkali oxides. An asbestos plug serves to confine the oxide fumes within the combustion area and prevents their being carried to the cooler parts of the apparatus. Both positive and negative errors can result if the oxide fumes are carried beyond the combustion area. Recovery tests indicate an average deviation of the procedure of 0.005%.

A procedure for free carbon in sodium, which employs wet combustion, has also been described (317). The sodium sample is cut into small pieces, which are then dissolved one by one in a small volume of water under a stream of nitrogen. The resulting solution is neutralized with sulfuric acid until an excess of the acid is present. The mixture is evaporated to near dryness, and then Van Slyke combustion fluid (430) is added. Upon heating, the carbon is oxidized to carbon dioxide, which is collected and measured in a gasometer. A typical analysis reported (317) is 0.0051 ± 0.0014 wt. % carbon.

b. CARBIDE CARBON

The combustion methods measure only the total carbon content of the sample. There is evidence to the effect that the carbon impurity in lithium metal at elevated temperatures exists in the form of lithium carbide (326). When a sample of lithium metal containing lithium carbide is dissolved in water, hydrogen and acetylene gas are evolved. A method suitable for the determination of small amounts of acetylene in large amounts of hydrogen would therefore serve to determine the carbide content of lithium metal. Such a method has been developed (156). The sample of lithium is dissolved in water, and the evolved gases are passed through a $1.5M$ solution of silver perchlorate. The acetylene in the gas stream is absorbed and combines to form a silver perchlorate–acetylene complex. This complex shows strong light absorption in the ultraviolet. The acetylene content is determined by measuring the absorbance at 297 or 313 mμ. The method was tested with known amounts of acetylene in the range of 50 to 2500 γ.

6. Determination of Metallic Impurities in Alkali Metals

a. COLORIMETRIC METHODS

The first step consists in dissolving the alkali metal in water or alcohol (cf. Section VI-A). A solution is formed in which the alkali metal ion concentration is several orders of magnitude larger than the concentration of the trace impurities. The presence of relatively large quantities of alkali metals in solution is generally not detrimental to the analysis of trace impurities, provided that the impurity is present in fair concentration (about 50 p.p.m.). When the concentration of the impurity is below 10 p.p.m., removal of the bulk of the alkali metal becomes necessary (cf. Section IV-C-1). It should be noted that large amounts of alkali metals may reduce the color intensity of certain complexes, for example, chromium(VI) diphenylcarbazide.

An analytical scheme for the determination of iron and nickel in sodium has been described (346). A 6 g. sample of sodium is dissolved in methanol, neutralized with hydrochloric acid, and evaporated to dryness. The chlorides are dissolved in water, and the iron is precipitated as sulfide. The iron sulfide is dissolved in acid, and finally the iron thiocyanate complex is measured. For the determination of nickel, the residue of sodium and other chlorides is dissolved in a minimum quantity of water. Gaseous hydrochloric acid is then used to precipitate the bulk of the sodium chloride, which is discarded. The nickel, which remains in solution, is determined photometrically with dimethylglyoxime.

Traces of nickel in sodium metal can be determined by measuring the nickel cyanide complex, which absorbs strongly at 268 mμ (131a).

Trace quantities of iron in lithium hydride, hydroxide, and metal may be determined photometrically at a controlled pH by reduction of Fe^{+2} with hydroxylamine hydrochloride and formation of the ferrous o-phenanthroline complex (142b). If the concentration of iron is very low, preliminary concentration by carrier precipitation of ferric hydroxide on zirconium hydroxide may be necessary.

Microgram quantities of barium are determined by precipitation as $BaCrO_4$, followed by a spectrophotometric determination of the CrO_4^{-2} (110).

A procedure for the determination of submicrogram quantities of chromium and vanadium in alkali hydroxides uses ion exchange to isolate these elements (269). The chromium in the solution of alkali hydroxide is oxidized to the sexivalent state. The solution is passed through a column packed with Dowex 1 resin in the hydroxide form. Chromate is retained on the column and then eluted with ammonium carbonate solution. The eluate is concentrated, and the chromate determined with diphenylcarbazide. The procedure can be applied to 25 g. of sample containing as little as 0.03 p.p.m. chromium. It is equally applicable to alkali metals after solution of the sample in water or alcohols. The method for vanadium is similar to that for chromium. The vanadium in the quinquevalent state is eluted from the ion exchange column. The eluate is concentrated, and the vanadium determined indirectly with the ferrous phenanthroline complex. Another method of isolating chromium from alkali metal salts, prior to its colorimetric determination, uses solvent extraction with tri-octylphosphine oxide as the extractant (268).

In a method for the determination of boron in sodium metal that avoids the classical methyl borate distillation, the sodium is converted to sodium chloride, and the boron is extracted with ethyl alcohol. The boron is subsequently determined with curcumin reagent (353). With this method, a minimum of 0.9 p.p.m. boron is detectable. In another procedure for the determination of boron in sodium metal, the hydroxide is electrolyzed in the anode compartment of an electromigration cell fitted with a cation exchange membrane. The anode solution is purified with a small cation exchange column, and the alkaline eluate is evaporated prior to color development (258).

b. GRAVIMETRIC METHODS

For the determination of potassium, calcium, and magnesium in sodium metal, the sodium is first converted to sodium chloride. The metal is dissolved in a minimum quantity of water, and the sodium chloride precipitated with hydrogen chloride gas. The solution is filtered, and the filtrate concentrated. Potassium is determined as the perchlorate, calcium as the oxalate, and magnesium as the oxinate. This method was used to determine potassium in the range 3 to 8 mg., calcium in the range 0.1 to 0.4 mg. and magnesium in the 0.4 mg. range (385). It has been shown (352) that in the presence of large quantities of sodium chloride the oxalate precipitation of calcium is not quantitative. It was therefore suggested that the calcium be precipitated with 8-hydroxyquinoline prior to the precipitation as calcium oxalate. The method can be used to determine as little as 0.1 mg. of calcium.

c. FLAME PHOTOMETRIC METHODS

Flame photometric methods have been widely used to determine lithium, sodium, potassium, magnesium, calcium, and strontium, either as major constituents or as trace impurities. The composition of the sample can effect the results, and therefore the composition of the standards should closely match that of the unknowns. It has been shown, for instance, that in the determination of sodium and potassium in lithium metal the presence of large quantities of lithium causes a decrease of 7% in the sodium line intensity and 10% in the potassium radiation (191) (cf. Section IV-B-1).

d. Spectrographic Methods

The alkali metals are relatively volatile and have low excitation potentials (cf. Section IV-B-2). Consequently, their presence in large amounts is often objectionable in spectrographic analysis. Under certain experimental conditions, the presence of major amounts of alkali metals will reduce the sensitivity for some elements by as much as 10^4. One approach is to isolate the impurities from the alkali metals and then to analyze the impurities spectrographically. This method has been used (309) in developing a general spectrographic procedure for the determination of impurities in lithium metal and other alkali metals. The elements that can be determined are Be, Cr, Co, Fe, Ni, Nb, Mn, Mo, Ta, Ti, U, V, W, and Zr in the range 10^{-1} to $10^{-4}\%$. The alkali metal is dissolved in water and filtered. The insoluble residue contains all of the Co, Ti, U, V, Ta, and Zr. Some of the Be, Cr, Fe, Ni, Nb, Mn, Mo, and W are dissolved in the alkali hydroxide solution. Be and Nb are recovered by precipitation with 8-hydroxyquinoline, and the others by precipitation as the sulfides. The residue and precipitates are dissolved in mineral acids and analyzed by the porous cup technique. In a second approach to the spectrographic analysis of alkali metals (204), the sample is converted to the sulfate and well mixed with graphite powder. This mixture is then placed in a deep anode cup and burned to completion in a 15 amp. d.c. arc. The buffering effect of the graphite, the deep anode cup, the high amperage, and the complete burning all contribute to minimizing the suppressive effect of the alkali metal. Preliminary results show that the limits of detection of Mo, Mn, V, Cr, Ni, Fe, W, Zr, Ta, and Nb are in the range 1 to 10 p.p.m.

e. Activation Methods

Activation methods have been used to determine submicrogram quantities of alkali metal impurities (cf Section VI-D-1). For instance, a procedure has been described (92) for the determination of rubidium and cesium in sodium-potassium alloys. The sample is irradiated in a neutron flux and then dissolved in methanol. Rubidium and cesium carriers are then added, and sodium cobaltinitrite is used to separate the potassium, rubidium, and cesium from the sodium. Ion exchange is used to separate the potassium, rubidium, and cesium into fractions. The rubidium and cesium fractions are then precipitated as cobaltinitrites, and the beta-gamma activities of the ^{86}Rb and ^{136}Cs measured. Rubidium analysis in the range 1 to 60 p.p.m. and cesium analysis in the range 0.18 to 0.05 p.p.m. are reported. A neutron activation method for the determination of sodium in lithium metal has also been described (390).   This method is used for sodium in the range 0.02 to 300,000 p.p.m.

B. ALKALI SALTS

As would be expected, methods for the determination of various cations in alkali compounds are quite similar to those used for the free alkali metals, and techniques previously described for the free metals, such as spectrographic analysis, neutron activation, and ion exchange, are equally applicable to the compounds.   In addition to analysis for cations, the analysis of alkali salts frequently involves determination of or conformity tests for various anions.   A short summary of the more common chemical methods applicable to alkali salts follows.

Since virtually all alkali salts are water-soluble, sample preparation is rather simple and usually consists in dissolving an appropriate amount of sample (5 to 100 g.) in water or, in the case of hydroxides or carbonates, in dilute acids.   Fluorides or nitrites are converted to chlorides by evaporation with hydrochloric acid.   For the determination of extremely small amounts of impurities, it may be desirable to remove the bulk of the alkali metal by precipitation from a concentrated solution either as chloride (sodium) or perchlorate (potassium).

1. Cations

a. ALKALI METALS

The determination of small quantities of alkali metals occurring as impurities in alkali salts has been described in previous sections.

b. IRON

To the solution of the sample, free from nitrates, sufficient hydrochloric acid is added to reduce the pH to less than 1.   Hydroxylamine hydrochloride is added to reduce the iron, and then o-phenanthroline reagent and ammonium acetate are added.   Ammonium hydroxide is added to a pH of 7 to 8.   After half an hour, the absorbance of the solution is measured at 515 mμ.   The thiocyanate photometric procedure is preferred by some analysts and merely consists in adding a few milliliters of a 3% ammonium thiocyanate solution to a 0.5N hydrochloric acid solution of the sample. Ammonium persulfate is used to keep the iron oxidized.   By this method 0.01 mg. of iron can be detected (1).

c. Copper

The solution of the sample, containing from 2 to 60 γ of copper and citrate buffer, is transferred to a separatory funnel and neutralized with ammonia to a pH of about 9. Isoamyl alcohol is added, followed by a 0.2% solution of sodium diethyldithiocarbamate. After separation, the absorbance of the amyl alcohol layer is measured at 465 mμ (359,400).

Copper and zinc in sodium chloride have been determined polarographically after prior extraction with dithizone (416a).

d. Nickel

The solution of the sample, containing from 5 to 50 γ of nickel and citrate buffer, is transferred to a separatory funnel and neutralized with ammonia to a pH of about 9. Dimethylglyoxime solution is added, and the nickel complex is extracted with chloroform. The chloroform layer is washed with dilute ammonia and then shaken with dilute hydrochloric acid. The chloroform layer is discarded, citrate buffer is added, the pH is adjusted to 9, and nickel is extracted with sodium diethyldithiocarbamate and isoamyl alcohol. The transmittance is measured at 390 mμ (359).

e. Manganese

The solution of the sample, containing an excess of about 10 ml. of sulfuric acid, is evaporated to fumes. The solution is diluted and filtered, and the filtrate is diluted to about 100 ml. Then 0.3 g. of sodium paraperiodate is added, and the solution is heated to boiling and kept slightly below the boiling point for 30 minutes. The color is measured by comparison with standards in Nessler tubes or in a spectrophotometer at 525 mμ. For the determination of extremely small quantities of manganese, magnesium has been suggested as a collector prior to color development (471).

f. Other Cations

For the determination of various other metallic impurities in alkali salts, the methods used in the analysis of the free alkali metals may be applied. Since large amounts of alkali salts do not interfere with the photometric determination of most cations or can easily be removed, their presence can be tolerated in most procedures described in the literature.

2. Anions

a. TOTAL ALKALINITY

Total alkalinity contributed by Na_2CO_3, $NaOH$, K_2CO_3, and KOH is determined by titration with standard sulfuric acid with methyl orange as indicator.

b. CARBON DIOXIDE

Carbon dioxide can be determined indirectly by the method described for total alkalinity by precipitating the carbonate with barium chloride and titrating the sodium hydroxide with standard acid with phenolphthalein as indicator (400). Sodium bicarbonate is analyzed by titration with standard sodium hydroxide solution with silver nitrate as outside indicator.

c. CHLORIDE

Chloride is determined by the usual Volhard titration involving silver nitrate, ferric salt, and potassium thiocyanate reagents (400). Small amounts of chloride can be determined nephelometrically (1). The determination of sodium hypochlorite is performed by adding an excess of standard sodium arsenite solution in a sodium bicarbonate medium and back-titrating with standard iodine solution (13). Chlorate is determined by titrating with an excess of standard sodium arsenite solution and back-titrating the excess with standard ceric nitrate with ferroin as indicator and osmium tetraoxide as catalyst (400). Chlorate can also be determined by reduction with ferrous ethylenediamine sulfate and titration of the excess reducing agent with $0.1N$ sodium hypochlorite reagent (386a). Total chlorine in hypochlorites is determined by titration with silver nitrate in a nitric acid medium after reduction of the $NaOCl$ with sodium arsenite.

d. IODIDE AND BROMIDE

Iodide (I^-) is oxidized with ferric chloride to I_2, which is extracted with carbon tetrachloride. In the aqueous layer, the Br^- is oxidized with chromic acid and extracted with CCl_4. The violet color of I_2 and the yellow-brown color of Br_2 in the CCl_4 extracts are compared with standards (1).

e. NITROGEN

Total nitrogen in fertilizers containing $NaNO_3$ and/or KNO_3 is determined by digesting the sample with sulfuric acid containing salicylic acid, treating the solution with zinc dust or sodium thiosulfate and heating with mercury salt, distilling the ammonia into an excess of standard acid, and back-titrating the excess acid with standard alkali solution (13). Various methods have also been described to determine the amounts of nitrate nitrogen, ammoniacal nitrogen, and organic nitrogen (13). To determine traces of nitrate, it is frequently sufficient to use conformance tests to measure the degrees of oxidation of organic dyes by the nitrate ion (1).

f. SULFATE

Turbidimetric tests (1) for small amounts of sulfate or weighing of $BaSO_4$ for larger quantities (400) are usually adequate. Sulfur in the parts per million range, however, should first be converted into H_2S by a mixture of HI and H_3PO_2 and then distilled into a solution of zinc acetate. The sulfur is then determined colorimetrically after reaction with HCl, p-phenylenediamine, and $FeCl_3$ (47b).

g. PHOSPHATE

The molybdenum blue color method is well suited for minor quantities of phosphate (1). Methods are available for determining larger quantities of phosphorus by precipitation with ammonium molybdate and also for differentiating between hexameta-, trimeta-, ortho-, pyro-, and tripolyphosphates (400).

h. SILICA

SiO_2 is determined in the usual way by dehydration in acid solution or photometrically as molybdenum blue (1).

VIII. SELECTED LABORATORY PROCEDURES

As the preceding pages have demonstrated, there are a number of approaches to the determination of the alkali metals in various inorganic and organic substances. The choice of technique and the type and number of preliminary separations depends on the composition of the sample, the number of samples to be analyzed, the available equipment, the training of personnel, and the accuracy required.

In this section, detailed, selected laboratory procedures are presented that have been thoroughly tested in the author's laboratory and that require the minimum in equipment and experience of personnel. For suitable methods of decomposing the sample, Section IV, which contains a general discussion of methods of sample preparation, should be consulted.

A. SEPARATION OF THE ALKALI METALS FROM EACH OTHER

1. Separation of Lithium from the Other Alkali Metals

a. 2-ETHYLHEXANOL METHOD (73)

Concentrate the chloride solution of the alkali metals as far as possible by evaporation, add from 30 to 50 ml. of 2-ethylhexanol (the technical grade is satisfactory), and evaporate at about 135°C. until dehydration is complete.   Care should be taken that dehydration is not carried out at the boiling point of the solvent; otherwise, low extraction yields will result owing to conversion of part of the lithium chloride into lithium hydroxide.   During the dehydration, the chlorides of sodium and potassium are deposited while lithium chloride is held in solution.

Decant the cold solution through a sintered-glass or Gooch crucible, and wash thoroughly with successive small portions of the cold alcohol, which has been previously dehydrated by boiling.   If the lithium content exceeds 100 mg., dissolve the insoluble residue in a little water, and repeat the separation by heating with additional 2-ethylhexanol.   (If desired, dry the crucible and salts at 210°C., and when cool, weigh as combined chlorides of sodium, potassium, rubidium, and cesium.)

Evaporate the filtrate and washings containing the lithium to dryness in a platinum dish, and moisten the residue with a little dilute sulfuric acid.   If there remains organic matter, destroy it by adding a few drops of nitric acid, and again evaporate to dryness.   Finally, ignite cautiously at a low temperature until every trace of acid is expelled, and then at 600°C. for about 10 minutes.   Cool, and weigh as Li_2SO_4.

2. Separation of Lithium, Sodium, and Potassium

a. BUTANOL–ETHYL ACETATE METHOD (453)

Add to a small beaker containing the aqueous solution of the mixed chlorides of the alkali metals 2 ml. of perchloric acid, and evaporate to complete dryness.   Wash down the sides of the beaker with a little water, and again evaporate to dryness.   Add to the cold salts 20 ml. of a mixture of equal parts by volume of anhydrous n-butanol and ethyl acetate, and digest near the boiling point for 2 to 3 minutes.   Cool to room temperature, decant the supernatant liquid through a tared Gooch crucible, and wash the residue three times by decantation with 5 ml. portions of the alcohol-acetate mixture.   Reserve the filtrate.

Determination of Potassium.   Dissolve the residue in a minimum amount of hot water, evaporate the solution to dryness, and digest the residue with a 10 ml. portion of the solvent. After cooling, filter through the dry original crucible, and wash thoroughly with a mixed solvent. Dry the beaker, and brush any unremoved particles into the Gooch crucible. Dry first at 110°C. and then for 15 minutes at 350°C. to complete the dehydration of the potassium perchlorate. Cool and weigh as $KClO_4$ plus $RbClO_4$ plus $CsClO_4$.

Determination of Sodium. Evaporate the combined filtrates containing the sodium and lithium on a hot plate to 20 ml. Add dropwise 2 ml., and then at once an additional 6 ml., of a 20% solution of hydrogen chloride in n-butanol (prepared by passing dry HCl gas into butanol until the specific gravity is 0.905). Cool, filter through a dry Gooch crucible, and wash the precipitate thoroughly with 1 to 2 ml. portions of a 6 to 7% solution of hydrogen chloride in n-butanol (prepared by adding to butanol the proper amount of the 20% solution of hydrogen chloride in butanol). Reserve the filtrate. Dry the precipitate and crucible for a few minutes at 110°C. and then for 10 minutes at 600°C. Weigh as impure NaCl, dissolve the residue in hot water, dry the crucible at 110°C., and again weigh. The loss in weight represents pure NaCl. Correct for solubility losses by adding 0.6 mg. of NaCl for each 100 ml. of combined filtrates and washings.

Determination of Lithium. Add to the filtrate from the sodium determination one-third its volume of water, and evaporate on a steam bath in such a way as to avoid condensation on the upper part of the beaker. When completely dry, add 10 ml. of water, 5 ml. of nitric acid, 3 ml. of perchloric acid, and 1 ml. of sulfuric acid. Evaporate to complete dryness, cool, dissolve the salts in hot water, transfer the solution to a tared platinum dish, and evaporate to dryness. Finally ignite cautiously until every trace of acid is removed; then ignite in a muffle at 600°C. for about 10 minutes. Cool, and weigh as Li_2SO_4.

3. Separation of Potassium, Rubidium, and Cesium

a. CHLORIDE SEPARATION METHOD (438)

Precipitate potassium, rubidium, and cesium together as chloroplatinates. (cf. Section VI-A-3) thus providing a separation from sodium and lithium, which can be determined in the filtrate. After the insoluble chloroplatinates have been weighed, reconvert the alkali metals to chlorides by solution in water, treatment with formic acid, and filtration. As an alternative procedure, collect the three alkali metals as perchlorates, convert to chlorides by ignition at about 600°C., and dissolve the chlorides in hot water.

Evaporate the chloride solution to dryness in a small beaker, dissolve the salts in 0.4 ml. of water, saturate the solution with hydrogen chloride gas, and add 10 ml. of ethanol saturated with hydrogen chloride. Filter through a small Gooch crucible, and wash with 2 ml. of a mixture of absolute alcohol and ether. Evaporate the filtrate to dryness, ignite cautiously, cool, and weigh. If the residue weighs less than 0.6 mg., rubidium and cesium are absent. More than one separation is required if the sample contains appreciable rubidium or cesium.

If the residue weighs more than 0.6 mg., separate cesium from rubidium as follows. Add to the dry alkali chlorides 0.1 ml. of a 0.5% ammonium sulfate solution to dissolve the alkali chlorides. Add dropwise 5 ml. of a solution prepared by dissolving 1 g. of ammonium sulfate in 20 ml. of water and 100 ml. of 95% alcohol and filtering. After half an hour of standing, filter through a Gooch crucible, and wash the precipitate, beaker, and crucible three times with 0.5 ml. portions of a wash solution prepared the same way as the alcoholic solution but containing also 0.16 g. of ammonium chloride per 100 ml. of solution. Evaporate the filtrate, which has been collected in a tared platinum dish, to dryness. Finally heat cautiously until all the ammonium chloride and sulfate are expelled. Weigh the cool residue as Cs_2SO_4. If the weight of Cs_2SO_4 calculated to CsCl plus 0.6 mg. of KCl (solubility of KCl in alcohol and hydrogen chloride) accounts for the combined weight of RbCl and CsCl, rubidium, of course, is absent. If the weight of the combined chlorides is greater than the weight just calculated, the difference is due to RbCl. It is a good practice to dissolve the residue containing the rubidium in water, to evaporate the solution to dryness in a platinum dish, and to weigh finally as Rb_2SO_4.

The method was recently reinvestigated by means of ^{42}K, ^{86}Rb, and ^{134}Cs as traces (465a). Advantages were demonstrated for a radioactive control of the separations.

b. Phosphomolybdic Acid–Silicotungstic Acid Method (304)

Add to the mixed chlorides of the three heavy alkali metals, containing not more than 0.08 g. of rubidium chloride and not more than 1 g. of potassium chloride, 100 ml. of 5N nitric acid, heat to near boiling, and add sufficient 9-phosphomolybdic acid (prepared from 12-phosphomolybdic acid by heating at 300 to 350°C, extraction with water, oxidation with bromine water, and slow evaporation) until precipitation is complete. Filter the precipitate, $(Rb,Cs)_3PO_4 \cdot 9MoO_3 \cdot 7H_2O$, through a Gooch crucible, and wash with a 1% solution of sodium nitrate. The filtrate contains the potassium, which can be determined as the chloroplatinate.

Dissolve the phosphomolybdate precipitate in the least possible amount of a dilute sodium hydroxide solution, heat to boiling, saturate with hydrogen sulfide, and then just acidify with dilute nitric acid. Boil to coagulate the molybdenum sulfide, filter, and wash with slightly acidified hydrogen sulfide water. Evaporate the filtrate to about 20 ml. To separate the cesium and rubidium from the phosphate ion, precipitate the two alkali metals as chloroplatinates by adding 60 ml. of alcohol, a slight excess of chloroplatinic acid, and a few milliliters of ether. Filter, wash with 80% alcohol, and reduce the chloroplatinates on the Gooch crucible by the addition of water and a few drops of hydrazine sulfate. Add aqua regia to the alkali chloride solution to destroy the hydrazine sulfate, and evaporate several times to dryness, with intermittent addition of hydrochloric acid, to destroy residual nitric acid.

Dissolve the salts in 50 ml. of $6N$ hydrochloric acid, and add to the cold solution 1 g. of silicotungstic acid dissolved in a few milliliters of water. Allow to stand for 12 hours, filter through a Gooch crucible, and wash with $6N$ hydrochloric acid. Dissolve the residue containing the cesium in the least possible amount of sodium hydroxide solution, acidify slightly with nitric acid, and precipitate the silicotungstic acid by the addition of a slight excess of a 10% solution of mercurous nitrate. After filtration, oxidize the excess of mercurous nitrate in the filtrate by boiling with aqua regia. Evaporate to about 10 ml., add alcohol and ether, and precipitate the cesium with chloroplatinic acid.

To recover the rubidium in the filtrate of the cesium silicotungstate, add a little nitric acid and an excess of chloroplatinic acid. Evaporate to about 10 ml., and complete the precipitation by adding 30 ml. of alcohol and 3 ml. of ether.

B. DETERMINATION OF THE ALKALI METALS

1. Lithium

a. Volumetric Method Based on Precipitation of Complex Periodate
(347)

Remove all cations except those of the alkali group, and evaporate the solution of the sample in a small beaker to 2 ml. If more than a few milligrams of ammonium salts are present, boil with a slight excess of potassium hydroxide. If sodium is present in amounts less than 20 mg., heat to 60 to 70°C., and then add 2 ml. of reagent (prepared by dissolving 24 g. of potassium hydroxide in 100 ml. of water and then adding to the cold solution 10 g. of potassium metaperiodate). If more than 20 mg. of sodium is present, add the reagent at room temperature. Add more reagent if the precipitate is heavy. After standing for 20 minutes at 60 to 70°C. or room temperature, filter through a Gooch crucible, and wash with four 2 ml. portions of 3 to 5N potassium hydroxide, added dropwise. Transfer the pad to a beaker, add dilute sulfuric acid to dissolve the precipitate, then add potassium iodide, and titrate the liberated iodine with thiosulfate solution. Alternatively, titrate the iodine with standard sodium arsenite solution, after buffering the sulfuric acid solution of the precipitate containing potassium iodide with borax or sodium bicarbonate. In either volumetric method, standardize the titrating solutions with known amounts of lithium carried through all steps of the procedure.

b. Determination Based on Precipitation of Lithium Potassium Ferricyanide Hexamethylenetetraamine (135)

Macro Procedure. Remove the solvent containing LiCl, resulting from the 2-ethylhexanol separation (cf. Section VIII-A-1); other extractants can also be used, by distillation, dissolve the salts in a few milliliters of water, and transfer the solution to a tared 10 ml. beaker. Evaporate, dry, cool, and weigh the residue. Dissolve in solvent solution at 20°C., using 1 ml. for each 5 mg. of solid. (The solvent is prepared by mixing 100 ml. of 30% hexamine solution, 105 ml. of water, and 200 ml. of acetone.) Transfer 1 ml. of the lithium solution to a 5 ml. beaker, add 2 ml. of ferricyanide reagent, mix without wetting the sides of the beaker, cover the beaker, and let stand for 15 minutes. (The ferricyanide reagent is prepared by mixing 50 ml. of 30% hexamine solution, 50 ml. of water, and 100 ml. of potassium ferricyanide solution. Warm the mixture to about 35°C., add 150 ml. of acetone slowly, and let stand for 24 hours at 20°C. before using.) Filter through a small sintered-glass crucible. Wash the beaker first with one 0.5 ml. portion of solvent solution and then with 0.5 portions of wash solution until the precipitate has been quantitatively transferred to the crucible (the wash solution is prepared by mixing 100 ml. of 30% hexamine solution with 110 ml. of acetone). To remove the hexamine, wash five times with 1 ml. portions of acetone containing 6% water and, finally, once with pure acetone. Dry at 50°C., and weigh. The weight of precipitate divided by 48.905 equals the weight of lithium.

Small quantities of lithium are best determined photometrically. In this case it is unnecessary to wash the precipitate with the acetone solution. Dissolve the precipitate in hot water, transfer the solution to a suitable volumetric flask (about 1500 γ of lithium per 100 ml.), and measure the absorbance of the yellow color at 420 mμ. To establish a calibration curve, carry standard aliquots containing from 200 to 1400 γ of lithium through all steps of the procedure.

Micro Procedure. For amounts of lithium below 50 γ, use only 0.2 ml. of solvent and 0.5 ml. of reagent, collect the precipitate with the help of a filter stick, and, after washing with 0.5 ml. portions of wash solution, dissolve it in a little water. Transfer the solution to a 100 ml. volumetric flask, add 40 ml. of ethanol and 8 ml. of malachite green leuco base (0.4 g. of malachite green reduced with zinc in dilute hydrochloric acid and diluted to 500 ml.). Dilute to the mark with water, mix, and measure the optical density of the solution. To prepare a calibration curve, transfer 2 ml. portions of the yellow solutions used to calibrate the graph in the macro method to 100 ml. flasks, and develop the green color resulting from the reaction of ferricyanide and the leuco base.

c. Thoron Photometric Method (422)

Prepare a solution of the sample that is free from substances yielding precipitates in strongly alkaline medium (cf. Section VI-A-1 for interferences). Adjust the volume of the solution to contain lithium in concentrations from 1 to 10 γ/ml. Pipet a 1 ml. aliquot into a 10 ml. glass-stoppered volumetric flask. Add 0.2 ml. of a 20% potassium hydroxide solution and 7.0 ml. of acetone. Next add 1 ml. of a 0.2% Thoron solution, dilute to volume with water, and mix. After 30 minutes, measure the absorbance of the solution vs. that of a reference solution containing all of the reagents. Determine the amount of lithium by reference to a calibration curve that is obtained by plotting the absorbance of lithium standards treated by the same procedure.

2. Sodium

a. Zinc Uranyl Acetate Method (24,25,225)

Reagent

Dissolve 100 g. of uranyl acetate ($2H_2O$) in 60 g. of·30% acetic acid and 490 g. of water. Dissolve 300 g. of zinc acetate ($3H_2O$) in 30 g. of 30% acetic acid and 320 g. of water. Heating is required to effect solution of the reagents. Mix the two solutions. If, after 24 hours of standing, no precipitate due to a sodium content of the reagents forms, add a few milligrams of sodium chloride, and filter. It is essential that the reagent be used at the same temperature which prevails at the time it is filtered. A convenient temperature is 20°C.

Procedure

Add to the weakly acid solution containing not more than 8 mg. of sodium in 1 ml. 10 times its volume of zinc uranyl acetate reagent. The temperature should be 20°C. or the temperature prevailing when the reagent was filtered. Allow to stand for at least half an hour with intermittent stirring, and then filter through a glass or porcelain fritted crucible. Wash five to ten times with 2 ml. portions of the reagent, then five times with 95% ethyl alcohol saturated with triple acetate, and finally twice with ether. Allow air to draw through the crucible to remove the ether, wipe the crucible with a slightly damp cloth, allow to stand in a desiccator for 10 minutes, and weigh. The factor from triple acetate, $NaZn(UO_2)_3$-$(C_2H_3O_2)_9 \cdot 6H_2O$, to sodium is 0.01495.

b. Magnesium Uranyl Acetate Method (75)

Reagent

Dissolve 90 g. of uranyl acetate ($2H_2O$) in 60 g. of glacial acetic acid and water, and dilute to 1 liter. Dissolve 600 g. of magnesium acetate ($4H_2O$) in 60 g. of glacial acetic acid and water, and dilute to 1 liter. Mix the two solutions, allow to cool to 20°C., and filter through a dry paper.

Procedure

Evaporate the neutral solution containing from 0.5 to 50 mg. of sodium and no interfering substances (see Section VI-A-2) to a volume of 5 ml. If the sodium content is less than 1 mg., reduce the volume to 1 to 2 ml. Avoid, however, the formation of salts. Add rapidly the proper amount of reagent. (For 10 mg. of sodium, use about 125 ml. of reagent; for larger amounts of sodium, multiply the expected milligrams of sodium by 10 to find the required milliliters of reagent. If the volume of the sample solution is 5 ml., do not use less than 100 ml. of reagent. If the volume of the sample solution is 3 ml., 25 ml. of the reagent is sufficient.)

Mix the solution, and immerse the beaker in a water bath kept at 20°C., stirring vigorously for 30 to 45 minutes with a mechanical stirrer. Filter through a tared Gooch or sintered-glass crucible, and wash several times with 5 ml. portions of 95% alcohol saturated with the triple acetate salt until the washings are colorless. Dry the crucible and precipitate for half an hour at 105 to 110°C., cool, and weigh. The factor from triple acetate, $NaMg(UO_2)_3(C_2H_3O_2)_9 \cdot 6H_2O$, to sodium is 0.0153.

c. Photometric Method (14)

Dissolve the precipitate obtained by one of the two preceding methods in water, and transfer the solution or an aliquot containing up to 0.5 mg. of sodium to a 50 ml. volumetric flask. Add 5 ml. of ammonium carbonate solution (saturated solution in $2N$ ammonium hydroxide), followed by 5 ml. of 3% hydrogen peroxide. Dilute to the mark, and obtain the transmittance of the solution using a wavelength of 525 mμ. Prepare a calibration curve by carrying aliquots of a standard sodium solution through all steps of the procedure. (When determining small amounts of sodium, the analyst should work with small volumes in order to reduce the solubility losses. A filter stick is very convenient for handling small volumes and precipitates.)

3. Potassium

a. Chloroplatinate Method

Add a slight excess of 10% (w/v) chloroplatinic acid to the chloride solution of the alkali metals in a small porcelain dish. For 1 g. of potassium chloride, 13.1 ml. of reagent is needed. One g. of sodium chloride requires an additional 16.8 ml. of reagent. The chloroplatinic acid is prepared either (1) by dissolving platinum in aqua regia and evaporating the solution several times to dryness on a steam bath, with intermittent treatment of the salts with $6N$ hydrochloric acid and finally dilution with water, or (2) by anodic solution of platinum sponge in hydrochloric acid.

To avoid the occlusion of mother liquor by the K_2PtCl_6, dilute the sample solution sufficiently with water so that no precipitation occurs upon the addition of the reagent. Evaporate the solution to a syrupy consistency on a steam bath in an atmosphere free from ammonia and dust. Add to the residue 20 to 25 ml. of 80% ethyl alcohol free from aldehydes, crush the crystals with a small pestle or the widened round end of a stirring rod, and then decant the solution through a dry tared sintered-glass crucible or a small filter paper moistened with alcohol. Treat with further additions of alcohol until the color of the solution denotes the removal of chloroplatinic acid and soluble chloroplatinates. Retain the filtrate if a sodium determination is required. With a fine stream of alcohol, transfer the precipitate into the sintered-glass crucible. If the solution was decanted through a paper, dry the paper for a few minutes, dissolve the salt in a little hot water, receive the solution in a tared platinum crucible, evaporate to dryness, and add the dry salts from the porcelain dish. Finally dry the glass or platinum crucible at 130°C. to constant weight. To avoid decrepitation of the salt, it is necessary to cover the crucible at first. The theoretical factor from K_2PtCl_6 to K_2O is 0.3067.

For amounts of potassium less than 1 mg., micro techniques should be employed to precipitate and collect the K_2PtCl_6. The volume of the sample solution should be only a few drops, and 0.5 ml. or less of chloroplatinic acid is required for filtration.   Collect the precipitate by centrifugation or with a filter stick, and wash the precipitate with 0.5 ml. portions of alcohol saturated with potassium chloroplatinate.   Dissolve the dry precipitate in hot water, and transfer the solution to a 25 ml. volumetric flask.   Add 5 ml. of 1:10 hydrochloric acid, dilute to about 20 ml., and add 1.0 ml. of stannous chloride (10% solution in $2N$ hydrochloric acid). Dilute to volume, and measure the transmittance using a blue filter.   Establish a calibration graph by carrying known quantities of potassium through all steps of the procedure (360).

b. Cobaltinitrite Method

Reagent

Dissolve 25 g. of cobaltous nitrate in 50 ml. of water and 12.5 ml. of glacial acetic acid.   Dissolve 120 g. of sodium nitrite in 180 ml. of water. To all of the cobaltous nitrate solution add 210 ml. of the sodium nitrite solution.   After the strong evolution of nitrous oxides ceases, pass air through the solution until all gases are removed (233).   Store in a refrigerator, and filter before use.

Procedure

To the neutral or weakly acid solution having a volume of 10 ml. or less, add at least a fivefold excess of reagent.   Allow to stand cold for at least several hours, preferably overnight.   Then filter through a Gooch crucible, and wash with cold water containing a little reagent.   Finally wash with 80% alcohol to remove the reagent, dry at 110 to 120°C., cool, and weigh.   The factor from $K_2NaCo(NO_2)_6 \cdot H_2O$ to potassium is 0.17216.

Since the composition of the precipitate is in doubt, an empirical factor should be established.   The method just described is recommended only for small amounts of potassium where a high degree of accuracy is not required; in other cases, proceed by either A or B.

A. Volumetric Technique.   Dissolve the dried residue, previously collected on a small sintered-glass crucible, filter stick, or centrifuge tube, in 5 ml. of ceric sulfate solution (9 g. of anhydrous ceric sulfate dissolved in 530 ml. of $2N$ sulfuric acid) and 1 ml. of 1:1 sulfuric acid.   Heat on a water bath at 90 to 100°C. until the precipitate has completely dissolved.   Maintain an excess of ceric sulfate throughout the reaction (5 ml. of $0.02N$ ceric sulfate is sufficient for precipitates containing no more than 0.5 mg. of potassium).   Cool to room temperature, and titrate the excess ceric sulfate with $0.02N$ ferrous ammonium sulfate using 1 drop of o-phenanthroline as indicator. Find the equivalent of the ceric sulfate by carrying known amounts of potassium through all steps of the procedure (57).

B. Colorimetric Technique (381). Dissolve the potassium cobalti-nitrite precipitate, which has been freed from excess reagent by repeated washing with acetone, in hot dilute sulfuric acid. Evaporate an aliquot of this solution containing from 1 to 10 γ of cobalt to dryness. Dissolve the residue of 5 ml. of water, 0.25 ml. of 1:1 hydrochloric acid, and 0.25 ml. of 1:10 nitric acid. Heat to dissolve all salts, and add 0.5 ml. of nitroso-R salt solution (0.2% aqueous solution), and 1 g. of hydrated sodium acetate. Boil for 1 minute, add 1 ml. of concentrated nitric acid, boil again for 1 minute, cool to room temperature, dilute to 10 ml. in a volumetric flask, and measure the transmittance of the solution at 520 mμ. Because of the uncertainty of the composition of any potassium cobaltinitrite precipitate obtained under varying conditions, it is best to standardize this procedure with known amounts of potassium.

c. TETRAPHENYLBORON METHOD (157,223)

(1) Gravimetric Determination or Titration of $(Ph)_4B^-$ Content of $(Ph)_4BK$

Reagents

Sodium tetraphenylboron solution. Dissolve 1.5 g. of sodium tetraphenyl-boron in 250 ml. of water, add about 1 g. of c.p. aluminum hydroxide, stir, and filter. The clear, cold solution, which has a pH of about 5, remains stable and effective for several days. Aqueous solutions of the reagent of pH above 7 (about 8 to 9) can be stored at room temperature and in ordinary diffuse light for several weeks without marked decomposition (95,362,404).

Wash solution. Precipitate potassium tetraphenylboron, $(Ph)_4BK$, with $(Ph)_4BNa$ from a $0.1N$ hydrochloric acid solution. Filter through a fritted-glass crucible, and store the dry salt in a desiccator. Shake 20 to 30 mg. of this salt with 250 ml. of water for 30 minutes. Add 0.5 to 1 g. of aluminum hydroxide, stir, and filter. The clear solution can be stored in glass bottles.

Procedure

For 10 mg. of K_2O in the sample dilute or concentrate the solution to about 40 ml. For 30 mg. of K_2O dilute to 100 ml., for 50 mg. to 200 ml., for 75 mg. to 300 ml., and for 100 mg. to 500 ml. Add enough concentrated hydrochloric acid to make the solution $0.1N$. Add from a pipet and with constant stirring 10 ml. of reagent for every 5 mg. of K_2O.   After a few minutes' standing, proceed by A, B, or C.

A. Gravimetric Technique.   Filter through a tared glass filtering crucible. Wash with water saturated with the precipitate, dry for 30 minutes at 105°C., cool in a desiccator, and weigh.   The factor from (Ph)₄BK to potassium is 0.1091, and to K_2O, 0.1314.

B. Titration with Silver Nitrate.   If a volumetric finish is preferred, filter the (Ph)₄BK precipitate through filter paper, and wash it free of reagent with $0.1N$ acetic acid (silver nitrate test).   Transfer the paper and precipitate to the original beaker, and dissolve the (Ph)₄BK with 10 ml. of acetone per 25 mg. of potassium.   Add 5 ml. of $2N$ acetic acid, 1 ml. of $0.1N$ potassium bromide solution, and 2 drops of 1% eosin indicator, and titrate with $0.05N$ silver nitrate ($0.1N$ if K > 25 mg.) until the color of the indicator changes.   Deduct the 1 ml. addition of $0.1N$ potassium bromide. One ml. of $0.1N$ AgNO₃ is equivalent to 3.9096 mg. of potassium.   It was recently shown (214a) that a sharper end point is obtained when the (Ph)₄BK is titrated potentiometrically in the acetone-water mixture than when the eosin indicator is used.

C. Alkalimetric Titration (127).   Dissolve the (Ph)₄BK, collected on a Gooch crucible or filter stick, in as little acetone as possible, collecting the solution in a platinum crucible.   Evaporate the acetone, and ignite the dry residue, first over a small flame and then with the full heat of a Bunsen burner.   During the ignition, ammonium tetraphenylboron, if present, is volatilized completely, and the (Ph)₄BK is quantitatively converted into potassium metaborate.   Dissolve the metaborate in a measured amount of standard hydrochloric acid, rinse the solution into a beaker or flask, boil to expel carbon dioxide, and immediately titrate the excess acid with standard sodium hydroxide solution using methyl red as indicator.   This method is particularly suitable for biological fluids.

(2) Excess Reagent Titration Technique (362,386)

The following procedure is detailed for the determination of acid-soluble potassium in manganese ore.   With minor variations, the method can be applied to other materials and different concentrations of potassium (386).

Reagents

Bromophenol blue indicator.   Dissolve 0.040 g. of bromophenol blue in 3 ml. of $0.1N$ sodium hydroxide, and dilute to 100 ml. with water.

Standard potassium chloride solution.   Dissolve 0.4767 g. of potassium chloride in water, transfer the solution to a 500 ml. volumetric flask, dilute to volume with water at 20°C., and mix.

Cetyltrimethylammonium bromide solution (CTAB). Dissolve 2.5 g. of the reagent in water, and dilute to 100 ml. Alternatively, a Zephiran Chloride (ZCl) solution can be used; transfer 50 ml. of 12.8% Zephiran Chloride to a 250 ml. volumetric flask, dilute to volume with water at 20°C., and mix.

Transfer 2 ml. of $(Ph)_4BNa$ solution to a 125 ml. Erlenmeyer flask. Add 20 ml. of water, 2 ml. of 20% sodium hydroxide solution, and 8 to 10 drops of bromophenol blue indicator. Titrate to a blue end point with the CTAB or ZCl solution. Adjust the concentration of the titrant so that 1 ml. equals 1 ml. of $(Ph)_4BNa$.

Sodium tetraphenylboron solution, 2.3%. Dissolve 23 g. of $(Ph)_4BNa$ in 800 ml. of water. Add 20 to 25 g. of aluminum hydroxide, stir 10 minutes, and filter. Collect the first 100 to 200 ml. of filtrate, and re-filter with the rest of the solution into a 1000 ml. flask. Add 2 ml. of 20% sodium hydroxide, dilute to volume with water at 20°C. and mix.

Transfer a 50 ml. aliquot of standard potassium chloride solution to a 100 ml. volumetric flask, add 4 ml. of 20% sodium hydroxide, and 10 ml. of $(Ph)_4BNa$ reagent. Dilute to volume with water, mix, allow to stand for 5 to 10 minutes, and pass through a dry filter. Transfer a 50 ml. aliquot of the filtrate to a 125 ml. Erlenmeyer flask, add 8 to 10 drops of bromophenol blue indicator, and titrate the excess reagent with the CTAB or ZCl standard solutions.

Calculation (Example)

2 ml. of $(Ph)_4BNa \sim$ 1.82 ml. of CTAB or ZCl
1 ml. of $(Ph)_4BNa \sim$ 0.91 ml. of CTAB or ZCl

0.20 ml. of CTAB or ZCl used in titration of 50 ml. aliquot
$0.20 \times 2 = 0.40$ ml. of CTAB or ZCl $\sim$ total excess $(Ph)_4BNa$

1 ml. of $(Ph)_4BNa \sim$ 0.91 ml. of CTAB or ZCl
0.44 ml. of $(Ph)_4BNa \sim$ 0.40 ml. of CTAB or ZCl

$10.0 - 0.44 = 9.56$ ml. of $(Ph)_4BNa$ used to precipitate K
9.56 ml. of $(Ph)_4BNa \sim$ 25 mg. of K

Procedure

Treat 2.5 g. of manganese ore with 100 ml. of concentrated hydrochloric acid, and boil down to dryness. Add an additional 50 ml. of hydrochloric acid, and again evaporate to dryness. Dissolve the salts in 100 ml. of water, boil, filter into a 250 ml. flask, and wash the residue with hot water. Dilute to volume with water at 20°C., and mix.

Add to a 100 ml. volumetric flask containing a 50 ml. aliquot, equivalent to 9.5 g. of sample, 4 ml. of 20% sodium hydroxide and 6.00 ml. of (Ph)₄-BNa. Dilute to volume, mix, and allow to stand for 5 to 10 minutes. Filter through a dry paper into a dry beaker. If the filtrate is cloudy, re-filter into another dry beaker. Transfer a 50 ml. aliquot of the filtrate to a 125 ml. Erlenmeyer flask, add 8 to 10 drops of bromophenol blue indicator, and titrate to a blue end point. If more than 5 ml. of CTAB or ZCl is required, the end point is likely to be indistinct. In this case, another 50 ml. aliquot of the ore solution should be taken, and the amount of (Ph)₄BNa should be decreased so that the excess will require less than 2 ml. of CTAB or ZCl.

Calculation (Example)

6.00 ml. of (Ph)₄BNa is added to 50 ml. aliquot (0.5 g. sample)
0.61 ml. of CTAB or ZCl used in titration of 50 ml. of filtrate
$0.61 \times 2 = 1.22$ ml. of CTAB or ZCl $\sim$ total excess (Ph)₄BNa

From Standardization

0.91 ml. of CTAB or ZCl $\sim$ 1 ml. of (Ph)₄BNa
1.22 ml. of CTAB or ZCl $\sim$ 1.34 ml. of (Ph)₄BNa
$6.00 - 1.34 = 4.66$ ml. of (Ph)₄BNa used to precipitate K

From Standardization

9.56 ml. of (Ph)₄BNa $\sim$ 25 mg. of K
4.66 ml. of (Ph)₄BNa $\sim$ 12.18 mg. of K

0.5 g. sample contains 12.18 mg.
The sample contains 2.44% K.

(3) Spectrophotometric Technique (325)

Adjust the pH of the sample solution to 4.0 to 5.0 with dilute sulfuric acid and sodium hydroxide. Add 5 ml. of 1% reagent to 5 ml. of sample solution (10 to 150 γ) in a 15 ml. graduated centrifuge tube. Centrifuge for 3 minutes in a high-speed centrifuge, and remove the supernatant liquid by pipet. Wash the precipitate twice with 3 ml. of a cold saturated solution of the potassium salt, again removing the supernatant liquid by pipet. A constant volume of liquid (0.5 ml.) is left with the precipitate.

Dissolve the precipitate by adding 5 ml. of a mixture of 75% acetonitrile and 25% water, and transfer to a 25 ml. volumetric flask. Rinse the centrifuge tube with additional solvent, transferring the washings into the flask, and dilute the solution in the flask to 25 ml. Prepare a blank solution by an identical procedure. Measure the absorbance at 266 mμ. Determine the potassium concentration from a calibration curve established with known amounts of potassium.

4. Cesium

a. SPECTROPHOTOMETRIC METHOD

Prepare a solution approximately 6N in hydrochloric acid. If necessary, dilute with 6N hydrochloric acid in a volumetric flask to such a volume that a 5 ml. aliquot will be in the range 0.5 to 4.5 mg. of cesium. Transfer the solution to a 15 ml. centrifuge tube. Add slowly, and with constant shaking of the tube, 1.00 ml. of freshly prepared 5% tungstosilicic acid reagent (5 g. dissolved in 95 ml. of 6N hydrochloric acid). Stir the solution by bubbling air into the tube for 2 minutes. Allow to stand for 35 minutes, and then centrifuge for 3 minutes. By means of a pipet transfer 5.00 ml. of the supernatant liquid, containing the excess of unreacted tungstosilicic acid, into a 25 ml. volumetric flask. To this liquid add 8 ml. of 3N sodium hydroxide while constantly shaking the flask. The pH of the solution should be approximately 0.2. Develop the heteropoly blue color by adding 8 ml. of a freshly prepared 0.2% titanium trichloride solution (1 ml. of 20% solution of titanium trichloride and 1 ml. of hydrochloric acid diluted to 100 ml.). Dilute to the mark with distilled water. The color develops immediately. Transfer some of the solution to a 1 cm. cell, and measure the absorbance at 725 mμ. Use distilled water as a blank in the reference cell. Prepare a calibration curve by carrying known amounts of cesium (0.5 to 4.5 mg.) through all steps of the procedure.

5. Use of Ion Exchange Resins in Analysis of Rocks and Minerals

a. ISOLATION OF SODIUM AND POTASSIUM (341)

Apparatus

Ion exchange column. Place a pad of glass wool in the bottom of a 50 ml. buret measuring 11 $\times$ 600 mm. Nearly fill with water; then add a slurry of Amberlite IR-120 resin (0.45 to 0.6 mm. grain size) until 10 ml. of settled resin bed is obtained. Wash the resin with 4N hydrochloric acid and then with water until the eluate is only slightly acid.

Procedure

Decompose 0.25 to 0.5 g. of sample in a platinum dish or crucible by heating for 4 hours on a water bath with 10 ml. of hydrofluoric acid, keeping the vessel tightly covered with a platinum or polyethylene lid. After 4 hours, evaporate to dryness, add 2 ml. of 1:1 sulfuric acid and 25 ml. of water, and again evaporate to dryness. Repeat the treatment with an additional 2 ml. of 1:1 sulfuric acid and water. Dissolve the salts by heating with 0.5 ml. of hydrochloric acid and 25 ml. of water. If necessary, filter, and wash the residue with hot water.

Dilute the filtrate to 50 ml., and pass the solution through the cation exchange column at a rate of approximately 2 to 4 ml./minute. Adjust the stopcock as the head of the liquid changes to maintain an even rate of flow throughout the exchange. Rinse the column with 100 ml. of water to remove sulfates, and discard the eluate.

Elute the sodium and potassium by passing 850 ml. of 0.12N hydrochloric acid through the column at a constant rate of 4 ml./minute. Evaporate the eluate to a convenient volume, transfer to a tared platinum dish, evaporate to dryness, and then determine the combined chlorides by gentle ignition and weighing. If only one of the two alkali metals is determined, omit the weighing of the combined chlorides, and determine the sodium or potassium by one of the specific methods described earlier.

b. DETERMINATION OF LITHIUM, SODIUM, AND POTASSIUM IN SILICATES
(420)

Decompose 1 g. of sample as outlined in the previous procedure, using more acid here to achieve complete decomposition of the sample. Moisten the dry residue with a little water, add hydrochloric acid, and evaporate to dryness. Dissolve the residue in 5 to 10 ml. of 0.7M hydrochloric acid. Heat until clear, and then add small portions of cadmium oxide until an excess of the brown cadmium powder is indicated. Boil the solution continuously during this step to facilitate the precipitation of aluminum, iron, and titanium. Cool, transfer the mixture to a 50 ml. volumetric flask, dilute to the mark, mix, and filter through a dry filter paper.

Evaporate a 25 ml. aliquot to 5 to 10 ml. Transfer the solution to a cation exchange column (37 cm. × 2.4 cm.²) containing Dowex 50 resin, sieved through 120 mesh and washed with 0.7M hydrochloric acid. Elute the cations with 0.7M hydrochloric acid at a flow rate of 0.6 cm./minute. The first 130 ml. of eluate contains all the cadmium of the aliquot. Discard this fraction, which contains no other metallic ions. Collect the next 50 ml., which contains the lithium, and the subsequent 60 ml., which contains the sodium. Discard the following 90 ml. fraction, which contains only dilute hydrochloric acid, but collect the next 100 ml., which contains the potassium. Determine the three alkali metals in their respective fractions by standard procedures.

6. Typical Flame Photometric Procedure for the Determination of Sodium, Potassium, and Lithium in Glass and Similar Materials (386)

Apparatus

Beckman Model DU Spectrophotometer, flame and photomultiplier attachments, and acetylene-oxygen burner.

Preparation of Standards

Into a 1000 ml. volumetric flask weigh 0.5324 g. of Li_2CO_3, 0.2305 g. of Na_2CO_3, and 0.1767 g. of K_2CO_3. Add approximately 100 ml. of water and sufficient 70% perchloric acid to dissolve the salts and render the solution slightly acid. Add 1 ml. excess of perchloric acid, and dilute to the mark with distilled water. This solution contains 100 p.p.m. sodium, potassium, and lithium. Store in a polyethylene bottle. Instead of perchloric acid, some analysts prefer to acidify the solution with sulfuric acid.

From the stock solution, pipet 0.00, 5.00, 10.00, 15.00, etc., ml. into 500 ml. volumetric flasks. Add 2 ml. of 72% perchloric (or sulfuric) acid, and dilute to the mark with distilled water. Store in polyethylene bottles. These solutions are equivalent to 0, 1, 2, 3, etc., p.p.m., respectively, of sodium, potassium, and lithium.

Preparation of Sample

Weigh 0.5000 g. of sample into a platinum dish, moisten with water, add 5 ml. of 70% perchloric acid (or 2 ml. of sulfuric acid, unless barium or calcium are present) and 25 ml. of 48% hydrofluoric acid. Evaporate to dryness under an infrared heater. Wash down the sides of the dish with water, add 5 ml. of perchloric acid (or 1 ml. of sulfuric acid), and evaporate again to dryness. Finally dissolve the residue in water and 1 ml. of perchloric (or sulfuric) acid, transfer the solution to a 250 ml. volumetric flask, and dilute to the mark with water.

Procedure

Determination of Sodium. From the sample solution prepared above, pipet a 25.00 ml. aliquot into a 500 ml. volumetric flask. Add 2.0 ml. of perchloric acid (or 1 ml. of sulfuric acid), and dilute to the mark with water.

Burning Conditions. Sensitivity knob at mid-point (five turns), photomultiplier sensitivity at 3, zero suppression control off, slit 0.0125 mm., selector switch at 0.1, $\lambda = 589$ (scan for maximum reading). These settings are typical and do not necessarily give maximum sensitivity. N.B.S. standard sample No. 91, opal glass (8% Na_2O), should burn between the 6 and 7 p.p.m. standards.

Typical Readings:

				Av.
6 p.p.m. Na, K, Li	836	838	837	837
Opal glass	864	864	864	864
7 p.p.m. Na, K, Li	980	980	980	980

Calculation:

$$6 + 864 - 837 \times \frac{1}{980\text{–}837} = 6.189 \text{ p.p.m. Na}$$

$$\frac{6.189 \times 250 \times 20 \times 100 \times 1.3479}{0.5 \times 10^6} = 8.34\% \text{ Na}_2\text{O}$$

Determination of Potassium. From the sample solution, pipet a 25.00 ml. aliquot into a 250 ml. volumetric flask. Add 1 ml. of 70% perchloric (or sulfuric) acid, and dilute to the mark with water.

Burning Conditions: Red-sensitive tube, sensitivity knob one turn back from fully counterclockwise, photomultiplier off, zero suppression control off, slit 0.20 mm., selector switch at 0.1, $\lambda = 766$ mμ (scan for maximum reading). N.B.S. standard sample No. 91, opal glass, should burn between the 5 and 6 p.p.m. standards.

Typical Readings:

				Av.
5 p.p.m. Na, K, Li	470	468	468	468
Opal glass	524	525	525	525
6 p.p.m. Na, K, Li	570	571	570	570

Calculation:

$$5 + 525 - 468 \times \frac{1}{570\text{–}468} = 5.559 \text{ p.p.m. K}$$

$$\frac{5.559 \times 250 \times 10 \times 100 \times 1.2046}{0.5 \times 10^6} = 3.35\% \text{ K}_2\text{O}$$

Determination of Lithium. The opal glass standard does not contain a known amount of lithium. This same procedure, with the same standards, has been applied to the determination of lithium in glass sand. The sample solution is used without further dilution. When lithium is to be determined in ores containing larger amounts of lithium than does glass sand, the burning conditions given here must be correspondingly modified.

Burning Conditions: Sensitivity knob at mid-point (five turns), photo-multiplier sensitivity at full, zero suppression control off, slit 0.2 mm., selector switch at 0.1, λ = 670.8 mμ (scan for maximum reading).

Typical Readings:

0	142	142	142
Sample	589	589	589
1 p.p.m. Na, K, Li	981	981	981

Calculation:

$$0 + 589 - 142 \times \frac{1}{981-142} = 0.532 \text{ p.p.m. Li}$$

$$\frac{0.532 \times 250 \times 100 \times 2.1527}{0.5 \times 10^6} = 0.06\% \text{ Li}_2\text{O}$$

REFERENCES

1. A.C.S. Specifications, *Reagent Chemicals*, American Chemical Society, Washington, D.C., 1955.
2. Adams, J., A. A. Benedetti-Pichler, and J. T. Bryant, *Mikrochemie*, **26**, 29 (1939).
3. Adams, J., M. Hall, and W. F. Bailey, *Ind. Eng. Chem., Anal. Ed.*, **7**, 310 (1935).
4. Aleksandrov, G. P., and M. D. Lyntaya, *Ukrain. Khim. Zhur.*, **21**, 518 (1955); *Anal. Abstr.*, **3**, 3272 (1956).
5. Alkemade, C. T. J., Doctoral thesis, Univ. of Utrecht, Utrecht, Holland, 1945.
6. Alten, F., H. Weiland, and B. Kurmies, *Z. Pflanzenernähr. Düng. Bodenk.*, **32**, 171 (1933).
7. Amin, A. M., *Chemist Analyst*, **43**, 4 (1954).
8. Amin, A. M., *Chemist Analyst*, **46**, 6 (1957).
8a. Amos, W. R., and R. F. Sympson, *Anal. Chem.*, **31**, 133 (1959).
9. *Am. Soc., Testing Materials ASTM Standards*, **1955**, Part 3.
10. Anderson, E. C., *Science*, **128**, 882 (1958).
11. Anderson, E. C., R. L. Schuch, W. R. Fisher, and W. Langham, *Science*, **125**, 1273 (1957).
12. Anderson, E. C., Schuch, R. L., J. D. Perrings, and W. H. Langham, *Nucleonics* **14** (1), 26 (1956).
12a. Angot, J., *Mikrochim. Acta* **1959**(3), 346.
13. *A.O.A.C. Official Methods of Analysis*, 8th ed., Association of Official Agricultural Chemists, Washington, D. C., 1955.
14. Arnold, E., and A. R. Pray, *Ind. Eng. Chem., Anal. Ed.*, **15**, 294 (1943).
15. Arons, W. L., and A. K. Solomon, *J. Clin. Invest.*, **33**, 995 (1954).
16. Arons, W. L., R. J. Vanderlinde, and A. K. Solomon, *J. Clin. Invest.*, **33**, 1001 (1954).
17. Ashton, W. M., and J. H. Williams, *J. Sci. Food Agr.*, **6**, 311 (1955).
18. *A.S.T.M. Methods for Emission Spectrochemical Analysis*, American Society for Testing Materials, Philadelphia, 1957.

19. Atchison, G. J., and W. H. Beamer, *Anal. Chem.*, **24**, 1812 (1952).
20. *Atomic Energy Can. Ltd., Tech. Bull.* NS-1.
21. Axelrod, J. M., and I. Adler, *Anal. Chem.*, **29**, 1280 (1957).
22. Ball, W. C., *J. Chem. Soc.*, **95**, 2126 (1909).
23. Ball, W. C., *J. Chem. Soc.*, **97**, 1408 (1910).
24. Barber, H. H., and I. M. Kolthoff, *J. Am. Chem. Soc.*, **50**, 1625 (1928).
25. Barber, H. H., and I. M. Kolthoff, *J. Am. Chem. Soc.*, **51**, 3233 (1929).
26. Barnabas, T., M. G. Badve, and J. Barnabas, *Naturwissenschaften*, **41**, 478 (1954).
27. Barnes, R., and D. D. Salley, *Ind. Eng. Chem., Anal. Ed.*, **15**, 4 (1943).
28. Beerstecher, E., *Anal. Chem.*, **22**, 1200 (1950).
29. Belcher, R., *Ind. Chemist*, **22**, 731 (1946).
30. Belcher, R., *Ind. Chemist*, **23**, 673 (1947).
31. Benedict, S. R., *J. Am. Chem. Soc.*, **32**, 480 (1904).
32. Bergstresser, K. S., and G. R. Waterbury, *U. S. Atomic Energy Comm. Rept.* LAMS 1698 (1954).
33. Berkhout, H. W., *Chem. Weekblad*, **48**, 909 (1952).
34. Berkhout, H. W., *Z. Anal. Chem.*, **152**, 248 (1956).
35. Berkhout, H. W., and G. H. Jongen, *Chemist Analyst*, **45**, 6 (1956).
36. Berry, J. W., C. D. Chappell, and R. B. Barnes, *Ind. Eng. Chem., Anal. Ed.*, **18**, 19 (1946).
37. Beukenkamp, J., and W. Rieman III, *Anal. Chem.*, **22**, 582 (1950).
38. Berzelius, J. J., *Pogg. Ann.*, **1**, 169 (1824).
39. Berzelius, J. J., *Pogg. Ann.*, **4**, 245 (1825).
40. Best, C. H., and N. B. Taylor, *Physiological Basis of Medical Practice*, Wood, Baltimore, Md., 1937.
41. Biffen, F. M., *Anal. Chem.*, **22**, 1014 (1950).
42. Bills, C. E., F. G. McDonald, W. Niedermeyer, and M. C. Schwartz, *Anal. Chem.*, **21**, 1076 (1949).
43. Birks, L. S., E. J. Brooks, and H. Friedman, *Anal. Chem.*, **25**, 692 (1953).
44. Blackwell, A. T., C. L. Yeager, and M. Kraus, *J. Assoc. Offic. Agr. Chemists*, **36**, 898 (1953).
45. Blanchetiére, A., *Bull. soc. chim. France*, **33**, 807 (1923).
46. Block, R. J., E. L. Durrum, and G. Zweig, *A. Manual of Paper Chromatography and Paper Electrophoresis*, Academic Press, New York, 1955.
47. Blum, A. S., *Nucleonics*, **14** (7), 64 (1956).
47a. Bond, R. D., and J. T. Hutton, *Analyst*, **83**, 684 (1958).
47b. Booth, E., and T. W. Evett, *Atomic Energy Research Establ. (Gt. Brit.)*, Analytical Method A.E.R.E.-AM 5 (1959).
48. Borkowski, G. J., *Anal. Chem.*, **21**, 348 (1949).
49. Boyd, G. E., *Anal. Chem.*, **21**, 335 (1949).
50. Boyd, G. E., J. Schubert, and A. W. Adamson, *J. Am. Chem. Soc.*, **69**, 2818 (1947).
51. Brannock, W. W., and S. M. Berthold, *U. S. Geol. Survey Bull.* No. 992 (1953).
52. Bridges, R. W., and M. F. Lee, *Ind. Eng. Chem., Anal. Ed.*, **4**, 264 (1932).
53. Briggs, A. P., *J. Biol. Chem.*, **57**, 351 (1923).
54. Brode, W. R., *Chemical Spectroscopy*, Wiley, New York, 1943.
55. Brooksbank, W. A., *U. S. Atomic Energy Comm. Rept.* ORNL-867 (1950).
56. Brooksbank, W. A., and G. W. Leddicotte, *J. Phys. Chem.*, **57**, 819 (1953).
57. Brown, D. S., R. R. Robinson, and G. M. Browning, *Ind. Eng. Chem., Anal. Ed* **10**, 652 (1938).

58. Brown, J. G., and O. Lilleland, *Proc Am. Soc. Hort. Sci.*, **48**, 341 (1946).
59. Brown, M. H., and J. H. Reedy, *Ind. Eng. Chem., Anal. Ed.*, **2**, 304 (1930).
60. Brumbaugh, R. J., and W. E. Fanus, *Anal. Chem.*, **26**, 463 (1954).
60a. Buddhadev, S., *Anal. Chim. Acta*, **19**, 320 (1958).
61. Bultasova, H., and E. Konopasek, *Chem. listy*, **49**, 769 (1955); through *Anal. Abstr.*, **3**, 1812 (1956).
62. Burgess, L. L., and O. Kamm, *J. Am. Chem. Soc.*, **34**, 652 (1912).
62a. Burkser, E. S., and T. G. Kornienko, *Ukrain. Khim. Zhur.*, **24**, 375 (1958); *Referat. Zhur. Khim.*, **1959**, Abstr. No. 914; through *Anal. Abstr.*, **6**, 4281 (1959).
63. Burriel-Marti, F., and J. Ramirez-Muños, *Flame Photometry*, Elsevier, New York, 1957.
64. Burkser, E. S., and R. V. Feldman, *Zavodskaya Lab.*, **7**, 166 (1938); through *Chem. Abstr.*, **32**, 4461 (1938).
65. Burma, D. P., *Analyst*, **77**, 382 (1952).
66. Burstall, F. H., G. R. Davies, R. P. Linstead, and R. A. Wells, *J. Chem. Soc.*, **1950**, 516.
67. Buser, W., *Helv. Chim. Acta*, **34**, 1635 (1951).
68. Butler, A. M., and L. Tuthill, *J. Biol. Chem.*, **93**, 171 (1931).
69. Cabell, M. J. and A. Thomas, *Atomic Energy Research Establ. (Gt. Brit.)*, **1955**, C/R 1725; *Anal. Abstr.*, **2**, 925 (1956).
70. Caley, E. R., *J. Am. Chem. Soc.*, **51**, 1965 (1929).
71. Caley, E. R., *J. Am. Chem. Soc.*, **52**, 1349 (1930).
72. Caley, E. R., *J. Am. Chem. Soc.*, **53**, 539 (1931).
73. Caley, E. R., and H. D. Axilrod, *Anal. Chem.*, **14**, 242 (1942).
74. Caley, E. R., and W. O. Baker, *Ind. Eng. Chem., Anal. Ed.*, **11**, 604 (1939).
75. Caley, E. R., and C. W. Foulk, *J. Am. Chem. Soc.*, **51**, 1664 (1929).
76. Caley, E. R., and L. B. Rogers, *Ind. Eng. Chem., Anal. Ed.*, **15**, 32 (1943).
77. Caley, E. R., and G. A. Simmons, Jr., *Anal. Chem.*, **25**, 1386 (1953).
78. Calvert, J. T., *Trans. Faraday Soc.*, **26**, 509 (1930).
79. Cameron, F. K., and G. H. Failyer, *J. Am. Chem. Soc.*, **25**, 1063 (1903).
80. Carell, A. J., *Analyst*, **77**, 537 (1952).
81. Carnot, A., *Bull. soc. chim. France*, (3)**1**, 280 (1889).
82. Carolan, R. J., *Intern. Sugar J.*, **56**, 189 (1954).
83. Carr, D. R., and Kulp, J. L., *Bull. Geol. Soc. Am.*, **68**, 763 (1957).
84. Carruthers, C., *Ind. Eng. Chem., Anal. Ed.*, **15**, 70 (1943).
85. Chakrabarti, S., and D. P. Burma, *Sci. and Culture (Calcutta)*, **16**, 485 (1951).
85a. Champeix, L., R. Derras, and J. Duflo, *J. Nuclear Materials*, **2**, 113 (1959).
85b. Chang, T. C., and C. L. Tseng, *Sci. Quart. Natl. Univ. Peking*, **4**, 185 (1934); through *Chem. Abstr.*, **28**, 4333 (1934).
86. *Chem. Eng. News*, **33**, 648 (1955).
87. *Chem. Eng. News*, **34**(8), 1992 (1956); **36**(44), 40 (1958).
87a. *Chem. Eng. News*, **37**(22), 50 (1959).
87b. *Chem. Eng. News*, **38**(43), 40 (1960).
88. Cherkesov, A. I., *Referat. Zhur. Khim.*, **1956**, Abstr. No. 36143; *Anal. Abstr.*, **4**, 1122 (1957).
89. Christopherson, E. W., through J. C. Langford, *U. S. Atomic Energy Comm. Rept.* HW-49668 (1957); *Chem. Abstr.*, **52**, 1539 (19538).
90. Churchill, H. V., R. W. Bridges, and A. L. Miller, *Ind. Eng. Chem., Anal. Ed.*, **8**, 348 (1936).
91. Cluley, H. J., *Analyst*, **80**, 354 (1955).

92. Cabell, M. J., and A. Thomas, *Atomic Energy Research Establ. (Gt. Brit.) Rept.*, **1955**, C/R 1725.
93. Cohn, W. E., and H. W. Kohn, *J. Am. Chem. Soc.*, **70**, 1986 (1948).
94. Colin, J., *Bull. soc. chim. biol.*, **33**, 394 (1951).
95. Cooper, S. S., *Anal. Chem.*, **29**, 446 (1957).
96. Cuvelier, B. V. J., *Natuurw. Tijdschr. (Ghent)*, **14**, 107 (1932).
96a. Cyprès, R., and R. Wollast, *Bull. soc. chim. Belges*, **67**(5–6), 171 (1958).
97. Dalton, J. C., and G. A. Welch, *Anal. Chim. Acta*, **15**(4), 317 (1956).
98. Damon, P. E., Univ. of Ariz., Tucson, Ariz.   The preparation of this section was greatly aided by detailed data made available by Dr. Damon.
99. Dana, E. S., *Descriptive Mineralogy*, Wiley, New York, 1920.
100. Darnell, M. C., and S. Walker, *Ind. Eng. Chem., Anal Ed.*, **12**, 244 (1940).
101. Deal, S. B., *Anal. Chem.*, **26**, 598 (1954).
102. Dean, J. A., *Anal. Chem.*, **23**, 202 (1951).
102a. De Bruin, H. J., and L. E. Smythe, *Nature*, **182**, 387 (1958).
103. Denes, S., *Mikrochemie*, **26**, 277 (1939).
104 Diamond, J. J., and L. Bean, *Anal. Chem.*, **25**, 1825 (1953).
105. Dippel, W. A., C. E. Bricker, and N. H. Furman, *Anal. Chem.*, **26**, 553 (1954).
105a. Dobrowolski, J., and N. Wyszynski, *Chem. Anal. (Warsaw)*, **4**(1–2), 207 (1959); through *Anal. Abstr.*, **6**, 4869 (1959).
106. Doisy, E. A., and R. D. Bell, *J. Biol. Chem.*, **45**, 313 (1920).
107. Dranitskay, R. M., *Referat. Zhur. Khim.*, **1955**, Abstr. No. 5779; through *Anal. Abstr.*, **3**, 33 (1956).
107a. Druyan, R., T. G. Mitchell, and E. R. King, *J. Lab. Clin. Med.*, **52**(2), 304 (1958).
108. Duca, A., and N. Buruleanu, *Rev. chim. (Bucharest)*, **7**, 430 (1956); through *Anal. Abstr.*, **4**, 3563 (1957).
109. Dupuis, T., *Compt. rend.*, **237**, 256 (1953).
110. Dutina, D., *U. S. Atomic Energy Comm Rept.* KAPL-1425 (1955).
111. Eckel, R. E., *J. Biol. Chem.*, **195**, 191 (1952).
112. Eden, A., *Analyst*, **68**, 167 (1943).
113. Edwards, G., and H. C. Urey, *Geochim. et Cosmochim. Acta*, **7**, 154 (1955).
114. Eggertsen, F. T., G. Wyld, and L. Lykken, *Am. Soc. Testing Materials Spec. Tech. Publ.* No. 116 (1952).
115. Ellestad, R. B., and E. L. Horstman, *Anal. Chem.*, **27**, 1229 (1955).
116. Ellington, F., and L. Stanley, *Analyst*, **80**, 313 (1955).
117. Elving, P. J., and P. C. Chao, *Anal. Chem.*, **21**, 507 (1949).
118. Engelbrecht, R. M., and F. A. McCoy, *Anal. Chem.*, **28**, 1772 (1956).
119. Erlenmeyer, H., H. von Hahn, and E. Sorkin, *Helv. Chim. Acta*, **34**, 1419 (1951).
120. Evans, G. H., and H. H. Strain, *Anal. Chem.*, **28**, 63 (1956).
120a. Fabrikova, E. A., *Zhur. Anal. Khim.*, **14**, 41 (1959); through *Anal. Abstr.*, **6**, 4282 (1959).
121. Feldman, C., *Anal. Chem.*, **21**, 1041 (1949).
122. Feldstein, P., and A. M. Ward, *Analyst*, **56**, 245 (1931).
123. Findeis, A. F., and T. de Vries, *Anal. Chem.*, **28**, 1899 (1956).
124. Flaschka, H., *Mikrochemie ver Mikrochim. Acta*, **39**, 391 (1952).
125. Flaschka, H., *Chemist Analyst*, **44**, 60 (1955).
126. Flaschka, H., and A. Holasek, *Z. physiol. Chem.*, **303**, 9 (1956).
127. Flaschka, H., A. Holasek, and A. M. Amin, *Z. anal. Chem.*, **138**, 161 (1953).

128. Flaschka, H., A. Holasek, and A. M. Amin, *Z anol. Chem.*, **138**, 241 (1953).

129. Flaschka, H., and F. Sadek, *Chemist Analyst*, **45**, 20 (1956).

129a. Flaschka, H., and F. Sadek, *Chemist Analyst*, **47**(2), 30 (1958).

130. Fletcher, M. H., *Anal. Chem.*, **21**, 175 (1949).

131. Floger, R. L., and H. Hicks, in W. W. Meinke, *U. S. Atomic Energy Comm. Rept.* 2738 (1949).

131a. Florence, T. M., *Anal. Chim. Acta*, **19**, 548 (1958).

132. Forbes, G. B., and M. D'Ambruso, *J. Biol. Chem.*, **212**, 655 (1955).

132a. Ford, C. L., *ASTM Bull.* No. 233, 57 (1958).

133. Ford, O. W., *J. Assoc. Offic. Agr. Chemists*, **36**, 649 (1953); **37**, 363 (1954); **38**, 445 (1955).

134. Ford, O. W., *J. Assoc. Offic. Agr. Chemists*, **39**, 598 (1956).

135. Forster, C. F., *Analyst*, **79**, 629 (1954).

136. Fourage, J., and G. Duyckaerts, *Anal. Chim. Acta*, **14**, 527 (1956).

137. Fox, C. L., Jr., E. B. Freeman, and S. E. Lasker, *Am. Soc. Testing Materials Spec. Tech. Publ.* No. 116 (1952).

138. Frazer, J. W., C. W. Schoenfelder, and R. L. Tromp, *U. S. Atomic Energy Comm. Rept.* UCRL 4944 (1957).

139. Fred, M., N. A. Nachtrieb, and F. S. Tomkins, *J. Opt. Soc. Am.*, **37**, 279 (1947).

140. Fredholm, H., *Z. Anal. Chem.*, **104**, 400 (1936).

141. Fresenius, R., and G. Jander, *Handbuch der Analytischen Chemie*, Part 3, Vol. 1a (E. Brennecke, F. Busch, L. Fresenius, and R. Fresenius, *Elements of Group I*), Springer, Berlin, 1940.

142. Fresenius, R., and G. Jander, *Handbuch der Analytischen Chemie*, Part 2, Vol. 1a (H. Schilling, H. Spandau, and O. Tomicek, *Elements of Group I*), Springer, Berlin, 1944.

142a. Friedman, H. A., *U. S. Atomic Energy Comm. Rept.* Y-978 (1957).

142b. Friedman, H. A., *U. S. Atomic Energy Comm. Rept.* Y-1060 (1957).

143. Friedman, H., L. S. Birks, and E. J. Brooks, *Am. Soc. Testing Materials Spec. Tech. Publ.* No. 157 (1954).

144. Frierson, W. J., and J. W. Jones, *Anal. Chem.*, **23**, 1447 (1951).

145. Fukushima, S., S. Ivata, S., Kume, and M. Shigemoto, *Japan Analyst*, **5**, 704 (1965); through *Anal. Abstr.*, **4**, 3270 (1957).

146. Furman, N. H., E. R. Caley, and I. C. Schoonover, *J. Am. Chem. Soc.*, **54**, 1344 (1932).

147. Gabrielson, G., *Analyst*, **80**, 479 (1955).

148. Gabrielson, G., and O. Samuelson, *Svensk Kem. Tidskr.*, **62**, 221 (1950).

149. Gast, P., Ph.D. Thesis, Columbia Univ., New York, 1957.

150. Gastinger, E., *Z. anal. Chem.*, **140**, 335 (1953).

151. Gaudin, A. M., and J. H. Pannell, *Anal. Chem.*, **20**, 1154 (1948).

152. Geffken, G., *Z. anorg. Chem.*, **43**, 197 (1905).

153. Geilmann, W., and A. Ganssle, *Glastech. Ber.*, **27**, 80 (1954).

154. Geilmann, W., and W. Gebauhr, *Z. anal. Chem.*, **139**, 161 (1953).

155. Gilbert, P. T., *Ind. Labs.*, **3**, 41 (1952).

156. Gilbert, T. W., Jr., A. S. Meyer, Jr., and J. C. White, *Anal. Chem.*, **29**, 1627 (1957).

157. Gloss, G. H., *Chemist Analyst*, **42**, 50 (1953).

158. Gooch, F. A., *Proc. Am. Acad. Arts. Sci.*, **22**, 177 (1886).

159. Gordon, H. T., and C. A. Hewel, *Anal. Chem.*, **27**, 1471 (1955).

160. Grottle, H., and W. Savelsberg, *Z. Anal. Chem.*, **110**, 81 (1937).

161. Grove, E. L., Univ. of Ala., University, Ala., Private communication, based on paper given before Pittsburgh Conference on Analytical Chemistry and Applied Spectroscopy, Pittsburgh, Pa., 1959.

162. Gould, E. S., *Inorganic Reactions and Structure*, Holt, New York, 1955.

163. Grabar, P., *Bull. soc. chim. biol.*, **11**, 58 (1929).

164. Gubeli-Litscher, O., and K. Stammbach, *Helv. Chim. Acta*, **34**, 1245 (1951).

165. Gulbranson, L. B., *Anal. Chem.*, **28**, 1632 (1956).

166. Guter, G. A., and G. S. Hammond, *J. Am. Chem. Soc.*, **78**, 5166 (1956).

167. Hahn, R. B., and R. O. Baker, *Nucleonics*, **14**(5), 90 (1956).

168. Hale, C. H., *Ind. Eng. Chem., Anal. Ed.*, **15**, 516 (1943).

169. Halstead, W. J., and B. Chaiken, *Public Roads*, **26**(5), 99 (1950).

170. Handley, T. H., and C. L. Burros, *Anal. Chem.*, **31**, 332 (1959).

170a. Hara, T., *Bull. Chem. Soc. Japan*, **31**, 635 (1958); through *Anal. Abstr.*, **6**, 1630 (1959).

170b. Hara, T., *Bull. Inst. Chem. Research Koto Univ.*, **37**, 112 (1959); through *Anal. Abstr.*, **7**, 1662 (1960).

171. Hegedus, A. J., I. K. Thega, and E. E. Zapp, *Mikrochim. Acta*, 1956(7–8), 1247.

172. Hering, H., *Anal. Chim. Acta*, **6**, 340 (1952).

173. Herrmann, R., *Flammenphotometrie*, Springer, Berlin, 1956.

174. Hevesy, G. V., *Chemical Analysis by X-Rays and Its Application*, McGraw-Hill, New York, 1932.

175. Hevesy, G. V., and J. T. Calvert, *Naturwissenschaften*, **18**, 529 (1930).

176. Heyrowski, A., *Chem. listy*, **50**, 69 (1956).

177. Hicks, W. B., *Ind. Eng. Chem.*, **5**, 650 (1913).

178. Hillebrand, W. F., G. E. F. Lundell, H. A. Bright, and J. I. Hoffman, *Applied Inorganic Analysis*, Wiley, New York, 1953.

178a. Holasek, A., and M. Dugandzic, *Mikrochim. Acta*, 1959(3), 488.

179. Hollander, J. M., I. Perlman, and G. T. Seaborg, *Revs. Mod. Phys.*, **25**, 469 (1953).

180. Holt, B. D., "Determination of Hydrogen in Alkali Metals, Isotope Dilution Method," 133rd Meeting, ACS, San Francisco, Calif., April, 1958; *Anal. Chem.*, **31**, 51 (1959).

181. Honda, M., *J. Chem. Soc. Japan, Pure Chem. Sect.*, **71**, 118 (1950); through *Chem. Abstr.*, **45**, 5053 (1951).

182. Hood, S. L., and C. L. Comar, *U. S. Atomic Energy Comm. Agr. Research Program Rept.*, ORO-91 (1953).

183. Horstman, E. L., *Anal. Chem.*, **28**, 1417 (1956).

184. Hourigen, H. F., and J. W. Robinson, *Anal. Chim. Acta*, **13**, 179 (1955)

185. Hourigen, H. F., and J. W. Robinson, *Anal. Chim. Acta*, **16**, 161 (1957).

186. Ievins, A., and E. Gudriniece, *Zhur. Anal. Khim.*, **9**, 270 (1954); through *Chem. Abstr.*, **49**, 2940 (1955).

187. Ievinsh, A. F., and J. K. Ozols, *J. Anal. Chem. U. S. S. R. (English Translation)*, **8**, 53 (1953); through *Brit. Abstr.*, C377 (1953).

188. Ikeda, S., *J. Chem. Soc. Japan, Pure Chem. Sect.*, **76**, 354 (1955); through *Anal. Abstr.*, **3**, 364 (1956).

189. Indenbom, V. L., Ts. A. Karchmar, L. F. Yurkoo, and B. M. Glukhovskoi, *Zavodskaya Lab.*, **22**, 1293 (1956); through *Anal. Abstr.*, **4**, 1763 (1957).

190. Ingraham, M. G., *Ann. Rev. Nuclear Sc.*, **4**, (1954).

191. Inman, W. R., R. A. Rodger, and J. A. Fournier, *Anal. Chem.*, **23**, 482 (1951).

192. Iritani, N., *J. Pharm. Soc. Japan*, **68**, 63 (1948); through *Chem. Abstr.*, **44**, 478 (1950).

193. Ishidate, M., Y. Mashiko, and Y. Kanroji, *J. Pharm. Soc., Japan*, **75**, 1492 (1955); through *Anal. Abstr.*, **4**, 290 (1957).

194. Ismail, A. M., and H. F. Harwood, *Analyst*, **62**, 443 (1937).

195. Jackson, P. J., and A. C. Smith, *J. Appl. Chem.* (*London*), **6**, 547 (1956).

196. Jacobs, H. R. D., and W. S. Hoffman, *J. Biol. Chem.*, **93**, 685 (1931).

197. James, A. H., L. Brooks, I. S. Edelman, J. M. Ohney, and F. D. Moore, *Metabolism Clin. and Exptl.*, **3**, 313 (1954).

198. Jendrassic, L., and Holász, *Biochem. Z.*, **298**, 74 (1938).

199. Jendrassic, L., and A. Polgar, *Z. anal. Chem.*, **107**, 417 (1936).

200. Jenkins, L. N., and A. A. Smales, *Quart. Revs.* (*London*), **10**, 83 (1956).

201. Jentoff, R. E., and R. J. Robinson, *Anal. Chem.*, **28**, 2011 (1956).

202. Jones, N. E., *U. S. Atomic Energy Comm. Rept.* KAPL-1378 (1955).

203. Joy, A. B., *Ind. Eng. Chem., Anal. Ed.*, **16**, 383 (1944).

204. Jury, R. V., *Atomic Energy Research Estbl.* (*Gt. Brit.*), **1957**, C/R 1871.

205. Kahane, E., *Bull. soc. chim. France*, **47**, 382 (1930).

206. Kahane, E., *Bull. soc. chim. France*, **53**, 555 (1933).

207. Kahlenberg, L., and F. C. Krauskopf, *J. Am. Chem. Soc.*, **30**, 1104 (1908).

208. Kahn, B., D. K. Smith, and C. P. Straub, *Anal. Chem.*, **29**, 1210 (1957).

209. Kakihana, H., *J. Chem. Soc. Japan, Pure Chem. Sect.*, **72**, 255 (1951); through *Chem. Abstr.*, **46**, 847 (1951).

210. Kallmann, S., *Ind. Eng. Chem., Anal. Ed.*, **16**, 712 (1944).

211. Kallmann, S., *Ind. Eng. Chem., Anal. Ed.*, **18**, 678 (1946).

212. Kallmann, S., Unpublished data, 1953.

213. Kallmann, S., Unpublished data, 1956.

214. Kallmann, S., Unpublished data, 1957.

214a. Karrman, K. J., E. Bladh, and P. O. Gedda, *Mikrochim. Acta*, **1959**(5), 775; and J. Havir, *Collection Czechoslov. Chem. Communs.*, **25**, 595 (1960); through *Anal. Abstr.*, **7**, 4122 (1960).

215. Kayas, G., *Compt. rend.*, **228**, 1002 (1949).

216. Kayas, G., *J. chim. phys.*, **47**, 408 (1950).

217. Kaye, I. A., *Ind. Eng. Chem., Anal. Ed.*, **12**, 310 (1940).

218. Kingsley, G. R., and R. R. Schaffert, *Anal. Chem.*, **25**, 1738 (1953).

219. Kingsley, G. R., and R. R. Schaffert, *J. Biol. Chem.*, **206**, 807 (1954).

220. Kinsman, S., *Radiological Health Handbook*, Radiological Health Training Section, R. A. Taft Sanitary Engineering Center, Cincinnati, Ohio, 1954.

221. Koch, H. J., in J. H. Yoe and H. J. Koch, *Trace Analysis*, Wiley, New York, 1957.

222. Koenig, E. W., *Ind. Eng. Chem., Anal. Ed.*, **7**, 314 (1935).

223. Kohler, M., *Z. anal. Chem.*, **138**, 9 (1953).

224. Kolthoff, I. M., and G. H. Bendix, *Ind. Eng. Chem., Anal. Ed.*, **11**, 94 (1939).

225. Kolthoff, I. M., and J. J. Lingane, *J. Am. Chem. Soc.*, **55**, 1871 (1933).

226. Kolthoff, I. M., and J. J. Lingane, *Polarography*, Vol. II, Interscience, New York–London, 1952.

227. Komar, N., *Zavodskaya Lab.*, **6**, 1074 (1937).

228. Korenman, I. M., and M. M. Fursima, *J. Appl. Chem.* (*U. S. S. R.*), **10**, 1494 (1937); through *Chem. Abstr.*, **32**, 2052 (1938).

229. Korenman, I. M., F. R. Sheyanova, and Z. I. Glasunova, *Zavodskaya Lab.*, **21**, 774 (1955); through *Anal. Abstr.*, **3**, 1251 (1956).

230. Korenman, I. M., and E. I. Zorin, *Zavodskaya Lab.*, **21**, 1419 (1955); through *Anal. Abstr.*, **3**, 2412 (1956).

231. Kovalenko, P. N., and V. V. Tenkovtsev, *Ukrain. Khim. Zhur.*, **20**, 411 (1954); through *Anal. Abstr.*, **3**, 626 (1956).

232. Kramer, B., and I. Gittleman, *J. Biol. Chem.*, **62**, 353 (1924).

233. Kramer, B., and F. F. Tisdall, *J. Biol. Chem.*, **46**, 339 (1921).

234. Kramer, B., and F. F. Tisdall, *J. Biol. Chem.*, **46**, 467 (1921).

235. Kraus, C. A., and W. W. Lucasse, *J. Am. Chem. Soc.*, **43**, 2529 (1921).

236. Kraus, K. A., and F. Nelson, *Am. Soc. Testing Materials Spec. Tech. Publ.* No. 195 (1958).

236a. Kreisky, F., *Mikrochim. Acta*, **1959**(2), 243.

236b. Krichmar, S. I., and L. G. Kaistro, *Zavodskaya Lab.*, **24**, 925 (1958); through *Anal. Abstr.*, **6**, 1955 (1958).

237. Krochta, W. G., and M. G. Mellon, *Anal. Chem.*, **29**, 1181 (1957).

238. Kume, S., K. Otaza, and H. Watanabe, *Nature*, **166**, 1076 (1950).

239. Kulrich, R., L. Feinstein, and E. C. Anderson, *Science*, **127**, 338 (1958).

240. Kuznetsove, V. I., *Zhur. Anal. Khim.*, **3**, 295 (1948).

241. Lange, B., *Kolorimetrische Analyse*, Verlag Chemie, Weinheim, 1956.

242. Langford, J. C., *U. S. Atomic Energy Comm. Rept.* HW-49668 (1957).

243. Lavina, N. D., and L. I. Panteleeva, *Zavodskaya Lab.*, **23**, 285 (1957); through *Anal. Abstr.*, **4**, 3236 (1957).

244. Leddicotte, G. W., Oak Ridge National Laboratory, Oak Ridge, Tenn. The preparation of this section was greatly aided by detailed data made available by Dr. Leddicotte.

245. Leddicotte, G. W., Private communication, 1958.

246. Leddicotte, G. W., and S. A. Reynolds, *U. S. Atomic Energy Comm. Rept.* 3489.

247. Leddicotte, G. W., and S. A. Reynolds, *Nucleonics*, **8**(3), 62 (1951).

248. Lederer, E., and M. Lederer, *Chromatography*, Elsevier, New York, 1957.

249. Lederer, M., *Anal. Chim. Acta*, **11**, 528 (1954).

250. Lederer, M., *Mikrochim. Acta*, **1956**(1–3), 43.

251. Ledoux & Co., Teaneck, N. J., *Health Regulations Covering the Analysis of Beryllium Compounds*.

252. Lewis, A. H., and F. B. Marmoy, *J. Soc. Chem. Ind.*, **52**, 177 (1933).

253. Lewis, P. R., *Analyst*, **80**, 768 (1955).

254. Libby, W. F., *Science*, **123**, 657 (1956).

255. Liebhafsky, H. A., *Anal. Chem.*, **26**, 26 (1954).

256. Liebhafsky, H. A., and Winslow, G. H., *Anal. Chem.*, **28**, 583 (1956); **30**, 580 (1958).

257. Lindo, D., and T. S. Gladding, through ref. 14.

258. Logie, D., *Chem. & Ind.* (*London*), **1957**, 225.

259. Lopez de Azcona, J. M., *Mikrochim. Acta*, **1956**(1–3), 334.

260. Luckenbach, W. F., Jr., and R. G. Verdiek, *Lithium, Now and Next*, Research and Engineering, 1957.

261. Lundegardh, H., *Die Quantitative Spectralanalyse der Elemente*, Fischer, Jena, 1934, Part II.

262. Lyon, R. N., in *Liquid Metals Handbook*, A.E.C.–Dept. of the Navy, Washington, D. C., 1952; 2nd ed., 1954.

263. Lyon, R. N., in *Liquid Metals Handbook, Sodium NaK Supplement*, *TID 5277*, A.E.C.–Dept. of the Navy, Washington, D. C., 1955.

264. Magee, R. J., and J. B. Headridge, *Analyst*, **82**, 95 (1957).

265. Majer, V., *Z. anal. Chem.*, **92**, 321 (1933).

265a. Maksimycheva, Z. T., and N. Abdusalyamov, *Zavodskaya Lab.*, **24**, 403 (1958); through *Anal. Abstr.*, **6**, 457 (1959).

266. Mallet, M. H., F. Gerds, and C. B. Griffith, *Anal. Chem.*, **25**, 116 (1953).

267. Manasevit, H. M., *Anal. Chem.*, **27**, 81 (1955).

268. Mann, C. K., and J. C. White, *ORNL Rept.* CF-56-10-86 (1956).

269. Manning, D. L., W. K. Miller, and R. Rowan, Jr., *ORNL Rept.* 1396 (1952); *Nuclear Sci. Abstr.*, **10**, 3109 (1955).

270. Margoshes, M., and B. L. Vallee, *Methods of Biochemical Analysis*, Vol. 3, Interscience, New York–London, 1954.

271. Marvin, G. G., and L. B. Woodlaver, *Ind. Eng. Chem., Anal. Ed.*, **17**, 554 (1945).

272. Mavrodineanu, R., *Appl. Spectroscopy*, **10**, 51, 137 (1956).

273. McAlpine, R. K., and B. A. Soule, *Prescott and Johnson's Qualitative Chemical Analysis*, Van Nostrand, New York, 1933.

274. McCormick, D. R., and W. E. Carlson, *Chemist Analyst*, **31**, 15 (1942).

275. McCoy, W. J., and G. G. Christiansen, *Am. Soc. Testing Materials, Spec. Tech. Publ.* No. 116 (1951).

276. McKay, D. C., and W. A. de Long, *Can. J. Agr. Sci.*, **34**, 451 (1954).

277. McKenzie, T. R., *U. S. Atomic Energy Comm. Rept.* HW-47761 (1957).

278. McNabb, W. M., J. F. Hazel, and H. F. Dantro, *Anal. Chem.*, **23**, 1325 (1951).

279. Meloche, V. W., *Anal. Chem.*, **28**, 1844 (1956).

279a. Messner, A. E., and L. B. Eddy, *Anal. Chem.*, **30**, 1971 (1958).

280. Miller, C. C., and R. J. Magee, *J. Chem. Soc.*, **1951**, 3183.

281. Miller, C. C., and F. Traves, *J. Chem. Soc.*, **1936**, 1395.

282. Miller, C. E., and L. D. Marinelli, *Science*, **124**, 122 (1956).

283. Miller, H. S., and G. E. Kline, *J. Am. Chem. Soc.*, **73**, 2741 (1951).

284. Mitteldorf, A. J. Spex Industries, New York. The assistance of Mr. Mitteldorf with the preparation of this section is gratefully acknowledged.

285. Mitteldorf, A. J., *The Spex Speaker, II*, No. 2 (1957).

285a. Modreanu, F., S. Fisel, and A. Carpov, *Nature*, **181**, 1618 (1958).

286. Monnier, D., and Z. Besso, *Anal. Chim. Acta*, **7**, 380 (1952).

287. Monnier, D., Z. Besso, and P. E. Wenger, *Helv. Chim. Acta*, **34**, 433 (1951).

288. Morrison, G. H., Sylvania Electric Products, Bayside, N. Y., contributed valuable data to this section.

289. Morrison, G. H., *Appl. Spectroscopy*, **10**, 71 (1956).

290. Moser, L., and E. Ritschel, *Monatsh.*, **46**, 19 (1925).

291. Mulwani, B. T., and A. G. Pollard, *J. Soc. Chem. Ind.* (*London*), **56**, 128T (1937).

291a. Munro, D. S., H. Renschler, and G. M. Wilson, *Phys. in Med. Biol.*, **2**, 239 (1958).

292. Murthy, G. K., and R. M. Whitney, *J. Dairy Sci.*, **39**, 364 (1956).

293. Nakano, S., *J. Chem. Soc., Japan, Pur. Chem. Sect.*, **77**, 836 (1956); through *Anal. Abstr.*, **4**, 1100 (1957).

294. *Natl. Bur. Standards* (*U. S.*) *Handbook* No. 52 (1953).

295. Nazarenko, V. A., and V. Ya. Filatova, *Zhur. Anal. Khim.*, **5**, 234 (1950); through *Brit. Abstr.*, C473 (1950).

295a. Neeb, K. H., and W. Gebauhr, *Z. anal. Chem.*, **162**(3), 167 (1958).

296. Nelson, F., *J. Am. Chem. Soc.*, **77**, 813 (1955).

297. Nemec, A., *Biochem. Z.*, **189**, 50 (1927).

298. Nier, A. O., *Phys. Rev.*, **77**, 789 (1950).

299. Nievwenburg, C. J., and T. van der Hoek, *Mikrochemie*, **18**, 175 (1935).

300. Nikolaev, A. V., and A. A. Sorokina, *Doklady Akad. Nauk S. S. S. R.*, **77**, 427 (1951).

301. Nishita, H., *Soil Sci.*, **81**, 317 (1956).
302. Nozaki, T., *J. Chem. Soc. Japan, Pure Chem. Sect.*, **76**, 445 (1955); through *Anal. Abstr.*, **3**, 341 (1956).
303. Okuno, H., M. Honda, and T. Ishimori, *Japan Analyst*, **2**, 438 (1953); through *Chem. Abstr.*, **48**, 6320 (1954).
304. O'Leary, W. J., and J. Papish, *Ind. Eng. Chem., Anal. Ed.*, **6**, 107 (1934).
305. Oplinger, G., in ref. 18.
306. Osborn, G. H., and H. Johns, *Analyst*, **76**, 410 (1951).
307. Osthaus, B. B., *J. Am. Chem. Soc.*, **33**, 377 (1950).
308. Overman, O. R., and O. F. Garret, *Ind. Eng. Chem., Anal. Ed.*, **9**, 72 (1937).
309. Owen, L. E., and J. Y. Ellenburg, *Anal. Chem.*, **23**, 1823 (1951).
310. Pagliassotti, J. P., and F. W. Porsche, *Anal. Chem.*, **23**, 198 (1951).
311. Palkins, S., *J. Am. Chem. Soc.*, **38**, 2326 (1916).
311a. Palous, R., V. Pavelka, and M. Mara, *Collection Czechoslov. Chem. Communs.*, **24**, 3910 (1959); through *Anal. Abstr.*, **7**, 3627 (1960).
312. Parks, J. D., H. O. Johnson, and L. Lykken, *Anal. Chem.*, **20**, 822 (1948).
313. Pauling, L., *General Chemistry*, W. H. Freeman, San Francisco, 1954.
313a. Penceff, N. P., *Rev. chim. (Bucharest)*, **10**, 231 (1959); through *Anal. Abstr.*, **7**, 26 (1960).
314. Pepkowitz, L. P., *Anal. Chem.*, **26**, 574 (1954).
315. Pepkowitz, L. P., and W. C. Judd, *Anal. Chem.*, **22**, 1283 (1950).
316. Pepkowitz, L. P., W. C. Judd, and R. E. Downer, *Anal. Chem.*, **26**, 246 (1954).
317. Pepkowitz, L. P., and J. T. Porter II, *Anal. Chem.*, **28**, 1606 (1956).
318. Pepkowitz, L. P., and E. R. Preud, *Anal. Chem.*, **21**, 1000 (1949).
319. Peracchio, E. S., and V. W. Meloche, *J. Am. Chem. Soc.*, **60**, 1770 (1938).
320. Perey, M., *J. chim. phys.*, **43**, 155, 269 (1946).
321. Perkin, R. W., *U. S. Atomic Energy Comm. Rept.* HW-40544 (1955).
322. Perri, G., *Bull. soc. ital. biol. sper.*, **25**, 1414 (1949).
323. Perrin, C. H., *Anal. Chem.*, **21**, 984 (1949).
324. Pfaff, C. H., *Handbuch der Analytischen Chemie*, Vol. II, Altona, 1822; through ref. 142.
325. Pflaum, R. T., and L. C. Howick, *Anal. Chem.*, **28**, 1542 (1956).
326. Phdollov, P. I., and M. T. Su, *Acta Chim. Sinica*, **23**, 30 (1957).
327. Phynschev, V. E., and I. V. Shakhuo, *J. Anal. Chem. U.S.S.R. (English Translation)*, **8**, 293 (1953).
328. Piper, C. S., *J. Soc. Chem. Ind.*, **53**, 392 (1934).
329. Piper, E., and H. Hagedorn, *Arch. Eisenhüttenw.*, **22**, 299 (1951).
330. Podvinski, R., *Časopis lékáru českých*, **92**, 205 (1953); through, *Chem. Abstr.*, **49**, 1133 (1955).
331. Pollard, F. H., and J. F. W. McOmie, *Chromatographic Methods of Inorganic Analysis*, Academic Press, New York, 1953.
332. Polektov, N. S., and M. P. Nikonova, *Zavodskaya Lab.*, **24**(5), 528 (1958); through *Anal. Abstr.*, **6**, 841 (1959).
333. Press, R. E., and K. A. Murray, *J. S. African Chem. Inst.*, **6**, 17 (1953).
334. Pročke, O., and A. Slouf, *Collection Czech. Chem. Communs.*, **11**, 276 (1939).
335. Pročke, O., and R. Uzel, *Mikrochim. Acta*, **3**, 105 (1938).
336. Rammelsberg, C., *Pogg. Ann.*, **66**, 79 (1845).
337. Raff, P., and W. Brotz, *Z. anal. Chem.*, **133**, 241 (1951).
338. Reed, J. F., A. Mehlich, and J. R. Piland, *Soil Sci. Soc. Am. Proc.*, **9**, 56 (1944).

338a. Reeve, W., *Anal. Chem.*, **31**, 1066 (1959).

339. Reeve, W., and I. Christoffel, *Anal. Chem.*, **29**, 102 (1957).

340. Reichard, O., *Z. anal. Chem.*, **140**, 188 (1953).

341. Reichen, L. E., *Anal. Chem.*, **30**, 1948 (1958).

342. Reiffel, L., and C. A. Stone, *J. Lab. Clin. Med.*, **49**, 286 (1957).

342a. Rekus, A. F., *Appl. Spectroscopy*, **12**(5), 141 (1958).

343. Ring, S. A., *Anal. Chem.*, **28**, 1200 (1956).

344. Robinson, A. M., and T. C. J. Ovenston, *Analyst*, **79**, 47 (1954).

345. Robinson, C. V., W. L. Arons, and A. K. Solomon, *J. Clin. Invest.*, **34**, 134 (1955).

346. Rodgers, S. J., J. W. Mausteller, and E. F. Batutes, *Mine Safety Appliance Co. Publ.* (1954).

347. Rogers, L. B., and E. R. Caley, *Ind. Eng. Chem., Anal. Ed.*, **15**, 209 (1943).

348. Rosza, J. T., in ref. 18.

349. Rothermel, D. L., *Am. Soc. Testing Materials Spec., Tech. Publ.* No. 116 (1952).

350. Roy, N., *Anal. Chem.*, **28**, 34 (1956).

351. Rudorf, W., and H. Zannier, *Z. anal. Chem.*, **137**, 1 (1952).

352. Rynasciewics, J., and M. E. Polley, *Anal. Chem.*, **21**, 1398 (1949).

353. Rynasciewics, J., M. P. Sleeper, and J. W. Ryan, *Anal. Chem.*, **26**, 935 (1954).

353a. Ryss, I. G., and E. L. Hilus, *Zavodskaya Lab.*, **24**, 1349 (1958); through *Anal. Abstr.*, **6**, 2866 (1959).

354. St. John, J. L., and M. C. Midgley, *Ind. Eng. Chem., Anal. Ed.*, **14**, 300 (1942).

354a. Sadek, F. S., and C. N. Reilly, *Anal. Chem.*, **31**, 494 (1959).

355. Sakaguchi, T., and Y. Yasuda, *J. Pharm. Soc. Japan*, **71**, 1469 (1951); *Chem. Abstr.*, **46**, 3452 (1952).

356. Salomon, A. K., and D. C. Caton, *Anal. Chem.*, **27**, 1849 (1955).

357. Samuelson, O., *Ion Exchangers in Analytical Chemistry*, Wiley, New York, 1953.

358. Samuelson, O., and E. Sjöström, *Anal. Chem.*, **26**, 1908 (1954).

359. Sandell, E. B., *Colorimetric Determination of Traces of Metals*, Interscience, New York–London, 1950.

360. Sandell, E. B., *Colorimetric Determination of Traces of Metals*, 3rd ed., Interscience, New York–London, 1959.

361. Sato, I. S., *J. Chem. Soc. Japan, Pure Chem. Sect.*, **72**, 181 (1951); **72**, 450 (1951); **72**, 490 (1951); **72**, 492 (1951); *Chem. Abstr.*, **46**, 3452 (1952).

361a. Sax, N. I., N. Y. Chu, R. H. Miles, and R. W. Miles, *U. S. Atomic Energy Comm. Rept.* NDA-38 (1957).

361b. Sazonova, V. A., and V. N. Leonov, *Zhur. Anal. Khim.*, **14**, 483 (1959); through *Anal. Abstr.*, **7**, 2063 (1960).

362. Schall, E. D., *Anal. Chem.*, **29**, 1044 (1957).

363. Schier, O., *Z. angew. Chem.*, **68**, 63 (1956).

364. Schmidt, V., *Scand. J. Clin. & Lab. Invest.*, **3**, 352 (1951).

365. Scheider, R. A., *U. S. Atomic Energy Comm. Rept.* HW-46488 (1956).

366. Schober, R., and A. Fricker, *Z. Lebensm. Untersuch. u. Forsch.*, **95**, 107 (1952).

367. Schoeller, W. R., and A. R. Powell, *The Analysis of Minerals of the Rarer Elements*, Hafner, New York, 1955.

368. Scholes, S. R., and J. E. Wessels, *Chemist Analyst*, **25**, 38 (1936).

369. Schuhknecht, W., and H. Schinkel, *Z. anal. Chem.*, **143**, 321 (1954).

370. Schumacher, E., *Helv. Chim. Acta*, **39**, 538 (1956).

371. Schwaibold, I., and M. Kohler, *Landwirtsch. Jahrb. Bayern*, **30**, Heft 1–2 (1953).

372. Schweitzer, H., *Acta Brevia, Neerl. Physiol. Pharmacol. Microbiol.*, **6**, 110 (1936).

373. Scott, R. K., V. M. Marcy, and J. Hronas, *Am. Soc. Testing Materials, Spec. Tech. Publ.* No. 115 (1951).

374. Scott, W. W., *Standard Methods of Chemical Analysis*, Vol. I, Van Nostrand, New York, 1939.

375. Seay, W. A., O. J. Attoe, and E. Truog, *Soil Sci.*, **71**, 83 (1951).

376. Seiler, H., K. Artz, and H. Erlenmeyer, *Helv. Chim. Acta*, **39**, 783 (1956).

377. Seiler, H., E. Sorkin, and H. Erlenmeyer, *Helv. Chim. Acta*, **35**, 120 (1952).

378. Shead, A. C., and G. F. Smith, *J. Am. Chem. Soc.*, **53**, 483 (1931).

379. Shell, H. R., *Anal. Chem.*, **22**, 575 (1950).

380. Sideris, C. P., *Ind. Eng. Chem., Anal. Ed.*, **9**, 145 (1937).

381. Sideris, C. P., *Ind. Eng. Chem., Anal. Ed.*, **14**, 821 (1942).

382. Siebert, H., and S. Rapoport, *Z. anal. Chem.*, **150**, 81 (1956).

383. Siegbahn, M., and T. Magnusson, *Z. Physik*, **87**, 291 (1933).

384. Silverman, L., and M. Shidelen, *Anal. Chem.*, **27**, 1660 (1955).

385. Silverman, L., and K. Trego, *Analyst*, **78**, 717 (1953).

386. Simpson, P. H., Foote Mineral Co., Berwyn, Pa., Private communication.

386a. Singh, B., and S. Singh, *Z. anal. Chem.*, **162**, 325 (1958).

387. Sinka, A., *Z. anal. Chem.*, **80**, 430 (1930).

388. Sittig, M., *Sodium, Its Manufacture, Properties and Uses*, A.C.S. Monograph, Reinhold, New York, 1956.

389. Sloviter, H. A., and A. Sitkin, *J. Opt. Soc. Am.*, **34**, 400 (1944).

390. Smales, A. A., and B. A. Lovridge, *Anal. Chim. Acta*, **13**, 566 (1955).

391. Smales, A. A., and L. Salmon, *Analyst*, **80**, 37 (1955).

392. Smales, A. A., and R. K. Webster, *Anal. Chim. Acta*, **18**(6), 582 (1958).

393. Smales, A. A., and R. K. Webster, *Anal. Chim. Acta*, **18**(6), 587 (1958).

393a. Smit, J., C. T. J. Alkemade, and J. C. M. Verschure, *Biochim. et Biophys. Acta*, **6**, 508 (1951).

393b. Smith, D. L., D. R. Jamieson, and P. J. Elving, *Anal. Chem.*, **32**, 1253 (1960).

394. Smith, G. F., *J. Am. Chem. Soc.*, **45**, 2072 (1923).

395. Smith, G. F., and A. C. Shead, *J. Am. Chem. Soc.*, **53**, 947 (1931).

396. Smith, J. L., *Am. J. Sci.*, (3)**1**, 269 (1871).

397. Smith, R. W., and S. P. Mattarells, in ref. 8.

397a. Smythe, W. R., *Phys. Rev.*, **55**, 316 (1939).

398. Smyth, W. R., and A. Henmendinger, *Phys. Rev.*, **51**, 178 (1937).

399. *Sodium Carbonate*, Columbia Southern Chemical Corp., Pittsburgh, Pa.

400a. Specker, H., H. Hartkamp, and E. Jackwerth *Z. anal. Chem.*, **163**(2), 111 (1958).

400. *Solvay Technical and Engineering Service Bull.* No. 9 (1958).

401. Spector, J., *Anal. Chem.*, **27**, 1452 (1955).

402. Spier, H. W., *Biochem. Z.*, **322**, 467 (1952).

403. Sporek, K., and A. F. Williams, *Analyst*, **80**, 347 (1955).

404. Sporek, K. F., *Analyst*, **81**, 540 (1956).

405. Standen, G. W., *Ind. Eng. Chem., Anal. Ed.*, **16**, 675 (1944).

406. Steel, A. E., *Nature*, **173**, 315 (1954).

407. Steinmetz, H., and N. Y. Chu.   This paper is largely based on detailed data made available by ref. 408.

408. Steinmetz, H., and N. I. Sax, Division of Industrial and Engineering Chemistry, 133rd Meeting, ACS, San Francisco, Calif., April, 1958.

409. Stevens, R. E., *Ind. Eng. Chem., Anal. Ed.*, **12**, 413 (1940).

410. Stoffer, K. G., and J. H. Phillips, *Anal. Chem.*, **27**, 773 (1955).

411. Stone, I., P. Gray, and M. Kenigsberg, *Am. Soc. Brewing Chemists, Proc.*, **1951**.

412. Strain, H. H., "Chromatography and Electrochromatography," in J. H. Yoe and H. J. Koch, *Trace Analysis*, Wiley, New York, 1957.

413. Strain, H. H., and G. W. Murphy, *Anal. Chem.*, **24**, 50 (1952).

414. Strain, H. H., T. R. Sato, and J. Engelke, *Anal. Chem.*, **26**, 90 (1954).

415. Strange, E. E., *Anal. Chem.*, **25**, 650 (1953).

416. Strecker, W., and F. O. Diaz, *Z. anal. Chem.*, **67**, 321 (1925).

416a. Sugihara, K., and T. Saito, *Japan Analyst*, **7**(3), 139 (1958); through *Anal. Abstr.*, **6**, 33 (1959).

417. Sugihara, T. T., H. I. James, E. J. Troianello, and V. T. Bowen, *Anal. Chem.*, **31**, 44 (1959).

418. Suttle, J. F., "The Alkali Metals," in M. C. Sneed and R. C. Brasted, *Comprehensive Inorganic Chemistry*, Van Nostrand, New York, 1957.

419. Sutton, W. J. L., and E. F. Almy, *J. Dairy Sci.*, **36**, 1248 (1953).

420. Sweet, R. C., W. Rieman III, and J. Beukenkamp, *Anal. Chem.*, **24**, 952 (1952).

421. Taylor, T. I., and W. W. Havens, Jr., *Nucleonics*, **6**(4), 54 (1950).

422. Thomason, P. F., *Anal. Chem.*, **28**, 1527 (1956).

423. Thompson, F. C., and S. Rowland, *Nature*, **152**, 103 (1943).

424. Tinsley, J., *Analyst*, **73**, 86 (1948).

425. Tissier, M., and H. Bénard, *Compt. rend. soc. biol.*, **99**, 1144 (1928).

426. Tomicek, O., and R. Pulpan, *Chem. listy*, **49**, 497 (1955); through *Anal. Abstr.*, **3**, 1246 (1956).

427. Tschopp, B., *Helv. Chim. Acta*, **8**, 893 (1925).

427a. Uzumasa, Y., Y. Nasu, and T. Seo, *J. Chem. Soc. Japan, Pure Chem. Sect.*, **79**(11), 1292 (1958).

428. Vainshtein, E. E., and V. V. Korolev, *Zhur. Anal. Khim.*, **11**, 627 (1956); through *Anal. Abstr.*, **4**, 2091 (1957).

429. Vanatta, J. C., and C. C. Cox, *J. Biol. Chem.*, **212**, 599 (1955).

430. Van Slyke, D. D., and J. Folch, *J. Biol. Chem.*, **136**, 509 (1940).

431. Vender, M., *Chem. listy*, **49**, 777 (1955); *Anal. Abstr.*, **3**, 1873 (1956).

431a. Vishveshwaraiah, K. N., and C. C. Patel, *J. Ind. Inst. Sci.*, *Sect. A*, **41**, 16 (1959); through *Anal. Abstr.*, **7**, 872 (1960).

431b. Voinovitch, L. A., and J. Debras, *Ind. Céram.*, No. 502, 321 (1958).

432. Walters, S. L., and R. R. Miller, *Ind. Eng. Chem.*, *Anal. Ed.*, **18**, 468 (1946).

433. Wander, J. W., *Ind. Eng. Chem.*, *Anal. Ed.*, **14**, 471 (1942).

434. Wasserman, R. H., A. R. Twardock, and C. L. Comar, *Science*, **129**, 568 (1959).

434a. Waterbury, G. R., E. H. van Kooten, and B. Morosin, *Anal. Chem.*, **30**, 1627 (1958).

435. Weaver, J. R., and L. Lykken, *Anal. Chem.*, **19**, 372 (1947).

436. Wells, R. C., R. K. Bailey, and J. G. Fairchild, *Ind. Eng. Chem.*, **16**, 935 (1924).

437. Wells, R. C., and R. E. Stevens, *Ind. Eng. Chem.*, *Anal. Ed.*, **6**, 439 (1934).

438. Wells, R. C., and R. E. Stevens, *Ind. Eng. Chem.*, *Anal. Ed.*, **9**, 236 (1937).

439. West, P. W., P. Folse, and D. Montgomery, *Anal. Chem.*, **22**, 667 (1950).

440. Westhaver, J. W., *J. Research Natl. Bur. Standards*, **38**, 169 (1947).

441. White, C. E., M. H. Fletcher, and J. Parks, *Anal. Chem.*, **23**, 479 (1951).

442. White, J. C., "New Developments in the Analysis of the Alkali Metals," Division of Industrial and Engineering Chemistry, 133rd Meeting, ACS, San Francisco, Calif., April, 1958.

443. White, J. C., *ORNL Rept.* CF-56-4-31 (1956); *Nuclear Sci. Abstr.*, **11**, 8290 (1956).

444. White, J. C., and G. Goldberg, *Anal. Chem.*, **27**, 1188 (1955).
445. White, J. C., W. J. Ross, and R. Rowan, Jr., *Anal. Chem.* **26**, 210 (1954).
446. White, J. C., C. K. Talbott, and L. J. Brady, *Anal. Chem.*, **26**, 942 (1954).
447. Whittles, C. L., and R. C. Little, *J. Sci. Food Agr.*, **1**, 323 (1950).
448. Wickbold, R., *Z. anal. Chem.*, **132**, 401 (1951).
449. Wildy, D. C., *Atomic Energy Research Establishment (Gt. Brit.)*, **1956**, C/R 2114
449a. Wilkins, D. H., *Anal. Chim. Acta*, **20**(2), 116 (1959).
450. Wilkinson, G., and W. E. Grummit, *Nucleonics*, **9**(3), 55 (1951).
451. Willard, H. H., and A. J. Boyle, *Ind. Eng. Chem., Anal. Ed.*, **13**, 137 (1941).
452. Willard, H. H., L. M. Liggert, and H. Diehl, *Ind. Eng. Chem., Anal. Ed.*, **14**, 234 (1942).
453. Willard, H. H., and G. F. Smith, *J. Am. Chem. Soc.*, **44**, 2816 (1922).
454. Williams, D. D., and R. R. Miller, *Anal. Chem.*, **23**, 1865 (1951).
455. Wilson, H. N., P. S. Leco, and W. Broomfield, *Analyst*, **76**, 355 (1951).
456. Wilson, M. F., in ref. 8.
457. Winkler, L. W., *Z. anal. Chem.*, **52**, 628 (1913).
458. Wittig, G., *Z. angew. Chem.*, **62**, 231 (1950).
459. Wittig, G., G. Keicher, A. Rückert, and P. Raff, *Ann. Chem.*, **563**, 110, 126 (1949).
460. Wittig, G., and P. Raff, *Ann. Chem.*, **573**, 195 (1951).
461. Wolthorn, H. J., and A. J. Herdle, in ref. 8.
462. Woodhead, J. L., A. J. Fudge, and E. N. Jenkins, *Analyst*, **81**, 570 (1956).
463. Woodward, K. T., C. R. Richmond, and W. H. Langham, *Proc. Health Phys. Sci.*, **1**, 79 (1956).
464. Woodward, K. T., T. T. Trujillo, R. L. Schuch, and E. C. Anderson, *Nature*, **178**, 97 (1956).
465. Yamatera, H., *J. Chem. Soc. Japan, Pure Chem. Sect.*, **72**, 559 (1951); through *Chem. Abstr.*, **46**, 3453 (1952).
465a. Yashchenko, M. L., G. V. Ovchinnikov, and L. I. Afanaseva, *Akad. Nauk S. S. S. R.*, **1958**, 296; *Referat. Zhur. Khim.*, **13**, Abstr. No. 45506 (1959); through *Anal. Abstr.*, **7**, 871 (1960).
466. Yoshimatsu, S., *Tôhoku J. Exp. Med.*, **8**, 496 (1927); through ref. 142.
467. Zemany, P. D., W. W. Welbon, and G. L. Gaines, Jr., *Anal. Chem.*, **30**, 299 (1958).
468. Zimmer, H., *Z. anal. Chem.*, **155**, 337 (1957); **151**, 258 (1956).
469. Zlotowski, I., and I. M. Kolthoff, *Ind. Eng. Chem., Anal. Ed.*, **14**, 473 (1942).
470. Yasumori, Y., *Bull. Chem. Soc. Japan*, **24**, 107 (1951).
471. Yuasa, T., *Repts. Govt. Chem. Ind. Research Inst. Tokyo*, **53**, 360 (1958); through *Anal. Abstr.*, **6**, 2960 (1960).

SUBJECT INDEX

A